ELEMENTARY MATH MODELING
Functions and Graphs

SPECIAL EDITION FOR WESTERN ILLINOIS UNIVERSITY

MARY ELLEN DAVIS
C. HENRY EDWARDS

Taken from

*Elementary Mathematical Modeling
Functions and Graphs*
Mary Ellen Davis
C. Henry Edwards

Thinking Mathematically
Robert Blitzer

Prentice
Hall

Pearson
Custom
Publishing

Taken from:

Elementary Mathematical Modeling: Functions and Graphs
by Mary Ellen Davis and C. Henry Edwards
Copyright © 2001 by Prentice-Hall, Inc.
A Pearson Education Company
Upper Saddle River, New Jersey 07458

Thinking Mathematically
by Robert Blitzer
Copyright © 2000 by Prentice-Hall, Inc.

This special edition published in cooperation with Pearson Custom Publishing.

Printed in the United States of America

10 9 8 7 6 5 4 3

Please visit our web site at www.pearsoncustom.com

ISBN 0–536–68625-4

BA 995544

PEARSON CUSTOM PUBLISHING
75 Arlington Street, Suite 300, Boston, MA 02116
A Pearson Education Company

Contents

PREFACE

This textbook is for an entry-level college mathematics course at the same academic level as college algebra, but intended for students who are not necessarily preparing for subsequent courses in calculus. Our approach is based on the exploitation of graphing-calculator technology to engage students in concrete modeling applications of mathematics. The mathematical ideas of the course center on functions and their graphs—ranging from linear functions and polynomials to exponential and trigonometric functions—that we hope will seem familiar and friendly to students who complete the course.

BRIEF DESCRIPTION

Specifically, this textbook presents an introduction to mathematical modeling based on the use of elementary functions to describe and explore real-world data and phenomena. It demonstrates graphical, numerical, symbolic, and verbal approaches to the investigation of data, functions, equations, and models. We emphasize interesting applications of elementary mathematics together with the ability to construct useful mathematical models, to analyze them critically, and to communicate quantitative concepts effectively. In short, this is a textbook for

- A graphing technology intensive course that is
- An alternative to the standard college algebra course, and is
- Solidly based on functions, graphs, and data modeling.

RATIONALE FOR A NEW COURSE

The content of the traditional college algebra course is defined largely by the paper-and-pencil skills (mainly symbolic manipulation) that are needed by students whose curricula point them towards a subsequent calculus course. However, many of the students in a typical college algebra course are not really headed for calculus or never make it there. For too many of these students, college algebra consists of revisiting the skills and concepts, either mastered or not, which were "covered" in several previous mathematics courses. This experience leaves students with little enhancement of the quantitative skills they most need for their subsequent studies. It is a missed opportunity for them to begin college with a useful mathematics course that is interesting both to students and to instructors, and which offers a solid chance for progress and success.

There is wide agreement on the need for an alternative new approach to fill this void. Both the NCTM's *Principles and Standards for School Mathematics* and AMATYC's *Crossroads in Mathematics: Standards for Introductory College Mathematics Before Calculus* recommend that mathematics courses teach students to reason mathematically, to model real-world situations, and to make use of appropriate technologies. We offer this as an appropriate textbook for such a course. The evolution of these materials began with a web site that was originally developed (starting in 1996) to support University of Georgia students taking pilot sections of this new course. About two thousand students have now used preliminary versions of the textbook. Many of these students have reacted with enthusiasm belying their typical lack of success in prior mathematical experiences. We hope this apparent success and satisfaction will carry over to the students who use this published textbook.

PURPOSE AND OBJECTIVES

The primary objective of this new course is the development of the quantitative literacy and savvy that college graduates need to function effectively in society and workplace. The course exploits technology and real-world applications to motivate necessary skill development and the ability to reason and communicate mathematically, to use elementary mathematics to solve applied problems, and to make connections between mathematics and the surrounding world.

With a flavor combining functions and graphs with data modeling, the course is based largely on the use of graphing calculator methods in lieu of traditional symbolic manipulations to solve both familiar and nonstandard problems. The focus of the course is "mathematical modeling" and the use of elementary mathematics—numbers and measurement, algebra, geometry, and data exploration—to investigate real-world problems and questions.

As an alternative to the standard college algebra course—though at the same academic level—this course is intended for students who are not necessarily headed for calculus-based curricula, but still need a solid quantitative foundation both for subsequent studies and for life as educated citizens and workers. Graphing technology enables these students to experience the power of mathematics and to enjoy success in solving interesting and significant problems (an experience that they all too rarely enjoy in traditional college algebra courses).

CONTENT AND ORGANIZATION

The book consists of the following chapters:

1. Linear Functions and Models
2. Quadratic Functions and Models
3. Natural Growth Models
4. Exponential and Logarithmic Models
5. Polynomial Models and Linear Systems
6. Trigonometric Models
7. Bounded Growth Models
8. Optimization

Most of these chapters fit a single pattern:

- The first section is a low-key introduction to the type of function to be used as a mathematical model throughout the chapter.
- The next section or two illustrate real-world applications of this new function.
- The final section of the chapter is devoted to data modeling using this type of function.

For example, in Chapter 3:

- Section 3.1 begins with the concept of constant-percentage growth and exponential functions of the form

$$A(t) = A_0(1 + r)^t \tag{1}$$

that model the amount at time t in an account with annual growth rate r and initial investment A_0 (e.g., $r = 0.12$ for 12% annual growth).

- Sections 3.2 and 3.3 illustrate a wide variety of real-world problems, such as the prototype question of how long is required for an initial investment of \$1000 to double if it grows at a 12% interest rate compounded annually. This question calls for solving the equation

$$1000 \times 1.12^t = 2000. \tag{2}$$

In a traditional course one might use logarithms, but here we can simply use a graphing calculator's intersection-finding capability to locate the intersection of the two graphs $y = 1000 \times 1.12^x$ and $y = 2000$, and thereby see that this takes about 6.12 years:

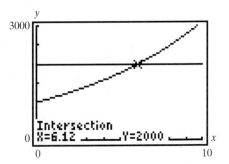

The conceptual core of this problem is the realization that Equation (2) must be solved, rather than the particular method used to do this. Essentially all students can successfully use graphing technology for this purpose, including many who might fail to use logarithms correctly. And graphical solution is a much more widely applicable approach than the use of logarithms.

- Section 3.4 (the final section of Chapter 3) is devoted to the problem of choosing the values of the parameters A_0 and r in Equation (1) so that the resulting natural growth function best fits given data. Again, this is done using available graphing calculator facilities.

As one chapter follows another, each developing the same theme with a new class of functions, the story of mathematical modeling comes to be a familiar one. Contrast this with the traditional algebra course, which many students perceive as a sequence of unrelated topics. In pilot sections, students selected mainly because of low placement test scores have exhibited success rates not frequently seen in traditional college algebra courses.

APPLICATIONS

The use of real-world applications is vital for making mathematics more lively and interesting to students and for helping them to see connections with the world around them. This text begins with a simple but very real example of a function that is taken from the menu of the popular Waffle House Restaurant chain. Throughout the book, combinations of simulated data and real (sourced) data are used in examples and problems. Contrived data are often more effective in providing clear and straightforward explanations of new concepts. Once concepts have been introduced, more robust data-based applications help to make these concepts more concrete and to underscore their connections to real life. Each chapter concludes with a data-based Activity that may be assigned as an individual or group exercise.

TECHNOLOGY

Graphing Calculators

This book assumes no technology other than student use of graphing calculators. Indeed, TI-83 syntax and calculator screens are seen throughout the text. However, it is entirely possible to mix different graphing calculators in the same class—and we have done so in pilot sections—if the instructor is willing and prepared to discuss all of them when necessary.

Spreadsheets

Perhaps it is worth remarking that in each historical era, real-world practitioners (if not teachers and academics) have always assimilated rapidly the best available technology to assist their mathematical computations—whether it be a sandbox, an abacus, a slide rule, or a desktop calculating machine. The principal computational instrument used in today's workplace is the spreadsheet (rather than the graphing calculator). We have therefore explored the use of spreadsheets to augment and reinforce graphing techniques initially introduced with calculators.

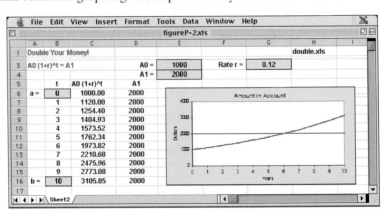

For instance, the preceding spreadsheet image illustrates the solution of Equation (2). Each of the five shaded cells is a "live cell" whose numerical content can be changed by the student. The accompanying graph and table then change dynamically. We can therefore "zoom in" by table and by graph, vividly and simultaneously. Thus if we enter the new endpoint values $a = 6.1$ and $b = 6.2$, the chart instantly changes as indicated in the spreadsheet image below, where we see the approximate solution $t \approx 6.12$.

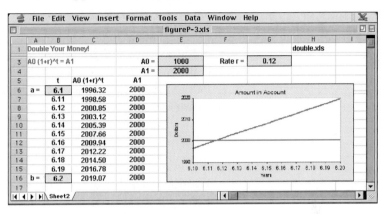

Where feasible, student use of spreadsheets can not only develop valuable familiarity with the modern world's predominant calculating technology, but also reinforce understanding of "solution by zooming" through comparison of several variants (ranging from tables to graphs). In particular, solution of the same problems using both graphing calculators and spreadsheets emphasizes that it is the general mathematical approach which we study, rather than the specific technology used to implement this approach.

The Web site *www.prenhall.com/davis* will provide a suite of spreadsheets that can be downloaded by students and instructors for use as described.

SUPPLEMENTS

Student Solutions Manual (ISBN 0-13-030771-8)

Written by Mary Ellen Davis and Henry Edwards
The Student Solutions Manual provides detailed solutions for all of the odd-numbered exercises in the text. Because these solutions were prepared by the textbook authors themselves, consistency in language and method of solution is guaranteed.

Instructor's Manual (ISBN 0-13-030760-2)

Written by Mary Ellen Davis and Henry Edwards
Solutions to all of the even-numbered problems appear in the Instructor's Solutions Manual. Sample exams and resource suggestions are also included.

Companion Web Site: www.prenhall.com/davis

In addition to the suite of spreadsheets described above, the Davis/Edwards Web Site will include additional resources including: On-line Graphing Calculator Help for various calculators, valuable resources for learning algebra, and a syllabus-building component for teachers.

ACKNOWLEDGEMENTS

Experienced and knowledgeable reviewers with extensive classroom teaching experience are crucial to the success of any textbook. We profited greatly from the advice, assistance, criticism, and enthusiasm of the following very fine reviewers and colleagues:

Virginia Carson, Georgia Perimeter College

Pete Casazza, University of Missouri–Columbia

Sandra Pryor Clarkson, Hunter College

Marko Kranjc, Western Illinois University

Kitt Powers Lumley, Columbus State University

Patty Monroe, Greenville Technical College

Charles Peters, University of Houston

Evelyn Pupplo-Cody, Marshall University

Susan Poss, Spartanburg Technical College

Sr. Barbara E. Reynolds, Cardinal Stritch University

Kim Robinson, Clayton College and State University

Behnaz Rouhani, Athens Area Technical Institute

Diane Van Nostrand, University of Tulsa

We thank Sally Yagan for her interest and enthusiasm for this project since its inception, and we owe a special debt of appreciation to our editor, Ann Heath, whose energy and ideas have shaped the finished book in ways that are too numerous to list. We also thank our production editor, Betsy Williams, for her extraordinary care and sensitivity in guiding this book through the production process. Finally, we must mention with gratitude the understanding, patience, and constant support of Alice Edwards and George, Matt, and Brian Davis.

Mary Ellen Davis
Georgia Perimeter College
mdavis@gpc.peachnet.edu
C. Henry Edwards
University of Georgia
hedwards@math.uga.edu

ABOUT THE AUTHORS

Mary Ellen Davis Georgia Perimeter College, received her Master of Arts degree in mathematics from the University of Missouri–Columbia in 1976. She has taught mathematics at the secondary level and at Georgia State University and the University of Birmingham (England). She joined the mathematics department at Georgia Perimeter College (then DeKalb College) in 1991 and has taught a wide range of courses from college algebra to calculus and statistics. She was instrumental in the piloting and implementing of the college's Introduction to Mathematical Modeling course in 1998. She was selected as a Georgia Governor's Teaching Fellow in 1996, and in 1999 received a GPC Distance Education Fellowship to develop web-based materials for applied calculus.

C. Henry Edwards (Ph. D. University of Tennessee) Emeritus professor of mathematics at the University of Georgia, Edwards recently retired after 40 years of undergraduate classroom teaching at the universities of Tennessee, Wisconsin, and Georgia. Although respected for his diverse research interests, Edwards' first love has always remained teaching. Throughout his teaching career he has received numerous college- and university-wide teaching awards, including the University of Georgia's *honoratus* medal in 1983 and its Josiah Meigs award in 1991. In 1997, Edwards was the first university-level faculty recipient of the Georgia Board of Regents newly-instituted state-wide award for teaching excellence.

A prolific author, Edwards is co-author of well-known calculus and differential equations textbooks and has written a book on the history of mathematics, in addition to several instructional computer manuals. During the 1990s, Edwards has worked on three NSF-supported projects that fostered a better integration of technology into the mathematics curriculum. The last three years of his long teaching career were devoted principally to the development of a new technology-intensive entry-level mathematics course on which this new textbook is based. Additional information is provided on his web page www.math.uga.edu/~hedwards.

ELEMENTARY MATHEMATICAL MODELING

FUNCTIONS AND GRAPHS

1

LINEAR FUNCTIONS AND MODELS

How hot is it *really?* Anyone who's ever visited Phoenix surely has heard the adage that the dry heat of the desert doesn't feel as hot as the temperature would suggest. Indeed, when it is 100° Fahrenheit in Phoenix, with a relative humidity of 10%, it "feels like" it is only 95°—a full five degrees cooler than the thermometer says!

The heat index is a number calculated by meteorologists to measure the effect of humidity on apparent temperature as felt by the human body. It is designed to report how hot you actually feel at a particular combination of air temperature and relative humidity. The chart in Fig. 1.0.1 shows the heat index for various levels of relative humidity at a fixed air temperature of 85°F.

The chart indicates that when the humidity is 10% the apparent temperature is only 80°F. However, if the humidity is 90% then a temperature of 85°F seems like 102°F. Thus the humidity has a big effect on how hot we actually feel.

We can see from the chart that as the relative humidity increases from 0% to 60%, the apparent temperature increases uniformly from 78°F to 90°F. Notice that this portion of the chart appears to be a straight line. But after we reach a relative humidity of 60%, the apparent temperature thereafter increases more rapidly as the relative humidity increases. That is, this portion of the chart appears to curve upward.

All around us we see quantities that seem, like apparent temperature and relative humidity, to be related to each other in some systematic way. We often describe this dependence of one quantity on another by using the word *function.* Thus, we might say that your weight is (ideally) a function of your

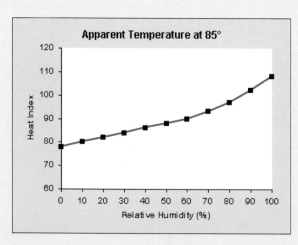

Figure 1.0.1   Source: National Weather Service, Buffalo, New York.

height; that your grade on a history test is a function of how long you studied; or that your income is a function of your education level. In each case we are noting a dependence of the first quantity on the second.

In this chapter, we will introduce the mathematical concept of a function, and we will study those functions that graph as straight lines.

1.1   FUNCTIONS AND MATHEMATICAL MODELING

The menu at a Waffle House restaurant gives the price of a breakfast of eggs, toast, jelly, and grits based on the number of eggs the customer orders, as illustrated in the following table of 1999 prices.

Number of Eggs	Price of Breakfast
1	$1.55
2	$2.00
3	$2.35
4	$2.65

Most applications of mathematics involve the use of numbers or *variables* to describe real-world quantities. In the aforementioned situation, suppose we let n represent the number of eggs ordered, and p the price of the breakfast. Then the table describes a relationship between n and p. This relationship is an example of a mathematical *function*, because for each number n of eggs ordered there is a corresponding price p charged for the breakfast.

The key concept here is that there is only **one price** associated with each number of eggs. The menu, in effect, provides a rule for determining price: If you know how many eggs were ordered, you know the price of the breakfast. If you and your friend each ordered a one-egg breakfast, then you would expect to be charged the same amount. Indeed, if one of you were charged more than $1.55 for your breakfast, then you surely would complain!

3

Definition: Function

A **function** f defined on a collection D of numbers is a rule that assigns to each number x in D a specific number $f(x)$.

The number $f(x)$—we say "f of x"—is called the *value* of the function f at the number x. The "rule" mentioned in the definition can be specified by a table, by a formula or graph, or even by a verbal description that tells how the value $f(x)$ is found when the number x is given. (While we frequently use x to denote the variable and f to denote the function, we can use any other letters that we like, or that seem more natural in a particular situation.)

Example 1

For the Waffle House function indicated previously, the set D is the collection of all possible numbers of eggs—the set of numbers $1, 2, 3$, and 4—which we denote here by n (rather than x). Given a number n in the first column of the table, we simply look in the second column to find the corresponding price $p(n)$. For instance, $p(3) = 2.35$ because $\$2.35$ is the price "assigned" to a three-egg breakfast.   ◪

Example 2

Rather than keeping a running total, the Bureau of the Public Debt uses a daily accounting method to calculate the public debt of the United States. At the end of each day, approximately 50 different agencies (such as Federal Reserve Banks) report certain financial information to the Bureau. At around 11:30 A.M. EST (Eastern Standard Time) the next morning, the accounting system produces a figure for the public debt, accurate to the nearest penny, for the previous day. Thus, to each date is assigned an official public debt amount, and we therefore can say that the debt depends on the day chosen. In other words, the debt is a function of the date. In particular, if g is the public debt function, then

$$g(9/30/1987) = \$2,350,276,890,953.00,$$

while

$$g(2/2/1998) = \$5,483,592,532,096.82.$$

(Thus the national debt increased by more than 3 trillion dollars between 1987 and 1998.) The rule defining the function g is the complicated process—described verbally previously—by which the Bureau of the Public Debt determines the national debt each day.   ◪

Example 3

The chart in Fig. 1.1.1 illustrates the population of St. Louis, Missouri, for the census years 1950 through 1990. This plot describes (at least approximately) a function P that is defined for each of the years 1950, 1960, 1970, 1980, and 1990—because for each of these years, there is *exactly one* population figure indi-

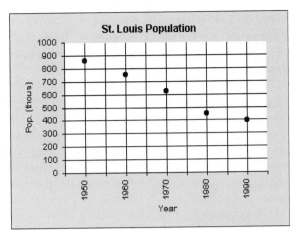

Figure 1.1.1   Source: Bureau of the Census.

cated by an appropriate dot. For instance, it appears that the 1990 population of St. Louis was approximately $P(1990) = 400$ thousand people.   ◼

Example 4

If a certain savings account earns 4% simple interest per year, then the interest I earned each year is given in terms of the amount A in the account by the formula $I = 0.04A$. This formula is a rule specifying I as a function of A. Thus, if the amount in the account is 500 dollars, then the interest earned that year is $(0.04)(500) = 20$ dollars.   ◼

Examples 1–4 illustrate functions that describe relationships between real-world variables. The key to using mathematics to analyze a real-world situation often is the recognition of such relationships among the variables that describe the situation. The following example illustrates functions defined by formulas that may be familiar from your previous studies in mathematics and science.

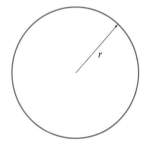

Figure 1.1.2   The area A of a circle is a function of its radius r.

Example 5

- The area A of a circle of radius r (Fig. 1.1.2) is given by

$$A = \pi r^2 \qquad \text{(where } \pi \approx 3.1416\text{)}.$$

We often write such a formula in *function notation* as $A(r) = \pi r^2$ to indicate that the area depends on the radius.

- If a rock is dropped from atop a high tower (Fig. 1.1.3) and the acceleration of gravity is 32 ft/sec², then its (downward) velocity v after t seconds and the distance d it has fallen are given by

$$v(t) = 32t \quad \text{and} \quad d(t) = 16t^2.$$

- If the temperature of a 3-gram sample of carbon dioxide is 27°, then its volume V in liters is given by

$$V(p) = \frac{168}{p}$$

where p is the pressure of the gas in atmospheres.   ◼

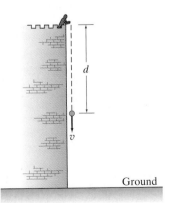

Figure 1.1.3   The distance d the rock has fallen is a function of time t.

Domain and Range of a Function

When we use functions to describe relationships between variables, it is important that we know what numbers are sensible values to substitute for those variables.

Definition: Domain

The collection (or set) D of all numbers for which the number $f(x)$ is defined is called the **domain** (of definition) of the function f.

Example 6

The domain of the volume function $V(p)$ of Example 5 is the set of all *positive real numbers*, because the pressure of a gas can be any positive number of atmospheres. But it would be meaningless to speak of a negative pressure, or even a zero pressure ("nature abhors a vacuum"). ◣

Example 7

The domain of the *reciprocal function* $f(x) = \frac{1}{x}$ is the set of all *nonzero real numbers*—that is, the set of all numbers except zero—since substitution of any nonzero number for x gives a real number value for $f(x)$. ◣

Definition: Range

The set of all possible values $y = f(x)$ is called the **range** of the function f.

Example 8

Suppose the total cost C of manufacturing n copies of a regional cookbook is 500 dollars to set up the printing press, plus 6 dollars for each book actually printed. Then C is given as a function of n by the formula

$$C(n) = 500 + 6n.$$

The domain of the cost function C is the set $\{1, 2, 3, \ldots\}$ of all *positive integers*, because it would be meaningless to speak of printing a negative or fractional number of books. Can you see that the range of C is the set of all numbers described by the list $\{506, 512, 518, \ldots\}$? ◣

Example 9

The range of the reciprocal function $f(x) = \frac{1}{x}$ is (like its domain) the set of all nonzero real numbers, because the expression $\frac{1}{x}$ can take on any value other than zero. ◣

Example 10

The *squaring function* defined by

$$f(x) = x^2$$

assigns to each number x its square x^2. Because every number can be squared, the domain of f is the set—often denoted by $\mathbb{R}$—of all (real) numbers. But only non-negative numbers are themselves squares, so the range of f is the set of all non-negative numbers.

Figure 1.1.4 shows a calculator graph of $y = x^2$. While the calculator shows only that portion of the graph visible in a standard viewing window (with x lying between -5 and 5 and y lying between -10 and 10), we can see that it confirms our observation that no negative numbers are in the range of f.

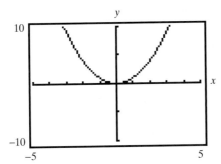

Figure 1.1.4   Calculator graph of $f(x) = x^2$.

Examples 8–10 illustrate the process of finding the range of a function. Frequently, however, we are more concerned with the domain of a function than with its range, because it is crucial for us to know what numbers we can use for the variable x to get "sensible" values for $f(x)$.

Formulas That Describe Functions

As opposed to a table or a graph, a formula provides a "symbolic description" of a function. The formula then specifies how to compute the value $f(x)$ in terms of the number x. Thus the symbol $f(\ )$ may be regarded as an operation that is to be formed whenever a number or expression is inserted between the parentheses.

When we describe the function f by writing a formula $y = f(x)$, we call x the *independent variable* and y the *dependent variable*—because the value of y depends (through the rule or formula of f) on the choice of x. As the independent variable x changes, or varies, then so does the dependent variable y. For instance, as x changes from -2 to 0 to 3, the value $y = x^2$ of Example 10 changes from 4 to 0 to 9.

You may find it useful to visualize the dependence of the value $y = f(x)$ on x by thinking of the function f as a kind of machine that accepts as *input* a number x and then produces as *output* the number $f(x)$, perhaps printed or displayed on a monitor (Fig. 1.1.5).

One such machine is (in effect) the square root key of a simple pocket calculator. When a number x is entered and this key is pressed, the calculator displays (a decimal approximation to) the number $\sqrt{x}$. This square root function $f(x) = \sqrt{x}$ has domain and range both equal to the set of all nonnegative numbers. A calculator like the TI-83 illustrates its knowledge of the domain by displaying an error message if we ask it to calculate the square root of a negative number.

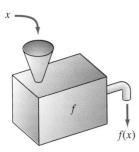

Figure 1.1.5
A "function machine"
with input x and
output $f(x)$.

Example 11

The formula

$$f(x) = x^3 - 3x^2 + 1$$

defines a function f whose domain is the whole real number line $\mathbb{R}$. Some typical values of f are

$$f(-2) = (-2)^3 - 3(-2)^2 + 1 = (-8) - 3(4) + 1 = -19$$

and

$$f(3) = (3)^3 - 3(3)^2 + 1 = (27) - 3(9) + 1 = 1.$$ ◼

Example 12

Not every function has a rule expressible as a simple one-part formula such as $f(x) = \sqrt{x}$. For instance, in 1999 the U.S. first-class postage rate was 33 cents for the first ounce plus 22 cents for each additional ounce or fraction thereof. Thus the postage $s(w)$ for a first-class letter weighing w ounces was given (in dollars) by

$$s(w) = \begin{cases} 0.33 & \text{if } 0 < w \le 1, \\ 0.55 & \text{if } 1 < w \le 2, \\ 0.77 & \text{if } 2 < w \le 3, \\ \vdots \end{cases} \tag{1}$$

Thus the postage-rate function s is described by a multipart formula. ◼

Example 13

The name of a function need not be a single letter. The **int** function on a calculator (Fig. 1.1.6) yields the integer part of the input x—that is, $\text{int}(x)$ is the largest integer that is not greater than x.

Figure 1.1.6 The **int** function on a graphing calculator.

If x is not itself an integer, then $\text{int}(x)$ is the integer just below x. Thus

$$\begin{array}{ll} \text{int}(-1.5) = -2, & \text{int}(0) = 0, \\ \text{int}(0.9) = 0, & \text{int}(1.3) = 1, \\ \text{int}(2) = 2, \text{ and} & \text{int}(\pi) = 3. \end{array}$$ ◼

Example 14

If we think of the function $\text{int}(x)$ as a "floor function" for the real number x, then closely related to it is the "ceiling function" $\text{roof}(x)$, which gives the smallest integer that is not less than x. If x is not itself an integer, then $\text{roof}(x)$ is the integer just above x. Thus

$$\begin{array}{ll} \text{roof}(-1.5) = -1, & \text{roof}(0) = 0, \\ \text{roof}(0.9) = 1, & \text{roof}(1.3) = 2, \\ \text{roof}(2) = 2, \text{and} & \text{roof}(\pi) = 4. \end{array}$$

◣

Example 15

The same function can have quite different descriptions. For a letter weighing $w > 0$ ounces, the number of additional ounces involved is $\text{roof}(w) - 1$. Therefore, the postage $s(w)$ due on this letter is given by

$$s(w) = 0.33 + 0.22 \cdot (\text{roof}(w) - 1) = 0.11 + 0.22 \cdot \text{roof}(w). \quad (2)$$

This is a single-part description of the postage-rate function $s(w)$, as compared with the multipart description in (1).

◣

Mathematical Modeling

The investigation of an applied problem often hinges on defining a function that captures the essence of a geometrical situation. The following problem illustrates this process.

The Dog Pen Problem

Suppose that you run a fencing business, and a customer hires you to build a rectangular dog pen for her Lakeland terrier. She wants the dog pen to have an area of 400 square feet and, after discussing her budget, you determine that she can afford only 60 feet of fence material. However, you can use the back wall of her house as one of the four sides of the pen. What then should be the dimensions of the pen you build, so that its area will be 400 ft² and the three new sides total 60 ft?

Figure 1.1.7 shows the dog pen and its dimensions x and y along and perpendicular to the existing wall. When confronted with a verbally stated problem such as this, our first question is, "How on earth do we get started on it?" The function concept is the key to getting a handle on such a situation. It involves a natural dependent variable—the area A of the rectangular pen. If we can express this dependent variable as a *function* of some (single) independent variable, then we have something tangible to do. We can equate this function to the specified numerical value of the dependent variable (here the area of 400 square feet), and then attempt to solve the resulting equation for the value of the independent variable.

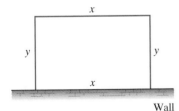

Figure 1.1.7   The dog pen.

Example 16

In connection with the dog pen problem, express the area A of the pen as a function of the length x of its wall side.

The area A of the rectangular pen of length x and width y is

$$A = xy. \tag{3}$$

This is a **formula** that expresses the dependent variable A in terms of the two variables x and y, and therefore does *not* define A as a function of any single independent variable. Some relation between x and y is needed in order to eliminate one of them—so that only one independent variable will remain.

By simply adding up the lengths of the three sides of the pen that must be constructed from the available 60 feet of fence material, we see (Fig. 1.1.7) that the total fence length L is

$$L = x + 2y = 60. \tag{4}$$

Selecting x as the independent variable, we can solve this **relation** for

$$y = \frac{1}{2}(60 - x). \tag{5}$$

Upon substituting this expression for y in (3) we obtain the desired equation

$$A(x) = \frac{1}{2}x(60 - x)$$

that expresses the area A as a **function** of the length x.

In addition to this formula for the function A, we must also specify its domain. Both side lengths of an actual rectangle are positive, so both $x > 0$ and $y > 0$. But we see from (5) that y is positive only if $x < 60$. Thus the complete definition of the area function—including both its formula and its domain—is

$$A(x) = \frac{1}{2}x(60 - x), \qquad 0 < x < 60. \tag{6}$$

It is important to note that the domain of a function is a necessary part of its definition. For each function we define we must therefore specify the domain of values of the independent variable. In applications, we use the values of the independent variable—as in (6)—that are relevant to the problem at hand. ◣

In Example 16 our goal was to express the dependent variable A as a function of the independent variable x. Initially, the geometric situation provided us instead with the following:

1. The **formula** in (3) expressing A in terms of both x and the additional variable y, and
2. The **relation** in (4) between x and y, which we used to eliminate y and thereby express A as a **function** of x alone.

We will see that this **formula-relation-function** pattern is common in many different applied problems.

Example 17

Solve the dog pen problem stated previously. That is, find the dimensions of the pen you should build for your customer.

Example 16 illustrates an important part of the solution of a typical applied problem—the formulation of a **mathematical model** of the situation under study. The area function $A(x)$ defined in (6) provides a mathematical model of the animal pen problem. The shape of the animal pen with the specified area 400 ft^2 can be determined by solving the equation $A(x) = 400$. Using (6), we get

$$\frac{1}{2}x(60 - x) = 400, \qquad (7)$$

$$60x - x^2 = 800, \quad \text{(simplifying)}$$

$$x^2 - 60x + 800 = 0. \qquad \text{(transposing)} \qquad (8)$$

We now have a quadratic equation to solve. We will review general quadratic equations in Chapter 2, but this is a simple one that we can solve by factoring:

$$(x - 20)(x - 40) = 0, \qquad (9)$$

so either

$$x - 20 = 0 \quad \text{or} \quad x - 40 = 0$$

(because a product of two numbers can be zero only if at least one of them is zero). Thus $x = 20$ or $x = 40$. If $x = 20$, then (5) gives $y = 20$ also, in which case our animal pen of area 400 ft^2 is a 20 ft by 20 ft square. But if $x = 40$, then (5) gives $y = 10$, in which case our animal pen of area 400 ft^2 is a 40 ft by 10 ft rectangle. As illustrated in Fig. 1.1.8, the original question as to the dimensions of the animal pen therefore has two answers: 20 ft × 20 ft and 40 ft × 10 ft. Your customer can choose whichever of these two shapes she prefers.

Figure 1.1.8   The two possible dog pens both having area 400 ft^2.

In Problems 1–6 the given formula defines a function. Identify the independent variable and the dependent variable.

1. $y = x^3 - 8$
2. $x = (t + 1)^3$
3. $v = 8\sqrt{h}$
4. $T = 4u - 7$
5. $C = 2\pi r$
6. $V = s^3$

In Problems 7–14, determine whether the given formula, table, or description defines y as a function of x.

7. The record high temperature y in Denver for each month x of the year.
8. The total cost y of purchasing x hamburgers at your favorite fast-food restaurant.

9. The total number y of calories in a chicken sandwich based on the number x of fat grams, according to the following table.

Fat Grams	20	29	5	33	9	33	26	43
Calories	430	550	320	680	300	750	530	710

Source: Chick-Fil-A Gram Comparison

10. The price y of a Christmas tree based on its height x, if

- a 6-foot tree costs between $20 and $50;
- an 8-foot tree costs between $25 and $75;
- an 11-foot tree costs between $100 and $200;
- a 13-foot tree costs $300 or more.

11. The year y that the Dow Jones Average first reached the level x, as indicated in the following table.

Dow Jones Ave.	500	1000	1500	3000	4000	5000	8000	9000
Yr. First Attained	1956	1972	1985	1991	1995	1995	1997	1999

Source: Dow Jones Industrial Average

12. $y = x^2$
13. $x = y^2$
14. $4x - 3y = 8$

In Problems 15–18, find and simplify each of the following values: $f(-1), f(0.5),$ $f(\sqrt{2}), f(a^2), f(2 - a)$.

15. $f(x) = 2x + 3$
16. $f(x) = x^2 + 1$
17. $f(x) = \dfrac{1}{2x + 1}$
18. $f(x) = \sqrt{x^2 + 2}$

In Problems 19–22, find all values of a such that $g(a) = 13$.

19. $g(x) = 3x + 4$
20. $g(x) = \dfrac{12}{1 - x}$
21. $g(x) = \sqrt{5x + 4}$
22. $g(x) = x^2 - 36$

In Problems 23–30, find the largest possible domain on which the given formula defines a real-valued function. (Remember that the square root of a negative number is not defined, and that division by zero is not allowed.)

23. $f(x) = 2x - 7$

24. $f(x) = x^2 - 7$

25. $h(x) = \sqrt{x - 3}$

26. $h(x) = \sqrt{x + 2}$

27. $f(x) = \dfrac{1}{x - 1}$

28. $g(t) = \dfrac{1}{t^2 + 1}$ $1^2 = 1 + 1$

29. $g(t) = \dfrac{1}{t^2 - 4}$

30. $f(x) = \dfrac{1}{\sqrt{x + 5}}$

In Problems 31–36, find the range of values of the function defined by the given formula.

31. The total cost function C for manufacturing n copies of a book, if $C(n) = 1000 + 10n$.

32. The area of a circle of radius r, $A(r) = \pi r^2$.

33. $f(x) = 10 - x$

34. $f(x) = 3x - 1$

35. $f(x) = 8 + x^2$

36. $f(x) = \sqrt{x} - 6$

37. A rectangle has base x and perimeter 100 (Fig. 1.1.9). Show that its area is given by the function

$$A(x) = x(50 - x), \qquad 0 < x < 50.$$

38. If the rectangle of Problem 37 has area 400, find the possible values of its base x. What are the possible dimensions (base and height) of this rectangle?

39. Suppose a rectangle has perimeter 200 and area 2500. Proceed as in Problems 37 and 38 to determine its dimensions.

40. Express the area A of a square as a function of its perimeter $P = 4x$.

41. Express the perimeter P of a square as a function of its area A.

42. Express the area $A = \pi r^2$ of a circle as a function of its circumference $C = 2\pi r$.

43. Express the total surface area $A = 6x^2$ of a cube as a function of its volume $V = x^3$.

44. Figure 1.1.10 shows a rectangular box of volume 125 with square base of edge length x and with height y. Then the volume formula $V = x^2 y$ implies that x and y satisfy the *relation*

$$x^2 y = 125. \tag{10}$$

Figure 1.1.9 $A = xy$ and $P = 2x + 2y$.

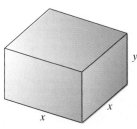

Figure 1.1.10 $V = x^2 y$ and $A = 2x^2 + 4xy$.

Both the top and the bottom of the box have area x^2, and each of its four vertical sides has area xy, so its total surface area is given by the *formula*

$$A = 2x^2 + 4xy. \tag{11}$$

Solve (10) for y in terms of x, and then substitute the result in (11) to show that the box's surface area A is given as a *function* of its base edge length x by

$$A(x) = 2x^2 + \frac{500}{x}.$$

What is the domain of this function?

45. Calculate roof(x) and $-$int($-x$) for $x = -4.5$, $x = -2$, $x = 0$, $x = 1.1$, and $x = 7$. What would you conclude about roof(x) and $-$int($-x$) for any real number x?

46. Use your conclusion from Problem 45 to rewrite the postage function $s(w)$ from Example 13 in terms of int($-x$) instead of roof(x). Then use your calculator to find the values $s(1.2), s(2), s(3.9)$, and $s(5.25)$.

1.2   LINEAR FUNCTIONS AND GRAPHS

Temperature is commonly measured in the United States in Fahrenheit degrees, but in much of the rest of the world it is measured in Celsius degrees. The following table illustrates the relation between the Celsius temperature C and the Fahrenheit temperature F.

C (degrees)	F (degrees)
0	32
10	50
20	68
30	86
40	104
50	122
60	140
70	158
80	176
90	194
100	212

Here, successive Celsius temperatures appear in the first column of the table at equal intervals of 10 degrees. Note also that successive Fahrenheit temperatures appear in the second column at equal intervals of 18 degrees. The fact that equal differences in one column correspond to equal differences in the other indicates a special kind of relationship between corresponding Celsius and Fahrenheit temperatures. Indeed, you can verify that if C and F are corresponding entries in the preceding table, then

$$F = 1.8C + 32. \tag{1}$$

One way would be to substitute each value $C = 0, 10, 20, \ldots, 100$ into (1) and verify in each case that the corresponding value of F shown in the table results.

Another way would be to rewrite (1) as

$$y = 1.8x + 32 \tag{2}$$

with x in place of C and y in place of F. With **Y1=1.8X+32** a calculator yields the table shown in Fig. 1.2.1, where we see the same columns of numerical values as in the preceding Celsius-Fahrenheit table.

If you proceed to graph the function in (2) in the calculator window defined by

Xmin=0	**Ymin=0**
Xmax=100	**Ymax=300**

you get the picture shown in Fig. 1.2.2, where it appears that the graph is a *straight line.* So what is special about the data in our original table of temperatures is this: It is described by a function whose graph is a straight line. Such a function is called *linear.*

X	Y1	
0	32	
10	50	
20	68	
30	86	
40	104	
50	122	
60	140	

X=0

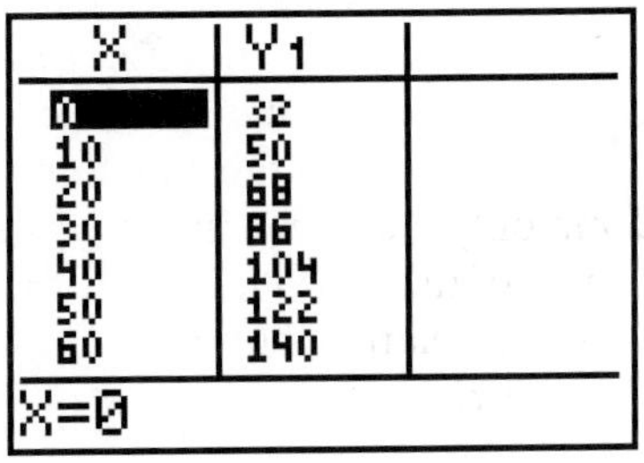

Figure 1.2.1 **Y1=1.8X+32** table with **TblStart=0** and **ΔTbl=10.**

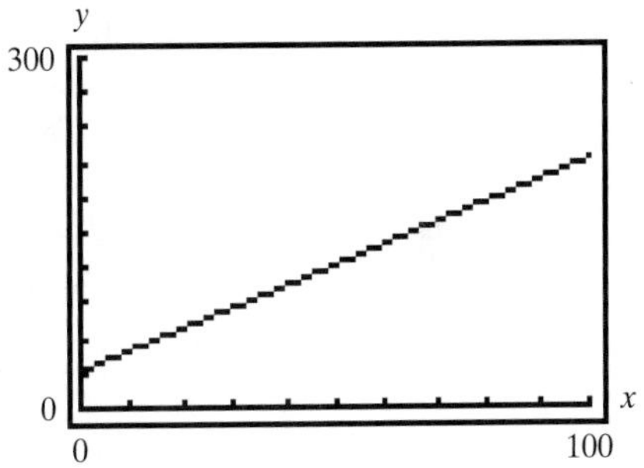

Figure 1.2.2 The graph $y = 1.8x + 32.$

Definition: Linear Function

A **linear function** is one of the form

$$f(x) = mx + b. \tag{3}$$

Note that the right-hand side in (3) contains both a constant term and an x-term (but no higher powers). A particular linear function f is determined when the values of the constant *coefficients* m and b are specified.

Just as two points in the plane determine a straight line, a linear function is determined when two of its values

$$y_1 = mx_1 + b \quad \text{and} \quad y_2 = mx_2 + b \tag{4}$$

are given. As illustrated in the following two examples, the two equations in (4) are then easily solved for the coefficients m and b.

Example 1

Find a linear function f such that $f(2) = 1$ and $f(4) = 15$.

If we substitute the values $x_1 = 2$ and $x_2 = 4$ of the independent variable x, together with the corresponding values $y_1 = 1$ and $y_2 = 15$ of the dependent variable y, into (4), we get the two equations

$$1 = 2m + b$$
$$15 = 4m + b$$

in the desired coefficients m and b. Subtraction of the first equation here from the second yields $14 = 2m$, so $m = 7$. Then substitution of $m = 7$ into the first equation gives $1 = 2(7) + b$, so $b = -13$. Thus the desired linear function is given by

$$f(x) = 7x - 13. \qquad \blacksquare$$

Example 2

The Celsius temperature C is defined as a linear function of the Fahrenheit temperature F such that $0°C$ corresponds to the freezing point $32°F$, while $100°C$ corresponds to the boiling point $212°F$ of water. Express C as a function of F.

Substitution of the corresponding values $C = 0$, $F = 32$ and $C = 100$, $F = 212$ into $C = mF + b$ yields the equations

$$0 = 32m + b,$$
$$100 = 212m + b.$$

Subtraction of the first equation here from the second equation gives $100 = 180\, m$, so it follows that $m = 100/180 = \frac{5}{9}$. Substitution of $m = \frac{5}{9}$ into the first equation gives $0 = 32(\frac{5}{9}) + b$, so it follows that $b = -160/9$. Consequently, the desired linear function expressing C in terms of F is given by

$$C = \frac{5}{9} F - \frac{160}{9}. \qquad (5)$$

You should verify that solution of this equation for F as a linear function of C gives the equation in (1) at the beginning of this section. $\qquad \blacksquare$

Straight Lines and Linear Graphs

The **graph** of the linear function $f(x) = mx + b$ is the straight line consisting of all points (x, y) in the xy-plane that satisfy the equation

$$y = mx + b. \qquad (6)$$

Although we often abbreviate and speak of "the straight line $y = mx + b$," it is important to understand the difference between

- the linear *function f*,
- its defining *formula* $f(x) = mx + b$,
- the *equation* $y = mx + b$, and
- the *graph* with equation $y = mx + b$.

In particular, the words *function, equation,* and *graph* should not be used interchangeably. In mathematics (as elsewhere), it's important to "say what you mean and mean what you say."

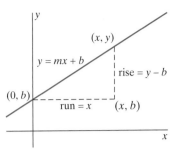

Figure 1.2.3   Slope = rise/run.

Substitution of $x = 0$ in $y = mx + b$ gives $y = b$, so the straight line intersects the y-axis in the point $(0, b)$. **Thus the constant b is the y-intercept of the line** (Fig. 1.2.3) and therefore measures its vertical location. If (x, y) is a second point on this line, then the (vertical) *rise* and (horizontal) *run* from the point $(0, b)$ to the point (x, y) are given by

$$rise = y - b = (mx + b) - b = mx,$$
$$run = x - 0 = x. \tag{7}$$

Recall that the **slope** of a line in the xy-plane is defined by

$$slope = \frac{rise}{run}. \tag{8}$$

Substitution of (7) in (8) therefore gives

$$slope = \frac{mx}{x} = m \quad \text{for the line} \quad y = mx + b. \tag{9}$$

Thus the coefficient m of x is the slope of the line and therefore measures the steepness of the line.

The Slope-Intercept Equation

The line with slope m and y-intercept b consists of all points in the xy-plane whose coordinates (x, y) satisfy the equation

$$y = mx + b. \tag{6}$$

Example 3

Define **Y1=M*X+B** in the ⌊Y=⌋ menu of your graphing calculator. Then enter several different pairs of slope-intercept values as indicated in Fig. 1.2.4, pressing ⌊GRAPH⌋ after each is entered.

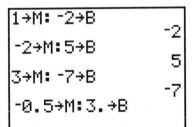

Figure 1.2.4   Various slopes m and y-intercepts b.

As illustrated in Figs. 1.2.5 and 1.2.6, you should find that

- the line *rises* (from left to right) if the slope m is *positive*;
- the *larger* is $m > 0$, the more *steeply* the line rises;
- the line *falls* (from left to right) if the slope m is *negative*;
- the *larger* (in the negative direction) is $m < 0$, the more *steeply* the line falls.

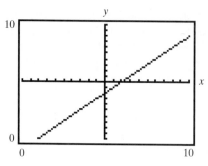

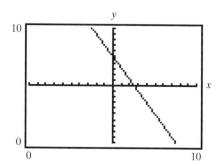

Figure 1.2.5   Slope $m = 1$ and y-intercept $b = -2$, so $y = x - 2$.

Figure 1.2.6   Slope $m = -2$ and y-intercept $b = 5$, so $y = -2x + 5$.   ◣

Figure 1.2.7 shows two points on a line with slope m. The point (x_0, y_0) is a fixed point, and (x, y) is any other point on the line. Using the indicated rise-run values, the slope of this line is given by

$$m = \text{slope} = \frac{\text{rise}}{\text{run}} = \frac{y - y_0}{x - x_0}.$$

If we equate the extreme members here and multiply the result by $x - x_0$, we get the equation $y - y_0 = m(x - x_0)$.

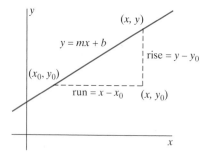

Figure 1.2.7   Slope $=$ rise/run.

The Point-Slope Equation

The line with slope m passing through the fixed point (x_0, y_0) consists of all points in the xy-plane whose coordinates (x, y) satisfy the equation

$$y - y_0 = m(x - x_0). \tag{10}$$

The rise and run between any two given points on a line can be used to determine its slope. Figure 1.2.8 shows two points (x_1, y_1) and (x_2, y_2) on a line.

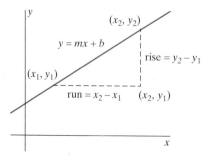

Figure 1.2.8   Slope $=$ rise/run.

Using the indicated horizontal run and vertical rise between these two points, we find that the slope of this line is given by

$$m = \frac{y_2 - y_1}{x_2 - x_1} = \frac{\Delta y}{\Delta x} \qquad (11)$$

where we use the capital Greek letter Δ to denote "difference." Thus

$$\Delta y = y_2 - y_1 \text{ and } \Delta x = x_2 - x_1 \qquad (12)$$

represent the differences of the y- and x-coordinates, respectively (in the same order).

Example 4

Find the slope-intercept equation of the line through the points $(2, 1)$ and $(4, 15)$. According to (11), the slope m of the line is given by

$$m = \frac{\Delta y}{\Delta x} = \frac{15 - 1}{4 - 2} = \frac{14}{2} = 7.$$

First we use the point-slope equation (10) with (x_0, y_0) being the point $(2, 1)$. This gives the equation

$$y - 1 = 7(x - 2),$$

which—upon solving for y—readily simplifies to the desired slope-intercept equation

$$y = 7x - 13$$

of the line. Note that we have found in another way the linear function $f(x)$ of Example 1, such that $f(2) = 1$ and $f(4) = 15$. You might also check that the *same* slope-intercept equation results if we use the point-slope equation with $(4, 15)$ rather than $(2, 1)$ as the given point (x_0, y_0) on the line. ∎

Graphs of Equations and Functions
A straight line is a simple example of a graph of an equation.

> **Definition:**   **Graph of an Equation**
> The **graph** of an equation involving two variables x and y consists of all points in the xy-plane whose coordinates (x, y) satisfy the equation.

For instance, there are three types of equations whose graphs are straight lines:

- Equations whose graphs are vertical lines
- Equations whose graphs are horizontal lines
- Equations whose graphs are slanted lines (neither vertical nor horizontal)

Example 5

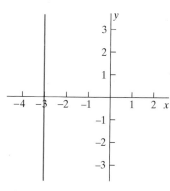

Figure 1.2.9   The graph of $x = -3$.

The graph of the equation $x = -3$, illustrated in Fig. 1.2.9, is a vertical line. Only ordered pairs (x, y) with first coordinate x equal -3 will satisfy this equation. The second coordinate y can be any real number. ∎

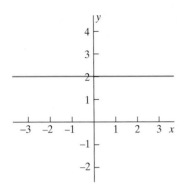

Figure 1.2.10   The graph of $y = 2$.

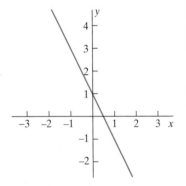

Figure 1.2.11   The graph of $y = -2x + 1$.

Example 6

The graph of the equation $y = 2$, illustrated in Fig. 1.2.10, is a horizontal line. Here the first coordinate x can be any real number, but the second coordinate y must equal 2. ◧

Example 7

Figure 1.2.11 shows the graph of the equation $y = -2x + 1$. Note that it is a slanted line, falling from left to right, with y-intercept 1. ◧

The graph of a function is a special case of the graph of an equation.

> **Definition: Graph of a Function**
> The **graph** of the function f is the graph of the equation $y = f(x)$.

Thus the graph of the function f consists of all points in the plane whose coordinates have the form $(x, f(x))$ with x being in the domain of f. Observe that the second coordinate of any such point is the value of f at its first coordinate (Fig. 1.2.12).

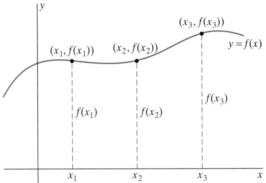

Figure 1.2.12   The graph of the function f.

Because the function has only one value $f(x)$ at x, **a vertical straight line in the plane cannot intersect the graph of a function in two or more points.** It follows, for instance, that a circle cannot be the graph of a *function,* even though it *is* the graph of an *equation*—for instance, the graph of the equation $x^2 + y^2 = 1$ is a circle of radius 1. Any horizontal or slanted straight line is the graph of a function, but a vertical line cannot be the graph of a function (though it is the graph of an equation).

Example 8

In 1999, Mindspring Enterprises offered a "light" plan for internet access, in which the monthly cost was $6.95 for up to 5 hours of connection time, with additional hours charged at $2.00 each. We can represent the monthly cost C as a function of the number h of hours used by writing the two-part formula

$$C(h) = \begin{cases} 6.95 & \text{if } 0 \le h \le 5, \\ 6.95 + 2(h - 5) & \text{if } h > 5. \end{cases}$$

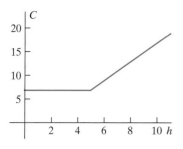

Figure 1.2.13   The graph of the cost function $C(h)$ for the Mindspring "light" plan.

Figure 1.2.13 shows the graph of this function. Note that the graph consists of two straight line pieces—one horizontal and one slanted—that meet at the point $(5, 6.95)$ and correspond to the two parts of the formula.   ◤

Example 9

Figure 1.2.14 shows the calculator graph **Y1=abs(X)** of the absolute value function defined mathematically by

$$|x| = \begin{cases} x & \text{if } x \geq 0, \\ -x & \text{if } x < 0. \end{cases}$$

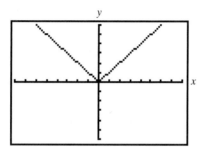

Figure 1.2.14   Graph of $y = |x|$.

The reason the graph "turns the corner" at the origin is that it consists of two straight line pieces:

- the left half of the line $y = -x$, which falls from left to right with slope -1, and
- the right half of the line $y = x$, which rises from left to right with slope $+1$.   ◤

Example 10

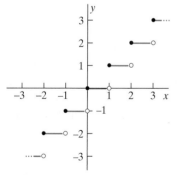

Figure 1.2.15   Graph of $y = \text{int}(x)$.

Figure 1.2.15 shows the graph of the integer part function $\text{int}(x)$ of Example 13 in Section 1.1. Note the "jumps" that occur at the integer values of x, causing the graph to consist of different pieces corresponding to different successive integer intervals on the x-axis. In particular, the part of the graph above the interval $n \leq x < n + 1$ (with n an integer) lies on the horizontal line $y = n$. The reason for this is that any number x in the given interval "rounds down" to the integer n.   ◤

Graphic, Numeric, and Symbolic Viewpoints

A formula $y = f(x)$ provides a *symbolic* description of the function f. A table of values of f is a *numeric* representation of the function. In this section we have introduced *graphic* representations of functions. Interesting applications often involve looking at the same function from at least two of these three viewpoints.

Example 11

Suppose that a car begins (at time $t = 0$ hr) in Danbury, Connecticut (position $x = 0$ mi) and travels to Hartford (position $x = 60$ mi) with a constant speed of 60 mi/hr. The car stays in Hartford for exactly one hour, and then returns to

Danbury, again with a constant speed of 60 mi/hr. Describe the car's position function both graphically and symbolically.

It should be fairly clear that the car's distance from Danbury is $x = 60t$ during the one-hour trip from Danbury to Hartford. For instance, after $t = \frac{1}{2}$ hr the car has traveled halfway, so $x = (\frac{1}{2})(60) = 30$. During the next hour, with $1 < t \leq 2$, the car's position is constant, $x \equiv 60$. Perhaps you can see that during the return trip of the third hour, with $2 < t \leq 3$, the car's position is given by

$$x = 60 - 60(t - 2) = 180 - 60t$$

because at time t it has been traveling for $t - 2$ hours at 60 mi/hr back toward Danbury from Hartford. Thus the position function is defined symbolically by the three-part formula

$$x(t) = \begin{cases} 60t & \text{if } 0 \leq t \leq 1, \\ 60 & \text{if } 1 < t \leq 2, \\ 180 - 60t & \text{if } 2 < t \leq 3. \end{cases}$$

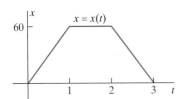

Figure 1.2.16 Graph of the position function in Example 11.

The domain of this function is the interval $0 \leq t \leq 3$, and its graph is shown in Fig. 1.2.16. ◼

1.2 PROBLEMS

In Problems 1–4, find a linear function $f(x) = ax + b$ having the given values.

1. $f(2) = 7$ and $f(5) = 13$
2. $f(3) = 5$ and $f(7) = 17$
3. $f(-2) = 19$ and $f(3) = -16$
4. $f(1) = 8$ and $f(3) = -10$

In Problems 5–8, find the slope-intercept equation $y = mx + b$ of the straight line passing through the given points.

5. $(1, 7)$ and $(5, 27)$
6. $(1, 7)$ and $(3, -1)$
7. $(-3, -2)$ and $(3, 50)$
8. $(2, 9)$ and $(6, 51)$

In Problems 9–14, write (in slope-intercept form) an equation of the line L described and sketch its graph.

9. L passes through the origin and the point $(2, 3)$.
10. L is vertical and has x-intercept 7.
11. L is horizontal and passes through the point $(3, -5)$.
12. L has x-intercept 2 and y-intercept -3.
13. L passes through $(-1, -4)$ and has slope $\frac{1}{2}$.
14. L passes through $(4, 2)$ and rises (left to right) at a 45 degree angle.

Three points A, B, and C lie on a single straight line if and only if the slope of AB equals the slope of BC. In Problems 15–18, plot the three given points and then determine whether they lie on a single line.

15. $A(-1, -2), B(2, 1), C(4, 3)$
16. $A(-2, 5), B(2, 3), C(8, 0)$
17. $A(-1, 6), B(1, 2), C(4, -2)$
18. $A(-3, 2), B(1, 6), C(8, 14)$

Sketch the graphs of the functions in Problems 19–22. Take into account the domain of definition of each function (either stated or implied), and plot points as necessary.

19. $f(x) = 2 - 5x, -1 \le x \le 1$

20. $f(x) = 2 - 5x, 0 \le x \le 3$

21. $f(x) = |x - 1|$

22. $f(x) = |2x|$

Sketch the graphs of the functions in Problems 23–25. Indicate any points where jumps or gaps in the graph occur.

23. $f(x) = \begin{cases} -2 \text{ if } x < 0, \\ 3 \text{ if } x \ge 0 \end{cases}$

24. $f(x) = \dfrac{|x|}{x}$

25. $f(x) = \text{int}(2x)$

26. The Fahrenheit temperature F and the absolute temperature K are linear functions of each other. Moreover, $K = 273.16$ when $F = 32$, and $K = 373.16$ when $F = 212$. Express K in terms of F. What is the value of F when $K = 0$ (absolute zero)?

27. The length L (in centimeters) of a copper rod is a linear function of its Celsius temperature C. If $L = 124.942$ when $C = 20$ and $L = 125.134$ when $C = 110$, express L in terms of C.

28. The owner of a grocery store finds that she can sell 980 gal of milk each week at \$1.69/gal and 1220 gal of milk each week at \$1.49/gal. Assume that sales S is a linear function of the price P per gallon. How many gallons would she then expect to sell at \$1.56/gal?

29. Assume the total daily production P of an oil field is a decreasing linear function of the number x of oil wells drilled (so long as any oil at all is produced). With 20 wells drilled the field has been producing 4000 barrels of oil daily. For each new well that is drilled, the daily production of each well decreases by 5 barrels per day. Write P as a function of x.

In Problems 30–32, write a symbolic description of the function whose graph is pictured. You may use the integer part function $\text{int}(x)$.

30.

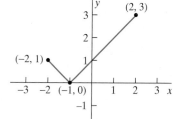

31.

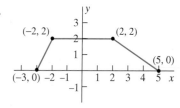

32.

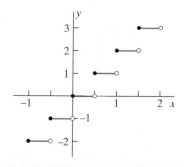

Each of Problems 33–36 describes a trip you made along a straight road connecting two cities 120 miles apart. Sketch the graph of the distance x from your starting point (in miles) as a function of the time t elapsed (in hours). Also describe the function $x(t)$ symbolically.

33. You traveled for one hour at 45 mph, then realized you were going to be late and therefore traveled at 75 mph for the next hour.

34. You traveled for one hour at 60 mph, were suddenly engulfed in dense fog, and therefore drove back home at 30 mph.

35. You traveled for one hour at 60 mph, stopped for a half hour while a herd of bison crossed the road, and then drove on toward your destination for the next hour at 60 mph.

36. You traveled for a half hour at 60 mph, suddenly remembered you'd left your wallet at home, drove back at 60 mph to get it, and finally drove two hours at 60 mph to reach your destination.

37. Suppose that the cost C of printing a pamphlet of at most 100 pages is a linear function of the number p of pages it contains. It costs $1.70 to print a pamphlet with 34 pages, whereas a pamphlet with 79 pages costs $3.05 to print.

   (a) Express C as a function of p.

   (b) Find the cost of printing a pamphlet with 50 pages.

   (c) The graph of the function $C(p)$ is a straight line. Tell what the slope and the C-intercept of this line mean—perhaps in terms of the "fixed cost" to set up the press for printing and the "marginal cost" of each additional page printed.

38. Suppose that the cost C of renting a car for a day is a linear function of the number x of miles you drove that day. The following table shows the cost of rental for various numbers of miles driven in a day.

Miles	100	150	200	250
Cost	$62.00	$79.50	$97.00	$114.50

   (a) Express C as a function of x.

   (b) How many miles did you drive if you were charged $90.70?

   (c) The graph of the function $C(x)$ is a straight line. Tell what the slope and the C-intercept of this line mean—perhaps in terms of the daily rental charge and the fee for each mile driven.

39. For a Federal Express letter weighing at most one pound sent to a certain destination, the charge C is $8.00 for the first 8 ounces plus 80 cents for each additional ounce or fraction thereof. Sketch the graph of this function C of the total number x of ounces.

40. In a certain city, the charge C for a taxi trip of at most 20 miles is $3.00 for the first 2 miles (or fraction thereof) plus 50 cents for each half-mile (or fraction thereof) up to a total of 10 miles, plus 50 cents for each mile (or part thereof) over 10 miles. Sketch the graph of this function C of the number x of miles.

1.3   CONSTANT CHANGE AND LINEAR GROWTH

Suppose the following table records the growth in the population of a certain city during the 1990s.

Year	Population (thous)
1990	110
1991	116
1992	122
1993	128
1994	134
1995	140
1996	146
1997	152
1998	158
1999	164
2000	170

It should be obvious that each number in the second column is found by adding 6 thousand to the previous one. Thus the population of this hypothetical city grew each year during the 1990s by the same amount of 6 thousand people.

In order to describe this city's population as a *function* of time t, let's take $t = 0$ in 1990. The result of starting with a population of $P(0) = 110$ thousand people, and adding 6 thousand people t times in succession—once each year—can be described by saying that after t years the population is given by

$$P(t) = 110 + 6t. \tag{1}$$

Thus the population of our city is a **linear** function of time t. Note that the constant term in (1) is the city's *initial population,* and the coefficient of t is its annual change in population.

More generally, suppose a city has an initial population of

$$P(0) = P_0$$

at time $t = 0$, and that its annual change in population is m (the same every year). Then after t years the population has increased by

$$\Delta P = m \cdot t \tag{2}$$

(using the Section 1.2 Δ-notation for differences). Therefore, the city's population after t years is

$$P = \text{initial population} + \text{change} = P_0 + \Delta P = P_0 + mt.$$

Thus a population $P(t)$ with **initial population** P_0 and (constant) **annual change** m is described by the linear function

$$P(t) = P_0 + mt. \tag{3}$$

Not all populations are described by linear functions. But a population model like the one in (3)—with a constant term and a t-term—is called a *linear population model*.

Definition: Constant Rate of Change

Whatever units of time we use, a population described by the function $P(t) = P_0 + mt$ changes by m during each unit of time. We therefore call m the population's **rate of change** (per unit of time).

Because the population changes by the same amount during each unit of time, we say that its rate of change is constant. Any quantity depending on time t with a **constant** rate of change is a **linear** function of t. In this section we mainly discuss linear population models. In Section 1.4 we discuss linear models for a wider variety of processes.

Example 1

On January 1, 1999 the population of Ajax City was 67,255 and had increased by 2935 people during the preceding year. Suppose this rate of increase continues—with 2935 more people added to the population of Ajax City each subsequent year. Find each of the following:

(a)   A linear function $P(t)$ modeling the population of Ajax City.

(b)   The predicted population of Ajax City on October 1, 2002, based on the model.

(c)   The month and the calendar year in which the population of Ajax City reaches 100 thousand.

(a)   In a given problem, we must decide when to start the clock, and we can count population however we wish—either by the person or by the thousand (for instance). If we take $t = 0$ on 1/1/1999 and measure population in thousands, then we need to substitute the initial population $P_0 = 67.255$ and the annual population change $m = 2.935$ in Eq. (2). This gives the linear model

$$P(t) = 67.255 + 2.935t \quad \text{(thousand)} \tag{4}$$

describing the growing population of Ajax City. (If we counted by the person rather than by the thousand, then the decimal points here would be replaced with commas.)

(b)   October 1, 2002 is 3 years and 9 months—that is, 3.75 years—after January 1, 1999. So we need only substitute $t = 3.75$ in (3) and calculate

$$P(3.75) = 67.255 + 2.935 \times 3.75 = 78.261.$$

Thus our linear model predicts an Ajax City population of 78.261 thousand, or 78,261 people on October 1, 2002.

(c)   We need to set

$$P(t) = 67.255 + 2.935t = 100$$

and solve for t:

$$2.935t = 100 - 67.255 = 32.745$$

so

$$t = \frac{32.745}{2.935} = 11.157 \text{ years.}$$

Starting with January 1, 1999 when $t = 0$, exactly 11 years later is January 1 of the year $1999 + 11 = 2010$. So the population of Ajax City hits 100 thousand

$$0.157 \text{ years} = 0.157 \text{ years} \times \frac{12 \text{ months}}{\text{year}} = 1.88 \text{ months}$$

into the year 2010. This is during February 2010.

Note that for the purpose of calendar-month problems like this, we will consider the year to be divided into 12 equal months. This is slightly inaccurate, but it is standard practice to take the differing lengths of individual months into account only when a question asks for a specific day of a particular month. ◣

Slope and Rate of Change

Recall from Section 1.2 the **slope-intercept equation**

$$y = mx + b \tag{5}$$

of a straight line in the xy-plane with coefficients

$$m = \text{slope} \quad \text{and} \quad b = y\text{-intercept} \tag{6}$$

as illustrated in Fig. 1.3.1.

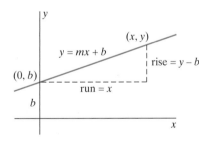

Figure 1.3.1   The slope-intercept equation $y = mx + b$ of a straight line.

The population equation

$$P = P_0 + mt \tag{7}$$

has the same linear form as the slope-intercept equation (5), but with independent variable t instead of x, and with dependent variable P instead of y. Also, the coefficients (or *parameters*) in the linear function (7) are

$$m = \text{rate of change} \quad \text{and} \quad P_0 = \text{initial population.} \tag{8}$$

Comparing (6) and (8), we note the correspondence between the **slope** of a straight line and the **rate of change** of a linear function. Indeed, the rate of change

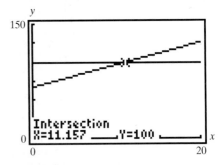

Figure 1.3.2   The graph of the linear function $P = P_0 + mt$.

m of the linear function $P = P_0 + mt$ is simply the slope of its straight line graph in the tP-plane (Fig. 1.3.2).

Example 2

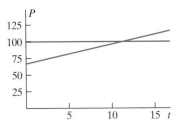

Figure 1.3.3   The graphs $P = 67.255 + 2.935t$ and $P = 100$.

Figure 1.3.3 shows the graph of the Ajax City population function

$$P = 67.255 + 2.935t$$

of Eq. (4) in Example 1, and also the horizontal line

$$P = 100.$$

The indicated point of intersection of these two lines is the point (t, P) where both equations give the same value of P, that is,

$$67.255 + 2.935t = 100. \qquad (9)$$

In Example 1(c) we solved this equation algebraically for $t = 11.157$. For variety and practice with a graphing calculator, we can also solve it graphically.

To do this, we need to plot the two sides of Eq. (9) simultaneously and see where the two graphs intersect. Because a graphing calculator requires that x and y (rather than t and P) be used as the independent and dependent variables, we need to plot the functions

$$y = 67.255 + 2.935x \quad \text{and} \quad y = 100.$$

Figure 1.3.4 shows the Y= menu. Figure 1.3.5 shows the resulting plot with viewing window

Xmin=0	**Ymin=0**
Xmax=20	**Ymax=150**

Figure 1.3.4   The Y= menu for the graphical solution of Example 1(c).

Figure 1.3.5   The graphs **Y1=67.255+2.935X** and **Y2=100** intersect at $(11.157, 100)$.

We have used the calculator's **CALC intersect** facility to locate the point of intersection. The indicated result $(11.157, 100)$ agrees with our previous algebraic solution $t = 11.157$ of Eq. (9). ∎

Example 3

We now proceed to solve Example 1(c) using our calculator's table-making facility. First we must enter the function we wish to tabulate. This is done in the same way as when we wish to graph a function—using the ⎡Y=⎤ menu. (In this case our function is already stored in **Y1** from Example 2; we can clear **Y2** since we no longer need it.)

To prepare to tabulate values of the function we've defined, we must specify the sort of table we want using the calculator's **TBLSET** (table-set) menu. We want to start our table at $x = 0$ and proceed by yearly increments of $\Delta x = 1$. Thus our table's *starting point* and its *increment* between successive entries are specified by entering these two parameters as shown in Fig. 1.3.6.

Figure 1.3.6 Initial table setting for the Ajax City population function.

Now we're ready to go! When we execute the calculator's **TABLE** command, we get the table shown in Fig. 1.3.7. This table doesn't go quite far enough to reach a population of 100 thousand, so we use the calculator's down arrow to scroll down. The calculator obligingly fills in additional values, with the result shown in Fig. 1.3.8. Again we see the population is closest to 100 thousand when $x \approx 11$ years (using the symbol $\approx$ for approximate equality, as opposed to $=$, which means exact equality). But the population is still a bit short of 100 thousand after precisely 11 years, so the exact population is hit sometime during the twelfth year after Jan. 1, 1999.

X	Y1
0.000	67.255
1.000	70.190
2.000	73.125
3.000	76.060
4.000	78.995
5.000	81.930
6.000	84.865

X=0

X	Y1
7.000	87.800
8.000	90.735
9.000	93.670
10.000	96.605
11.000	99.540
12.000	102.48
13.000	105.41

X=13

Figure 1.3.7 Initial table for the Ajax City population function.

Figure 1.3.8 Additional table values for the Ajax City population function.

To see more closely when during the twelfth year the population reaches 100 thousand, we use the calculator's table-set menu to specify the new starting value $x = 11$ and the new increment $\Delta x = 0.1$ (Fig. 1.3.9). The resulting table (Fig. 1.3.10) indicates that the population is closest to 100 thousand after

```
TABLE SETUP
 TblStart=11
 ∆Tbl=.1
Indent: Auto  Ask
Depend: Auto  Ask
```

```
  X    │  Y1   │
───────┼───────┤
11.000 │ 99.540│
11.100 │ 99.834│
11.200 │ 100.13│
11.300 │ 100.42│
11.400 │ 100.71│
11.500 │ 101.01│
11.600 │ 101.30│
───────┴───────┘
X=11
```

Figure 1.3.9   Second table setting for the Ajax City population function.

Figure 1.3.10   Second table for the Ajax City population function.

11.2 years (rounded off to the nearest *tenth* of a year). This is because 100.13 thousand after 11.2 years is closer to 100 thousand than is 99.834 thousand after 11.1 years.

To narrow it down still further—in the interval between $x = 11.1$ years and $x = 11.2$ years—we go back to the calculator's table-set menu and specify starting point $x = 11.1$ and increment $\Delta x = 0.01$. (Note that we typically divide our desired interval of x-values into ten "pieces.") Then the **TABLE** command yields the table shown in Fig. 1.3.11. Now we see that the population of Ajax City is closest to 100 thousand after $x \approx 11.16$ years (rounded off accurate to the nearest *hundredth* of a year).

```
  X    │  Y1   │
───────┼───────┤
11.100 │ 99.834│
11.110 │ 99.863│
11.120 │ 99.892│
11.130 │ 99.922│
11.140 │ 99.951│
11.150 │ 99.980│
11.160 │ 100.01│
───────┴───────┘
X=11.1
```

Figure 1.3.11   Third table for the Ajax City population function.

In order to satisfy yourself that we will obtain the same answer here as we did in Example 1(c) and Example 2, you should perform this "table zoom" procedure one more time, with starting point $x = 11.15$ and increment $\Delta x = 0.001$. Do you see that the population is closest to 100 thousand when $x = 11.157$ years? ◼

Perhaps it seems to you that this "table zooming" is a great deal more work than solving the linear equation $67.255 + 2.935t = 100$ algebraically. Most people (including the authors) would agree with you. The method is presented here to illustrate that you will have a choice of algebraic, graphic, and numeric methods for solving the problems you will encounter. In another situation, you may find using the table preferable.

The Linear Population Model

Figure 1.3.12 shows a line through the point (x_1, y_1) with slope

$$m = \frac{\text{rise}}{\text{run}} = \frac{y - y_1}{x - x_1}.$$

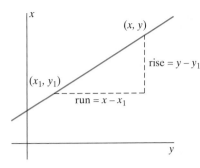

Figure 1.3.12   The point-slope equation $y - y_1 = m(x - x_1)$.

Cross multiplication then gives the **point-slope equation** (Section 1.2)

$$y - y_1 = m(x - x_1) \tag{10}$$

of a straight line that passes through the point (x_1, y_1) and has slope m.

If we replace x and y in (6) with t and P, we obtain the equation

$$P - P_1 = m(t - t_1) \tag{11}$$

describing a population P with rate of change m such that $P = P_1$ at time t_1. Solution for P yields the linear population function

$$P(t) = P_1 + m(t - t_1) \tag{12}$$

satisfying the condition $P(t_1) = P_1$ rather than the initial condition $P(0) = P_0$. But if we replace t_1 with 0 and P_1 with the initial population P_0, we get our original linear population function

$$P(t) = P_0 + mt. \tag{13}$$

Thus (13) is the special case $t_1 = 0$ of (12).

Which population model—(12) or (13)—do we use in a problem where the rate of change m is given? The population at some specified time must also be given. It depends on whether this specified time is $t = 0$ [in which case we use (13)] or some other time $t_1 \neq 0$ [in which case we use (12)].

Actually, we could just forget (13) and substitute $t_1 = 0$ in (12) when appropriate—that is, when the specified time is 0. However, most people prefer to have both (12) and (13) available for use. Sometimes one form seems easier to use, sometimes the other.

In many problems we can take our choice of formulas (in effect) by our selection of the starting time for our clock. For instance, suppose we are given the value of a population in the year 1990. If we take $t = 1990$ in the year 1990, then we should use (12), substituting for P_1 the given 1990 population. But if we restart our clock by setting $t = 0$ in 1990, then we use (13) and substitute for P_0 the given 1990 population.

Example 4

Maywood has a constant rate of growth of 125 people per year, and on October 1, 1990 its population was 3470 people. Find a population model for Maywood.

Since Maywood's constant rate of growth is 125 people per year, $m = 125$ in either (12) or (13). If we take

$$t_1 = 1990 \quad \text{and} \quad P_1 = 3470$$

then (12) yields

$$P(t) = 3470 + 125(t - 1990). \tag{14}$$

But if we take $t = 0$ in 1990, then (12) with $P_0 = 3470$ gives

$$P(t) = 3470 + 125t. \tag{15}$$

For instance, substitution of $t = 10$ in (15) gives a year 2000 population of $3470 + 1250 = 4720$, as does substitution of $t = 2000$ in (14). Of course, the results must be the same whether we reset our clock in 1990 or not. ◣

Frequently the values $P_1 = P(t_1)$ and $P_2 = P(t_2)$ of a linear population function $P(t)$ at two different specified times t_1 and t_2 are given, and we must calculate the population's (constant) rate of change

$$m = \frac{\Delta P}{\Delta t} = \frac{P_2 - P_1}{t_2 - t_1} \tag{16}$$

before proceeding. The change $\Delta P = P_2 - P_1$ in the population during the time interval $\Delta t = t_2 - t_1$ is illustrated in Fig. 1.3.13.

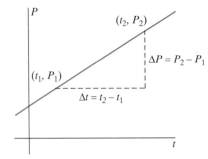

Figure 1.3.13 At time change Δt and the population change ΔP.

We originally defined the rate of change m to be the change in the population in a *unit* time interval—that is, a time interval of length 1. But if the rate of change is constant—that is, equal changes occur during equal time intervals—then the change during a time interval of length Δt is given by $\Delta P = m \cdot \Delta t$, so it follows that $m = \Delta P / \Delta t$ as in (16).

Example 5

On January 1, 1992 the population of Yucca City was 46,350 and on July 1, 1994 it was 56,925. Suppose this rate of population increase continues for the foreseeable future.

(a) Write a linear function $P(t) = \ldots$ giving the population of Yucca City at time t (where $t = 1992$ on January 1, 1992).
(b) Find the expected population of Yucca City on October 1, 2000.
(c) In what month of what calendar year will the population of Yucca City hit 100 thousand?

(a)   Note that July 1, 1994 is two and a half years after January 1, 1992. So if we measure population in thousands, then the population of Yucca City is

$$P_1 = 46.350 \quad \text{when} \quad t_1 = 1992.0 \text{ (on 1/1/1992), and}$$
$$P_2 = 56.925 \quad \text{when} \quad t_2 = 1994.5 \text{ (on 7/1/1994).}$$

Thus

$$\Delta P = 56.925 - 46.350 = 10.575 \text{ thous, and}$$
$$\Delta t = 1994.5 - 1992 = 2.5 \text{ years.}$$

Hence the rate of change of the population is

$$m = \frac{\Delta P}{\Delta t} = \frac{10.575}{2.5} = 4.230$$

thousand people per year. With $t_1 = 1992$ and $P_1 = 46.350$, substitution of this rate of change in (12) gives the linear model formula

$$P(t) = 46.350 + 4.230(t - 1992) \tag{17}$$

for the population of Yucca City in the calendar year t.

(b)   Because September is the ninth month of the calendar year, October 1, 2000 is 9 months $= \frac{3}{4}$ year into the year 2000. To find the population when $t = 2000.75$, we use (17) to calculate

$$P(2000.75) = 46.350 + 4.230 \times 8.75 \approx 83.363 \text{ (thous).}$$

Thus our linear model predicts 83,363 people in Yucca City on 10/1/2000.

(c)   We need to set

$$P(t) = 46.350 + 4.230(t - 1992) = 100$$

and solve for t. Thus

$$t = 1992 + \frac{100 - 46.350}{4.230} \approx 2004.683.$$

(Figure 1.3.14 shows a graphic solution, but in this case the algebraic solution may be quicker.)

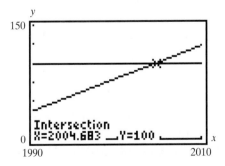

Figure 1.3.14   The graphs **Y1=46.350+4.230(X−1992)** and **Y2=100** plotted with **Xmin=1990** and **Xmax=2010** intersect at (2004.683, 100).

So the function $P(t)$ reaches the value 100

$$0.683 \text{ year} = 0.683 \text{ year} \times \frac{12 \text{ months}}{\text{year}} = 8.196 \text{ months}$$

into the year 2004. Therefore, the population of Yucca City should hit 100 thousand during the ninth month of the year 2004, that is, during the month of September 2004. (Since August is the eighth month of the year, we are 0.196 month into September.)   ◼

Example 6

On January 1, 1997 the population of Amityville was 27,255 and was increasing at the rate of 935 people per year. On the same date the population of Bittersville was only 21,765 but was increasing at the rate of 1465 people per year. Assuming these rates of increase continue, during what month of what calendar year will the population of Bittersville overtake that of Amityville?

Often there are different ways to answer the same question. Here we'll illustrate three slightly different approaches. It's a cliché that "different strokes work for different folks." Moreover, a problem is often clearer when it's viewed from multiple perspectives.

Solution 1   Let's take $t = 0$ on 1/1/97 and measure populations in thousands. We will write $A(t)$ and $B(t)$ for the population functions of Amityville and Bittersville, respectively, and use the general population function

$$P(t) = P_0 + mt$$

in Eq. (13). With rate of change $m = 0.935$ and initial population $A_0 = 27.255$, the population of Amityville is given by

$$A(t) = 27.255 + 0.935t.$$

With rate of change $m = 1.465$ and initial population $B_0 = 21.765$, the population of Bittersville is given by

$$B(t) = 21.765 + 1.465t.$$

To determine when these two populations are equal, we need to solve the equation $A(t) = B(t)$, that is,

$$27.255 + 0.935t = 21.765 + 1.465t.$$

The solution is

$$t = \frac{27.255 - 21.765}{1.465 - 0.935} = 10.358,$$

which is 10 years plus

$$0.358 \text{ year} = 0.358 \text{ year} \times \frac{12 \text{ months}}{\text{year}} = 4.296 \text{ months}.$$

Since $t = 0$ on 1/1/1997, and $1997 + 10 = 2007$, this is during the fifth month (May) of the year 2007. Thus the Amityville and Bittersville populations are equal some time during May 2007. [Although the question was not asked, you might like to verify that the common population then is $A(10.358) = B(10.358) = 36.940$ thousand people.]

Figure 1.3.15 shows a graphic solution for the intersection of the graphs of the two functions $A(t)$ and $B(t)$.

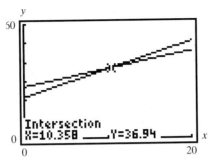

Figure 1.3.15   The graphs **Y1=27.255+0.935X** and **Y2=21.765+1.465X** plotted with **Xmin=0** and **Xmax=20** intersect at $(10.358, 36.94)$.

Solution 2   If we don't reset our clock, but simply take $t_1 = 1997$ on 1/1/97, then the general population function

$$P(t) = P_1 + m(t - t_1)$$

of (12) gives

$$A(t) = 27.255 + 0.935(t - 1997) \text{ and}$$
$$B(t) = 21.765 + 1.465(t - 1997)$$

for the two population functions. Now we solve the equation $A(t) = B(t)$,

$$27.255 + 0.935(t - 1997) = 21.765 + 1.465(t - 1997)$$

for

$$t = 1997 + \frac{27.255 - 21.765}{1.465 - 0.935} = 1997 + 10.358 = 2007.358.$$

Obviously, this is the same May 2007 result as before. The advantage to restarting the clock is that it makes the algebraic manipulations somewhat easier.

Solution 3   Sometimes ordinary common sense is worth more than fancy formulas. On 1/1/97 the population of Bittersville was $27.255 - 21.765 = 5.490$ thousand less than that of Amityville, but was gaining at the rate of $1.465 - 0.935 = 0.530$ thousand per year. It will therefore take $5.490/0.530 = 10.358$ years to catch up. As before, this brings us to May 2007. ∎

Piecewise-Linear Functions

Definition: Piecewise-Linear Function
A **piecewise-linear function** is one that is defined by different linear functions on different intervals. (For instance, a population P might grow at one constant rate on one time interval and at a different constant rate on another time interval.)

Example 7

Suppose that the population of Springfield was 150 thousand in 1970 and from 1970 to 1990 the population grew at the rate of 10 thousand per year. However, due to new industry acquired in 1990, new people started moving in steadily. As a net result, after 1990 the population of Springfield grew at the increased rate of 20 thousand people per year. Noting that the population of Springfield in 1990 was 350 thousand (why?), we see that the city's population is described by the piecewise-linear function

$$P(t) = \begin{cases} 150 + 10(t - 1970) & \text{if } 1970 \leq t \leq 1990, \\ 350 + 20(t - 1990) & \text{if } t > 1990. \end{cases} \tag{18}$$

Thus the function $P(t)$ is defined until 1990 by the linear function $150 + 10(t - 1970)$, but after 1990 it is defined by the different linear function $350 + 20(t - 1990)$.   ◣

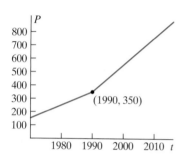

Figure 1.3.16   The piecewise-linear population function of Example 7.

The graph of a piecewise-linear function consists of different straight lines or straight line segments on different intervals. Figure 1.3.16 shows the graph of the population function defined in (18).

Most people encounter piecewise-linear functions when they pay their income tax on or before April 15 of each year.

Example 8

Schedule X on page 51 of the 1997 Form 1040 instructions specifies the tax paid by a single taxpayer and reads essentially as follows.

If Your Taxable Income Is Over	But Not Over	The Tax You Owe Is	Of the Amount Over
$0	$24,650	15%	$0
24,650	59,750	$3697.50 + 28%	24,650
59,750	124,650	$13,525.50 + 31%	59,750
124,650	271,050	$33,644.50 + 36%	124,650
271,050		86,348.50 + 39.6%	271,050

If we write T for tax and I for income, then this table is a description of the piecewise-linear function defined by

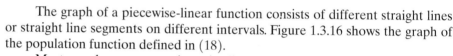

$$T(I) = \begin{cases} 0.15I & \text{if } 0 < I \leq 24,650, \\ 3697.50 + 0.28(I - 24,650) & \text{if } 24,650 < I \leq 59,750, \\ 13{,}525.50 + 0.31(I - 59,750) & \text{if } 59,750 < I \leq 124,650 \\ 336{,}44.50 + 0.36(I - 124,650) & \text{if } 124,650 < I \leq 271,050, \\ 86{,}348.50 + 0.396(I - 27,1050) & \text{if } I > 271,050. \end{cases} \tag{19}$$

For instance, a single taxpayer with a taxable income of $50,000 owes

$$T(50,000) = 3697.50 + 0.28(50,000 - 24,650) = \$10{,}795.50$$

in federal income tax, whereas a single taxpayer with a taxable income of $150,000 owes

$$T(150{,}000) = 33{,}644.50 + 0.36(150{,}000 - 124{,}650) = \$42{,}770.50.$$

The latter taxpayer has three times the taxable income, but owes almost four times as much tax. This illustrates the fact that the federal income tax is *progressive*—people with larger incomes pay larger percentages of their income in tax.   ◪

Linear Models: Summary

The slope-intercept equation

$$y = mx + b \tag{5}$$

of a straight line in the xy-plane with slope m and y-intercept b corresponds to the linear population model

$$P(t) = P_0 + mt \tag{13}$$

of a population with initial population P_0 and constant rate of change m. The point-slope equation

$$y - y_1 = m(x - x_1) \tag{10}$$

of the straight line passing through (x_1, y_1) with slope m corresponds to the linear population model

$$P(t) = P_1 + m(t - t_1) \tag{12}$$

of a population with constant rate of change m that has the value P_1 at time t_1. Either (12) or (13) can be applied in a problem where the population at a specified time is given. If we take $t_0 = 0$ at this specified time, then (13) applies. Otherwise, if we take t_1 equal to the calendar date at this specified time, then (12) applies.

1.3 PROBLEMS

In Problems 1–4, **(a)** first determine whether B is a function of A; and **(b)** if B is a function of A, decide (based on the average rate of change) whether B is a linear function of A.

1.

A	10	10.5	13	15	16	20
B	3	4	9	13	15	23

2.

A	10	10.5	13	15	16	20
B	3	4	4	9	13	23

3.

A	2	4	5	5	8	11
B	3	4	9	13	15	23

4.

A	2	4	6	8	10	12
B	3	3	3	3	3	3

In Problems 5–8, write a population function $P(t)$ with the given initial population P_0 and constant rate of change m.

5. $P_0 = 42$ and $m = 5$

6. $P_0 = 73$ and $m = -6$

7. $P_0 = 324.175$ and $m = 15.383$

8. $P_0 = 786.917$ and $m = -21.452$

In Problems 9–12, a population function $P(t)$ is given, with t in years and P in thousands. Find the initial population P_0 and its constant rate of change m.

9. $P(t) = 123 + 6t$

10. $P(t) = 387 - 8t$

11. $P(t) = 487.139 + 20.558t$

12. $P(t) = 666.333 - 42.789t$

In Problems 13–16, the value $P_1 = P(t_1)$ of a population at time t_1 and its constant rate of change m are given. Write the population function $P(t)$.

13. $P(1987) = 375$ and $m = 12$

14. $P(1983) = 685$ and $m = -24$

15. $P(1991) = 227.625$ and $m = 17.234$

16. $P(1993) = 847.719$ and $m = -60.876$

In Problems 17–20, the values (in thousands) of a population on the same calendar dates in two given years are given. First find the population's constant rate of change m. Then write its population function.

(a)   In the form $P(t) = P_0 + mt$ with P_0 being the first of the two given populations, and

(b)   In the form $P(t) = P_1 + m(t - t_1)$ with P_1 being the first of the two given populations.

17. $P = 23$ in 1985 and $P = 37$ in 1995

18. $P = 68$ in 1985 and $P = 53$ in 1995

19. $P = 137$ in 1978 and $P = 208$ in 1993

20. $P = 375$ in 1972 and $P = 545$ in 1992

In Problems 21–24, each population is measured in thousands and time is measured in years. Assuming 365 days per year, determine how long it takes the indicated population to *double* in size. Give your answer in the form ## years and ?? days, rounded off accurate to the nearest whole day.

21.   The population of Problem 5

22.   The population of Problem 7

23.   The population of Problem 9

24.   The population of Problem 11

In Problems 25–28, take your choice as to which of the linear growth model formulas $P(t) = P_0 + mt$ and $P(t) = P_1 + m(t - t_1)$ of this section to use.

25. City A had a population of 35,500 on January 1, 1985 and it was growing at the rate of 1700 people per year. Assuming that this annual rate of change in the population of City A continues, find

   (a) its population on January 1, 2000, and

   (b) the month of the calendar year in which its population reaches 85 thousand.

26. City B had a population of 375 thousand on January 1, 1992 and it was growing at the rate of 9250 people per year. Assuming that this annual rate of change in the population of City B continues, find

   (a) its population on January 1, 2000 and

   (b) the month of the calendar year in which its population reaches 600 thousand.

27. City C had a population of 45,325 on January 1, 1985 and a population of 50,785 on January 1, 1990. Assuming that this annual rate of change in the population of City C continues, find

   (a) its population on January 1, 2000 and

   (b) the month of the calendar year in which its population reaches 75 thousand.

28. City D had a population of 428 thousand on January 1, 1992 and a population of 455 thousand on January 1, 1997. Assuming that this annual rate of change in the population of City D continues, find

   (a) its population on January 1, 2000 and

   (b) the month of the calendar year in which its population reaches 600 thousand.

29. Find the month of the calendar year during which Cities A and C (of Problems 25 and 27) have the same population.

30. Find the month of the calendar year during which Cities B and D (of Problems 26 and 28) have the same population.

31. The following table gives the Alabama state tax rates for married persons filing jointly. (Source for this table and the tax tables following is *The World Almanac and Book of Facts 1998*.)

If Your Taxable Income Is Over	But Not Over	The Tax You Owe Is	Of the Amount Over
$0	$1000	2%	$0
1000	6000	$20 + 4%	1000
6000		220 + 5%	6000

   (a) Find the tax owed on a taxable income of $3350.

   (b) Find the tax owed on a taxable income of $6000.

   (c) Find the tax owed on a taxable income of $100,000.

   (d) Write a formula defining a piecewise-linear function $T(I) = \ldots$ that gives tax owed as a function of taxable income.

32. The following table gives the Kansas state tax rates for married persons filing jointly.

If Your Taxable Income Is Over	But Not Over	The Tax You Owe Is	Of the Amount Over
$0	$30,000	3.50%	$0
30,000	60,000	$1050 + 6.25%	30,000
60,000		2925 + 6.45%	60,000

(a) Find the tax owed on a taxable income of $3350.

(b) Find the tax owed on a taxable income of $45,000.

(c) Find the tax owed on a taxable income of $100,000.

(d) Write a formula defining a piecewise-linear function $T(I) = \ldots$ that gives tax owed as a function of taxable income.

33. The following table gives the basic state tax rate for taxpayers in the state of Virginia.

If Your Taxable Income Is Over	But Not Over	The Tax You Owe Is	Of the Amount Over
$0	$3000	2%	$0
3000	5000	$60 + 3%	3000
5000	17,000	120 + 5%	5000
17,000		720 + 5.75%	17,000

(a) Find the tax owed on a taxable income of $3350.

(b) Find the tax owed on a taxable income of $6375.

(c) Find the tax owed on a taxable income of $100,000.

(d) Write a formula defining a piecewise-linear function $T(I) = \ldots$ that gives tax owed as a function of taxable income.

1.4   FITTING LINEAR MODELS TO DATA

In Section 1.3 we saw that a population whose growth is modeled by a linear function grows with a **constant** rate of change—that is, with the same change in population each year. In this section we discuss the modeling of data of a sort that might be said to display an almost constant rate of change—with the annual changes from year to year being approximately but not exactly equal. As an example of data that might therefore be described as almost but not quite linear, the following table shows the population of Charlotte, North Carolina, as recorded in the decade census years of 1950 through 1990.

Year	Pop. (thous)	Change
1950	134	
1960	202	68
1970	241	39
1980	315	74
1990	396	81

Source: U.S. Census Bureau.

The third column of this table shows (for each decade year) the change in the population during the preceding decade. We see that the population of Charlotte increased by roughly 70 to 80 thousand people during the 1950s, the 1970s, and the 1980s. It increased by somewhat less during the 1960s, but still with a change measured in roughly comparable tens of thousands. We might wonder whether this qualifies as almost linear population growth. The way to answer such a question is to plot the data and take a look.

The data points corresponding to the preceding table are plotted in Fig. 1.4.1. Surely most people would agree that these points appear to lie on or near some straight line.

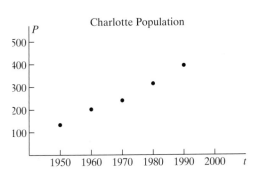

Charlotte Population

Figure 1.4.1   Dot plot of the Charlotte 1950–1990 population data.

But how can we find a straight line that passes through or near each data point in the figure? One way is simply to pass a straight line through the first and last data points—those for 1950 and 1990. The slope of this line will be the average rate of change of the population of Charlotte during the 40-year period from 1950 to 1990.

Definition: Average Rate of Change
The **average rate of change** of a population P during a time interval is the change ΔP in the population divided by the length Δt of the time interval,

$$\text{average rate of change} = \frac{\Delta P}{\Delta t}. \qquad (1)$$

Example 1

The average rate of change in the population of Charlotte during the 1950–1990 period was

$$\frac{\Delta P}{\Delta t} = \frac{396 - 134}{1990 - 1950} = \frac{262}{40} = 6.55 \text{ thousand/year}. \qquad (2)$$

Using $m = 6.55$ as a constant rate of change, along with $t_1 = 1950$ and $P_1 = 134$, Eq. (12) of Section 1.3 gives the linear population model

$$P(t) = 134 + 6.55(t - 1950). \qquad (3)$$

Figure 1.4.2 shows the corresponding straight line $P = 134 + 6.55(t - 1950)$ plotted in the tP-plane along with our original census population data points for Charlotte.

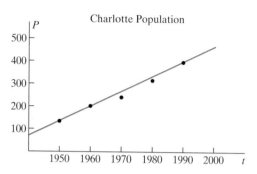

Figure 1.4.2   The straight line $P = 134 + 6.55(t - 1950)$ approximating the 1950–1990 growth of Charlotte.

The linear function we found looks like a "good fit" to the data—the 1950 and 1990 data points automatically lie on the line (why?), while the 1960 point seems to lie on the line and the 1970 and 1980 points lie just below the line. The following table shows the *discrepancies* between the actual populations and those predicted by the linear function in (3) for each of the 1950–1990 census years. We see that the actual 1960 population is just 2.5 thousand (only about 1%) larger than the 1960 population predicted by the linear model in (3), whereas the actual 1970 and 1980 populations are 24 thousand and 15.5 thousand (respectively) less than the corresponding linear predictions.

t	P (Actual)	$P(t)$ (Predicted)	Discrepancy $P - P(t)$
1950	134	134	0
1960	202	199.5	2.5
1970	241	265	−24
1980	315	330.5	−15.5
1990	396	396	0

Note that the figures in each (horizontal) row of the figure satisfy the formula

$$P_{\text{actual}} = P(t) + \text{error} \tag{4}$$

writing *error* (in the predicted population) for *discrepancy*.

Smaller Errors and Fitting Data Better

Now we discuss the concept of a linear model that **best fits** given population (or other) data such as

t (*years*)	t_1	t_2	t_3	t_4
P (*thous*)	P_1	P_2	P_3	P_4

In the case of the Charlotte population, there were five given data points. However, here we assume for simplicity in the general discussion that four data points are given. The final procedure will be analogous whatever the number of data points.

The preceding table gives the actual populations P_1, P_2, P_3, P_4 specified at $n = 4$ different times t_1, t_2, t_3, t_4. We may ask what linear model of the form

$$P(t) = mt + b \tag{5}$$

best fits the given data. That is, what should the numerical values of the coefficients m and b be in order that the model best fits the data? But the real question is, What does this mean? What does it mean for the model to fit the data well?

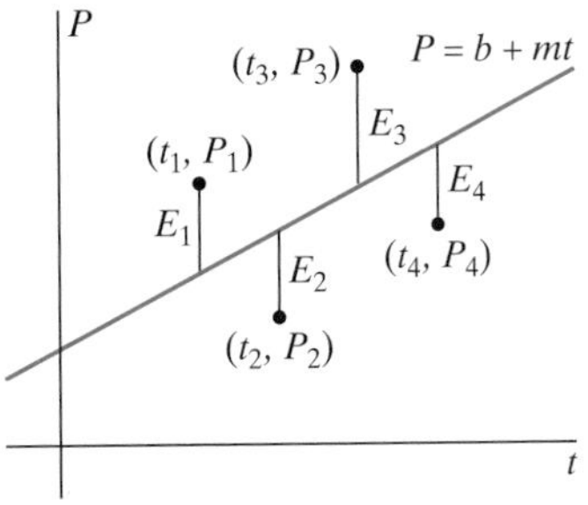

Figure 1.4.3 shows the errors that correspond to the discrepancies between the given data points in the tP-plane and the straight line graph of (5). The ith error E_i is the vertical distance

$$E_i = P_i - P(t_i) = P_i - (mt_i + b) \qquad (6)$$

Figure 1.4.3   The errors in the linear model $P(t) = mt + b$.

between the actual data point (t_i, P_i) and the corresponding point $(t_i, P(t_i))$ on the line that is predicted by the linear model. It is worth emphasizing in (6) that P_i is the actual observed value of the population at time t_i while $P(t_i)$ is the value predicted by the linear model, so

$$\text{error} = \text{actual} - \text{predicted}. \qquad (6')$$

One might suspect that the linear model fits the data well if the *sum of the errors* is small. However, observe that the error E_i defined in (6) is *signed*. It is positive if the ith data point lies above the line $P = mt + b$ but is negative if the data point lies below the line. Consequently, it is possible for large positive errors to cancel out large negative errors in the sum of all the errors. For instance, Fig. 1.4.3 indicates two large positive errors (data points above the line) and two large negative errors (data points below the line). Although each of these four errors is numerically large, their sum may be quite small, or even 0 just as

$$(+72) + (-54) + (+29) + (-47) = 0.$$

Thus the fact that the sum of the errors is small does *not* guarantee that all the individual errors are small.

It is therefore customary to use the sum of the *squares* of the errors as a measure of the overall discrepancy between the given data points and a proposed linear model.

Definition: Sum of Squares of Errors
The phrase "**Sum of Squares of Errors**" is so common in data modeling that it is abbreviated to **SSE**. Thus the **SSE** associated with a data model based on n data points is defined by

$$\text{SSE} = E_1^2 + E_2^2 + E_3^2 + \ldots + E_n^2. \qquad (7)$$

Note that however many data points are given, **the SSE is the sum of the squares of all their errors.** In plain words, if we write the actual populations in one column and the predicted populations in a second column, then the SSE is the sum of the squares of the differences between corresponding entries in the two columns.

t_i	Actual P_i	Linear $P(t_i)$	Error E_i	E_i^2
1950	134	134	0	0
1960	202	199.5	2.5	6.25
1970	241	265	−24	576
1980	315	330.5	−15.5	240.25
1990	396	396	0	0

Example 2

The preceding table shows the Charlotte census data again. Recall that the linear model used here is

$$P(t) = 134 + 6.55(t - 1950) = 6.55t - 12{,}638.5. \tag{8}$$

We have added a final column showing the squares of the errors; the sum of the numbers in this final column is

$$\text{SSE} = 0 + 6.25 + 576 + 240.25 + 0 = 822.5. \qquad ◥$$

The linear function $P(t) = 6.55t - 12{,}638.5$ in (8) corresponds to choosing the numerical values $m = 6.55$ and $b = -12{,}638.5$ in the general linear model $P(t) = mt + b$. We wonder if it is possible to find different numerical values of m and b that yield a smaller SSE than the value 822.5 found in Example 2.

Example 3

Find a linear function with a smaller SSE for the Charlotte population data.

Looking at Fig. 1.4.2 as well as at the table for Example 2, we see that the line $P = 6.55t - 12{,}638.5$ passes right through the first and last data points, but passes 24 units above the third data point. Let's think of a line that splits the difference and passes 12 units below the first and last data point as well as 12 units above the third data point. Can you see that we can make this change by subtracting 12 from the value $b = -12{,}638.5$ in (8), so that the new line lies 12 units lower in the tP-plane? Our new linear model is

$$P(t) = 6.55t - 12{,}650.5 \tag{9}$$

with $m = 6.55$ as in (8) but now $b = -12{,}650.5$ (rather than $-12{,}638.5$). The following table shows the computation of the SSE for this new altered linear model.

t_i	Actual P_i	Linear $P(t_i)$	Error E_i	E_i^2
1950	134	122	12	144
1960	202	187.5	14.5	210.25
1970	241	253	-12	144
1980	315	318.5	-3.5	12.25
1990	396	384	12	144

(We have started with the previous table, then recalculated the numbers in the third, fourth, and fifth columns in turn. You should verify the results shown for yourself.) Now the sum of the numbers in the final column is

$$\text{SSE} = 144 + 210.25 + 144 + 12.25 + 144 = 654.5.$$

Thus we have succeeded in reducing somewhat the SSE.   ◥

So although either of the functions

$$P(t) = 6.55t - 12{,}638.5 \quad \text{and} \quad P(t) = 6.55t - 12{,}650.5 \tag{10}$$

can be used as a linear model for the growth of Charlotte during the 1950–1990 period, the latter one fits the observed census data at least slightly better, because it has a smaller sum of squares of errors.

But exactly *what* does the SSE really mean? Well, the SSE for either of the models in (10) is a sum of 5 "squared errors,"

$$\text{SSE} = E_1^2 + E_2^2 + E_3^2 + E_4^2 + E_5^2.$$

We should therefore divide by 5 to get the average of these squared errors,

$$\text{average squared error} = \frac{E_1^2 + E_2^2 + E_3^2 + E_4^2 + E_5^2}{5} = \frac{\text{SSE}}{5}.$$

But then we should take the *square root* of the average *squared* error to get the average error itself,

$$\text{average error} = \sqrt{\frac{\text{SSE}}{5}}.$$

This is for Charlotte with $n = 5$ data points. To define the average error for a model fitting n given data points, we need only divide the SSE instead by n.

Definition: Average Error
The **average error** in a linear model fitting n given data points is defined in terms of its SSE by

$$\text{average error} = \sqrt{\frac{\text{SSE}}{n}}. \tag{11}$$

This formula says simply that **the average error is the square root of the average of the squares of the individual errors** (or discrepancies between predicted and actual data values).

Example 4

For the first linear model $P(t) = 6.55t - 12638.5$ in (10), we calculated its SSE $= 822.5$, so with $n = 5$ in (11) we find that its average error is

$$\text{average error} = \sqrt{\frac{822.5}{5}} \approx 12.826.$$

But the SSE for the second linear model $P(t) = 6.55t - 12650.5$ in (10) is only 654.5, so its average error is

$$\text{average error} = \sqrt{\frac{654.5}{5}} \approx 11.441.$$

These average errors—like the populations themselves—are measured in thousands. We may therefore say that the populations predicted by our first model for the five census years 1950, 1960, 1970, 1980, and 1990 err by an average of 12,826 people, whereas the predictions of our second model err by an average of 11,441 people. This is a tangible statement of the extent to which the second model fits the actual census data better than does the first model.   ∎

The Best Fit—The Least Possible Average Error

The question is this: What choice of the numerical parameters b and m in the linear model $P(t) = mt + b$ will minimize the average error—that is, will result in the least possible average error? This optimal linear model will be the one that we say best fits the given data.

Students in past generations often plotted data points on a piece of graph paper, then carefully maneuvered a ruler so that it appeared visually to come as close as possible to these points "on the average." But now the modern graphing calculator comes equipped with the facility to solve best-fitting problems more precisely. Here we describe how this is done. You should carry out with your own graphing calculator the steps we describe.

Figure 1.4.4 shows how to enter the Charlotte population data in a calculator. The list of census years from 1950 to 1990 is stored as a list **L1**, and the corresponding list of recorded populations is stored as a list **L2**. (Note that calculator "lists" are enclosed in curly braces.) Figure 1.4.5 shows the resulting **STAT EDIT** menu displaying the data in table form. Here the individual items—either a year or the corresponding population—can be changed or edited one at a time (for instance, if an error was made in entering either list originally).

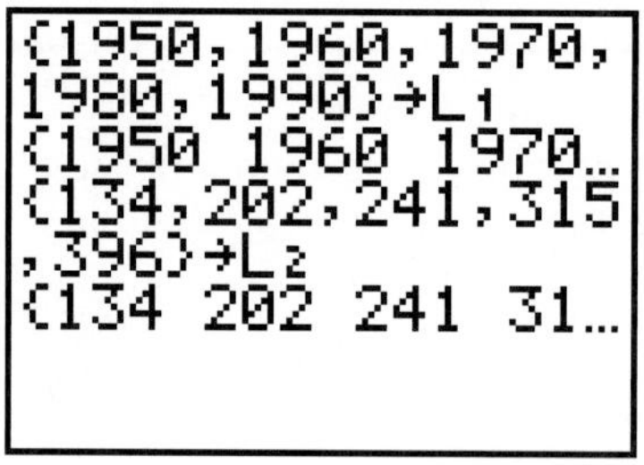

| ```
{1950,1960,1970,
1980,1990}→L₁
{1950 1960 1970…
{134,202,241,315
,396}→L₂
{134 202 241 31…
``` | ```
L1      L2      ------ 1
1950    134
1960    202
1970    241
1980    315
1990    396
------  ------
L1(1)=1950
``` |

Figure 1.4.4   Storing the 1950–1990 population census data for Charlotte.

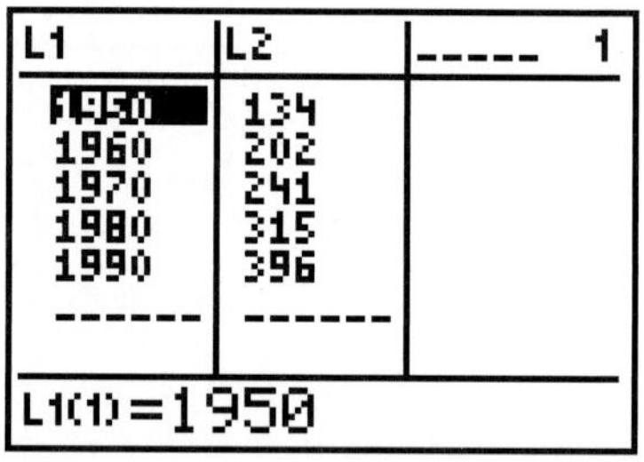

Figure 1.4.5   TI-83 **STAT EDIT** menu showing the Charlotte population data in table form.

Figure 1.4.6 shows the calculator's **STAT CALC** menu. Item **4: LinReg(ax+b)** on this menu is the calculator's so-called linear regression facility for finding the straight line **y=ax+b** that best fits the selected data. (Curve fitting is called regression in statistics and calculator lingo.) When we select item **4** on this menu, the **LinReg(ax+b)** function is entered on the home calculating screen. As shown in Fig. 1.4.7, we must then enter the names of our list **L1** of **X**-coordinates, our list **L2** of **Y**-coordinates, and the name **Y1** of the Y= menu variable where we want the resulting linear formula saved.

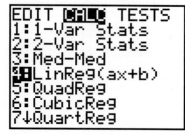

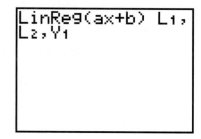

Figure 1.4.6   The TI-83 **STAT CALC** menu.

Figure 1.4.7   Fitting the **X**-data in list **L1** and the **Y**-data in list **L2**.

Figure 1.4.8 shows the display that results when this command is entered. With *a* written instead of *m* for slope, the straight line that best fits our data is

$$y = 6.37x - 12{,}291 \qquad (12)$$

(rounding off the 12,291.30 shown in Fig. 1.4.8 to 12,291, which seems precise enough for our purpose of predicting whole numbers of people).

The **LinReg(ax+b) L1, L2, Y1** command automatically enters Eq. (12) in the $\boxed{Y=}$ menu, ready for plotting as shown in Fig 1.4.9. With **Plot 1** turned **On** in the **STAT PLOT** menu (Fig. 1.4.10), $\boxed{\text{GRAPH}}$ then gives the plot of the best-fitting straight line shown in Fig. 1.4.11, where the original census data points are shown as small squares.

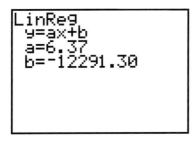

Figure 1.4.8 The best straight-line fit to our data points.

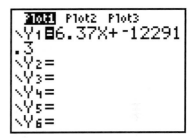

Figure 1.4.9 The best-fit straight line ready for plotting.

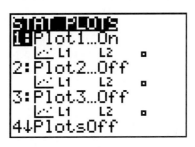

Figure 1.4.10 Preparing to plot the data with the best-fit straight line.

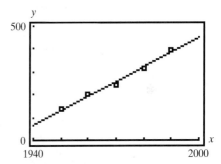

Figure 1.4.11 The line of best fit.

The calculator automatically uses **X** as the independent variable and **Y** as the dependent variable. In terms of calendar year as the independent *t*-variable and population as the dependent *P*-variable, Eq. (12) says that the linear model that best fits the 1950–1990 Charlotte census data is given by

$$P(t) = 6.37t - 12{,}291. \qquad (13)$$

The following table compares the original census data with the population figures predicted by this linear model.

t (year)	Actual P (thous)	P(t)	Error	Error Squared
1950	134	130.2	3.8	14.4
1960	202	193.9	8.1	65.6
1970	241	257.6	−16.6	275.6
1980	315	321.3	−6.3	39.7
1990	396	385	11	121.0

Example 5

You should verify the values shown in the preceding table. The final column shows the *squares* of the errors. Hence the SSE associated with the optimal linear model in (13) is

$$14.4 + 65.6 + 275.6 + 39.7 + 121.0 = 516.3.$$

Therefore, the average error is given by

$$\text{average error} = \sqrt{\frac{516.3}{5}} \approx 10.162.$$

Thus the linear model $P(t) = 6.37t - 12291$ predicts 1950–1990 census year populations that differ (on the average) by 10,162 people from those actually recorded for Charlotte. Note that this minimal average error of 10.162 (thousands) is necessarily less than the average errors calculated in Example 4 for the first two linear models $P(t) = 6.55t - 12,638.5$ (with average error 12.826) and $P(t) = 6.55t - 12,650.5$ (with average error 11.441) that we considered.   ◼

Once we have a linear model that predicts the 1950–1990 census year populations for Charlotte, we can use it to predict the population of Charlotte in years for which we have no data. This is really the point of mathematical modeling, since it would be foolish to use an approximate value for the population in 1970 when we have the exact value.

This issue raises several points of which you should be aware. First, your calculator will always find you a "best" linear model, whether your data "looks" linear or not. Before constructing such a model, you should consider whether it is appropriate. You can do this by plotting your data, or finding the average rates of change between consecutive data points to verify that the average rate of change is more or less constant. (A set of data that increases and decreases at noticeably different rates is not a good candidate for a linear model.)

Second, you should pay attention to the type of prediction you plan to make. If you are making a prediction about a year between two data points, say 1962 (between census years 1960 and 1970), this is called **interpolation.** It is generally safe to make such a prediction because, barring some unusual circumstance, the population is not likely to fluctuate wildly over this 10-year period. If you make a prediction about a year earlier or later than all of your data, this is called **extrapolation.** You must be careful about predicting too far beyond (or before) the information you have, because circumstances that affect the actual population may be very different from those existing when the data is collected.

Applications of Linear Modeling

Thus far, we have discussed only the modeling of linear population growth. But the world is full of other apparently linear data waiting to be modeled.

Example 6

The per capita consumption of cigarettes in 1930 and the lung cancer death rates (deaths per million males) for 1950 in the four Scandinavian countries were as follows:

Country	Cigarette Consumption in 1930 x	Death Rate in 1950 y
Norway	250	95
Sweden	300	120
Denmark	350	165
Finland	1100	350

It is hard to ignore the fact that higher cigarette consumption appears to be correlated with higher lung cancer death rates 20 years later. We wonder whether the relationship is approximately linear.

We do **MEM ClrAllLists** to purge the Charlotte population data from our calculator, and then enter the x- and y-data from the preceding table in the lists **L1** and **L2** (Fig. 1.4.12). Then the **STAT CALC** command **LinReg(ax+b) L1, L2, Y1** produces the straight line

$$y = 0.28x + 40.75 \tag{14}$$

that best fits our data. With an appropriate window and the same **STAT PLOT** settings as before, we get the plot of this straight line and the table data points that is shown in Fig. 1.4.13.

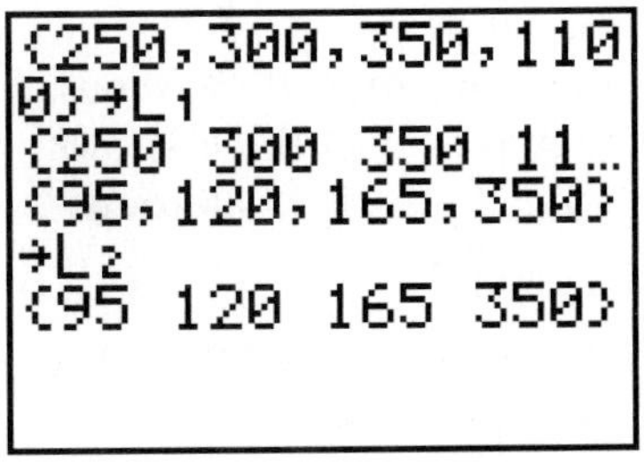

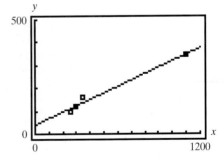

Figure 1.4.12   The cigarette consumption and lung cancer death data of Example 6.

Figure 1.4.13   The line best fitting the cigarette consumption versus lung cancer deaths data.

The calculator also calculates automatically the discrepancies between the data and the predictions of the linear model in (14). These errors are

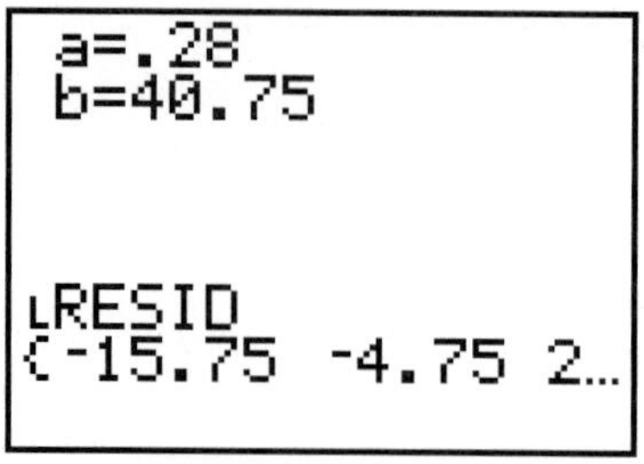

```
a=.28
b=40.75




LRESID
{-15.75  -4.75  2...
```

Figure 1.4.14   The errors or "residuals" in Example 6.

stored in the **LIST** menu under the name **RESID**. If you scroll through the list indicated in Fig. 1.4.14, you see that these errors or "residuals" are -15.75, $-4.74, 26.25$, and 1.25. Hence the average error of our linear model is

$$\text{average error} = \sqrt{\frac{(-15.75)^2 + (-4.75)^2 + (26.25)^2 + (1.25)^2}{4}} = 15.50.$$

Thus the average error in the linear model's predictions (for the four Scandinavian countries) is 15.5 lung cancer deaths per million males. For a comparison, the 1930 per capita cigarette consumption in Australia was 470, so the linear model in (14) predicts

$$(0.28)(470) + 40.75 = 172.35 \approx 172$$

lung cancer deaths per million males in Australia. The actual number of such deaths in Australia in 1950 was 170. (Given an average error of 15.50, this agreement is better than we have any right to expect, especially ignoring any differences there may be between Australian and Scandinavian health and lifestyles.)

   Finally, let us note what the linear model $y = 0.28x + 40.75$ *means*. If we substitute $x = 0$ (no cigarette consumption), we get $y(0) = 40.75$. Thus we should expect 40.75 lung cancer deaths per million males even if no cigarettes at all are smoked. Then the rate of change (or slope) $m = 0.28$ implies an additional 0.28 death per unit increase in per capita cigarette consumption. That is, since $4 \times 0.28 = 1.12$, there should be approximately one additional death for each 4-unit increase in per capita cigarette consumption. This sort of *interpretation* of a linear model frequently is more important than any specific numerical predictions of the model.   ◼

1.4 PROBLEMS

In Problems 1–4, the population P (in thousands) of a city in three different years is given, thereby providing three known (t, P) data points. Calculate the SSE for the straight line $P = mt + b$ through

   (a)   the first and third of these points,
   (b)   the second and third of these points.

1.

t (years)	0	10	20
P (thous)	200	270	320

2.

t (years)	0	10	20
P (thous)	300	390	460

3.

t (years)	1970	1980	1990
P (thous)	435	605	715

4.

t (years)	1970	1980	1990
P (thous)	615	805	1155

In Problems 5–8, the population P (in thousands) of a city in four different years is given, thereby providing four known (t, P) data points. Calculate the average error for the straight line $P = mt + b$ through

(a)   the first and fourth of these points,

(b)   the second and third of these points.

5.

t (years)	0	10	20	30
P (thous)	240	300	300	360

6.

t (years)	0	10	20	30
P (thous)	240	320	360	360

7.

t (years)	1960	1970	1980	1990
P (thous)	600	800	950	1050

8.

t (years)	1960	1970	1980	1990
P (thous)	265	385	485	565

9–12.   Find the linear model $P(t) = mt + b$ that best fits the data in Problems 5–8, as well as the average error of this optimal linear model.

In each of Problems 13–16, the 1950–1990 population census data for a U.S. city is given.

(a)   Find the linear model $P(t) = mt + b$ that best fits this census data.

(b)   Use the model from part (a) to predict the year 2000 population of this city.

(c)   Construct a table showing the actual and predicted populations (and errors) for the decade years 1950–1990.

13.   San Diego, California:

t (years)	1950	1960	1970	1980	1990
P (thous)	334	573	697	876	1111

14. Santa Anna, California:

t (years)	1950	1960	1970	1980	1990
P (thous)	46	100	156	204	294

15. Riverside, California:

t (years)	1950	1960	1970	1980	1990
P (thous)	47	84	140	171	227

16. Garland, Texas:

t (years)	1950	1960	1970	1980	1990
P (thous)	11	39	81	139	181

17. The following table gives the number of compact discs (in millons) sold in the United States for the even-numbered years 1988 through 1996.

t (years)	1988	1990	1992	1994	1996
S (millions)	149.7	286.5	407.5	662.1	778.9

Source: The World Almanac and Book of Facts 1998.

(a) Find the linear model $S(t) = mt + b$ that best fits this data.
(b) Compare the model's prediction for the year 1995 with the actual 1995 CD sales of 722.9 million.
(c) Use the model to predict compact disc sales for the year 2002.
(d) Which prediction, the one for 1995 or the one for 2002, is likely to be closer to actual sales? Why?

18. The following table gives the number of cassette tapes (in millions) sold in the United States for the even-numbered years 1988 through 1996.

t (years)	1988	1990	1992	1994	1996
S (millions)	450.1	442.2	366.4	345.4	225.3

Source: The World Almanac and Book of Facts 1998.

(a) Find the linear model $S(t) = mt + b$ that best fits this data.
(b) Explain the meaning of the rate of change m for this linear model.

19. The following table gives the military monthly pay scale for a Lieutenant General based on years of service.

Y (years of service)	2	4	8	12	16	20
P (pay in dollars)	6693.90	6836.70	7010.40	7302.00	7911.60	8349.90

Source: The World Almanac and Book of Facts 1998.

(a)   Find the linear model that best fits this data.

(b)   Use a graph or a table of values for this model to find the years in which the model underestimates the officer's pay.

20.   The Consumer Price Index is a measure of the cost to consumers of various goods and services in comparison to the cost of those items in previous years. The following table gives the CPI for all urban consumers for housing for selected years from 1987 to 1996. The years 1982–1984 serve as the base years for comparison, with the cost of housing in those years equal to 100.

T (years)	1987	1990	1991	1994	1996
CPI	115.6	130.5	135.0	145.4	154.0

(a)   Find the linear model that best fits this data.

(b)   Use this linear model to predict the CPI for housing in 1989. Is your answer a reasonable approximation to 124.9, the actual 1989 CPI for housing? Explain your answer in terms of the plot of the data or the average rates of change between consecutive table entries.

(c)   Use the linear model to predict the year in which the CPI for housing will reach 165. What assumption are you making when you make this prediction?

(d)   Use the linear model to predict when the CPI for housing will reach 250. Why is it *not* a good idea to make such a prediction?

21.   Thus far we have constructed linear models for data that represent a function of some independent variable. Frequently in the real world, we are confronted with data that does not actually describe a function, but that suggests an underlying relationship that might be modeled by a function. An example of such data is the relationship between height and weight for the seven infielders on the Los Angeles Dodgers roster on July 12, 1997.

Height in Inches, h	70	74	71	71	76	70	73
Weight in Pounds, W	163	170	180	145	222	185	200

(a)   Find the linear model that best fits this data.

(b)   Use the linear model to predict the weight of a major league infielder who is 6 feet tall.

(c)   Should you use this model to predict the height of any American male who is 6 feet tall? Why or why not?

CHAPTER 1 REVIEW

In this chapter, you learned about functions and linear function models. After completing the chapter, you should be able to

- Determine whether a relation described numerically, graphically, or symbolically represents a function.
- Find the domain and range of a function.
- Find the output value of a function for a given input value.
- Find the input value(s) of a function for a given output value.
- Determine whether a function described numerically, graphically, or symbolically represents a linear function.
- Determine the rate of change of a linear function.
- Find a linear function that models given linear data.
- Find a best least squares linear model fitting data that is approximately linear.
- Interpret the slope and y-intercept of a linear model in terms of the situation modeled.

REVIEW PROBLEMS

In Problems 1–7, (a) decide whether, based on the table, graph, or formula, y is a function of x; and (b) if y is a function of x, decide whether y is a linear function of x. Explain your answer.

1.

x	2	4	5	6	8	11
y	3	4	9	13	15	23

2.

x	2	4	6	8	10	12
y	3	1.5	0	−1.5	−3	−4.5

3.

x	1	2	3	4	5	6
y	300	150	75	37.5	18.75	9.375

4.

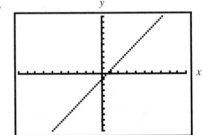

5.

6. $y = x^2 - 4$

7. $3x + 4y = 2$

In Problems 8–10, find the domain and range of each function.

8. The number of fat grams $F(x)$ in a sandwich based on the number of calories x, according to the following table.

Calories	430	550	320	680	300	750	530	710
Fat Grams	20	29	5	33	9	33	26	43

Source: Chick-Fil-A Fat Gram Comparison

9.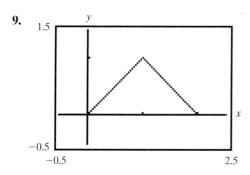

10. $f(x) = |x| - 3$

11. Find a linear population model for the population of Libertyville if its population was 227,352 in 1981 and 376,778 in 1993.

12. For many years, insurance companies published guidelines of ideal weights (W) for various heights (h). The most common rule for calculating ideal weight for a woman was 100 pounds for a woman 60 inches tall, and 5 additional pounds for each inch over 60 inches.
    (a) Write a function rule $W(h)$ to determine the ideal weight for a woman who is at least 60 inches tall.
    (b) Use your rule to determine the ideal weight for a woman who is 66 inches tall.

13. The cost function for the Mindspring Enterprises "light" plan for internet access is given by

$$C(h) = \begin{cases} 6.95 & \text{if } 0 \leq h \leq 5, \\ 6.95 + 2(h - 5) & \text{if } h > 5, \end{cases}$$

where C is in dollars and h is the number of hours used. If a subscriber's bill for April 1999 was $23.65, how many hours of internet time did she use?

14. Economists frequently use linear functions to construct models for the relationship between price and demand for a small business. Generally, we consider the selling **price** p of the item to be a linear function of the **demand** x (the number of units consumers will purchase). Pomelia has begun a home business making decorative lawn sprinklers out of copper tubing. She has found that she can sell 20 sprinklers a month if they are priced at $60 each, but only 12 sprinklers if they are priced at $70.
    (a) Find a linear function $p(x)$ giving the price of the sprinklers as a function of the number sold.
    (b) How many sprinklers will Pomelia sell if the sprinklers are priced at $55?
    (c) If Pomelia wants to sell at least 30 sprinklers per month, what price should she charge?
    (d) Explain what the intercepts of the line mean in this situation.

15. Nambe Mills in Santa Fe, New Mexico manufactures tableware made of a metal alloy. The pieces are sand casted, and then shaped, ground, buffed, and polished. The following table gives the total grinding and polishing times (in minutes) for various pieces of Nambeware and their corresponding prices (in dollars).

Time	109.38	16.41	23.77	13.25
Price	260	39	49.50	31

Time	44.45	64.30	34.16
Price	89	165	75

Source: Nambe Mills

(a) Find the best least squares linear model for price as a function of grinding and polishing time.
(b) According to your model, what should be the price of a piece of Nambeware if its grinding and polishing time is 53.18 minutes?
(c) Interpret the slope of your model in terms of the situation.

Reading: Rates of Change in the Real World

The following radio interview illustrates the fact that real people in the real world actually talk about rates of change. To emphasize this, you might count (or even underline) the references of this sort in this brief conversation.

This is an excerpt of the transcript of "Morning Edition," National Public Radio, January 6, 1999.

BOB EDWARDS, HOST: A new study in the *Journal of the American Medical Association* tracks the number of Americans killed by infectious diseases such as pneumonia, influenza, and tuberculosis over the past century. The pattern in the death rates suggests humans have won only a partial victory.

NPR's Joanne Silberner reports.

JOANNE SILBERNER, NPR REPORTER: Several years ago, the Centers for Disease Control and Prevention looked at the deaths from infectious diseases in the United States from 1980 to 1992. Researchers saw an increase in the death rate. They suspected it was the first such increase in this century. So they undertook a more detailed study. They found as expected that before 1980 infectious diseases took less of a toll as the century wore on, but they also discovered that the rate of change was uneven.

DR. JEFFREY ARMSTRONG (Ph.D.), EPIDEMIOLOGIST, CENTERS FOR DISEASE CONTROL AND PREVENTION: What we found was that from 1900 to the late 1930s the infectious disease mortality rate was dropping by a fairly steady $2\frac{1}{2}$ percent.

SILBERNER: Dr. Jeffrey Armstrong is an epidemiologist with the CDC.

ARMSTRONG: I believe it's most likely due to a general improvement in living conditions and to improvements in public health and sanitation.

SILBERNER: Then came antibiotics and the era of modern medicine and some dramatic changes.

ARMSTRONG: Following the late 1930s, there was an even more rapid drop in infectious disease mortality; it fell by about 8 percent per year. And this actually corresponded to the time when the first antimicrobials were introduced and also the time when vaccines first came into widespread use.

SILBERNER: After that, the decline in the infectious disease death rate slowed again—and then came AIDS. For the first time this century, AIDS pushed the death rate from infectious diseases up, though that may soon reverse again since the rate of death from AIDS fell in 1996 and 1997.

The AIDS impact was not surprising to the study's authors, but they did uncover a new, unexpected, and unexplained trend. Since 1980, the rate of death from pneumonia and influenza among the elderly has also gone up.

These uneven cycles in the rate of death tell epidemiologists one thing: that they can't just extend lines on their graphs to predict the future; infectious diseases are simply too unpredictable.

ACTIVITY

Activity: Exploring Rate of Change

In this chapter, you have learned that a linear function is one whose rate of change is constant. What does a graph of a function look like if its average rate of change is not constant? This activity will allow you to investigate situations with different rates of change.

In order to supplement her income as a school counselor, Mrs. Gould decided to sell cookies at her neighborhood swimming pool during the summer. After the first week of sales, she examined her sales record and made a chart that includes the number of cookies sold per day along with the change from the previous day. Complete a chart like the one shown for each of the situations described. Then make a plot that shows the day on the x-axis and the number of cookies sold on the y-axis. Describe in words how each graph looks.

Day	Cookies Sold	Avg. Rate of Change (Cookies per Day)
1	40	N/A
2		
3		
4		
5		
6		
7		

1. Mrs. Gould's sales remained constant.
2. Mrs. Gould's sales increased at a constant rate.
3. Mrs. Gould's sales increased at an increasing rate.
4. Mrs. Gould's sales increased at a decreasing rate.
5. Mrs. Gould's sales decreased at a constant rate.
6. Mrs. Gould's sales decreased at an increasing rate.
7. Mrs. Gould's sales decreased at a decreasing rate.

2 QUADRATIC FUNCTIONS AND MODELS

What happens when you toss a ball straight up into the air? Does it travel upward (and then down) with a constant rate of speed? Does it take longer for the ball to reach its highest point than it does to fall back to where it was thrown?

Figure 2.0.1 shows a plot of data obtained in an experiment in which a ball was tossed into the air over a motion detector. The motion detector was attached to a unit that recorded the ball's height (above the motion detector) as a function of time.

What does this graph tell us about the motion of the ball? First, we can see that the ball was thrown upward from a height of about 3 feet, and was caught (before it hit the motion detector) at a slightly lower height. Second, the ball was not moving at a constant rate of speed because the distance it traveled from 0.6 second to 0.7 second is much greater than the distance traveled in the same length of time between 0.9 second to 1.0 second. And, finally, it took (essentially) the same amount of time to travel up as it did to travel down.

If we were to construct a mathematical model for the relationship between time and height of the ball, we would surely not choose a linear model. It appears that the curve we used to connect our data points is an "upside down" variation of the parabolic graph of the simple quadratic function $f(x) = x^2$. Indeed, the situation of dropping or throwing a ball (or any other object) always yields a quadratic function model of this type.

In this chapter we will study quadratic functions and the relationships for which they provide suitable models.

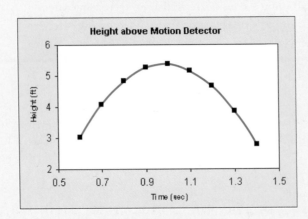

Figure 2.0.1 The motion detector measures the height of the ball every tenth of a second.

2.1	Quadratic Functions and Polynomials
2.2	Quadratic Models and Equations
2.3	Fitting Quadratic Models to Data

2.1 QUADRATIC FUNCTIONS AND POLYNOMIALS

In this section we briefly survey some of the simpler nonlinear functions that are used to portray data that describe phenomena in the world around us. Our viewpoint here is largely graphic and pictorial. The objective is for you to gain some general feeling for major differences between different types of functions. In later sections and chapters we will further investigate these functions and graphs and their applications.

Quadratic Functions and Parabolas

Let us take a closer look at the dropping/throwing situation considered previously. Suppose a rock is dropped from the top of a tall tower. The following table shows (on the basis of careful measurements) the distance d (in feet) the rock has fallen after t seconds.

t (sec)	d (feet)
0	0
1	16
2	64
3	144
4	256
5	400

Note that equal 1-second differences between successive entries in the first column do *not* correspond to equal differences between successive entries in the second column. You might therefore infer that d is not a linear function of t. Indeed, you can verify that d is given as a function of t by the formula

$$d = 16t^2,$$

which involves the *second* (rather than the first) power of the variable t.

Definition: Quadratic Function
A **quadratic function** is one of the form

$$f(x) = ax^2 + bx + c \tag{1}$$

with $a \neq 0$, so its formula involves a *square term* as well as linear and constant terms.

The graph of a quadratic function is a parabola whose shape resembles that of the particular parabola in the following example.

Example 1

Figure 2.1.1 shows the graph of the quadratic function

$$y = 16x^2$$

[where $a = 16$ and $b = c = 0$ in (1)]. With x and y in place of t and d, the right half of this parabola corresponds to the distance function of the falling rock discussed previously. The xy-points corresponding to the tabulated td-data are marked on the graph. ◼

The parabola $y = -16x^2$ would look similar to the one in Fig. 2.1.1 but would open downward rather than upward. More generally the graph of the equation

$$y = ax^2 \quad \text{(with } a \neq 0\text{)} \tag{2}$$

is a parabola with its *vertex* (the point where it appears to change direction) at the origin $(0, 0)$. This parabola opens upward if $a > 0$ and downward if $a < 0$.

The size of the coefficient a in (2) determines the "width" of the parabola. Specifically, the larger $a > 0$ is, the more steeply the curve rises, and hence the narrower the parabola is. (See Fig. 2.1.2.)

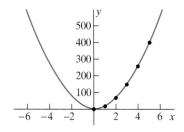

Figure 2.1.1 The parabola $y = 16x^2$ and the points $(0, 0)$, $(1, 16), (2, 64), (3, 144), (4, 256),$ $(5, 400)$.

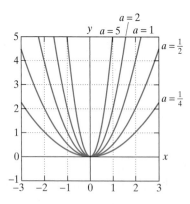

Figure 2.1.2 Parabolas with different widths.

The parabola in Fig. 2.1.3 has its vertex located at the point (h, k) instead of at the origin. In the indicated uv-coordinate system its equation is of the form $v = au^2$, in analogy with Eq. (2) but with u and v instead of x and y.

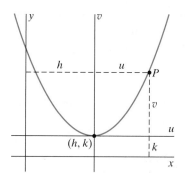

Figure 2.1.3   A translated parabola.

It is evident in the figure that the uv- and xy-coordinates are related by

$$u = x - h, \quad v = y - k.$$

Substitution of these relations in $v = au^2$ then gives the xy-equation

$$y - k = a(x - h)^2 \tag{3}$$

of this "translated parabola" with vertex (h, k).

If Eq. (3) is solved for y and simplified, then clearly there will result a square term, a linear term, and a constant term. More generally, the graph of any equation of the form

$$y = ax^2 + bx + c \quad \text{(with } a \neq 0\text{)} \tag{4}$$

can be recognized as a translated parabola by completing the square in x to obtain an equation of the form in (3).

Example 2

Determine the shape of the graph of the equation

$$y = 2x^2 - 4x - 1.$$

If we complete the square in x,

$$y = 2(x^2 - 2x \qquad) - 1$$
$$= 2(x^2 - 2x + 1) - 1 - 2 = 2(x - 1)^2 - 3,$$

we obtain the equation

$$y + 3 = 2(x - 1)^2$$

having the form in (3) with $a = 2$ and $h = 1, k = -3$. Hence the graph is the parabola shown in Fig. 2.1.4, opening upward from its vertex at $(1, -3)$. ∎

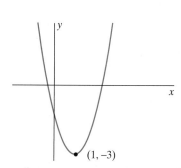

(1, –3)

Figure 2.1.4   The parabola of Example 2.

Power Functions

The linear function $f(x) = x$ and the quadratic function $g(x) = x^2$ are both examples of *power functions*.

Definition: Power Function
A **power function** is one of the form

$$f(x) = x^k \qquad (5)$$

where k is a given constant, which can be either positive or negative, either integral or fractional (or even irrational, like $\sqrt{2}$ or π).

Example 3

We have already pointed out the cases $k = 1$ (with graph the line $y = x$) and $k = 2$ (with graph the parabola $y = x^2$). If $k = 0$ then, because $x^0 \equiv 1$, (5) reduces to the constant-valued function $f(x) \equiv 1$ whose graph is the horizontal straight line $y = 1$. If $k = 3$ then we have the function $f(x) = x^3$ whose graph is shown in Fig. 2.1.5.

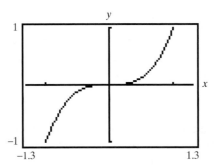

Figure 2.1.5   The graph $y = x^3$ of Example 3.

Note that the parabola $y = x^2$ and the cubic graph $y = x^3$ are fairly illustrative of the graph of any power function whose exponent k is a *positive integer*. The graphs of the *even*-degree power functions x^2, x^4, x^6, and so forth all "cup upward" like a parabola (Fig. 2.1.6). But the larger is the *even* exponent, the flatter is the graph near the origin. The graphs of the *odd*-degree power functions x, x^3, x^5, and so forth all go "from southwest to northeast" like the cubic graph in Fig. 2.1.5. But the larger is the *odd* exponent, the flatter is the graph near the origin (Fig. 2.1.7).

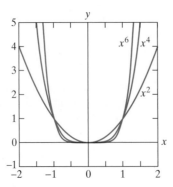

Figure 2.1.6   Graphs of power functions with even exponents.

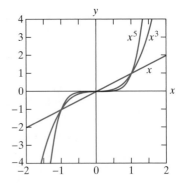

Figure 2.1.7   Graphs of power functions with odd exponents.

The situation is different if the exponent k in (5) is not an integer. If $k = \frac{p}{q}$, where p and q are integers, then the fractional power x^k is defined by

$$x^{p/q} = (\sqrt[q]{x})^p = \sqrt[q]{x^p}. \qquad (6)$$

One way to remember the roles of p and q here—which is the power and which the root—is to say "p is for *power*" (so q must be for root).

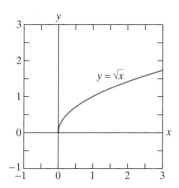

Figure 2.1.8   The graph $y = x^{1/2}$.

Example 4

With $p = 1$ and $q = 2$ in (6) we get the *square root function*

$$f(x) = x^{1/2} = \sqrt{x}$$

whose graph is shown in Fig. 2.1.8. Because negative numbers do not have (real) square roots, this square root function is defined only for $x \geq 0$. This is why the figure shows the graph only in the right half of the plane.   ◼

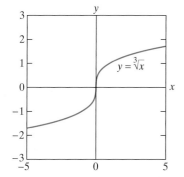

Figure 2.1.9   The graph $y = x^{1/3}$.

Example 5

With $p = 1$ and $q = 3$ in (6) we get the *cube root function*

$$f(x) = x^{1/3} = \sqrt[3]{x}$$

whose graph is shown in Fig. 2.1.9. By contrast with the square root function, the cube root function is defined *for all x*—positive numbers have positive cube roots (like $\sqrt[3]{8} = 2$) while negative numbers have negative cube roots [like $\sqrt[3]{-1} = -1$, because $(-1)^3 = -1$].   ◼

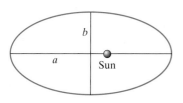

Figure 2.1.10   An (exaggerated) elliptical planet orbit.

Example 6

The orbit of a planet about the sun is an ellipse like that shown in Fig. 2.1.10 (though the sun is located off-center as indicated in the picture). An *ellipse* can be regarded as a "squashed circle" with *major radius a* and *minor radius b < a* (as contrasted with a circle whose radii are all equal). In the year 1619 the German mathematician (and court astrologer) Johann Kepler calculated the major radii of the orbits of the six planets then known, and also tabulated the observed time (or period) T of revolution of each of these planets about the sun. The following table shows these major radii measured in astronomical units (AUs)—one AU being the major radius of the Earth's orbit—with the planetary times of revolution measured in (Earth) years.

Planet	Period T (Years)	Major Radius a (AU)
Mercury	0.241	0.387
Venus	0.615	0.723
Earth	1.000	1.000
Mars	1.881	1.524
Jupiter	11.862	5.201
Saturn	29.456	9.538

Thus the period of revolution of Mercury about the sun is less than 3 months (why?), while the period of revolution of Jupiter is almost a dozen years. Thinking of the major radius as the planet's "average distance" from the sun, we see that Venus is less than $\frac{3}{4}$ as far from the sun as is the Earth, while Mars is a bit over one and one half times as far. Kepler's third law of planetary motion says that (with the units used in the table) **the *square* of a planet's period *T* (of revolution) equals the *cube* of the major radius *a* of its orbit about the sun.** That is, $T^2 = a^3$, so—upon taking cube roots—we see that the major radius is given as a function of the period T by

$$a = \sqrt[3]{a^3} = \sqrt[3]{T^2} = (T^2)^{1/3} = T^{2/3}. \tag{7}$$

Use your calculator to verify for yourself that $a = T^{2/3}$ for each of the six planets shown in the preceding table.   ◼

Isaac Newton showed that the relation $a = T^{2/3}$ must hold for *any* planet, comet, or asteroid in the solar system. So suppose an asteroid is discovered that lies exactly 4 times as far from the sun as the Earth. How long does it take this asteroid to complete one revolution about the sun?

Polynomials

Many varied and complicated functions can be assembled out of simple building block functions like the elementary power functions

$$1, \; x, \; x^2, \; x^3, \cdots, \; x^n, \cdots \tag{8}$$

with nonnegative integer exponents.

A *polynomial function* (or simply a *polynomial*) is a sum of constant multiples of the power functions shown in (8). A *first-degree polynomial* is a combination

$$p(x) = ax + b$$

of the first two power functions 1 and x in (8)—with a and b being constants—and thus is simply a linear function. A *second-degree polynomial* is a quadratic function of the form

$$p(x) = ax^2 + bx + c$$

with *coefficients a, b,* and *c.* A *third-degree* or *cubic polynomial*

$$p(x) = ax^3 + bx^2 + cx + d$$

has highest-degree term involving x^3, while a *fourth-degree* or *quartic polynomial*

$$p(x) = ax^4 + bx^3 + cx^2 + dx + e$$

with five constant coefficients a, b, c, d, e has in addition a fourth-degree term involving x^4. In general, the *degree* of a polynomial equals the exponent of the highest power appearing among its terms.

Example 7

It is not necessary that all terms of lower degree actually appear in a polynomial. Thus

$$q(x) = 2x^5 - 3x^2 + 17$$

is a fifth-degree polynomial (though it contains no terms of degrees 1, 3, or 4). ◼

Solving Polynomial Equations

Much of the content of traditional algebra courses deals with solving polynomial equations of the form $p(x) = 0$ where $p(x)$ is a polynomial. Thus one learns that the *quadratic equation*

$$ax^2 + bx + c = 0 \quad \text{(with given coefficients } a, b, c\text{)}$$

has *two* solutions obtained by taking (separately) the plus and minus signs in the **quadratic formula**

$$x = \frac{-b \pm \sqrt{b^2 - 4ac}}{2a}. \tag{9}$$

In Section 2.2 we will take a fresh look at this famous formula.

There also are known formulas that give solutions of a *cubic equation* like

$$ax^3 + bx^2 + cx + d = 0$$

or a *quartic equation* like

$$ax^4 + bx^3 + cx^2 + dx + e = 0.$$

However, in contrast with the quadratic formula, these cubic and quartic formulas are so complicated that practically no one knows or uses them for solution of equations. For instance, one of the three solutions of the specific cubic equation

$$x^3 - 3x^2 + 1 = 0 \tag{10}$$

is given by the formula

$$x = 1 + \frac{1}{\sqrt[3]{\frac{1}{2}(1 + i\sqrt{3})}} + \sqrt[3]{\frac{1}{2}(1 + i\sqrt{3})} \tag{11}$$

(where $i = \sqrt{-1}$). You should not worry about where this mysterious-looking formula comes from, or even about what it means.

In this book we'll largely use graphic (rather than formula-based symbolic) methods to solve our equations. Graphic equation-solving is based on the following principle.

Principle: Graphic Solution of Equations

The solutions of the equation

$$f(x) = 0 \tag{12}$$

are precisely the x-intercepts of the graph

$$y = f(x). \tag{13}$$

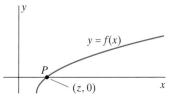

Figure 2.1.11   Solution of $f(x) = 0$ and x-intercept of $y = f(x)$.

Figure 2.1.11 illustrates the truth of this principle. The fact that z is an x-intercept of Eq. (13) means that the curve $y = f(x)$ intersects the x-axis at the point $P(z, 0)$. But then the fact that the y-coordinate $f(z)$ of P is 0 means precisely that $f(x) = 0$, so the x-intercept z is a solution of Eq. (12).

Consequently, a major reason for interest in the graph of a function $f(x)$ is to see visually the number and approximate locations of the solutions of the equation $f(x) = 0$. A polynomial equation of degree n cannot have more than n (real number) solutions, but it can have less than n real solutions. Sometimes a glance at a graph can tell us exactly how many real solutions a given equation has.

Example 8

Figure 2.1.12 shows the graphs $y = x^2 - 2x - 2$, $y = x^2 - 2x + 1$, and $y = x^2 - 2x + 3$. Because we recognize each as a parabola opening upward, it's clear that no x-intercepts are missing from these pictures.

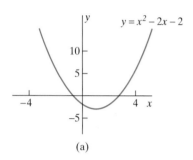

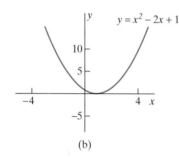

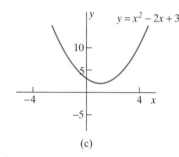

(a)   (b)   (c)

Figure 2.1.12   (a) Two real solutions; (b) one real solution; (c) no real solutions.

It follows that

- the equation $x^2 - 2x - 2 = 0$ has two real solutions;
- the equation $x^2 - 2x + 1 = 0$ has exactly one real solution (assuming that the graph does, indeed, just touch the x-axis at a single point); and
- the equation $x^2 - 2x + 3 = 0$ has no real solutions at all.

If you wish, you can use the quadratic formula to verify these observations.   ◼

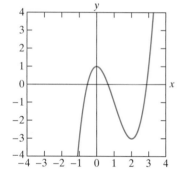

Figure 2.1.13
$y = x^3 - 3x^2 + 1$.

Example 9

Figure 2.1.13 shows the graph $y = x^3 - 3x^2 + 1$. Because we see *three* x-intercepts, we conclude that the cubic equation $x^3 - 3x^2 + 1 = 0$ has exactly *three* real solutions (since it cannot have more than three). Indeed, the calculator solution shown in Fig. 2.1.14 indicates that the one on the right (near $x = 3$) is approximately $x \approx 2.8794$. It turns out that this is the one represented by the complex expression in (11).

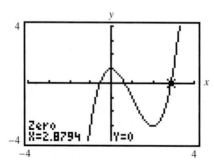

Figure 2.1.14   The right-hand intercept of $y = x^3 - 3x^2 + 1$.

◼

Example 10

Figure 2.1.15 shows the graph $y = x^4 - 4x^2 + x + 1$. Because we see *four x*-intercepts, we conclude that the quartic equation $x^4 - 4x^2 + x + 1 = 0$ has exactly *four* real solutions (since it cannot have more than four).

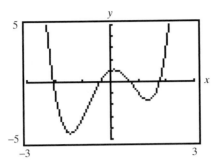

Figure 2.1.15 $y = x^4 - 4x^2 + x + 1$.

Certain characteristics of Figs. 2.1.13 and 2.1.15 are typical of polynomial graphs. Like the cubic in Fig. 2.1.13, the graph of any polynomial of *odd* degree *n* with positive "leading coefficient" (the highest-degree coefficient) goes from southwest to northeast—just like the graph of an odd-degree power function. And between southwest and northeast it can have as many as $n - 1$ "bends" (like the two bends of the third-degree polynomial graph in Fig. 2.1.13).

But like the quartic in Fig. 2.1.15, the graph of any polynomial of *even* degree *n* with positive leading coefficient rises in both directions—to the left and to the right—just like the graph of an even-degree power function. And in between it can have as many as $n - 1$ bends (like the three bends of the fourth-degree polynomial graph in Fig. 2.1.15).

Calculator/Computer Graphing

A typical calculator or computer graphing utility shows (on its graphics screen or monitor) only that portion of a graph $y = f(x)$ that lies within a selected rectangular **viewing window** of the form

$$a \leq x \leq b, \quad c \leq y \leq d.$$

The parts of the graph that lie outside this viewing window remain unseen (Fig. 2.1.16).

Figure 2.1.16   The viewing window $a \leq x \leq b$, $c \leq y \leq d$.

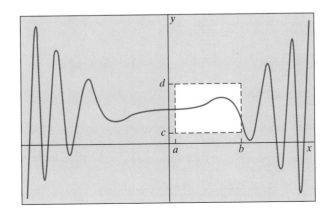

With a graphing calculator the maximum and minimum x- and y-values may be entered explicitly in the form

$$\textbf{Xmin} = a \qquad \textbf{Ymin} = c$$
$$\textbf{Xmax} = b \qquad \textbf{Ymax} = d$$

Frequently the user must specify the **x-range** $[a, b]$ and the **y-range** $[c, d]$ carefully so that the viewing window will show the desired portion of the graph. The calculator or computer's default window may provide only a starting point.

Example 11

Construct a graph that exhibits the principal features of the cubic polynomial

$$y = x^3 + 12x^2 + 5x - 66. \tag{14}$$

We anticipate a graph that looks somewhat like the cubic graph in Fig. 2.1.13—one that goes from southwest to northeast, perhaps with a couple of bends in between. But upon entering (14) in the $\boxed{Y=}$ menu of a typical graphing calculator with default viewing window $-10 \le x \le 10, -10 \le y \le 10$, we get the result shown in Fig. 2.1.17. Evidently, our viewing window is not large enough to show the expected behavior.

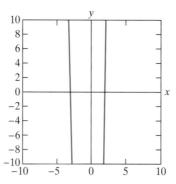

Figure 2.1.17 The cubic in Example 11 with the viewing window $-10 \le x \le 10, -10 \le y \le 10$.

Doubling its size in each dimension, we get the result in Fig. 2.1.18. Now we see the three zeros that a cubic polynomial can have, as well as some possibility of two bends, but it appears that magnification in the y-direction is indicated. Perhaps we need a y-range measuring in the hundreds rather than the tens. With

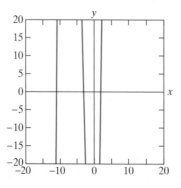

Figure 2.1.18 With the viewing window $-20 \le x \le 20, -20 \le y \le 20$.

the viewing window $-20 \leq x \leq 20, -200 \leq y \leq 200$ we finally get the satisfying graph shown in Fig. 2.1.19.

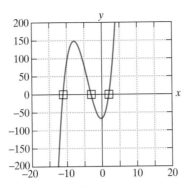

Figure 2.1.19   With the viewing window $-20 \leq x \leq 20, -200 \leq y \leq 200$.

Once we have zoomed out to see the big picture, we can zoom in on points of interest. For instance, Fig. 2.1.19 indicates "zoom boxes" locating the three zeros of the polynomial in (14). Apparently they are located at or near the points $x = -11, x = -3$, and $x = 2$. Each can be approximated graphically as closely as you please by the method of zooming. (See whether you can convince yourself that these three zeros are *exactly* the indicated integers. How could you verify that this actually is true?)   ◼

Example 12

Investigate the graph of the quartic polynomial

$$f(x) = (x^2 - 1)(x - 10)(x - 10.1) \\ = x^4 - 20.1x^3 + 100x^2 + 20.1x - 101. \quad (15)$$

Here we know the zeros $x = -1, +1, 10, 10.1$ in advance, so it makes sense to choose an x-range that includes all four. Noting that $f(0) = -101$, we suspect that a y-range measuring in the hundreds is indicated. Thus with the viewing window $-5 \leq x \leq 15, -1000 \leq y \leq 1000$ we get the nice graph shown in Fig. 2.1.20. Observe that with its three bends it resembles the quartic graph in Fig. 2.1.15.

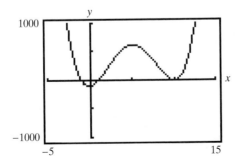

Figure 2.1.20   The quartic in Example 12 with the viewing window $-5 \leq x \leq 15, -1000 \leq y \leq 1000$.

But now the behavior of the graph near the point $x = 10$ is unclear. Does it dip beneath the x-axis or not? We select the viewing window $9.5 \leq x \leq 10.5$, $-1 \leq y \leq 1$ to magnify this area and get the result shown in Fig. 2.1.21. This is a

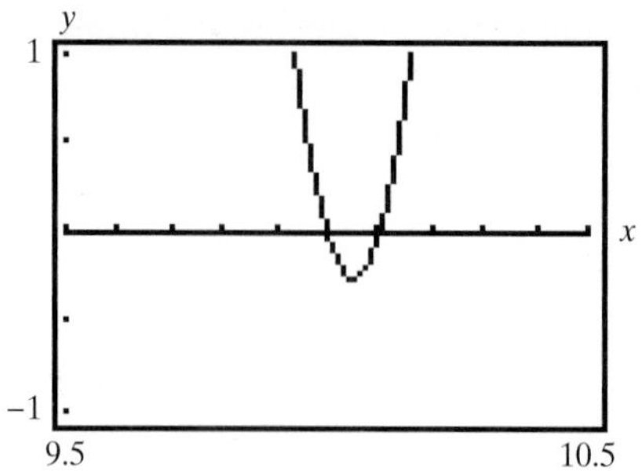

Figure 2.1.21   With the viewing window $9.5 \leq x \leq 10.5, -1 \leq y \leq 1$.

case where it appears that different plots on different scales are required to show visually all the behavior of the graph.   ◨

Our graphs in Examples 11 and 12 exhibit the maximal possible number of zeros and bends for the polynomials in (14) and (15), so we can feel fairly confident that our investigations reveal the main qualitative features of the graphs of these polynomials. But we will need to investigate polynomial graphs further in subsequent chapters. For instance, a polynomial graph can exhibit less than the maximum possible number of bends, but at this stage we cannot be certain that more bends are not hidden somewhere, perhaps visible only on a different scale than the viewing window we have selected.

2.1 PROBLEMS

In Problems 1–4, determine the value of the coefficient a so that the parabola $y = ax^2$ passes through the point P with given coordinates.

1. $P(3, 18)$
2. $P(-2, 24)$
3. $P(4, -64)$
4. $P(-5, -250)$

In Problems 5–8, determine the values of the coefficients b and c so that the graph of the quadratic function $f(x) = x^2 + bx + c$ passes through the points P and Q with given coordinates. *Suggestion:* Note that substitution of either coordinate pair gives a linear equation in b and c, so you will have two equations in two unknowns to solve. Start by adding these two equations.

5. $P(-1, 2)$ and $Q(1, 6)$
6. $P(-3, -1)$ and $Q(3, 23)$
7. $P(-4, 35)$ and $Q(4, 11)$
8. $P(-5, 150)$ and $Q(5, 50)$

In Problems 9–14, match the given quadratic function $f(x)$ with its graph among those shown in Figs. 2.1.22 through 2.1.27. Don't use a graphing calculator. Instead, use information such as the value $f(0)$ and whether the parabola in the figure opens upward or downward.

9. $f(x) = x^2 + 1$
10. $f(x) = 4 - x^2$
11. $f(x) = x^2 - 2x$
12. $f(x) = -x^2 - 2x$
13. $f(x) = x^2 - 2x - 3$
14. $f(x) = 3 - 2x - x^2$

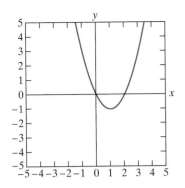

Figure 2.1.22

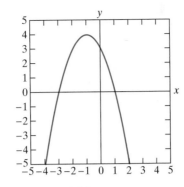

Figure 2.1.23

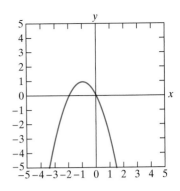

Figure 2.1.24

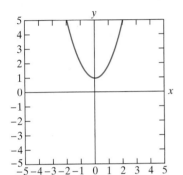

Figure 2.1.25

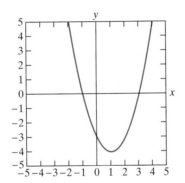

Figure 2.1.26

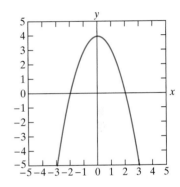

Figure 2.1.27

In Problems 15–20, match the given polynomial with its graph among those shown in Figs. 2.1.28–2.1.33. Don't use a graphing calculator. Instead, consider the degree of the polynomial, its number of zeros that you see on the graph, and its indicated behavior when x is numerically large.

15. $f(x) = x^3 - 3x + 1$

16. $f(x) = 1 + 4x - x^3$

17. $f(x) = x^4 - 5x^3 + 13x + 1$

18. $f(x) = 2x^5 - 10x^3 + 6x - 1$

19. $f(x) = 16 + 2x^2 - x^4$

20. $f(x) = x^5 + x$

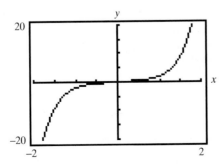

Figure 2.1.28

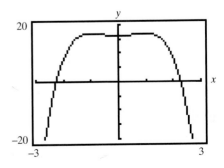

Figure 2.1.29

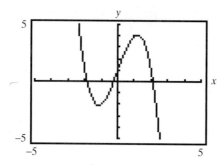

Figure 2.1.30

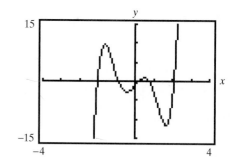

Figure 2.1.31

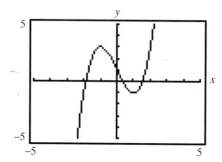

Figure 2.1.32

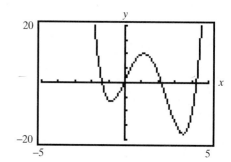

Figure 2.1.33

In each of Problems 21–26, a brief table of values of a function $f(x)$ is given. The function f is either linear or is a quadratic or cubic polynomial. Determine *which* (perhaps by graphing the points).

21.

x	-3	-1	2	5	7
$f(x)$	11	-3	-9	3	21

22.

x	-4	-2	2	3	4
$f(x)$	-17	17	-11	-3	23

23.

x	-4	-2	1	2	5
$f(x)$	13	7	-2	-5	-14

24.

x	-5	-1	1	3	4
$f(x)$	-13	-5	-1	3	5

25.

x	-2	0	2	3	5
$f(x)$	18	-10	2	8	-10

26.

x	-3	-1	0	2	4
$f(x)$	-35	5	10	-10	-70

In each of Problems 27–30, use a graphing calculator or computer to determine one or more appropriate viewing windows to exhibit the principal features of the graph $y = f(x)$. In particular, determine thereby the number of real solutions of the equation $f(x) = 0$ and the approximate location (to the nearest integer) of each of these solutions.

27. $f(x) = x^3 - 3x + 1$
28. $f(x) = x^3 - 3x + 2$
29. $f(x) = 2x^4 - 6x^3 + 10x - 10$
30. $f(x) = 2x^4 - 6x^3 + 10x + 8$

In each of Problems 31–35, determine (and describe briefly) how the graph $y = f(x)$ changes when the value of c is changed—for values of c between -5 and 5. With a graphing calculator or computer you should be able to plot several graphs on the same screen with different values of c.

31. $f(x) = 3x + c$
32. $f(x) = x^2 - 3x + c$
33. $f(x) = cx^2 - 3x$
34. $f(x) = x^3 - 3x + c$
35. $f(x) = x^3 + cx$
36. Determine a value of c such that the equation $x^2 - 10x + c = 0$ has
   (a) two solutions
   (b) exactly one solution
   (c) no solutions

Suggestion: Use your graphing calculator. Start by constructing graphs with different values of c.

37. Determine a value of c such that the equation $x^3 - 4x + c = 0$ has
   (a) three solutions,
   (b) exactly two solutions,
   (c) exactly one solution.

2.2 QUADRATIC MODELS AND EQUATIONS

In Section 1.4 we analyzed the 1950–1990 population of Charlotte and found that it is reasonably well fitted by a linear model of the form

$$P(t) = P_0 + mt \tag{1}$$

where P_0 is the initial population (at time $t = 0$) and m is the annual change in the population. But a linear model is appropriate only when the rate of change is *constant* (or at least approximately so). The following table displays the 1950–1990 census data for Austin, Texas.

Year	Population (thous)	Change
1950	132	
1960	187	55
1970	254	67
1980	346	92
1990	466	120

The final column shows the population change in the preceding decade. Observe that the population was *not* increasing at a constant rate. Indeed, it appears that the rate of change *itself* was increasing throughout the 1950–1990 period. This is why neither of the straight lines plotted in Fig. 2.2.1 appears to fit the Austin population data points well. The following example describes how these lines were plotted.

Example 1

To plot a line through the 1950 and 1960 data points, we take $t = 0$ in 1950 and note first that the rate of change in the Austin population during the 10-year period 1950–1960 was

$$m_1 = \frac{187 - 132}{10} = \frac{55}{10} = 5.5.$$

With $P_0 = 132$, Eq. (1) gives the equation

$$P = 132 + 5.5t. \tag{2}$$

In Fig. 2.2.1 we see that this line—though it passes through the 1950 and 1960 data points—"rides below" the last three data points. The rate of change in the population from 1980 to 1990 was

$$m_2 = \frac{466 - 346}{10} = \frac{120}{10} = 12.$$

Since $t = 0$ in 1950, the year 1980 corresponds to $t_1 = 30$ when the population was $P_1 = 346$. Hence the form $P(t) = P_1 + m(t - t_1)$ of the linear population model [Eq. (12) in Section 1.3] gives the equation

$$P = 346 + 12(t - 30) \tag{3}$$

of the second line shown in Fig. 2.2.1. Though it passes through the 1980 and 1990 data points, it rides below the first three data points. It appears that no single straight line fits well all five of Austin's 1950–1990 population data points. ◼

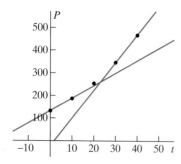

Figure 2.2.1   No single straight line appears to fit the Austin population data.

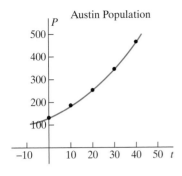

Figure 2.2.2 The Austin population data is better fitted by the parabola $P(t) = 132 + 3.84t + 0.113t^2$.

Perhaps a close inspection of Fig. 2.2.1 will suggest to you that any smooth curve drawn through all five Austin data points must bend upward like a parabola does. Indeed, Fig. 2.2.2 shows how well the quadratic function

$$P(t) = 132 + 3.84t + 0.113t^2 \qquad (4)$$

appears to fit the actual 1950–1990 population growth of Austin. (In Section 2.3 we will talk about how to find such a quadratic model, but here we take it as given.)

Quadratic Population Models

Equation (4) illustrates the general **quadratic model**

$$P(t) = P_0 + at + bt^2. \qquad (5)$$

Assuming that the coefficients are all positive, this model describes a population that—roughly speaking—grows more rapidly as t increases than any linear function. Note that (5) differs from the linear model (1) only in the inclusion of a t^2-term.

In Section 2.1 we wrote the typical quadratic function in the form

$$f(x) = ax^2 + bx + c \qquad (6)$$

and observed that, if the coefficient of the square term in (6) is positive, then the graph $y = f(x)$ is a parabola opening upward. The function $P(t)$ in (5) is a quadratic function of t, whereas the function $f(x)$ in (6) is a quadratic function of x. The coefficients P_0, a, b in (5)—and the coefficients a, b, c in (6)—denote numerical constants, and these constants can be denoted by any letters we choose. We denote the constant term in the quadratic population model (5) by P_0 simply because substitution of $t = 0$ yields $P(0) = P_0$.

Example 2

Suppose that the future population of Kempton t years after January 1, 1990 is described (in thousands) by the quadratic model

$$P(t) = 110 + 4t + 0.07t^2. \qquad (7)$$

(a) What was the population of Kempton on January 1, 2000?
(b) In what month of what calendar year will the population of Kempton reach 200 thousand?

(a) We need only substitute $t = 10$ in (7) and calculate

$$P(10) = 110 + 4(10) + 0.07(10)^2 = 110 + 40 + 7 = 157.$$

Thus our quadratic model predicts a 1/1/2000 Kempton population of 157 thousand people.

(b) We need to find the value of t when $P(t) = 200$, that is, so that

$$110 + 4t + 0.07t^2 = 200. \qquad (8)$$

Figure 2.2.3 shows the graphs of the two sides of this equation—the parabola $P(t) = 110 + 4t + 0.07t^2$ and the horizontal line $P(t) = 200$. (Since our graphing calculator's independent variable is x instead of t, we used **Y1=100,**

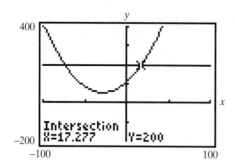

Figure 2.2.3   The line $y = 200$ and the parabola $y = 110 + 4x + 0.07x^2$.

Y2=110+4X+0.07X^2 and the graphing calculator window $-100 \le x \le 100$, $-200 \le y \le 400$ to construct this figure.)

To solve Eq. (8)—with x in place of t—we need only find the x-coordinates of the two intersection points of the line and parabola that we see in Fig. 2.2.3. Remember why this is so. It's because any point (x, y) lying *both* on the line and on the parabola has *both* $y = 200$ (because it lies on the line) and $y = 110 + 4x + 0.07x^2$ (because it lies on the parabola). Thus x satisfies the equation $110 + 4x + 0.07x^2 = 200$, because both sides equal the (single) y-coordinate of the intersection point.

One of the intersection points in Fig. 2.2.3 has a negative x-coordinate and the other has a positive x-coordinate. Hence Eq. (8) has both a negative solution and a positive solution. However, because $t = 0$ is 1/1/1990, the negative solution $t < 0$ would be in the past—rather than in the future. We therefore seek the positive solution of the equation.

Figure 2.2.3 indicates that we have already used our graphing calculator's intersection-finding feature to locate the intersection point $(17.277, 200)$ on the right (corresponding to the positive solution). Remembering that the calculator's x is our t, we therefore see that the positive solution of Eq. (8) is

$$t = 17.277 \text{ years}$$
$$= 17 \text{ years} + (0.277 \times 12) \text{ months}$$
$$= 17 \text{ years} + 3.32 \text{ months}.$$

Thus Kempton should reach a population of 200 thousand 17 years, 3.32 months after Jan. 1, 1990. But 17 years after Jan. 1, 1990 is Jan. 1, 2007, and 3.32 months later is sometime during April, 2007.   ◼

We have described a *graphic solution* of Eq. (8). However, you may recall using the quadratic formula to solve similar equations in previous mathematics courses. For a *symbolic solution,* we could start with our equation

$$110 + 4t + 0.07t^2 = 200$$

and transpose the constant 200 to get the *quadratic equation*

$$0.07t^2 + 4t - 90 = 0.$$

You might check that substitution of the coefficient values $a = 0.07$, $b = 4$, and $c = -90$ in the *quadratic formula*

$$t = \frac{-b \pm \sqrt{b^2 - 4ac}}{2a} \tag{9}$$

gives the two solutions $t = -74.419$ (if we take the minus sign before the radical) and $t = +17.277$ (if we take the plus sign). The positive solution agrees with our graphic solution. You should use your own calculator to verify the negative solution graphically.

The Quadratic Formula

Recall that the **quadratic equation**

$$ax^2 + bx + c = 0 \tag{10}$$

with coefficients a, b, and c has *two* solutions r and s given by

$$r = \frac{-b + \sqrt{b^2 - 4ac}}{2a} \quad \text{and} \quad s = \frac{-b - \sqrt{b^2 - 4ac}}{2a}.$$

This fact—that *both* values $x = r$ and $x = s$ given by these *two* formulas satisfy the given quadratic equation—is what is meant by the **quadratic formula** written in its usual form

$$x = \frac{-b \pm \sqrt{b^2 - 4ac}}{2a}, \tag{11}$$

which describes both solutions simultaneously.

It is important to observe that—however a given quadratic equation may be written—the symbol a in (11) denotes the coefficient of the *square* of the variable in the equation. For instance, in the equation

$$P_0 + at + bt^2 = 0$$

the roles of a, b, and c in (11) are played by b, a, and P_0, respectively, so the quadratic formula gives its two solutions as

$$t = \frac{-a \pm \sqrt{a^2 - 4bP_0}}{2b}.$$

Thus the key to correct use of the quadratic formula is realizing that a, b, and c in (11) are merely placeholders, with

- a being the coefficient of the square term,
- b being the coefficient of the first-power term, and
- c being the constant term in the quadratic equation being solved.

How Many Solutions?

The solutions of the quadratic equation $ax^2 + bx + c = 0$ are the x-intercepts of the parabola $y = ax^2 + bx + c$, that is, the points of this graph on the x-axis where $y = 0$. Geometrically, it is easy to see that a parabola can intersect the x-axis either

- at **two points,** as in Fig. 2.2.4, where the parabola dips beneath the x-axis, or
- at **a single point,** as in Fig. 2.2.5, where it just touches the x-axis, or
- at **no points,** as in Fig. 2.2.6, where it lies completely above the x-axis.

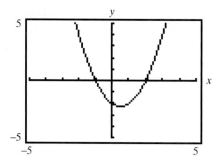

Figure 2.2.4   The graph
$y = x^2 - x - 2$.

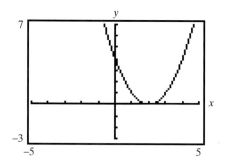

Figure 2.2.5   The graph
$y = x^2 - 4x + 4$.

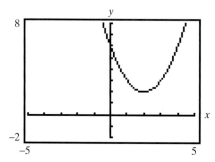

Figure 2.2.6   The graph $y = x^2 - 4x + 6$.

(You might like to verify each of these graphs with your own graphing calcula-tor.) These three geometric cases correspond to three algebraic possibilities—as to whether the quantity $b^2 - 4ac$ under the radical in (11) is

- **positive,** so there are two different solutions of the equation;
- **zero,** so the equation has only one solution;
- **negative,** so the equation has no real solutions at all.

(If it's zero, then whether we add or subtract the radical, we get the same thing. If it's negative, then the radical represents the square root of a negative number and thus is an imaginary number, which means the equation has no real solutions.)

Most of the quadratic equations we'll see in applications will have two real solutions that can be found either

- *algebraically*—by using the quadratic formula, or
- *graphically*—by locating the intersection points of a parabola and either the x-axis (like those in Fig. 2.2.4) or some other horizontal line (like those in Fig. 2.2.3), or
- *numerically*—by the method of tabulation illustrated in Example 3 of Section 1.3.

In the next several examples we illustrate typical calculations using the quadrat-ic formula.

Example 3

Solve the quadratic equation $x^2 - 10x - 119 = 0$.

Here $a = 1$, $b = -10$, and $c = -119$ so the quadratic formula gives the two solutions

$$r, s = \frac{-(-10) \pm \sqrt{(-10)^2 - 4(1)(-119)}}{2(1)}$$

$$= \frac{10 \pm \sqrt{100 + 476}}{2}$$

$$= \frac{10 \pm \sqrt{576}}{2}$$

$$= \frac{10 \pm 24}{2}$$

$$= \frac{34}{2}, \frac{-14}{2} \quad \text{(taking the two signs separately)}$$

$$r, s = 17, -7.$$

We write r, s here to emphasize that we're calculating two different solutions simultaneously. In plain language, the quadratic equation $x^2 - 10x - 119 = 0$ has the two solutions $x = -7$ and $x = 17$.

We all make algebraic mistakes from time to time. (The authors of this text-book have made more algebraic mistakes than any student reader has ever thought of, but we hope to have found them before the book was printed.) There-fore, you should always check your algebraic solutions. Substitute them into the equation to verify that they really do satisfy it:

$$(-7)^2 - 10(-7) - 119 = 49 + 70 - 119 = 0$$
$$(17)^2 - 10(17) - 119 = 289 - 170 - 119 = 0. \qquad \blacksquare$$

The **factor theorem** of elementary algebra says that *if* the quadratic equa-tion $ax^2 + bx + c = 0$ has solutions r and s *then* the quadratic polynomial $ax^2 + bx + c$ factors as

$$ax^2 + bx + c = a(x - r)(x - s). \tag{12}$$

Example 4

It follows that the quadratic polynomial $x^2 - 10x - 119$ (with $a = 1$) in the equation of Example 3 has factors $x - (-7) = x + 7$ and $x - 17$. It there-fore factors as

$$x^2 - 10x - 119 = (x - 17)(x + 7).$$

If (for some reason) we'd been asked to factor this quadratic but could not find the factorization by the usual trial-and-error approach, we could have used the quadratic formula as in Example 3 to discover it. The point is that—as opposed to the usual hit-or-miss method of factoring—the quadratic formula provides a clear-cut way that always succeeds in doing the job. $\blacksquare$

Example 5

Solve the quadratic equation $60x^2 + 171x - 1275 = 0$, and thereby discover how to factor the quadratic polynomial on the left.

Here $a = 60, b = 171$, and $c = -1275$ so the quadratic formula gives the two solutions

$$r, s = \frac{-(171) \pm \sqrt{(171)^2 - 4(60)(-1275)}}{2(60)}$$

$$= \frac{-171 \pm \sqrt{335241}}{120}$$

$$= \frac{-171 \pm 579}{120}$$

$$= \frac{408}{120}, \frac{-750}{120} = \frac{17}{5}, -\frac{25}{4}.$$

Writing (12) with $a = 60$, we therefore get the factorization

$$60x^2 + 171x - 1275 = 60\left(x - \frac{17}{5}\right)\left(x + \frac{25}{4}\right).$$

We can clean this up a bit by first writing $60 = 3 \times 5 \times 4$, then multiplying the 5 times the first factor and the 4 times the second factor. This gives

$$60x^2 + 171x - 1275 = 3 \cdot 5\left(x - \frac{17}{5}\right) \cdot 4\left(x - \frac{25}{4}\right).$$

Multiplying out, we finally get the factorization

$$60x^2 + 171x - 1275 = 3(5x - 17)(4x - 25)$$

with all the coefficients being *integers*. This factorization might have been difficult to find using the hit-or-miss approach. ◼

Example 6

Solve the quadratic equation $169x^2 - 806x + 961 = 0$ and thereby discover how to factor the quadratic on the left.

Here $a = 169, b = -806$, and $c = 961$, so the quadratic formula gives the two solutions

$$r, s = \frac{806 \pm \sqrt{(-806)^2 - 4(169)(961)}}{2(169)}$$

$$= \frac{806 \pm \sqrt{0}}{2(169)} = \frac{403}{169} = \frac{31 \times 13}{13 \times 13} = \frac{31}{13}.$$

Hence our quadratic equation has only the single solution $r = s = 31/13$. The factor theorem therefore gives the factorization

$$169x^2 - 806x + 961 = 169\left(x - \frac{31}{13}\right)\left(x - \frac{31}{13}\right)$$

$$= 13\left(x - \frac{31}{13}\right) \cdot 13\left(x - \frac{31}{13}\right)$$

$$= (13x - 31)(13x - 31)$$

$$169x^2 - 806x + 961 = (13x - 31)^2,$$

which is hardly apparent at first glance. ◧

Applications

Just solving quadratic equations by themselves—though necessary for practice—can seem like pretty dry stuff. But such equations appear in real-world problems.

For instance, suppose an object—like a ball or a bullet—is thrown or fired straight upward at time $t = 0$ from a point y_0 feet above the ground (Fig. 2.2.7). (We take $y_0 = 0$ if it starts from the ground.) If the projectile's initial (upward) velocity is v_0 feet/sec, then (neglecting air resistance) its height y feet above the ground after t seconds is given by the formula:

$$y(t) = -16t^2 + v_0 t + y_0. \tag{13}$$

Everyone knows that what goes up must come back down. If the values of y_0 and v_0 are given, then Eq. (13) is all we need in order to find out how long the ball stays in the air before returning to the ground.

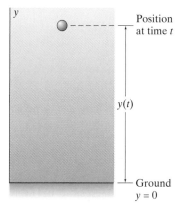

Figure 2.2.7 The position function of a particle moving vertically.

(margin labels:) Position at time t — $y(t)$ — Ground $y = 0$

Example 7

Suppose an arrow is shot straight upward from a point on the ground beside a building 256 feet high. If the arrow's initial velocity is 160 ft/sec, then substitution of $y_0 = 0$ and $v_0 = 160$ in (13) yields

$$y(t) = -16t^2 + 160t. \tag{14}$$

(a) How high is the arrow after 5 seconds?
(b) How long is the arrow in the air before it returns to the ground?
(c) When does the arrow pass the top of the building on the way up? On the way back down?

(a) Substitution of $t = 5$ in (14) gives

$$y(5) = -16(5)^2 + 160(5) = 400 \text{ feet}$$

for the ball's height after 5 seconds.
(b) Note that $y = 0$ again when the arrow returns to ground level. The time t at which it hits the ground therefore satisfies the equation

$$y(t) = -16t^2 + 160t = -16t(t - 10) = 0,$$

when $t = 0$ or when $t = 10$. But $t = 0$ when the arrow was originally shot upward, so it remains in the air for 10 seconds.
(c) If we set $y(t) = 256$ in (14) we find that the arrow is 256 feet high when

$$-16t^2 + 160t = 256.$$

We could use the quadratic formula, but this equation is easy to solve by factoring:

$$-16t^2 + 160t - 256 = 0,$$
$$-16(t^2 - 10t + 16) = 0,$$
$$-16(t - 2)(t - 8) = 0.$$

(Even if factoring like this is not easy for you, it should be easy to multiply out and verify that the indicated factorization is correct.) The two solutions $t = 2$ and $t = 8$ are the times when the arrow is 256 feet high. So it passes the top of the building on the way up after 2 seconds, and on the way back down 8 seconds after it was shot upward.   ◨

Example 8

You have a 100 ft by 50 ft flower garden that you plan to enclose with a sidewalk costing 25 cents per square foot. If you have \$250 to spend, determine accurate to the nearest 1/8 inch how wide you can make this sidewalk.

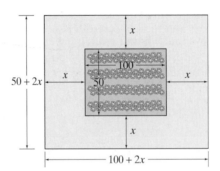

Figure 2.2.8   The flower garden and its sidewalk.

Figure 2.2.8 shows the flower garden enclosed with a sidewalk of width x. The big rectangle consisting of the garden plus the sidewalk has dimensions

$$100 + 2x \quad \text{and} \quad 50 + 2x,$$

so its area is given by

$$(100 + 2x)(50 + 2x) = 4x^2 + 300x + 5000.$$

The area of the 100 ft by 50 ft rectangular garden alone is $100 \times 50 = 5000$. The area of the sidewalk is the difference obtained by subtracting the area of the inner rectangle from the area of the outer rectangle

$$A = (4x^2 + 300x + 5000) - 5000 = 4x^2 + 300x. \tag{15}$$

Now with \$250 at 25 cents/ft^2 = \$0.25/ft^2 available, we can afford to buy

$$A = \frac{\$250}{\$0.25/\text{ft}^2} = \frac{250}{0.25} \text{ ft}^2 = 1000 \tag{16}$$

square feet of sidewalk. Equating the final expressions for A in (15) and (16), we get the equation

$$A = 4x^2 + 300x = 1000. \tag{17}$$

Thus we see that we need to solve the quadratic equation

$$4x^2 + 300x - 1000 = 0. \tag{18}$$

The quadratic formula now gives

$$x = \frac{-(300) \pm \sqrt{(300)^2 - 4(4)(-1000)}}{2(4)} = \frac{-300 \pm \sqrt{90000 + 16000}}{8}$$

$$= \frac{-300 \pm \sqrt{106000}}{8} = 3.1971, -78.1971.$$

But x here denotes the width of the sidewalk—a physical dimension. A physical dimension cannot be negative (!), so it's the *positive* solution of Eq. (18) that measures the width of the sidewalk. This gives a sidewalk width of

$$x = 3.1971 \text{ ft}$$
$$= 3 \text{ ft plus } (12 \times 0.1971) \text{ in}$$
$$= 3 \text{ ft } 2.3652 \text{ in.}$$

This might look like the answer. But recall that we were asked to find the width of the sidewalk accurate to the nearest *eighth* of an inch.

It therefore remains only to see which multiple of $\frac{1}{8}$ inch is closest to 0.3652 inches. But $\frac{1}{8} = 0.125$, $\frac{2}{8} = 0.250$, and $\frac{3}{8} = 0.375$. We see that 0.3652 in is between $\frac{2}{8}$ (or $\frac{1}{4}$) and $\frac{3}{8}$ in, but closer to the latter. Hence the proper width of our sidewalk is 3 feet, $2\frac{3}{8}$ inches. ◼

We have mentioned that any quadratic equation can be solved either *algebraically* (using the quadratic formula) or *graphically* (using a graphing calculator), as well as *numerically* (by "table zooming"). So an interesting alternative to using the quadratic formula to solve the equation in (18) is to graph each side **Y1=4x^2+300X** and **Y2=1000** of the equation in (17). With an appropriate window we get the picture shown in Fig. 2.2.9, with two apparent intersections of the line and parabola. You might like to use your calculator's intersection-finding facility to verify the two solutions found in Example 8.

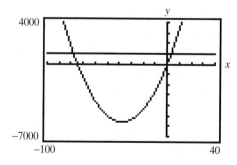

Figure 2.2.9 The graphs $A = 4x^2 + 300x$ and $A = 1000$.

Summary

A quadratic population model is one of the form

$$P(t) = P_0 + at + bt^2$$

where P_0 denotes the initial (time $t = 0$) population. In order to find when the population is P_1, we need to solve the equation

$$P_0 + at + bt^2 = P_1.$$

This is a quadratic equation—after tranposition of P_1 to the other side—that you can solve either

- graphically, using a graphing calculator,
- numerically, using a table of function values, or
- symbolically, using the quadratic formula.

Apply the quadratic formula to solve the quadratic equations in Problems 1–6. Try to express each root x as a **rational number**—that is, as a quotient $x = p/q$ of two **integers.** For variety, solve several of these equations graphically, and then verify that your graphically found roots agree with those given by the quadratic formula.

1. $x^2 - 2x - 15 = 0$
2. $x^2 - 10x - 119 = 0$
3. $2x^2 - 5x + 2 = 0$
4. $6x^2 - 5x - 6 = 0$
5. $20x^2 + 57x - 425 = 0$
6. $54x^2 + 105x - 621 = 0$

In Problems 7–10, the given quadratic population model predicts the population (in thousands) of a city t years after January 1, 1997. Find how long it takes this city's population to reach the given level P_1. Give your answer in the form m years and n days. (Assume exactly 365 days per year.)

7. $P(t) = 0.25t^2 + 5t + 100;$ $P_1 = 200$
8. $P(t) = 0.3t^2 + 6t + 150;$ $P_1 = 250$
9. $P(t) = 0.7t^2 + 12t + 200;$ $P_1 = 350$
10. $P(t) = 1.5t^2 + 21t + 300;$ $P_1 = 500$

In Problems 11 and 12, the population $P(t)$ of a city t years after January 1, 1997 is given. In what month of what year does the city's population reach twice its initial (1/1/1997) population?

11. $P(t) = 80 + 6t + 0.3t^2$
12. $P(t) = 90 + 7t + 0.5t^2$

In Problems 13–20, use $y(t) = -16t^2 + v_0t + y_0$ as in Example 7.

13. A powerful crossbow fires a bolt straight upward from the ground with an initial velocity of 320 ft/sec. Then its height after t seconds is given by $y(t) = -16t^2 + 320t$. How long is the bolt in the air?

14. A ball is thrown straight upward from the ground beside a 100-foot tree. Its initial velocity is $v_0 = 96$ ft/sec. When does it pass the top of the tree on the way up? On the way down?

15. A ball is thrown straight upward (at time $t = 0$) from the top of a 100-foot building with initial velocity 100 ft/sec, so $y_0 = v_0 = 100$. When does the ball pass the top of the building on its way back down? How long until it hits the ground?

16. A ball is thrown or dropped from the top of the Empire State Building, which is 960 feet tall.

(a) If it is simply dropped with $v_0 = 0$, how long does it take to hit the ground?

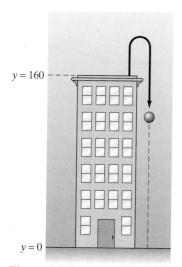

$y = 160$

$y = 0$

Figure 2.2.10   The building of Problem 20.

(b) If it is thrown downward with $v_0 = -50$ ft/sec (note the minus sign), how long does it take to hit the ground?

17. In each part of Problem 16, when does the ball pass the fiftieth floor (480 feet above the ground) on its way down?

18. Cezar drops a stone into a well, and it hits the water at the bottom after 3 seconds. How deep is the well?

19. Sydney drops a rock into a well in which the water surface is 300 feet below ground level. How long does it take the rock to hit the water at the bottom?

20. Maria throws a ball upward with an initial velocity of 48 ft/sec from the top of a building 160 feet high (Fig. 2.2.10).The ball soon falls to the ground at the base of the building. How long does the ball remain aloft?

21. You have a rectangular 175 ft by 75 ft flower garden that you plan to enclose with a sidewalk costing 20 cents per square foot. If you have $340 to spend, determine how wide you can make this sidewalk, rounded off accurate to the nearest $\frac{1}{8}$ inch.

22. Figure 2.2.11 shows a 65 ft by 45 ft rectangular garden with one long side along a creek. A concrete sidewalk is to be built along the other three sides of the garden.

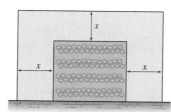

Figure 2.2.11   The flower garden in Problem 22.

(a) If the width of the sidewalk is x feet, write a formula $A(x) = \cdots$ giving the area of the sidewalk in square feet.

(b) If the sidewalk will cost $1.70 cents per square foot of area, what area of sidewalk will cost a total of exactly $920?

(c) Given the cost figures in (b), express the sidewalk width x in feet and inches, rounded off accurate to the nearest quarter-inch.

23. Figure 2.2.12 shows a circular flower garden with a radius of 50 feet. It is to be surrounded with a sidewalk having an area of exactly 1000 square feet. Find the width x of the sidewalk, rounded off accurate to the nearest eighth of an inch. Remember that the area of a circle of radius r is given by $A = \pi r^2$, where $\pi \approx 3.1416$.

24. This problem is a personal challenge. Suppose the population of Your City t years after January 1, 1998 is given (in thousands) by

$$P(t) = 100 + kt + \left(\frac{k}{10}\right)^2 t^2$$

where k is the largest digit in your student ID number. On what calendar day of what year will the population of Your City reach 200 thousand? For the purpose of this problem you can ignore leap years and assume that every year has 365 days, but you will need to take into account the differing number of days in a month.

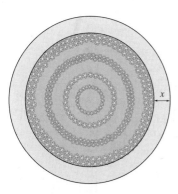

Figure 2.2.12   The circular flower garden of Problem 23.

2.3   FITTING QUADRATIC MODELS TO DATA

In Section 2.2 we discussed the data in the following table, which shows the population of Austin, Texas as recorded in the decade census years of 1950 through 1990.

Year	Population (thous)	Change
1950	132	
1960	187	55
1970	254	67
1980	346	92
1990	466	120

The change figures in the final column of the table show that the population of Austin was changing at a steadily increasing rate. Thus the population of Austin does *not* exhibit the constant rate of change that is characteristic of a linear model. Indeed, we indicated in Figs. 2.2.1 and 2.2.2 that this data is better fitted by a **quadratic model** of the form

$$P(t) = P_0 + at + bt^2. \tag{1}$$

In this section we discuss the fitting of data by quadratic models. Much of this discussion will parallel the discussion in Section 1.4 of fitting linear models to data.

Example 1

Ordinary people frequently use spreadsheets to record and analyze data. Figure 2.3.1 shows a spreadsheet that we prepared to analyze the Austin population data. It is set up so that—when the population census figures are entered in the Population column, and the desired numerical coefficients P_0, a, and b in (1) are entered in the first three shaded cells—the resulting predicted populations are automatically calculated and displayed in the $P(t)$ column, as well as the errors and finally the Average Error that is shown in the final shaded cell.

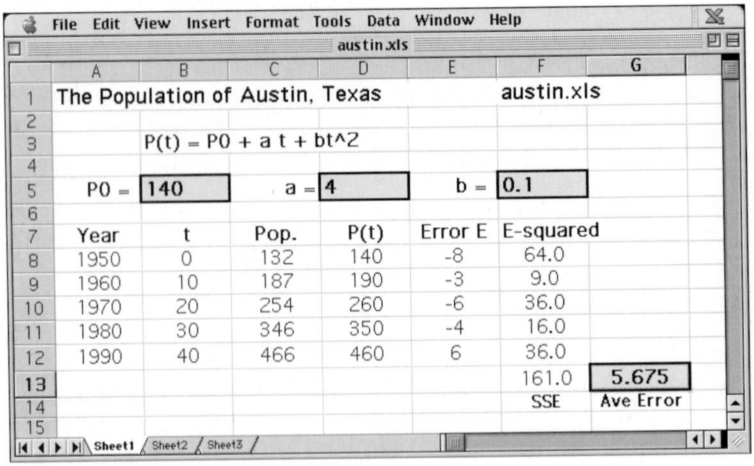

Figure 2.3.1   Spreadsheet modeling the population of Austin, Texas.

We chose the indicated values $P_0 = 140, a = 4$, and $b = 0.1$ by a process of trial and error. We actually started with the value $P_0 = 130$ (close to Austin's actual initial population in the table) and the outright guesses $a = 5$ and $b = 0.1$. Then we adjusted slightly the values of P_0 and a so as to decrease the calculated average error. In this way we discovered that the specific quadratic model

$$P(t) = 140 + 4t + 0.1t^2 \qquad (2)$$

fits the 1950–1990 Austin census data with an average error of 5.675 thousand people.

t	Actual P	$P(t)$	Error E	E^2
0	132	140	−8	64
10	187	190	−3	9
20	254	260	−6	36
30	346	350	−4	16
40	466	460	6	36

The meaning of the term *average error* here is the same as in Section 1.4. The preceding table was copied from the spreadsheet of Fig. 2.3.1 and lists in its P-column the *actual* 1950–1990 census populations P_1, P_2, P_3, P_4, P_5 at the successive times t_1, t_2, t_3, t_4, t_5. The $P(t)$-column lists the *predicted* populations $P(t_1), P(t_2), P(t_3), P(t_4), P(t_5)$ calculated using the quadratic model in (2). For instance,

$$t_1 = 0, P_1 = 132, P(t_1) = 140 \quad \text{and} \quad t_4 = 30, P_4 = 346, P(t_4) = 350.$$

The E-column of the table lists the successive **errors** E_1, E_2, E_3, E_4, E_5 defined by

$$E_i = P_i - P(t_i) \quad (= \text{actual} - \text{predicted}) \qquad (3)$$

for each i. Finally, the last column of the table lists the *squares* of these errors. As in Section 1.4, the SSE (**sum of squares of errors**) is defined by

$$\text{SSE} = E_1^2 + E_2^2 + E_3^2 + E_4^2 + E_5^2 \qquad (4)$$

and the **average error** is then

$$\text{average error} = \sqrt{\frac{\text{SSE}}{n}} \qquad (5)$$

where n is the number of original data points. ◼

Example 2

In the case of the Austin data shown in the preceding table, we have

$$\text{SSE} = (-8)^2 + (-3)^2 + (-6)^2 + (-4)^2 + (6)^2 = 64 + 9 + 36 + 16 + 36 = 161.$$

Since $n = 5$ here, Eq. (5) gives

$$\text{average error} = \sqrt{\frac{161}{5}} \approx 5.675$$

for the average error with which the quadratic model $P(t) = 140 + 4t + 0.1t^2$ fits the actual Austin census population data for the years 1950–1990. Thus we verified with our own calculations the average error displayed in the spreadsheet of Fig. 2.3.1. ∎

The Best Fit—The Least Possible Average Error

Of course, the optimal quadratic model is the one that best fits the actual data. As in Section 1.4, the better of two models is the one giving the lesser average error.

Example 3

Which of the two quadratic models

$$P(t) = 140 + 4t + 0.1t^2 \quad \text{or} \quad P(t) = 125 + 4.5t + 0.1t^2 \qquad (6)$$

fits the Austin census data best?

We saw in Example 2 that the average error of the first quadratic model in (6) is 5.675 thousand people. You should use your calculator to verify that the second of these quadratic models yields the figures shown in the following table.

t	Actual P	$P(t)$	Error E	E^2
0	132	125	7	49
10	187	180	7	49
20	254	255	−1	1
30	346	350	−4	16
40	466	465	1	1

Consequently, the second model in (6) has sum of squares of errors

$$\text{SSE} = 49 + 49 + 1 + 16 + 1 = 116$$

and the resulting average error

$$\text{average error} = \sqrt{\frac{116}{5}} \approx 4.817.$$

Thus the average error in the second model is only 4.817 thousand people as compared with the average error of 5.675 in the first model. Thus the quadratic model $P(t) = 125 + 4.5t + 0.1t^2$ fits the Austin population data better than does the first model $P(t) = 140 + 4t + 0.1t^2$ in (6). ∎

For best fit, the question is this: What choice of the numerical parameters $P_0, a,$ and b in the quadratic model $P(t) = P_0 + at + bt^2$ will minimize the average error? That is, what values of these three coefficients will give the quadratic model with the least possible average error? This optimal quadratic model will be the one that we say best fits the given data.

Figure 2.3.2 shows how to enter the Austin population data in a calculator. The t-values 0, 10, 20, 30, 40 corresponding to the decade years from 1950 to 1990 are stored as a list **L1**, and the corresponding list of census population figures is stored as a list **L2**. (Note that calculator lists are enclosed in curly braces.) Figure 2.3.3 shows the resulting **STAT EDIT** menu displaying the data in table form. Here the individual items—either a year or the corresponding population—can be changed or edited one at a time (for instance, if an error was made in entering either list originally).

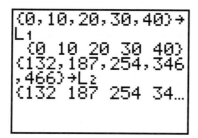

Figure 2.3.2   Storing the 1950–1990 population census data for Austin.

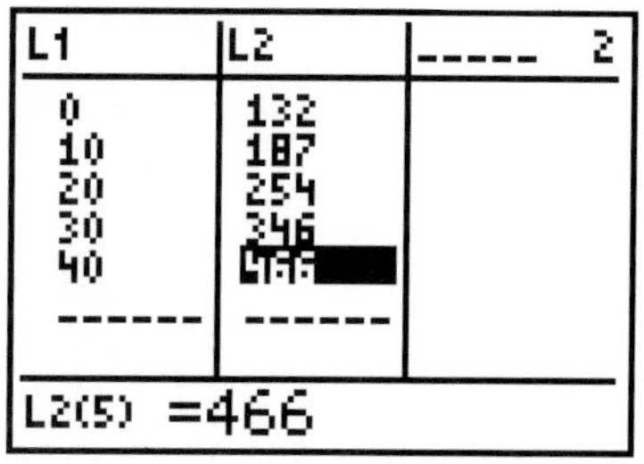

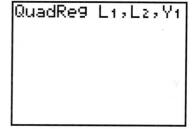

Figure 2.3.3   TI-83 **STAT EDIT** menu showing the Austin population data in table form.

Figure 2.3.4 shows the calculator's **STAT CALC** menu. Item **5: QuadReg** on this menu is the calculator's quadratic regression facility for finding the parabola $y = ax^2 + bx + c$ that best fits the selected data. When we select item **5** on this menu, the **QuadReg** function is entered on the home calculating screen. As shown in Fig. 2.3.5, we must then enter the names of our list **L1** of **X**-coordinates, our list **L2** of **Y**-coordinates, and the name **Y1** of the $\boxed{Y=}$ menu variable where we want the resulting quadratic function saved.

Figure 2.3.4   The TI-83 **STAT CALC** menu.

Figure 2.3.5   Fitting the **X**-data in list **L1** and the **Y**-data in list **L2**.

Figure 2.3.6 shows the display that results when this command is entered. Observe that the calculator has its own notation, using a for the coefficient of the x^2-term, b for the coefficient of the x-term, and c for the coefficient of the constant term.

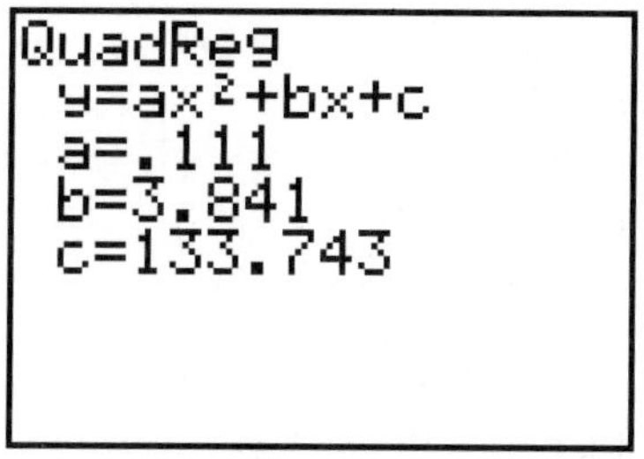

```
QuadReg
 y=ax²+bx+c
 a=.111
 b=3.841
 c=133.743
```

Figure 2.3.6   The best quadratic polynomial fit to our data points.

With this notation, the displayed results say that the quadratic polynomial best fitting the given data is

$$y = 0.111x^2 + 3.841x + 133.743. \qquad (7)$$

The **QuadReg L1, L2, Y1** command automatically enters Eq. (7) in the Y= menu, ready for plotting as shown in Fig 2.3.7. With **Plot 1** turned **On** in the **STAT PLOT** menu (Fig. 2.3.8), GRAPH then gives the plot of the best-fitting parabola (quadratic polynomial graph) shown in Fig. 2.3.9, where the original census data points are shown as small squares.

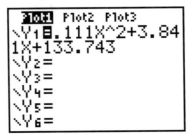

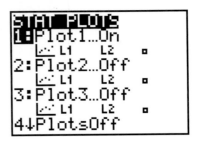

Figure 2.3.7   The best-fit quadratic polynomial ready for plotting.

Figure 2.3.8   Preparing to plot the data together with the optimal quadratic fit.

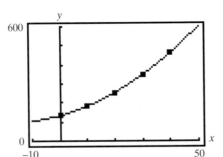

Figure 2.3.9   The optimal quadratic fit.

The calculator automatically uses **X** as the independent variable and **Y** as the dependent variable. In terms of calendar year as the independent t-variable and population as the dependent P-variable, Eq. (7) says that the quadratic model that best fits the 1950–1990 Austin census data is given by

$$P(t) = 133.743 + 3.841t + 0.111t^2. \qquad (8)$$

The following table compares the original census data with the population figures predicted by this linear model.

t	Actual P	$P(t)$	Error E	E^2
0	132	133.743	−1.743	3.038
10	187	183.253	3.747	14.040
20	254	254.963	−0.963	0.927
30	346	348.873	−2.873	8.254
40	466	464.983	1.017	1.034

Example 4

You should use a calculator to calculate the indicated values of $P(t)$ and to verify the other values shown in this table. As usual, the final column shows the *squares* of the errors. Hence the SSE associated with the optimal linear model in (8) is

$$3.038 + 14.040 + 0.927 + 8.254 + 1.034 = 27.293.$$

Therefore, the average error is given by

$$\text{average error} = \sqrt{\frac{27.293}{5}} \approx 2.336.$$

Thus the quadratic model $P(t) = 133.743 + 3.841t + 0.111t^2$ predicts 1950–1990 census year populations that differ (on the average) by 2336 people from those actually recorded for Austin. Note that this minimal average error of 2.336 (thousands) is necessarily less than the average errors calculated in Example 3 for the first two quadratic models $P(t) = 140 + 4t + 0.1t^2$ (with average error 5.675) and $P(t) = 125 + 4.5t + 0.1t^2$ (with average error 4.817) that we considered.　　　　　　　　　　　　　　　　　　　　　　　　　　　　◤

Applications of Quadratic Modeling

Thus far, we have discussed only the quadratic modeling of population growth. But the world is full of other apparently quadratic data waiting to be modeled.

Example 5

The per capita consumption of cigarettes in 1930 and the lung cancer death rates (deaths per million males) for 1950 in the four Scandinavian countries were as follows:

Country	Cig. Consumption x	Death Rate y
Norway	250	95
Sweden	300	120
Denmark	350	165
Finland	1100	350

It is hard to ignore the fact that higher cigarette consumption appears to be correlated with higher lung cancer death rates. In Section 1.4 we found that the optimal linear model fitting this data is

$$y = 0.28x + 40.75. \tag{9}$$

This straight line fit to the data is shown in Fig. 2.3.10. We note that this straight line appears to go through the second and fourth data points but does not fit the first and third points so well. Perhaps a parabola that levels off a bit as it approaches the fourth point would fit all of the points better.

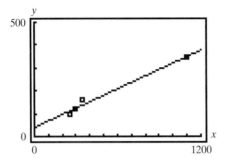

Figure 2.3.10   Straight line $y = 0.28x + 40.75$ fitting the cigarette data.

We therefore explore a *quadratic* model fitting this same data. We do **MEM ClrAllLists** to purge the Austin population data from our calculator, and then enter the *x*- and *y*-data in the lists **L1** and **L2** (Fig. 2.3.11). Then the **STAT CALC** command **QuadReg L1, L2,Y1** produces the parabola

$$y = -0.000521x^2 + 1.01x - 127.99 \tag{10}$$

that best fits our data. With an appropriate window and the same **STAT PLOT** settings as before, we get the plot of this parabola and the table data points that is shown in Fig. 2.3.12.

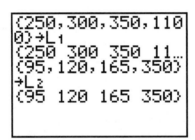

Figure 2.3.11   The cigarette consumption and lung cancer death data of Example 5.

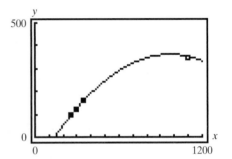

Figure 2.3.12   The parabola best fitting the cigarette consumption versus lung cancer deaths data.

Figure 2.3.13 shows a calculator table of values of the quadratic function in (10).

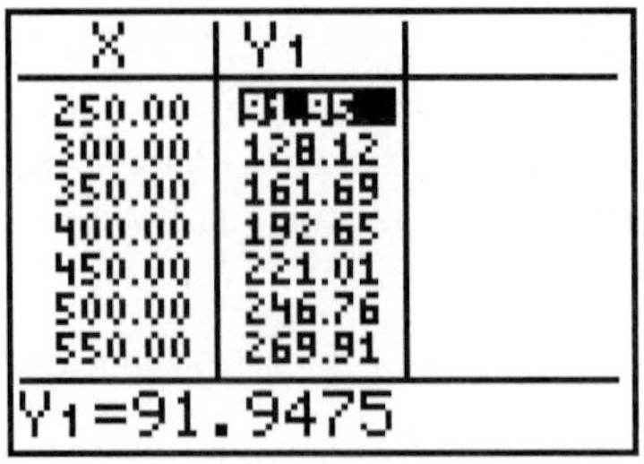

X	Y1
250.00	91.95
300.00	128.12
350.00	161.69
400.00	192.65
450.00	221.01
500.00	246.76
550.00	269.91

Y1=91.9475

Figure 2.3.13   Table of values of the optimal quadratic model $y = -0.000521x^2 + 1.01x - 127.99$.

In the following table we have added these values to our original data.

Cig. Consumption x	Actual Death Rate y	Predicted Death Rate $y(x)$	Error E	Squared Error E^2
250	95	91.95	3.05	9.30
300	120	128.12	−8.12	65.93
350	165	161.69	3.31	10.96
1100	350	352.60	−2.60	6.76

The final column shows the squares of the individual errors. Hence the average error of our quadratic model (10) is

$$\text{average error} = \sqrt{\frac{9.30 + 65.93 + 10.96 + 6.76}{4}} = 4.82.$$

Thus the average error in the quadratic model's predictions (for the four Scandinavian countries) is only 4.82 lung cancer deaths per million males. ◼

In Example 6 of Section 1.4 we found that the average error in the linear model (9) was 15.50. Thus it appears that the optimal quadratic model fits the data considerably better than does the optimal linear model.

But does it really? When we look at the graph in Fig. 2.3.12 it appears that the rate of cancer deaths peaks *before* we reach the fourth point consumption of $x = 1100$. Indeed, by tracing the graph as indicated in Fig. 2.3.14, we see that the quadratic model appears to predict a maximum of about 361.5 cancer deaths per million at a cigarette consumption level of about $x = 969$. Does it sound reasonable that you are worse off if you smoke 969 cigarettes, but every additional cigarette smoked thereafter improves your chances? Surely not!

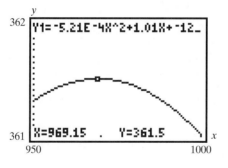

Figure 2.3.14   Consumption $x = 969$ appears to yield the maximum predicted death rate of $y = 361.5$.

So the important lesson is this: There's more to the validity of a mathematical model than its average error. If we wanted to predict the effect of cigarette consumption at higher levels than $x = 1100$, we might well rely more on the linear model—despite its greater average error for the known data points—because at least it predicts a further increase in death rates for greater consumption rates.

Example 6

From 1820 through 1950, the median age of the U.S. population was increasing; data from selected years is shown in the accompanying table.

Year t	1820	1840	1860	1870	1880	1890
Median Age (years) M	16.7	17.8	19.4	20.2	20.9	22.0

We can see from the table that the median age is increasing, but not at a constant rate. (The average rate of change over the first 20 years is 0.055 year per year, while over the last 10 years it is 0.11 year per year.) Thus median age is not a linear function of year.

If we reset our starting point, so that $t = 0$ represents the year 1820, and view our data in the window **Xmin=−10**, **Xmax=100**, **Ymin=15**, **Ymax=25** (Fig. 2.3.15), it appears to have a slight upward bend. Hence, we suspect that a quadratic function might fit this data better than a linear function would.

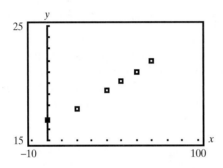

Figure 2.3.15   The median age data of Example 6.

Using the method of Example 5, we find that the quadratic function that best fits this data is given by

$$y = 0.00031x^2 + 0.054x + 16.68,$$

where y represents median age in years and x represents years after 1820. So the quadratic function we are looking for (in terms of t and M) is

$$M(t) = 0.00031t^2 + 0.054t + 16.68,$$

where t denotes years after 1820. For instance, to estimate the median age of the population in 1920, we take $t = 100$ and evaluate $M(100)$,

$$M(100) = 0.00031(100)^2 + 0.054(100) + 16.68 = 25.18 \text{ years.}$$

Thus the median age of the U.S. population in 1920 was approximately 25.18 years. ◣

Example 7

Find the year in which the median age of the population was 27.
Here we need to solve the equation $M(t) = 27$, that is,

$$0.00031t^2 + 0.054t + 16.68 = 27.$$

As always, we have a choice of methods with which to solve this equation.

Graphic Method   Enter the left-hand side of the equation ($0.00031t^2 + 0.054t + 16.68$) as **Y1**, and the right-hand side 27 as **Y2**. Since **Ymax** is set at 25, we must reset our window to include $y = 27$; an **Xmax** of 100 may not be big enough either. Let **Xmax=130** (since we originally said that the median age was increasing from 1820 to 1950) and **Ymax=30**. Then use the calculator's intersection-finding command to find the intersection point (Fig. 2.3.16) of $(115.08, 27)$. Thus, the median population is predicted to reach 27 years of age 115.08 years after 1820, or during the year 1935.

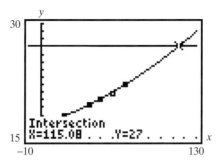

Figure 2.3.16   Finding the intersection point.

Numeric Method   With $0.00031t^2 + 0.054t + 16.68$ in **Y1**, we look in the table and zoom in on $y = 27$. Since our last data point is $(70, 22)$, we start the table at $x = 70$ and increment by steps of $\Delta x = 10$ (Fig. 2.3.17).

X	Y1
70.000	21.979
80.000	22.984
90.000	24.051
100.00	25.180
110.00	26.371
120.00	27.624
130.00	28.939

X=110

Figure 2.3.17   Table of median ages, with 10-year increments.

We see that the median age reaches 27 somewhere between 110 and 120 years, so we reset the table to start at 110 and increment by steps of $\Delta x = 1$ (Fig. 2.3.18).

Here we find that at $x = 115$, $y = 26.99$, so we reset the table to start at 115. Since 26.99 is so close to 27, we now increment by steps of $\Delta x = 0.01$. Thus we again find (Fig. 2.3.19) that 115.08 years after 1820, the median age reaches 27.

X	Y1
110.00	26.371
111.00	26.494
112.00	26.617
113.00	26.740
114.00	26.865
115.00	26.990
116.00	27.115

X=115

Figure 2.3.18   Table of median ages, with 1-year increments.

X	Y1
115.04	26.995
115.05	26.996
115.06	26.997
115.07	26.999
115.08	27.000
115.09	27.001
115.10	27.002

X=115.08

Figure 2.3.19   Table of median ages, with one-hundredth-year increments, after scrolling down to the target value.

Symbolic Method   If we transform the quadratic equation $0.00031t^2 + 0.054t + 16.68 = 27$ into standard form, we get $0.00031t^2 + 0.054t - 10.32 = 0$. We can then use the quadratic formula to obtain the two solutions

$$t = \frac{-0.054 + \sqrt{0.0157128}}{0.00062} \quad \text{or} \quad t = \frac{-0.054 - \sqrt{0.0157128}}{0.00062}.$$

Approximating these solutions gives $t = 115.08$ years (as before) and $t = -289.28$ years. Since the latter negative solution corresponds to approximately 289 years *before* 1820, it does not make sense in the context of this problem, and we discard it.

Thus, no matter which method we use, we arrive at the same conclusion—that the median age is predicted to be 27 sometime during the year 1935.   ◣

Note that this is an example where hindsight is available as a check. Because we are using selected data to model population trends in the past, we can check the reasonableness of our model using any additional data available to us. As it happens, the median age of the population in 1920 was 25.3 years, quite close to our prediction of 25.18 years. Furthermore, the median age of the U.S. population was 26.5 in 1930 and 29.0 in 1940, so our prediction of sometime in 1935 for a median age of 27 looks quite reasonable.

The only reason to use a mathematical model to predict a data value that we know is to check its reasonableness to predict values we don't know. As always, we must be careful about predicting too far beyond our known data. Since recent data is readily available, we would not use the model from Example 6 to predict the current median age of the U.S. population. We have used the example here to illustrate the principle of modeling data with a quadratic function.

2.3 PROBLEMS

In Problems 1–8, both a quadratic polynomial $p(x) = ax^2 + bx + c$ and several (x, y) data points are given. Find the average error with which the indicated polynomial approximates these points. If you wish, you may use the table facility of your calculator to compute an appropriate table of values of $p(x)$.

1. $p(x) = 2x^2 - 5$

x	-2	0	1	3
y	2	-4	-2	12

2. $p(x) = 3x^2 - 7x$

x	-3	-1	4	5
y	45	13	17	43

3. $p(x) = 5 - 3x + x^2$

x	-1	2	4	6
y	11	2	6	25

4. $p(x) = 17 - 3x + 2x^2$

x	-2	1	3	5
y	35	15	30	50

5. $p(x) = 3x^2 + 7x - 10$

x	-10	-5	0	5	10
y	225	35	-15	100	350

6. $p(x) = 25 - 10x + 5x^2$

x	-2	0	1	3	6
y	50	30	20	50	150

7. $p(x) = 2x^2 - 7x + 10$

x	0	1	2	3	4	5
y	15	0	0	10	15	30

8. $p(x) = 100 + 5x - x^2$

x	-4	-2	0	2	4	6
y	60	80	110	110	100	90

9–16. Find the quadratic model $q(x) = Ax^2 + Bx + C$ that best fits the data in Problems 1–8 (respectively), as well as the average error of this optimal quadratic model.

In each of Problems 17–20, the 1950–1990 population census data for a U.S. city is given. (**a**) Find (as in Example 4 and the preceding discussion) the quadratic model $P(t) = P_0 + at + bt^2$ (with $t = 0$ in 1950) that best fits this census data. (**b**) Also, construct a table showing the actual and predicted populations (and errors) for the decade years 1950–1990. (**c**) Use the model to predict the year 2000 population of this city.

17. Mesa, Arizona:

t (years)	1950	1960	1970	1980	1990
P (thous)	17	34	63	152	288

18. St. Petersburg, Florida:

t (years)	1950	1960	1970	1980	1990
P (thous)	96	181	216	239	240

19. Arlington, Texas:

t (years)	1950	1960	1970	1980	1990
P (thous)	8	45	90	160	262

20. Corpus Christi, Texas:

t (years)	1950	1960	1970	1980	1990
P (thous)	108	168	205	232	257

21. The annual production of tobacco (in millions of pounds) in the United States for selected years is given in the following table.

t (years)	1988	1990	1992	1994	1996
P (millions of lb)	1370	1626	1722	1583	1517

Source: World Almanac and Book of Facts 1998

(a) Find the quadratic function that best fits this data, and its average error.

(b) Use the model to find the year in which tobacco production falls to 1400 million pounds.

22. The number of U.S. bank failures (banks closed or assisted) in the years from 1935 to 1940 is given in the following table.

t (years)	1935	1936	1937	1938	1939	1940
B (banks)	32	72	84	81	72	48

Source: World Almanac and Book of Facts 1998

(a) Find the quadratic function that best fits this data, and its average error.

(b) Use the model to predict the number of bank failures in 1945.

23. The following table gives the per capita value of money in circulation in the United States in selected years.

t (years)	1985	1990	1994	1996	1997
P (dollars)	779	1029	1428	1573	1665

Source: World Almanac and Book of Facts 1998

(a) Find the quadratic function that best fits this data.

(b) Use the model to predict the year in which the per capita value of money is $650, and the year in which the per capita value of money is $900.

(c) Which of your predictions is likely to be more accurate? Why?

C H A P T E R   2   R E V I E W

In this chapter, you learned about quadratic functions and models. After completing the chapter, you should be able to

- Determine whether a relation described numerically, graphically, or symbolically represents a quadratic function.
- Find the domain and range of a quadratic function.
- Find the output value of a quadratic function for a given input value.
- Find the input value(s) of a quadratic function for a given output value.
- Solve an equation or inequality involving a quadratic function.
- Find a quadratic function that models given quadratic data.
- Find the best-fitting quadratic model for data that is approximately quadratic.

REVIEW PROBLEMS

In Problems 1–7, determine whether, based on the table, graph, or formula, y is a quadratic function of x.

1.

x	2	4	5	6	8	11
y	−2	−8	−12.5	−18	−32	−60.5

2.

x	−2	−1	1	3	4	5
y	9	2	0	−26	−63	−124

3.

x	1	2	3	4	5	6
y	300	150	75	37.5	18.75	9.375

4.

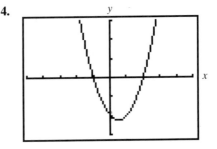

5.

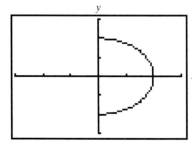

6. $x^2 + y - 4 = 0$

7. $y = 3(x + 2)(x - 7)$

In Problems 8–10, find the domain and range of each function.

8. The height h (in feet) of a math book dropped from a second floor window as a function of the time t (in seconds), according to the following table.

t	0	0.2	0.4	0.6	0.8	1.0
h	16	15.36	13.44	10.24	5.76	0

9.

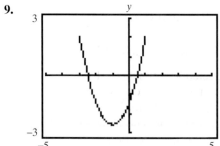

10. $f(x) = -3(x - 2)^2 + 4$

11. In Problem 15 of the Chapter 1 Review, we found that the relationship between price and demand (number of items sold) for Pomelia's decorative lawn sprinkler business was given by $p(x) = -1.25x + 85$, where x was the number of items sold and p was the price per item. Since **revenue** (the money resulting from sales) is given by the product

$$(\text{number of items}) \cdot (\text{price per item}) = x \cdot p(x),$$

we see that the revenue is a quadratic function of the number of items sold.

(a) Find a quadratic function $R(x)$ giving revenue as a function of x, the number of sprinklers sold per month.

(b) What is the revenue when 20 sprinklers are sold?

12. The population data from the U.S. census for Stockton, California is given in the following table.

t (years)	1950	1960	1970	1980	1990
P (thous)	71	86	110	148	211

(a) Find the quadratic population model that best fits this data.

(b) Use your model to predict the year in which the population of Stockton reaches 250 thousand.

13. The table below displays the percentage P of the U.S. population that was foreign-born in the year y.

(a) Find the quadratic model that best fits this data.

(b) Use your model to predict the percent of the population that was foreign-born in 2000.

y	1930	1940	1950	1960	1970	1980	1990	1996
P	11.6	8.8	6.9	5.4	4.8	6.2	7.9	9.3

Source: *World Almanac and Book of Facts 1998*

ACTIVITY

Quadratic Models in Baseball

In this chapter, you have learned about quadratic models for a dropped or thrown ball. Does a batted ball behave in the same manner? In this activity you will investigate what happens when a ball is batted under different conditions.

You may have observed, either from watching or playing baseball, that when a ball is hit, in the air, it appears to travel in a parabolic path. A fly ball to the warning track looks like a "wide" parabola, while a pop-up to the third baseman looks more like a narrow one. If we ignore air resistance and any wind that may be blowing, a batted baseball does indeed follow a parabolic path.

In the discussion that follows, we will also assume that the ball is hit on the "sweet spot," that place on the bat that minimizes the loss of energy of the pitched ball contacting the bat. The distance that the ball travels depends on both the angle at which it is batted and velocity of the bat.

If a ball is batted at an angle of 35°, the distance that the ball travels, as a function of the bat speed, is given approximately by

$$D(v) = 0.029v^2 + 0.021v - 1,$$

where v is the bat speed in miles per hour and D is distance traveled in feet.

1. Find the distance a batted ball will travel if the ball is batted with a velocity of 90 miles per hour.

2. With what velocity must you hit the ball in order for it to travel at 400 feet?

Each of the following tables gives data for distance traveled as a function of the angle at which the ball is hit for various bat velocities. (An average bat velocity is about 100 miles per hour.) For each of the tables, (a) find the quadratic function of best fit, and (b) use this quadratic model to determine the maximum distance the ball can be hit and the angle in degrees at which it must be hit to achieve the maximum distance.

3. Velocity = 90 mph

Angle (A)	30	40	55	70	75	80
Distance (D)	219	249	238	163	127	87

4. Velocity = 100 mph

Angle (A)	35	40	55	65	70	75
Distance (D)	294	308	294	239	201	156

5. Velocity = 110 mph

Angle (A)	30	40	55	70	75	80
Distance (D)	327	372	355	243	189	129

6. If you were to advise an aspiring player on how to increase the distance of his or her hits, what would you suggest?

In constructing these models, we have considered the force of gravity acting on the ball, but not the effect of air resistance. The air causes a drag force on the ball, which slows it down. Interestingly enough, this drag force is typically a quadratic function of the velocity of the ball—still another example of a quadratic function. Another factor in the drag force function is the density of the air through which the ball is traveling. The denser the air, the greater the drag force. This explains why balls travel farther in the "thin" air of Denver, the home of the Colorado Rockies.

Colorado Rockies Online—the homepage of the Colorado Rockies—provides the chart shown in Fig. 2.R.1, which shows the effect of altitude on the distance a ball travels. (Go to **www.coloradorockies.com/rockies** and look under **Baseball 101** at the **Physics of Baseball** link.) The graph in the chart curves upward, suggesting that a quadratic function might be a good model.

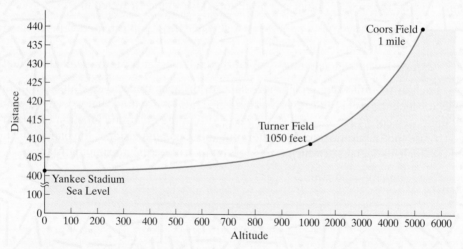

Figure 2.R.1 Distance a batted baseball travels, as a function of altitude above sea level. *Source:* Colorado Rockies Online.

7. Find the quadratic function of best fit for the data that is summarized in the following table.

Stadium	Altitude in Feet (x)	Distance in Feet (y)
Yankee Stadium	0	400
Turner Field	1050	408
Coors Field	5280	440

8. Use your quadratic model to predict the distance a ball would travel in Wrigley Field, where the altitude is approximately 600 feet.

9. Find the linear function of best fit for the altitude-distance data, and use it to predict the distance the ball would travel in Wrigley Field.

10. Look at the models from items (7) and (9) to explain why the estimates were virtually the same. Does distance traveled appear to be a quadratic function of altitude?

3

NATURAL GROWTH MODELS

Have you ever used the internet to complete a class assignment or research a term paper? Chances are, if a student were asked this question 10 years ago, the answer would have been no. Today, you would probably answer yes. During the 1990s the use of the internet literally exploded. It seems that you now can use the World Wide Web to explore almost anything—from the current U.S. debt to growth charts for someone's pet iguana.

The chart in Fig. 3.0.1 shows a plot of data portraying the growth of the internet since 1993. The Internet Software Consortium considers a host to be a computer system connected directly to the internet. We can see from the increasing steepness of the graph that the growth of the internet was rather slow at first, but then began to increase more rapidly. We might think, at first glance, that this data should be modeled by a quadratic function. However, to a mathematician, a graph with this shape suggests a different kind of function, one that grows at the same percentage rate each year.

In this chapter, we will study functions that model such growth and illustrate their applicability to a wide variety of real-world situations.

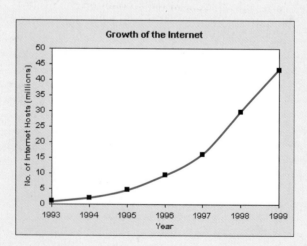

Figure 3.0.1 Internet growth from 1993 to 1999.

Source: Based on data from the Internet Software Consortium. (http://www.isc.org/)

3.1 Percentage Growth and Interest
3.2 Solving Growth Problems with Tables and Graphs
3.3 Natural Growth and Decline in the World
3.4 Fitting Natural Growth Models to Data

3.1 PERCENTAGE GROWTH AND INTEREST

Suppose that $1000 is invested on July 1, 2000 in a savings account that pays 10% annual interest. This means that, on each subsequent July 1, the amount in the account is increased by 10%—that is, interest equal to $\frac{1}{10}$ of the current amount is added to the account. Thus, $(1/10)(\$1000) = \$100$ in interest is added to the account on July 1, 2001, so the new amount then is $1000 + $100 = $1100. Next, $(1/10)(\$1100) = \$110$ in interest is added to the account on July 1, 2002, so the new amount then is $1100 + $110 = $1210. The following table shows the resulting amount in the account on each July 1 (after the year's interest has been added) for the first 10 years. The third column of the table shows the change in the amount from the previous year. You should use your calculator to verify all the entries in this table. That is, add $\frac{1}{10}$ of each year's amount to that amount to calculate the subsequent year's amount.

Date	Amount	Change
July 1, 2000	$1000.00	
July 1, 2001	$1100.00	$100.00
July 1, 2002	$1210.00	$110.00
July 1, 2003	$1331.00	$121.00
July 1, 2004	$1464.10	$133.10
July 1, 2005	$1610.51	$146.41
July 1, 2006	$1771.56	$161.05
July 1, 2007	$1948.72	$177.16
July 1, 2008	$2143.59	$194.87
July 1, 2009	$2357.95	$214.36
July 1, 2010	$2593.74	$235.79

Observe that the annual change increases from each year to the next. Indeed, the change in each of the last two years is over twice the change in the first year. Hence the amount in the account is *not* changing at a constant rate. Thus growth at a constant *percentage* rate—10% annually in this case—is quite different from a constant rate of change.

Many changing quantities—ranging from bank accounts to animal populations—are very different in appearance, but very similar in the way they change. In equal units of time—such as during any one-year period, from one year to the next—they grow by the same *percentage*. In this section we review the language that is needed to measure and analyze the growth or decline (the opposite of growth) of such quantities.

Simple Percentages

For a brief review of percentages, recall first that a **cent** is $1/100$ of a dollar. This helps us remember that the word **percent** means "one hundredth." Thus **1 percent of something is 1/100 of it.** Then p percent of it is p times 1 percent of it, which is the same as $p/100$ of it. So, if we're talking about a quantity denoted by A, then

$$p \text{ percent of } A = \frac{p}{100} \times A. \tag{1}$$

But we often use the abbreviation % for the word *percent*. Thus **the symbol % simply stands for the number 1/100.** That is,

$$\% = \frac{1}{100} = 0.01. \tag{2}$$

So, whenever we see the symbol % we can replace it with the number 0.01 if we wish. For instance,

$$7\% = 7 \times \% = 7 \times 0.01 = 0.07.$$

This fact is all we need to clear up the air of mystery that surrounds percentages. The phrase *percent of* simply means "% times." Hence

$$p\% \text{ of } A = p \text{ times } \% \text{ times } A$$
$$= p \times \frac{1}{100} \times A = p \times 0.01 \times A. \tag{3}$$

For those who remember (3), there really is no mystery to percentages. It may help to regard the symbol % as a combination of the division symbol / and the two zeroes in the quantity $1/100$ in (2).

Example 1

$$6\% \text{ of } 100 = 6 \times \tfrac{1}{100} \times 100$$
$$= 0.06 \times 100 = \tfrac{6}{100} \times 100 = 6 \times 1 = 6$$
$$15\% \text{ of } 270 = 15 \times \tfrac{1}{100} \times 270 = 0.15 \times 270 = 40.5$$
$$7.6\% \text{ of } 385 = 7.6 \times \tfrac{1}{100} \times 385 = \tfrac{7.6}{100} \times 385$$
$$= \tfrac{76}{1000} \times 385 = 0.076 \times 385 = 29.26$$

(Whenever you see such calculations here, you should use your own calculator to check them—to make sure you know what's going on.)

We can simply replace the word **percent** with the symbol $\% = \mathbf{0.01}$ when translating an appropriate sentence into a mathematical equation. The following table includes some additional pairs of corresponding words and symbols that should be familiar.

Word	Symbol
percent	%
of ("times")	$\times$
and ("plus")	$+$
is ("equals")	$=$

Percentage Increase and Decrease

Often we need to find the result of increasing some quantity by a given percentage. **To increase A by $p\%$ means to increase A by adding $p\%$ of A to itself.** This means that we calculate

$$A + (p\% \text{ of } A) = A + (p \times 0.01A) = A(1 + 0.01p). \tag{4}$$

So to increase A by $p\%$ we multiply A by $(1 + 0.01p)$.

Similarly, **to decrease A by $p\%$ means to decrease A by subtracting $p\%$ of A from A.** Thus

$$A - (p\% \text{ of } A) = A - (p \times 0.01A) = A(1 - 0.01p). \tag{5}$$

So to decrease A by $p\%$ we multiply A by $(1 - 0.01p)$.

Note the difference in signs between (4) and (5). The plus in (4) corresponds to an increase in the quantity, while the minus in (5) corresponds to a decrease.

Example 2

(a) Suppose a shirt is priced at \$26.50. If this price is increased by 6%, then by using (4) with $A = 26.50$ and $p = 6$ we find that the new price is

$$(26.50)(1 + 0.06) = (26.50)(1.06) = 28.09 \text{ (dollars)}.$$

Figure 3.1.1 illustrates the use of calculator variables to make this computation. It is useful to store the values of p and A if several such computations are to be carried out. Then we can simply recall each of the commands shown and change

```
6→P
                 6.00
26.50→A
                26.50
A(1+0.01P)
                28.09
```

Figure 3.1.1 Graphing calculator computation for Example 2.

only the appropriate numerical value. In particular, the command **A(1+0.01P)** can simply be recalled and reentered (with no retyping required).

(b) Suppose a car is priced at $9500. If this price is decreased by 4%, then by using (5) with $A = 9500$ and $p = 4$ we find that the new price is

$$(9500)(1 - 0.04) = (9500)(0.96) = 9120 \text{ (dollars)}. \qquad \blacksquare$$

Example 3

A new circular walkway around a circular garden increases the total enclosed area by 96%. The walkway is 4 feet wide. What was the original radius r the garden?

In Fig. 3.1.2 we see that the original circular garden plus the circular walkway form together a larger circle of radius $r + 4$. We are given that the area $A_1 = \pi(r + 4)^2$ of the larger circle is 96% larger than the area $A_0 = \pi r^2$ of the original smaller circle. Hence

$$A_1 = (1 + 96\%)A_0 = 1.96A_0,$$

so

$$\pi(r + 4)^2 = 1.96\pi r^2.$$

If we divide both sides by π and use the square root property, we see that

$$r + 4 = 1.4r \quad (\text{because } \sqrt{1.96} = 1.4).$$

It follows that $0.4r = 4$ (why?) and hence that $r = 10$. Thus the original garden itself had a radius of 10 feet. $\qquad \blacksquare$

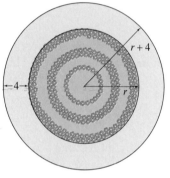

Figure 3.1.2   The sidewalk around the garden of Example 3.

Interest and Constant Percentage Growth

We now begin our study of quantities that grow by equal percentages during equal time intervals. A typical such quantity is the amount A invested in a savings account that draws interest that is compounded annually. If the **annual interest rate** is $p\%$, this means that at the end of each year, $p\%$ of the amount at the beginning of the year is added to the account as interest. **That is, the amount in the account at the beginning of the year is increased by $p\%$ at the end of the year.** If A denotes the amount in the account at the beginning of the year, then it is seen from Eq.(4) that the new amount—after interest is added at the end of the year—is given by

$$A_{new} = A(1 + 0.01p). \qquad (6)$$

Thus the effect of $p\%$ annual interest is to multiply the amount A each year by the factor $(1 + 0.01p)$.

If we start with an initial deposit of A_0 dollars in the account, then after 1 year the amount in the account is

$$A_1 = A_0(1 + 0.01p). \qquad (7)$$

During the second year the amount A_1 is itself multiplied by $(1 + 0.01p)$, so at the end of 2 years the amount in the account is

$$A_2 = A_1(1 + 0.01p) = A_0(1 + 0.01p) \cdot (1 + 0.01p) = A_0(1 + 0.01p)^2. \quad (8)$$

During the third year the amount A_2 is multiplied by $(1 + 0.01p)$, so at the end of 3 years the amount in the account is

$$A_3 = A_2(1 + 0.01p) = A_0(1 + 0.01p)^2 \cdot (1 + 0.01p) = A_0(1 + 0.01p)^3. \quad (9)$$

And at the end of 4 years the amount in the account is

$$A_4 = A_3(1 + 0.01p) = A_0(1 + 0.01p)^3 \cdot (1 + 0.01p) = A_0(1 + 0.01p)^4. \quad (10)$$

It's often said that mathematics is more about **patterns** than about numbers. Can you spot the pattern in Eqs. (8)–(10)? In each, the **final exponent** on the right equals the **initial subscript** on the left. **Therefore, the amount in the account after interest is added at the end of the nth year is**

$$A_n = A_0(1 + 0.01p)^n. \quad (11)$$

Note that (8) is the case $n = 2$ of (11), while (9) is the case $n = 3$ of (11), and (10) is the case $n = 4$ of (11).

Example 4

Suppose you deposit $A_0 = 1000$ dollars in a savings account that draws 5% interest compounded annually. How long will you have to wait until you have $1300 in the account?

If we substitute $A_0 = 1000$ and $p = 5$ in (11) we get the formula

$$A_n = 1000(1.05)^n \quad (12)$$

for the amount in the account after n years. It suffices to calculate this amount with the successive values $n = 1, 2, 3, \ldots$ until our money reaches $1300. The calculator screen in Fig. 3.1.3 shows the first three steps in this process. Note the use of the ⌐ key for raising the number 1.05 to a power. Only the first line in Fig. 3.1.3 had to be typed "in toto" on our calculator. At each subsequent step we simply pressed the reentry key to retrieve the previous command line; then it was necessary only to type in the desired new exponent before entering the new line to get the next result.

```
1000*1.05^1
           1050.00
1000*1.05^2
           1102.50
1000*1.05^3
           1157.63
```

Figure 3.1.3   Starting the computation in Example 4.

Figure 3.1.4 shows the results of the next three steps. We see that we had almost reached $1300 after 5 years, but 6 years were required to exceed our goal of $1300. So the answer to the question is 6 years. But if we had asked after what year is the amount in the account closest to $1300, the answer would have been 5 years.   ◼

```
1000*1.05^4
            1215.51
1000*1.05^5
            1276.28
1000*1.05^6
            1340.10
```

Figure 3.1.4   Finishing the computation in Example 4.

Iteration

Modern calculators and computers provide especially simple ways to carry out repetitive calculations like the one in Example 4. Indeed, this is exactly what modern computers were invented (in the 1940s and 1950s) to do. Suppose we enter

5→P
$$5.00$$

1000→A
$$1000.00$$

in our calculator to record the initial deposit A and the annual interest rate of $p\%$; this is "initialization" of the variables **P** and **A**. Then we enter the command

A*(1+0.01P)→A
$$1050.00$$

to calculate and store (as the value of **A**) the amount in the account after one year.

Now comes the punch line: If we simply press the ENTER key again, this same command line is executed again! That is, the value 1050.00 currently stored as **A** is itself multiplied by **(1+0.01P)** and the result stored as the new value of **A**. Having started the process, each press of the ENTER key carries out the computation for another year and stores the result. So in order to find out how much is in the account after 6 years, we need only type the line **A*(1+0.01P)→A** *once,* and then press the ENTER key six times in succession (keeping careful count of how many times we've entered the command). Figure 3.1.5 shows the result and provides the same conclusion as in Example 4.

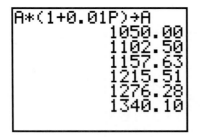

Figure 3.1.5   Example 4 by iteration.

This is our first example of **iteration**—doing the same thing again and again. Specifically, the successive results A_0, A_1, A_2, A_3, . . . are calculated **iteratively** when the same formula is used repeatedly to calculate each new result from the preceding one. In Example 4 this **iterative formula** is the formula

$$A_{n+1} = A_n(1 + 0.01p), \tag{13}$$

that is,

$$A_{new} = A_{old}(1 + 0.01p),\qquad(14)$$

which says that each amount is multiplied by $(1 + 0.01p)$ to get the next amount. Doing this over and over is called **iterating** the formula. So Fig. 3.1.5 shows the result of iterating (13) six times, starting with $A_0 = 1000$ (and using the constant value $p = 5$).

To solve any problem like Example 4—with a given interest rate $p\%$ and initial deposit A_0—you can use the same method to find how long it takes the account to grow to a desired target amount. For instance, if the interest rate is 3% and the initial amount is \$500, you initialize **P** and **A** by entering the lines

3→P
500→A

and then iterate the command

A*(1+0.01P)→A

until the target value of A is reached.

Input-Output Processes

The iterative formula in (13) or (14) can be visualized as an **input-output process** as illustrated in Fig. 3.1.6. We think of a "black box" with a hidden mechanism inside that performs the computation described by (14). Specifically, when an **input** $A = A_{old}$ is fed into the box, the iteration is performed and the **output** A_{new} is produced. We often will find it useful to interpret a complicated iteration as a simple input-output process—simple in that for many purposes we need not think explicitly of what is happening inside the box. It may only be important that, whatever the input, the same process always produces the corresponding output.

The Babylonian Iteration

When we repeat the iteration of Fig. 3.1.6, we "plow" the output back into the right-hand side of the equation $A_{new} = A_{old}(1 + 0.01p)$. Indeed, the word *iterate* apparently stems from the Latin verb *iterare,* meaning "to plow again." And the concept of iteration is as old as the word. Two thousand years ago the ancient Babylonians introduced the iteration

$$x_{n+1} = \frac{1}{2}\left(x_n + \frac{A}{x_n}\right),\qquad(15)$$

which can be used to calculate more and more accurate approximations to the square root $\sqrt{A}$ of a given positive number A. One starts with an initial guess x_0 and then uses (15) to calculate the successive iterates $x_1, x_2, x_3, \ldots$. It happens that the initial guess x_0 need not be especially accurate—any nonzero guess will do for a start. For instance, $x_0 = A/2$ is a convenient starting point, and then the **Babylonian square algorithm** can be implemented with the calculator commands

2→A
A/2→X
(1/2)(X+A/X)→X

to approximate the square root of the number $A = 2$. The first two commands here initialize the variables **A** and **X,** and the last one is the iterative command.

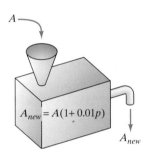

A

$A_{new} = A(1+0.01p)$

A_{new}

Figure 3.1.6 Iteration as an input-output process.

The results shown in Fig. 3.1.7 indicate that the 6-place value $\sqrt{2} \approx 1.414214$ is reached quickly. With any positive number A and any initial guess x_0 the successive approximations generated by the iteration in (15) eventually "stabilize" in this way, agreeing to the number of decimal places displayed.

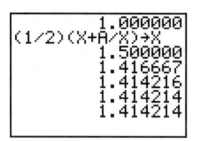

Figure 3.1.7   Approximating the square root of 2.

The Babylonian iteration would provide a way of calculating square roots if you were marooned on a desert island and found that your calculator's square root key no longer worked. Calculation of the right-hand side in (15) requires only the basic arithmetic operations $+, -, \times, \div$, so we could still calculate accurately the square root of any desired number.

The motivation behind the Babylonian iteration is easy to describe. Consider a specific initial guess x at the value of $\sqrt{A}$. We're unlikely to hit it on the nose, so this guess is either too large or too small. Now note that

- if x is larger than $\sqrt{A}$, then A/x is smaller than $\sqrt{A}$, while
- if x is smaller than $\sqrt{A}$, then A/x is larger than $\sqrt{A}$.

In either case one of the two numbers x and A/x is an overestimate and the other is an underestimate of the true value of $\sqrt{A}$. So why not take their *average* $\frac{1}{2}(x + \frac{A}{x})$ to get an improved estimate? This is just where the right-hand side in (15) comes from.

3.1

PROBLEMS

1. Calculate the following numbers.
    (a) 5% of 200
    (b) 7% of 350
    (c) 3.5% of 50
    (d) 6.5% of 75
    (e) 2.25% of 18
    (f) 3.75% of 47
    (g) 6.66% of 27.5
    (h) 4.19% of 58.35

2. Calculate the new price (rounded off to the nearest cent) if
    (a) The old price of $6.70 is increased by 10%.
    (b) The old price of $39.00 is increased by 7.5%.
    (c) The old price of $1720 is increased by 5.75%.
    (d) The old price of $110 is increased by 10%.
    (e) The old price of $69.50 is decreased by 6.6%.
    (f) The old price of $2567 is decreased by 8.25%.

3. Explain why the following method works to calculate the amount to be paid in a restaurant if you wish to add a 15% tip to the original bill amount A. First, write down the amount A. Then move the decimal point in A one unit to the left, and write this amount under A. Finally, divide this second amount by 2 and write this amount also. The total amount (including tip) to be paid is then the sum of the three amounts you have written down.

4. A sale price of $27.90 for a shirt was obtained upon reducing the original price by 10%. What was the original price?

5. A sale price of $19,760 for a car was obtained upon reducing the original price by 5%. What was the original price?

6. A class contains 18 boys and 55% of the class members are girls. How many class members are there?

7. The edge x of a square is 10 inches. By what percentage must its edge be increased in order to increase its perimeter P by 10%?

8. The edge x of a square is 10 inches. By what percentage must its edge be increased in order to increase its area $A = x^2$ by 10%?

9. The area of a square is 400 square inches. By what percentage must its edge be decreased in order to decrease its area by 20%?

10. The radius r of a circle is 10 inches. By what percentage must its radius be decreased in order to decrease its perimeter $P = 2\pi r$ by 25%?

11. The area of a circle is 200 square inches. By what percentage must its radius be increased in order to increase its area $A = \pi r^2$ by 30%?

12. The base b of a rectangle is 25 inches and its height h is 15 inches. By what percentage should each be increased in order to increase the rectangle's area $A = bh$ by 40%?

13. A cube has a volume of 1000 cubic inches. By what percentage should its edge x be increased in order to increase its volume $V = x^3$ by 50%?

14. A new circular walkway around a circular garden increases the total enclosed area by 69%. The original garden's radius was 7 feet. Find the width of the walkway, accurate to the nearest tenth of an inch.

15. If $500 is deposited in an account paying 10% interest annually, how long will you have to wait until your initial deposit is doubled? (Give the year after which the amount is *at least* $1000.)

16. If $1000 is deposited in an account paying 6% interest annually, how long will you have to wait until your initial deposit is doubled? (Give the year after which the amount in the account is *closest to* $2000.

17. The same as in Problem 16, except with 8% annual interest.

18. The same as in Problem 16, except with 9% annual interest.

19. Do you see a pattern in the results of Problems 16 through 18? What is the product in each case of the annual interest rate r and the number N of years required (accurate to the nearest year) to double your original deposit? What might the **rule of 72** say?

20. How long (rounded off accurate to the nearest year) does it take to *triple* an initial deposit of $1000 if the annual interest rate is 10%?

21. If you invest $1000 at 12% annual interest, show that you will have $1973.82 after 6 years and $2210.68 after 7 years. What initial deposit (accurate to the nearest cent) would lead to precisely $2000 (accurate to the nearest dollar) after 6 years? To answer this question, you will need to carry out several iterations, starting with successively better estimates of the needed initial deposit; obviously, you need to start with a bit more than $1000.

22. Let A be the number of dollars specified by the last three nonzero digits of your student ID number. Let k be the largest digit, and p the next largest digit in this ID. If you invest A dollars at p% annual interest, what will you have after k years?

23. Let A be the number of dollars specified by the last three nonzero digits of your student ID number. Let k be the next-to-largest digit in this ID. If $p = 10 + k$, and you invest A dollars at $p\%$ annual interest, how long (rounded off accurate to the nearest year) will it take to triple your investment?

24. A 1996 presidential primary candidate proposed a flat tax under which a family of four would pay as its federal income tax each year an amount equal to 17% of the portion of its taxable income in excess of $36,000. Suppose that a family's 1996 taxable income this year was $50,000.

   (a) Under this proposal, what percent of the family's total taxable income would be owed as income tax?

   (b) Suppose that this family's actual federal income tax bill for 1996 was $6015 plus 28% of the amount of their taxable income over $40,100. Then what percent of their total taxable income was owed as income tax?

25. Repeat Problem 24 for a family whose taxable income was $200,000, on which the actual federal income tax bill was $37,667 plus 36% of the excess over $147,700.

26. Apply the Babylonian square root algorithm to approximate square roots of several numbers, both quite large (like 3,456,789) and quite small (like 0.0003456). Try different initial guesses with the same number A whose square root is sought. For instance, to approximate the square root of 10, you might try both the initial guess $x_0 = 0.01$ and the initial guess $x_0 = 1000$. How does the accuracy of the initial guess affect the number of iterations required to get 6-place accuracy?

27. What happens with the Babylonian algorithm if a negative (rather than a positive) initial guess is used?

28. If stranded on a desert island you also could calculate cube roots with a basic four-function calculator. Verify empirically (that is, by experimentation) that the iteration

$$x_{new} = \frac{1}{3}\left(2x + \frac{A}{x^2} \right)$$

suffices. Pick a fixed number A and an initial guess $x_0 \approx \sqrt[3]{A}$, and verify that the resulting sequence of iterates appears to approach the cube root of A.

29. Verify empirically that the iteration

$$x_{new} = \frac{1}{q}\left((q - 1)x + \frac{A}{x^{q-1}} \right)$$

could be used to calculate qth roots on a desert island. Try out various values of the positive number A and the positive integer q.

3.2   SOLVING GROWTH PROBLEMS WITH TABLES AND GRAPHS

In Section 3.1 we discussed a savings account in which an amount of A_0 dollars is initially deposited, and thereafter draws interest at the annual rate of $p\%$. We saw that the amount A_n in the account after n years is given by

$$A_n = A_0(1 + 0.01p)^n. \tag{1}$$

In Example 4 we used the value $p = 5$ corresponding to an annual interest rate of $5\% = 0.05$, and the initial deposit $A_0 = 1000$, so (1) gives

$$A_n = 1000(1.05)^n.$$

The symbol p in (1) denotes the number of **percentage points** of annual interest. A common alternative for describing interest is to include the factor $\% = 0.01$ in the single symbol $r = p\%$ that denotes the annual **interest rate.** Thus we may say that $r = 0.05$ to specify an interest rate of 5%, so an annual interest rate of

$$r = 0.05 = 5(0.01) = 5\%$$

corresponds to $p = 5$ percentage points of annual interest. Similarly, an annual interest rate of 6% is the same as 6 percentage points of annual interest, and we can write either $r = 0.06 = 6\%$ or $p = 6$ to describe this annual interest. Whether we describe the situation in terms of **interest rate** or in terms of **percentage points** is a matter of choice.

To rewrite (1) in terms of the interest rate r instead of in terms of the number p of percentage points, we need only substitute $0.01p = r$. This gives

$$A_n = A_0(1 + r)^n \tag{2}$$

for the amount A_n in the account after n years. If $r = 0.05$ and $A_0 = 1000$, this version gives the same result $A_n = 1000(1.05)^n$ as before.

Formulas (1) and (2) both are used in the real world, and they are simply two slightly different ways of saying the same thing, because of the relation

$$r = p\% = 0.01p \quad (\text{since } \% = 0.01) \tag{3}$$

between the interest rate r and the number p of percentage points. One way to remember it is this: Whether we write

- $A_n = A_0(1 + r)^n$ in terms of the interest rate r, or
- $A_n = A_0(1 + 0.01p)^n$ in terms of the percentage points p,

the placeholder . . . in the formula $A_n = A_0(1 + \ldots)^n$ contains the percentage factor $\% = 0.01$, either visibly as in (1) or hidden in the interest rate r as in (2).

Hereafter, we'll concentrate mainly on interest rates instead of percentage points, and therefore primarily use the form $A_n = A_0(1 + r)^n$. Remember "r for rate" instead of "p for points."

If we assume that the formula in (2) is valid not only for the amount in the account after an integer number of years, but also after a fractional or decimal number of years, then we may write it in the form

$$A(x) = A_0(1 + r)^x, \tag{4}$$

which describes the amount A as a **function** of the number x of years elapsed since the initial deposit. We henceforth assume that the amount in our account grows "continuously" as described by (4), rather than "discretely" (that is, with interest added only at the end of each year).

We now discuss more fully the problem stated in Example 4 of Section 3.1.

Example 1

Suppose you deposit $A_0 = 1000$ dollars in a savings account that draws 5% annual interest. How long will you have to wait until you have $1300 in the account?

In Section 3.1 we answered this question by calculating the amount $A(x) = 1000(1.05)^x$ with the successive values $x = 1, 2, 3, \ldots$. Figures 3.1.3 and 3.1.4 show the results of these calculations:

x Years	A(x) Dollars
0	$1000.00
1	$1050.00
2	$1102.50
3	$1157.63
4	$1215.51
5	$1276.28
6	$1340.10
7	$1407.10

When we scan the columns of this table of values of the function $A(x)$, we see immediately that—among the values shown—the amount A is closest to 1300 dollars after $x = 5$ years (because 1276.28 differs from 1300 by less than 24 dollars, while 1340.10 differs from 1300 by more than 40 dollars).

But clearly it really takes a bit more than 5 years for the amount to reach 1300 dollars, since after *precisely* 5 years we have only $1276.28 in our account. Suppose we want to know the value x more accurately, say, during which week of the sixth year the amount $A(x)$ reaches $1300. To focus in on the sixth year—between $x = 5$ and $x = 6$—we will calculate values of the amount $A(x)$ for the successive values $x = 5.0, 5.1, 5.2, 5.3, \ldots, 5.9, 6.0$ and look to see when (to the nearest tenth of a year) the target value of 1300 is exceeded.   ◼

This kind of repetitive calculation quickly gets tedious to do by hand, so we usually use a calculator or spreadsheet to tabulate a function automatically.

Using Tables
We now proceed to solve Example 1 numerically.

Example 1 Revisited

As we have seen before, first we must enter the function $A(x) = 1000(1.05)^x$ we wish to tabulate into our ⃞Y= menu, as illustrated in Fig. 3.2.1. Since we already

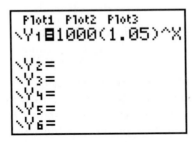

Figure 3.2.1   The function $A(x) = 1000(1.05)^x$ of Example 1.

know that the $1000 grows to $1300 sometime during the sixth year, we want to start our table at $x = 5$ and proceed by yearly increments of $\Delta x = 0.1$, as shown in Fig. 3.2.2.

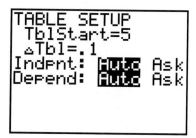

Figure 3.2.2   Preparing to tabulate our function—the TI-83 **TBLSET** (table set) menu.

When we execute the calculator's **TABLE** command, we get the table shown in Fig. 3.2.3. We see that A is closest to 1300 when $x \approx 5.4$ years (rounded off to the nearest *tenth* of a year) because 1301.4 dollars after 5.4 years is closer to 1300 than is 1295.1 after 5.3 years.

X	Y1	
5.0	1276.3	
5.1	1282.5	
5.2	1288.8	
5.3	1295.1	
5.4	1301.4	
5.5	1307.8	
5.6	1314.2	

X=5.4

Figure 3.2.3 A is close to $1300 after 5.4 years.

In order to determine when in the interval between $x = 5.3$ years and $x = 5.4$ years the money grows to $1300, we zoom in on the table once again, starting at $x = 5.3$ and incrementing by $\Delta x = 0.01$. Since this table does not go all the way to 1300, we scroll down until it does (Fig. 3.2.4). So we see finally—in this table—that A is closest to 1300 dollars after $x \approx 5.38$ years (rounded off accurate to the nearest *hundredth* of a year).

X	Y1	
5.34	1297.6	
5.35	1298.3	
5.36	1298.9	
5.37	1299.5	
5.38	1300.2	
5.39	1300.8	
5.40	1301.4	

X=5.38

Figure 3.2.4 A is closer to $1300 after 5.38 years.

The Answer

What does this result mean? Well,

$$0.38 \text{ year} = 0.38 \times 52 \text{ weeks} \approx 19.76 \text{ weeks,}$$

so we conclude that the amount in our savings account reaches 1300 dollars sometime during the twentieth week of the sixth year.

Everyday calendar computations sometimes require more care than you might expect initially. Are you *sure* that the amount in our account reaches $1300 during the twentieth week of the sixth year, rather than during the nineteenth week or during the twenty-first week? To see what this question involves, let's consider also the adjacent entries in the table of Fig. 3.2.4:

$$A \approx 1299.5 \text{ after 5 years plus } 0.37 \text{ year} = 0.37 \times 52 \text{ weeks} \approx 19.24 \text{ weeks}$$
$$A \approx 1300.2 \text{ after 5 years plus } 0.38 \text{ year} = 0.38 \times 52 \text{ weeks} \approx 19.76 \text{ weeks}$$
$$A \approx 1300.8 \text{ after 5 years plus } 0.39 \text{ year} = 0.39 \times 52 \text{ weeks} \approx 20.28 \text{ weeks.}$$

So A is precisely 1300 sometime *more than* 19.24 weeks and *less than* 19.76 weeks into the sixth year. In this case we are certain that it's during the twentieth week of the sixth year that our money grows to $1300.

Sometimes, in order to be absolutely sure, you need to proceed—using one more table—to find x accurate to the nearest *thousandth* of a year. Because a thousandth of a year is only about a third of a day (why?), it is then absolutely clear which week of which year an initial amount grows to a certain level.   ◼

Repeated Tabulation

Thus far this section has been devoted to the solution of the equation

$$A(x) = 1000(1.05)^x = 1300$$

to find (at least approximately) the time x it takes an initial investment of $1000 to grow to $1300 at an annual interest rate of 5%. Some of you may have seen in previous mathematics courses the use of logarithms to solve such equations. Here we have used the power of modern technology instead, in the form of a table-generating facility. Each table of values of $A(x)$ brackets the desired x within an interval between consecutive x-values in the table, and we can improve the accuracy by further tabulating values of $A(x)$ within this interval so as to obtain a still smaller interval that contains the desired solution of our equation. This is the *method of repeated tabulation.*

The square root $\sqrt{A}$ of the positive number A is that number x such that $x^2 = A$. We might therefore attempt to approximate the value of $\sqrt{A}$ by tabulating values of x^2 by a range of values of x whose squares bracket A.

Example 2

For instance, suppose we want to approximate the square root $\sqrt{10}$, whose value lies between $x = 3$ and $x = 4$ (why?). From the table

x	x^2
3.0	9.00
3.1	9.61
3.2	10.24
3.3	10.89
3.4	11.56
3.5	12.25
3.6	12.96
3.7	13.69
3.8	14.44
3.9	15.21
4.0	16.00

that results when we tabulate values of x^2 in this interval, we conclude that $\sqrt{10}$ lies between $x = 3.1$ and $x = 3.2$ (why?). The further tabulation

x	x^2
3.10	9.61
3.11	9.67
3.12	9.73
3.13	9.80
3.14	9.86
3.15	9.92
3.16	9.99
3.17	10.05
3.18	10.11
3.19	10.18
3.20	10.24

now shows that $\sqrt{10} \approx 3.16$ rounded off accurate to 2 decimal places. It should be apparent that we can obtain an additional decimal place of accuracy with each further tabulation. Why don't you use your calculator to carry out two more tabulations, and thereby find the value of $\sqrt{10}$ rounded off accurate to 4 decimal places? ◼

Using Graphs

Once again we discuss a savings account in which an amount of A_0 dollars is initially deposited, and thereafter draws interest at the annual rate of $r = p\%$. The amount in the account after x years is given by the now familiar formula

$$A(x) = A_0(1 + r)^x. \tag{4}$$

In particular, if the initial amount is $A_0 = 1000$ (dollars) and the annual interest rate is $r = 0.05 = 5\%$, then

$$A(x) = 1000(1.05)^x. \tag{5}$$

In our discussion of Example 1 we used the method of repeated tabulation to explore the question of how long it will take our account to grow in value from $1000 to $1300. For the remainder of this section, we will use graphic methods to analyze this same question afresh.

Figure 3.2.5 shows a computer-plotted graph of the amount function $A(x)$. As usual, the x-axis is horizontal, but the vertical axis is the A-axis. The rising curve in the figure portrays the increasing amount in the account—its height above the point x on the horizontal axis is the amount A in our account after x years have elapsed.

We have also plotted the horizontal line of height $A = 1300$. The instant when our account value reaches 1300 dollars corresponds to the point where the rising graph of $A(x)$ intersects the horizontal line. The reason is that this point is precisely where the height functions $A(x) = 1000(1.05)^x$ of the curve and $A(x) = 1300$ of the line are equal. In other words, this intersection point is exactly where the desired condition

$$1000(1.05)^x = 1300 \tag{6}$$

is satisfied.

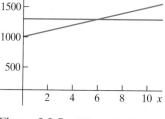

Figure 3.2.5 When do the two graphs cross?

From a graphic viewpoint, our job therefore is to find the x-coordinate of the intersection point in Fig. 3.2.5. We can see at a glance that $x \approx 5$ years. A closer look shows that x seems to be a bit larger than 5, but closer to 5 than to 6.

Now suppose we magnify the region near the intersection point in Fig. 3.2.5, so that the resulting picture shows only the graphs from $x = 5$ to $x = 6$. Then perhaps we could see, with our own eyes, much more accurately where the intersection point lies—maybe to the nearest tenth rather than just to the nearest integer. This is the basic idea of the *method of magnification*. It would surely be "no go" if we had to construct each new graph by hand, but fortunately we live in a technological age when graphs are readily constructed automatically by our handy graphing calculators.

Figure 3.2.6 shows a calculator screen where we've entered the two functions $A(x) = 1000(1.05)^x$ and $A(x) = 1300$, which appear on either side of the equation in (6) that we need to solve in order to find how long it takes our money to grow to $1300.

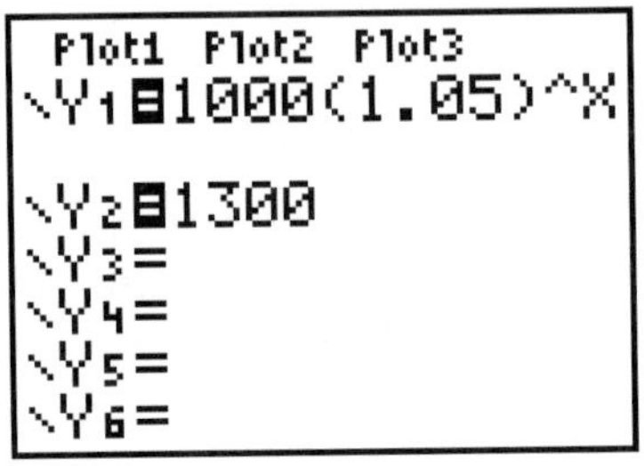

```
Plot1  Plot2  Plot3
\Y1目1000(1.05)^X

\Y2目1300
\Y3=
\Y4=
\Y5=
\Y6=
```

Figure 3.2.6   The two functions we want to graph.

In principle, if you simply press the graph key your calculator should plot the desired graphs. However, you should know by now that it is important to choose the proper viewing window in the plane in order to see the portion of the graph you are interested in.

Figure 3.2.7 shows window settings chosen to yield a calculator picture similar to Fig. 3.2.5. We want to see the x-range from $x = 0$ to $x = 10$ because we certainly hope that our money will grow to $1300 within 10 years! We select the y-range from $y = 0$ to $y = 2000$ because it's big enough to contain our target value of $y = 1300$. (Of course, the calculator uses y rather than A to denote the dependent variable.) **Caution:** Often it's not easy to decide what viewing window will give an informative picture, and you then must try different possibilities until you discover a good one. The key is not to get discouraged and not to quit trying.

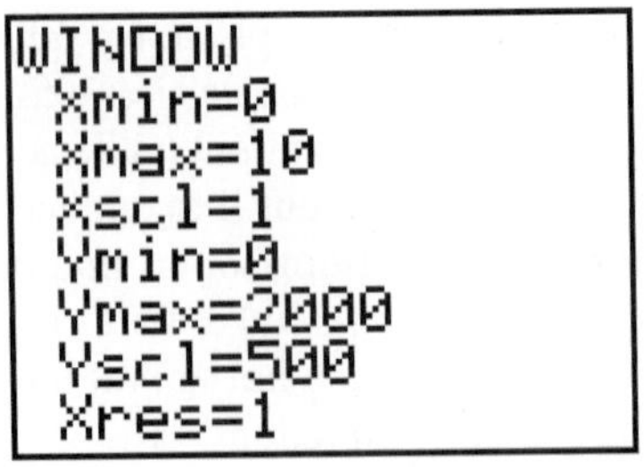

```
WINDOW
 Xmin=0
 Xmax=10
 Xscl=1
 Ymin=0
 Ymax=2000
 Yscl=500
 Xres=1
```

Figure 3.2.7   Specifying our viewing window.

Figure 3.2.8 shows the plot that results. It looks just like the computer plot in Fig. 3.2.5, except that the calculator provides no labels on the axes. Hence we've got to remember for ourselves what the viewing window is.

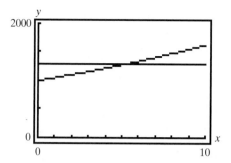

Figure 3.2.8   Plot for $0 \leq x \leq 10$.

If we press ⬚TRACE⬚ on the calculator, then a blinking cursor shows up on this screen. We can locate the intersection point (approximately) by moving this cursor (with the arrow-designated cursor keys) until it coincides (as nearly as possible) with the intersection point. As we do so, the calculator shows the (changing) coordinates of the cursor location at the bottom of the screen. Fig. 3.2.9 shows the result, and it gives $x = 5$ as the approximate location of our point.

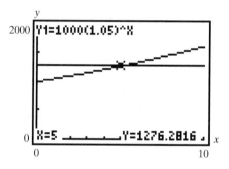

Figure 3.2.9   So x is, indeed, approximately 5.

In this case it's tempting to jump the gun and plot the graphs from $x = 4.9$ to $x = 5.1$, but let's proceed a bit more cautiously and magnify by only one factor of 10. Thus we want to plot our graphs from $x = 5$ to $x = 6$. But what vertical range of values should we show? The "factor of 10" idea is often the key. The vertical scale in Fig. 3.2.9 is measured in thousands. So why not divide by 10 and think of a new vertical scale measured in hundreds? This thought motivates the new viewing window defined in Fig. 3.2.10, with the y-range from $y = 1200$ to $y = 1400$ again including our target value of $y = 1300$.

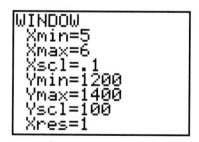

Figure 3.2.10   Our new viewing window.

We now graph and trace the curve to locate the intersection point as closely as possible. Figure 3.2.11 shows the result. It now appears that $x = 5.37$. If this is so, then it certainly would have been a mistake to plot the graphs from $x = 5.0$

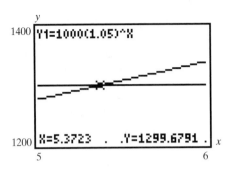

Figure 3.2.11   Now we see that x is approximately 5.37.

to $x = 5.1$—we wouldn't have seen anything useful. (Try it yourself to see what this remark means.)

If you move the cursor back and forth—above and below the horizontal line of height 2000 in the figure—and watch the changing x-value, it becomes clear that the desired value is, indeed, somewhere between $x = 5.3$ and $x = 5.4$. Figure 3.2.12 shows the result of another zoom, after having defined the new viewing window $5.3 \le x \le 5.4$, $1290 \le y \le 1310$. (Can you see that we've again divided each dimension by 10?) Now each tick mark on the x-axis repre- sents an increment of $\Delta x = 0.01$, so this final picture makes it clear that the value of x we've been seeking is $x \approx 5.38$, rounded off accurate to 2 decimal places (on the right of the decimal point). Note that we write $x \approx 5.38$ (which means "ap- proximately equal") and *not* $x = 5.38$ (which would mean "exactly equal").

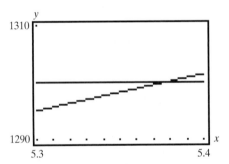

Figure 3.2.12   Plot for $5.30 \le x \le 5.40$.

Summary—Repeated Magnification

By repeated graphing we have magnified our two graphs near their point of in- tersection sufficiently to see that our account has grown to $1300 after approxi- mately 5.38 years (accurate to two decimal places). Since the second decimal place represents hundredths, and a hundredth of a year is about 3.65 days, we would need another decimal place of accuracy to determine the magic moment accurate to the nearest day of the sixth year. An answer accurate to 4 or 5 decimal places would give it accurate to the nearest hour.

But it's *your* calculator and *your* time. You can keep at it as long as you wish, constructing repeated graphs to focus in on the point of intersection more and more closely. This is the **method of magnification**—sometimes called the **method of repeated graphing,** or simply the **method of zooming**—to solve an equation of the form $f(x) = g(x)$ approximately. Simply graph the expressions **Y1=f(x)** and **Y2=g(x)** and zoom in on the point of intersection of their graphs.

Automatic Intersection Finding

As we have done earlier, we can let the calculator find the intersection point. To do this, we press **CALC** and get the menu shown in Fig. 3.2.13. When we select the calculator's **intersect** facility, the result is the screen shown in Fig. 3.2.14. We press ENTER—it makes no difference here which is the **First curve** and which the **Second curve**—until the calculator shows **Guess?**. We then move the blinking cursor to the apparent intersection of the two curves (using the calculator's cursor keys), and then press ENTER to record that location as our best guess.

Figure 3.2.13   The **CALCULATE** menu.

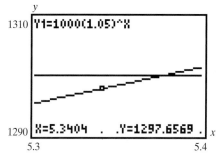

Figure 3.2.14   Preparing to solve for x.

The result $x \approx 5.3774$ is shown in Fig. 3.2.15. Since our calculator is set in 4-decimal place mode, our answer 5.3774 is rounded off accurate to 4 decimal places.

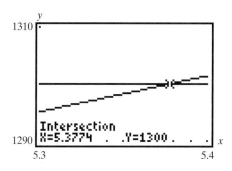

Figure 3.2.15   The final solution in Example 1.

To see what accuracy to the nearest $0.0001 = 1/10,000$ of a year tells us, we note that

$$0.0001 \text{ year} = (0.0001 \text{ year})(365 \text{ days/year}) = 0.0365 \text{ days}$$
$$= (0.0365 \text{ days})(24 \text{ hours/day}) = 0.876 \text{ hours}$$

using the conversion factors of 365 days/year and 24 hours/day. Thus if we convert our calculator's approximate answer of 5.3774 years to years, days, and hours, we should be within an hour of the true answer:

$$5.3774 \text{ years} = 5 + (0.3774 \text{ year})(365 \text{ days/year}) = 5 \text{ years} + 137.7510 \text{ days}$$
$$= 5 \text{ years}, 137 \text{ days} + (0.7510 \text{ days})(24 \text{ hours/day})$$
$$= 5 \text{ years}, 137 \text{ days} + 18.0240 \text{ hours}$$
$$5.3774 \text{ years} \approx 5 \text{ years}, 137 \text{ days}, 18 \text{ hours}.$$

For instance, suppose we electronically deposited our original $1000 just after the stroke of midnight on the morning of January 1, 2000. Since the 138th day of a non–leap year is May 18, it follows that our account will reach $1300 in value at about 6 P.M. during the evening of May 18 in the year 2005. This is our "final answer"—to the nearest hour—for Example 1 at the beginning of this section.

Really Getting It Right

This "final answer" ignores the fact that the intervening years 2000 and 2004 will be leap years with an extra 366th day (since leap years are those noncentury years that are divisible by 4 and those century years that are divisible by 400). Hence two of our days are used up by these leap days, so when the magic moment occurs the calendar has advanced two days less than we calculated. Therefore, the honest-to-goodness true answer is May 16, 2005.

Finding Roots Graphically

The square root $\sqrt{A}$ of the positive number A is that number x such that $x^2 = A$. We might therefore attempt to approximate the value of $\sqrt{A}$ by zooming in on the intersection of the graphs of the curve $y = x^2$ and the horizontal straight line $y = A$. For instance, suppose we want to approximate the square root of 10. We used numerical tables to do this in Example 2, but now we want to do it graphically. The calculator plot traced in Fig. 3.2.16 indicates that the square root of 10 is probably between $x = 3.1$ and $x = 3.2$.

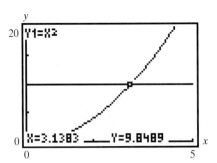

Figure 3.2.16   The graphs **Y1=X^2** and **Y2=10.**

When we use the window $3.1 \leq x \leq 3.2, 9.5 \leq y \leq 10.5$ we get the plot shown in Fig. 3.2.17. It now appears that $\sqrt{10} \approx 3.16$ rounded off accurate to 2 decimal places. It should be apparent that we can obtain an additional decimal place of accuracy with each further zoom. You might check that your calculator's intersect facility gives $\sqrt{10} \approx 3.1623$ rounded off accurate to 4 decimal places. Is this what your calculator's square root key gives?

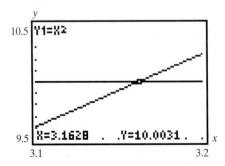

Figure 3.2.17   Between $x = 3.1$ and $x = 3.2$.

Solve Problems 1–5 by the method of repeated tabulation. In each problem, the interest accumulates continuously, as assumed in this section. First find the answer accurate to the nearest hundredth of a year. Then state the answer in years and weeks (rounded off accurate to the nearest week).

1. Starting with $500 deposited at 10% annual interest rate, how long will you have to wait until your initial deposit is doubled?

2. The same as in Problem 1, except with 6% annual interest.

3. The same as in Problem 1, except with 8% annual interest.

4. How long does it take to triple an initial deposit of $1000 if the annual interest rate is 10%?

5. The same as in Problem 4, except with 5% annual interest.

6–10. These are the same as Problems 1–5, except that you are to solve them graphically—that is, by the method of repeated magnification, tracing the curve to determine the solution with the required accuracy.

11–15. These are the same as Problems 1–5, except that you are to solve them graphically with automatic intersection finding. First find the answer accurate to the nearest thousandth of a year. Then state the answer in years and days (rounded off accurate to the nearest day). (Assume 365 days per year, and ignore leap years.)

In Problems 16–20, use the method of tabulation to find the indicated root accurate to 2 decimal places.

16. $\sqrt{2}$

17. $\sqrt{1000}$

18. $\sqrt[3]{100}$ *Hint:* Tabulate the function $f(x) = x^3$.

19. $\sqrt[5]{500}$ *Hint:* Tabulate the function $f(x) = x^5$.

20. $\sqrt[10]{1000}$ *Hint:* Tabulate the function $f(x) = x^{10}$.

21–25. These are the same as Problems 16–20, but solve them graphically with automatic intersection finding. Now find the indicated roots accurate to 4 decimal places.

26. If you invest $1000 at 12% annual interest, you will have $1973.82 after 6 years and $2210.68 after 7 years. What initial deposit would lead to precisely $2000.00 (accurate to the nearest cent) after 6 years? To answer this question, you will need to tabulate the function $A(x) = A_0(1.12)^6$, varying the initial amount A_0 until you hit $2000 on the nose after 6 years.

27. Use the method of Problem 26 to find the amount (accurate to the nearest cent) you would need to invest at 10% annual interest, in order to have exactly $2500 after 10 years.

28. Suppose you invest $1000. Use the method of Problem 26 to find the interest rate r (accurate to 4 decimal places) your investment must earn in order to double in 5 years. But now you will need to tabulate the function $A(x) = 1000(1 + r)^5$, varying the interest rate r until you hit $2000 on the nose after 5 years.

29. The same as in Problem 28, except that now you want to triple your investment in 10 years.

3.3   NATURAL GROWTH AND DECLINE IN THE WORLD

The U.S. constitution as adopted in 1783 decrees that a census (or count) of the people shall be conducted every 10 years. The third column of the following table records the results from the first six census counts—in the decade years 1790, 1800, 1810, 1820, 1830, and 1840. The fourth column shows the results of an annual growth rate of 3%, starting with the initial 1790 population $P_0 = 3.9$ (million). Note the close correspondence—in these early decades of our nation's history—between the actual population figures and those predicted by the 3% mathematical model $P(t) = 3.9\,(1.03)^t$.

t (years)	Year	Census Population (millions)	$P(t) = 3.9\,(1.03)^t$ (rounded)
0	1790	3.9	3.9
10	1800	5.3	5.2
20	1810	7.2	7.0
30	1820	9.6	9.5
40	1830	12.9	12.7
50	1840	17.1	17.1

The world is full of quantities that—like savings accounts and the early U.S. population—appear to grow at a constant percentage rate per unit of time. For instance, this is so common for many other populations—of people, of animals, of insects, of bacteria—that such growth is called **natural growth.** If a population starts at time $t = 0$ with initial population numbering P_0 and thereafter grows "naturally" at an annual rate of $r = p\%$, then the number of individuals in the population after t years is given by

$$P(t) = P_0(1 + r)^t. \qquad (1)$$

Observe that this formula is the same as Eq. (4) in the Section 3.2, except that here we write "P for population" instead of "A for amount," and "t for time" instead of "x for whatever." However, we often will continue to write x for time—for one reason, because a graphing calculator typically requires that **X** (rather than **T**) be used for the independent variable in its ⌐Y=⌐ functions menu. But you should realize that the formula

$$P(x) = P_0(1 + r)^x \qquad (2)$$

defines exactly the same function as (1), because it says to do precisely the same thing with x or t (whichever may denote the independent variable). The independent variable by any other name is (like a rose?) still the independent variable.

Population Examples

Example 1

Use a graphing calculator to verify the entries in the final column of the U.S. population table at the beginning of this section.

To simplify matters, we take $t = 0$ in 1790 so that the census dates 1790 through 1840 correspond to the times $t = 0$ through $t = 50$. With $P_0 = 3.9$ (counting population in millions rounded off to 1 decimal place) and $r = 0.03$, Eq. (1) is

$$P(t) = 3.9 \times 1.03^t. \tag{3}$$

Figure 3.3.1 shows a calculator implementation—incrementing t by 10 (years) for each step—to calculate the predicted populations 5.2, 7.0, 9.5, and 12.7 (in millions) for the census years 1800 through 1830. Figure 3.3.2 shows an alternative calculator approach—realizing that in every 10-year period the population will be multiplied 10 times by 1.03 (once for each year), and hence by 1.03^{10} altogether, we simply iterate this latter multiplication and don't bother to recalculate t each time.

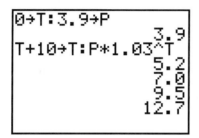

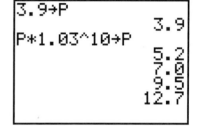

Figure 3.3.1   Applying (3) every 10 years.

Figure 3.3.2   Multiplying repeatedly by 1.03^{10}.

Figure 3.3.3 illustrates using a calculator table. Here we tabulate **Y1=3.9*1.03^X**, with **TblStart=0** and **ΔTbl=10** in the tableset menu. Then the **TABLE** command yields the table of results shown in the figure, with the last two lines predicting U. S. populations of 17.1 and 23.0 million in the years 1840 ($= 1790 + 50$) and 1850 ($= 1790 + 60$), respectively.   ◼

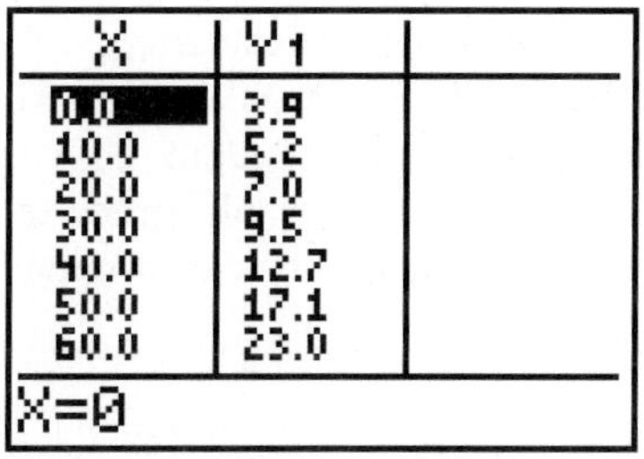

X	Y1
0.0	3.9
10.0	5.2
20.0	7.0
30.0	9.5
40.0	12.7
50.0	17.1
60.0	23.0

X=0

Figure 3.3.3   A calculator table of predicted population figures.

Example 2

Suppose the U.S. population, starting at 3.9 million in 1790, had continued indefinitely to grow at a constant 3% annual rate. Then determine when the country's population would have reached 100 million.

We want to find the value of t such that

$$P(t) = 3.9 \times 1.03^t = 100. \tag{4}$$

We can do this by graphing both sides and then zooming in on the point of intersection (as in Section 3.2). In Fig. 3.3.4 we have plotted the graphs **Y1=3.9*1.03^X** and **Y2=100** in the viewing window $0 < x, y < 150$ and have then used our calculator's intersection-finding facility to determine the indicated coordinates (109.8, 100) of the point of intersection. Thus it would take about 109.8 years (starting in 1790) for the U.S. population to reach 100 million.

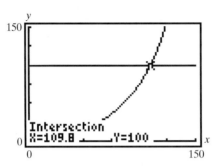

Figure 3.3.4 $P = 100$ when $t = 109.8$.

Let's assume for the sake of discussion that each calculated population occurs at the midpoint (July 1) of the corresponding year. Then 109 years after July 1, 1790 would be July 1, 1899 (because $1790 + 109 = 1899$). The population of 100 million would then occur about 0.8 year later, early in the year 1900. ◼

But a prediction based on an assumed formula is one thing, and actual reality may be another. The results shown in the preceding figures could have been calculated (perhaps using a slide rule instead of a modern calculator) early in the nineteenth century—as soon as enough census data was available to suggest a 3% annual growth rate. But how could we then have been sure that the U.S. population would continue to grow at this same 3% constant annual rate? Did it? We should never merely accept mathematical predictions without wondering about the possibility of a reality check. We cannot be sure of the validity of a mathematical model until we have checked its predictions against real-world facts.

In this case—sitting here almost a century later—we *know* how it turned out. Figure 3.3.5 exhibits a spreadsheet (available at this book's Web site as **USpop.xls**) showing both the population predicted by the 3% formula in (3) and the actual population recorded in U.S. census data at 10-year intervals through the year 1900. In the graph, predicted populations are plotted as a smooth curve, whereas the actual census populations are plotted as square dots.

Figure 3.3.5   Predicted and actual U.S. populations for 1790–1900.

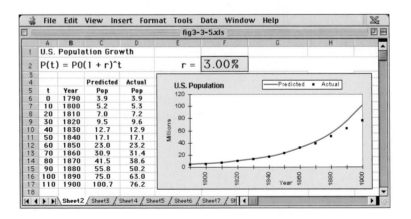

We observe that the assumed 3% rate of growth appears to have been maintained initially—perhaps through the first half of the nineteenth century—but the actual U.S. population growth seems to have slowed appreciably during the second half of the century. Indeed, in the year 1900 the actual population of the United States was about 76 million rather than 100 million, which is predicted by the 3% mathematical model $P(t) = 3.9 \times 1.03^t$.

In Section 3.4 we'll discuss the problem of fitting a constant-percentage growth model to a collection of data points. However, in many problems we suspect (or assume) constant-percentage growth but know the actual population at only a couple of different times. The following example illustrates several different methods that can then be used to determine the population's growth rate r.

Example 3

The city of Bethel had a population of 25 thousand in 1980 and 40 thousand in 1990.

(a)   What was the city's percentage rate of growth (rounded off accurate to 1 decimal place in percentage points) during this decade?

(b)   Assuming that this rate of growth continues for another decade, what population can the Bethel city planners expect in the year 2000?

We take $t = 0$ in 1980 to get started. Then substitution of $P_0 = 25$ (thousand) and $t = 10$ in Eq. (1) gives

$$P(10) = 25(1 + r)^{10} = 40 \tag{5}$$

since the population 10 years later in 1990 was 40 thousand. We need to solve this equation for r. Various methods are available to us.

Graphic Method   We graph the functions **Y1=25(1+X)^10** and **Y2=40**, with x instead of r denoting the unknown in Eq. (5). As usual, we can either zoom in on the intersection or use our calculator's automatic intersection-finding facility. Figure 3.3.6 shows a plot in the viewing window $0 < x < 0.10, 0 < y < 60$. (For sake of investigation, we estimate initially that the unknown rate $r = x$ is less than $10\% = 0.10$.) The rising curve is the curve $y = 25(1 + x)^{10}$. We have asked the calculator to solve automatically for the intersection point and have obtained the point $(0.048, 40)$. Thus $x = 0.048$, and hence the growth rate $r = 4.8\%$ satisfies Eq. (5). This answers question (a). With this rate in (5) we get the mathematical model

$$P(t) = 25 \times 1.048^t \tag{6}$$

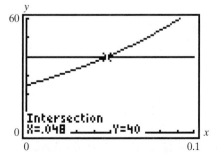

Figure 3.3.6   The graphs $y = 25(1 + x)^{10}$ and $y = 40$.

for the population (in thousands) of Bethel. To answer question (b), we substitute of $t = 20$ and get

$$P(20) = 25 \times 1.048^{20} \approx 63.9. \tag{7}$$

Thus, Bethel should plan for a population of about 64 thousand people in the year 2000.

Numerical Method Another approach is to solve Eq. (5) by the method of tabulation. We use our calculator to tabulate values of the function **Y1=25*(1+X)^10** that corresponds to the left-hand side in (5), with x instead of r as the unknown. Figure 3.3.7 shows the result when we construct a table with **TblStart=0** and **ΔTbl=0.001** and then scroll down in this table until the population figures (in the **Y1** column) approach the target of 40 (thousand). Obviously, the second column entry that is closest to 40 corresponds to the first column entry of $x = 0.048 = 4.8\% = r$ for the annual percentage growth rate. This is the same growth rate we found graphically and leads to the same results shown in Eqs. (6) and (7).

X	Y1	
.045	38.824	
.046	39.197	
.047	39.574	
.048	39.953	
.049	40.336	
.050	40.722	
.051	41.112	

X=.048

Figure 3.3.7 P is closest to 40 when $r = 0.048$.

Symbolic Method Finally, we illustrate an entirely algebraic approach. In order to solve the equation

$$25(1 + r)^{10} = 40,$$

we divide each side by 25 and obtain the equation

$$(1 + r)^{10} = \frac{8}{5}.$$

Taking the tenth root, or the 1/10 power, of each side now yields

$$1 + r = \left(\frac{8}{5}\right)^{\frac{1}{10}}, \text{ so } r = \left(\frac{8}{5}\right)^{\frac{1}{10}} - 1.$$

A calculator then gives $(8/5)^\wedge(1/10) - 1 = 0.0481$ (approximately), so once again we see that $r \approx 4.8\%$. ◩

As we have seen previously, it is the rule rather than the exception when a choice of different methods is available to solve a given problem. The preceding remarks illustrate the **rule of three**—which advocates the consideration of graphic and numeric methods as well as the symbolic methods of ordinary algebra. Of course, plotting the graph of a function is graphic; calculating a table of values is numeric, and solving an equation algebraically (as we did previously) is symbolic. It is important that you develop—through experience and practice—some judgment as to which of the available methods of approach is likely to work best (or easiest) in a given situation.

Natural Growth Models

We have introduced the function

$$P(t) = P_0(1 + r)^t \tag{1}$$

as a mathematical model for the *natural growth* of a population that starts (at time $t = 0$) with population P_0 and thereafter grows at an annual percentage rate of $r = p\%$. In this case we call r the population's *natural growth rate*.

There are situations where the growth rate r itself is not of specific interest, and it may then be easier to simply think of the base constant

$$a = 1 + r \tag{8}$$

that appears (raised to the tth power) in (1). Then (1) takes the simpler-looking form

$$P(t) = P_0 \cdot a^t. \tag{9}$$

Definition: Exponential Function
An **exponential function** is one of the form

$$f(x) = a^x, \tag{10}$$

with base a and exponent x (its independent variable). Note that *an exponential function is a constant raised to a variable power.* By contrast, an ordinary power function like x^3 is a *variable raised to a constant power.*

Equation (9) then says that **a natural growth population function is** (a constant multiple of) **an exponential function.**

Example 4

If $r = 1$ so the annual growth rate is 100%, then (8) gives $a = 2$, so by (9) the population after t years is given by

$$P(t) = P_0 \cdot 2^t. \tag{11}$$

Thus

$$P(1) = 2P_0, \quad P(2) = 4P_0, \quad P(3) = 8P_0, \ldots$$

and hence we see that the population is **doubling** every year. For instance, suppose that $P_0 = 100$ and we want to know the population after 4 years and 8 months. This is when $t = 4\frac{2}{3} = \frac{14}{3}$, so using the exponentiation key $\boxed{\wedge}$ on our calculator we get

100*2^(14/3)

2539.84

If we're talking about a population of rabbits (say) then—there being no such thing as a fractional rabbit—we should round off and conclude that there are about 2540 rabbits in the population after 4 years 8 months.   ◼

Warning
The parentheses enclosing the exponent 14/3 are vital! If we omitted them we would get

100*2^14/3
                    546133.33

instead. Here the calculator first raises 2 to the fourteenth power before dividing by 3 (instead of first dividing 14 by 3 and using the result as the exponent of 2). Thus this second calculation is **100*(2^14)/3** instead of **100*2^(14/3)**. Most people dislike superfluous parentheses because they complicate typing (and also make the eyes glaze over) and therefore try not to use them unless actually necessary to tell the calculator precisely what to do. But a good practice is, "When in doubt, use parentheses" to make sure the calculator does what you intend.

Example 5

If $r = 2$ so the annual growth rate is 200% (instead of the 100% in Example 1), then (8) gives $a = 3$ so by (9) the population after t years is given by

$$P(t) = P_0 \cdot 3^t. \qquad (12)$$

Thus

$$P(1) = 3P_0, \quad P(2) = 9P_0, \quad P(3) = 27P_0, \ldots$$

and hence we see that the population is **tripling** every year.   ◤

Compare $P(t) = P_0 \cdot 2^t$ in (11) for a doubling population with $P(t) = P_0 \cdot 3^t$ in (12) for a tripling population. These situations are more intuitively described by the base constants $a = 2$ and $a = 3$ than by the annual percentage growth rates of the populations. Consequently, use of the base constant form of the function—$P(t) = P_0 \cdot a^t$—seems clearer than using the rate constant form, $P(t) = P_0(1 + r)^t$.

Natural Growth Model: Multiplication by a Every Year
As we see in Examples 4 and 5, the base constant a in $P(t) = P_0 \cdot a^t$ is the factor by which the population is multiplied every year (or whatever is the unit of time). In short, the function

$$P(t) = P_0 \cdot a^t \qquad (9)$$

models a population with *annual multiplier a*.

Thus a population that quadruples every year would be described by $P(t) = P_0 \cdot 4^t$, and one that quintuples annually by $P(t) = P_0 \cdot 5^t$. Obviously, the larger is the base constant a the faster the exponential function a^t grows in value as t increases. Thus we see in Fig. 3.3.8 more steeply rising graphs as the base constant $a > 0$ gets larger.

There's no reason that it—whatever *it* is—has to happen in a single year. For instance, a population could double every 3 years, or triple every 5 years. Can you see that the formula

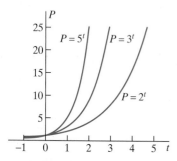

Figure 3.3.8   Natural growth curves with $a = 2, 3, 5$.

$$P(t) = P_0 \cdot b^{t/N} \tag{13}$$

describes a population that is multiplied by the factor b every N years?

Natural Growth Model: **Multiplication by b Every N Years**
If a population with initial (time $t = 0$) value P_0 grows naturally and is multiplied by the number b every N years (or other appropriate unit of time), then it is described by the function

$$P(t) = P_0 \cdot b^{t/N}. \tag{13}$$

For instance, a population that doubles every 3 years is described by

$$P(t) = P_0 \cdot 2^{t/3},$$

because we see that this formula gives

$$P(3) = P_0 \cdot 2^{3/3} = 2P_0, \quad P(6) = 4P_0, \quad P(9) = 8P_0, \ldots.$$

Similarly, a population that triples every 5 years is described by

$$P(t) = P_0 \cdot 3^{t/5}, \tag{14}$$

because this formula gives

$$P(5) = P_0 \cdot 3^{5/5} = 3P_0, \quad P(10) = 9P_0, \quad P(15) = 27P_0, \ldots.$$

Example 6

By what factor a is the population in (14) multiplied each year?
  If the population is multiplied by a each year, then Eqs. (9) and (14) yield

$$P(t) = P_0 \cdot a^t = P_0 \cdot 3^{t/5} = P_0 \cdot (3^{1/5})^t.$$

Therefore, $a = 3^{1/5} = \sqrt[5]{3} \approx 1.2457$. For instance, if $P(0) = 100$ rabbits, then after one year there are approximately 125 rabbits.   ◼

Example 7

The rapidly growing town of Tuckersville grew in population from 10 thousand in 1980 to 27 thousand in 1992. Assuming natural population growth, what population should Tuckersville's planners expect in the year 2005?
  With $t = 0$ in 1980 we have $P_0 = 10$ (in thousands) and $P(12) = 27$. Thus the population has grown by a factor of $b = 27/10 = 2.7$ in a period of $N = 12$ years. Therefore, (13) yields the population formula

$$P(t) = 10 \cdot (2.7)^{t/12}$$

for Tuckersville. (This is a case where the parentheses on the right are unnecessary but seem to make the expression look a bit better.) Then the population in the year 2005 should be

$$P(t) = 10 \times 2.7^{25/12} \text{ (thousands)}.$$

Consequently, our calculator—again being careful with parentheses—gives

10*2.7^(25/12)

$$79.191$$

thus indicating a Tuckersville population of 79,191 persons in the year 2005.   ◣

The following method illustrates how we can determine the annual percentage growth of a population if we know its population at two different times.

Example 8

Suppose that on January 15, 1998 you invested $1600 in a stock account, and on July 15, 2000 your account value was $2100.

(a) What was the annual percentage rate of growth in your account in the $2\frac{1}{2}$-year period from 1/15/1998 to 7/15/2000?

(b) On what calendar date will the value of your account reach $3000?

(a) Think of your account as a naturally growing "population" of dollars. It increased in value by a factor of $b = 2100/1600 = 1.3125$ in a period of $N = 2.5$ years (from 1/15/1998 to 7/15/2000). If we write A for amount (instead of P for population) and hence $A_0 = 1600$ for your initial amount (in dollars) at time $t = 0$ on 1/15/1998, then Eq. (13) gives

$$A(t) = A_0 \cdot b^{t/N} = 1600(1.3125)^{t/2.5} = 1600(1.3125^{1/2.5})^t$$

using the law $(b^r)^s = b^{rs}$ of exponents. Now a calculator gives 1.3125^(1/2.5) = 1.1149. Thus we see that the amount in our account after t years is given by

$$A(t) = 1600 \times 1.1149^t. \tag{15}$$

Comparing this result with Eq. (9), we get

$$a = 1 + r = 1.1149$$

for our account's natural growth base constant. Hence (subtracting 1 to get r) our annual percentage rate of growth is $r = 0.1149 = 11.49\%$.

(b) Let's determine graphically when our account reaches $3000 in value. Using (15), we need to solve the equation

$$1600 \times 1.1149^t = 3000. \tag{16}$$

Using calculator notation, we want to find where the graph **Y1= 1600*1.1149^X** corresponding to the left-hand side crosses the horizontal line **Y2=3000** corresponding to our target value. We select a viewing window defined by

- $0 < x < 10$ (hoping that it will take no longer than 10 years)
- $0 < y < 4000$ (so we'll be able to see the line $y = 3000$)

As usual, the question is when (or where) the rising growth curve in Fig. 3.3.9 crosses the horizontal line of height 3000. The figure indicates that

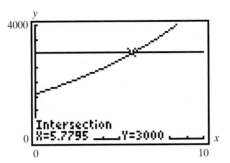

Figure 3.3.9   Solving Eq. (16).

our calculator's automatic intersection finder has found the intersection point (5.7795, 3000). To see what this means, we must remember the following correspondence:

	Calculator	Us
Independent variable	**X**	t
Dependent variable	**Y**	A

Thus the fact that **X=5.7795** means that our account reaches the target value of $A = \$3000$ in $t = 5.7795$ years. Since $0.7795 \times 365 \approx 285$ days, we must count 285 days forward from January 15 in the year 2003 (which is 5 years forward from 1998). Starting with the remaining 16 days in January and adding 28 days in February, 31 days in March, ..., 30 days in September, we first calculate

$$16 + 28 + 31 + 30 + 31 + 30 + 31 + 31 + 30 = 258 \text{ days.}$$

This takes us from January 15 to September 30. Then $285 - 258 = 27$ more days takes us to October 27. Thus our account will reach $3000 in value on October 27, 2003.   ◣

Natural Decline

The growth rate r in the equation $P(t) = P_0(1 + r)^t$ of (1) can be *negative* as well as positive. Whereas a population increases as time passes if its growth rate is positive, a negative growth rate $r < 0$ means a decreasing population. We often describe a decreasing population or other quantity as *declining* or *decaying*.

Example 9

Suppose you invested $10,000 in a stock account early on the morning of March 1, 2000, and instructed your broker to sell if and when the value of your stock fell to $9000. When will this occur, assuming that the value of your stock immediately started decreasing at a rate of 3.5% per year and continued at this rate?

Here we have the negative growth rate $r = -3.5\% = -0.035$, so $1 + r = 1 - 0.035 = 0.965$. Therefore, Eq. (1) with $P_0 = 10$ and $1 + r = 0.965$ gives

$$A(t) = 10 \times 0.965^t \tag{17}$$

for the amount A (in thousands) in your account after t years. We therefore need to solve the equation

$$10 \times 0.965^t = 9. \tag{18}$$

Figure 3.3.10 shows the graphs **Y1=10*0.965^X** and **Y2=9** in the viewing window defined by $0 < x < 5$ (the first 5 years) and the interval $8 < y < 10$ selected to bracket the target value $y = 9$. Our calculator's automatic intersection-finding facility gives the intersection point $(2.9573, 9)$.

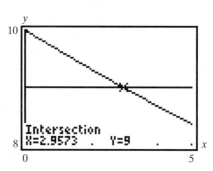

Figure 3.3.10   Solving Eq. (18).

We therefore see that $A = 9$ after $t = 2.9573$ years, that is, after 2 years plus $0.9573 \times 365 \approx 349$ days. This is 16 ($= 365 - 349$) days short of 3 full years. Now 3 years from March 1, 2000 is March 1, 2003. This latter day is the sixteenth day after February 13, 2003. (Most people will need to start with February 13 and count forward 16 days to verify this.) Thus you'll need to tell your broker to issue a sell order on February 13, 2003.   ◼

Summary

We say that a population **grows or declines** *naturally* provided that

$$P(t) = P_0 \cdot a^t \tag{9}$$

for some base constant $a > 0$. Recalling the relation $a = 1 + r$ in (8) between the growth rate r and the (positive) base constant a, we see that (as x increases) the value of the exponential function $f(x) = a^x$

- **increases** if $r > 0$ and hence $a > 1$,
- **decreases** if $r < 0$ and hence $a < 1$.

This means that—as we scan the graph $y = a^x$ from left to right—the curve

- **rises** if $a > 1$ (natural growth),
- **falls** if $0 < a < 1$ (natural decline).

We have seen "typical growth" curves for values $a > 1$ in Fig. 3.3.8. Figure 3.3.11 shows some typical "decay curves" for several values $a < 1$.

Many quantities other than populations and investment accounts grow or decline naturally—that is, are multiplied by equal factors in equal times—and are therefore described by exponential functions.

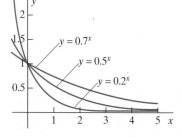

Figure 3.3.11   Decay curves with $a = 0.7, 0.5, 0.2$.

Example 10

Suppose a nuclear reactor accident at the state's engineering school has left its campus contaminated with three times the maximal amount S of radiation that is safe for human habitation. Two and a half months after the accident, the campus radiation level has declined to 75% of its original level. Assuming natural decline of this radiation level, how long must students and faculty members wait before it will be safe for them to return to campus?

Let us write $A(t)$ for the amount of radiation still present after t months. If we measure A as a multiple of the maximal safe amount S, then we won't need to know exactly what S is (who knows this sort of thing offhand?). For in terms of these safe units (su) we're given that $A(0) = 3$ su and we want to find when $A(t) = 1$ su, so it's safe for people to come back to campus.

In addition to the initial amount $A_0 = 3$, we're given that the amount of radiation is multiplied by the factor $b = 75\% = 0.75$ every $N = 2.5$ months. Therefore, Eq. (13) gives

$$A(t) = 3 \times 0.75^{t/2.5}. \tag{19}$$

Notice that here time is measured in months rather than in years. To find when $A = 1$ we define **Y1=3*0.75^(X/2.5)** and **Y2=1** with the idea of seeing where the amount graph crosses the horizontal line $y = 1$. Figure 3.3.12 shows a plot in the viewing window defined by $0 < x < 12, 0 < y < 4$. Automatic intersection-finding yields the intersection point $(9.5471, 1)$. Thus we see that A falls to 1 su in just over $9\frac{1}{2}$ months. With human lives at stake, we probably ought to add a margin for safety and wait at least 10 months, maybe a full year, before reoccupying the campus. ◥

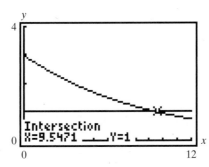

Figure 3.3.12   Solving the equation $3 \times 0.75^{t/2.5} = 1$ in Example 10.

In Problems 1–8, write a mathematical model of the form $P(t) = P_0 \cdot a^t$.

1. $P(0) = 75$ and P doubles every year.
2. $P(0) = 125$ and P triples every year.
3. $P(0) = 100$ and P doubles every two and a half years.
4. $P(0) = 50$ and P triples every three and a third years.
5. $P(0) = 100$ and $P(1) = 175$.
6. $P(0) = 120$ and $P(3) = 180$.
7. $P(0) = 400$ and $P(1) = 155$.
8. $P(0) = 120$ and $P(4) = 40$.

In each of Problems 9–16, the population of a city, state, or region in two different years is given. Find both its annual percentage increase and—assuming this rate of increase continues—its expected population in the years 1990 and 2000. Look in an almanac or other source to compare the predicted and actual populations.

9. The population of Knoxville, Tennessee was 112 thousand in 1960 and 175 thousand in 1980.

10. The population of Austin, Texas was 254 thousand in 1970 and 345 thousand in 1980.

11. The population of Georgia was 3.94 million in 1960 and 5.46 million in 1980.

12. The population of California was 19.97 million in 1970 and 23.67 million in 1980.

13. The population of Africa was 375 million in 1970 and 491 million in 1980.

14. The population of South America was 168 million in 1965 and 242 million in 1980.

15. The population of the world's more developed regions was 1.002 billion in 1965 and 1.176 billion in 1985.

16. The population of the world's less developed regions was 2.356 billion in 1965 and 3.706 billion in 1985.

In each of Problems 17–20, the actual 1985 population of a world city and its projected population in the year 2000 are given. Find both its annual percentage increase and—assuming this rate of increase continues—its expected population in the years 2010 and 2020.

17. Sao Paulo, Brazil: 14.9 million in 1985 and 25.4 million in 2000

18. Seoul, South Korea: 13.7 million in 1985 and 22.0 million in 2000

19. Los Angeles, USA: 9.64 million in 1985 and 10.71 million in 2000

20. Bangkok, Thailand: 5.00 million in 1985 and 7.59 million in 2000

21. How long does it take a naturally growing bacteria population to triple if it doubles in 1.5 hours?

22. The number of bacteria in a culture increased sixfold in 10 hours. Assuming natural growth, how long did it take their number to double?

23. Suppose a naturally growing rabbit population increases in 3.5 months from an initial population of 4 rabbits to 10 rabbits. How many rabbits will there be after 1 year (starting when there were 4 rabbits)?

24. Suppose a couple plans, upon the birth of their first child, to make a deposit in a savings account guaranteed to continue to pay 4% annual interest. How much should they deposit in order for the account to contain $25,000 when the child is ready to begin college at age 18?

25. A naturally growing bacteria population $P(t)$ numbers 49 at 12 noon.

   (a) Write a formula giving $P(t)$ after t hours if there are 294 bacteria at 1 P.M.

   (b) How many bacteria are there at 1:40 P.M.?

   (c) At what clock time (nearest minute) that afternoon are there 20 thousand bacteria?

26. The English language evolves naturally in such a way that 77% of all words disappear (or are replaced) every 1000 years. Of a basic list of words used by Chaucer in A.D. 1400, what percentage should we expect to find still in use today?

27. The amount $A(t)$ of atmospheric pollutants in a certain mountain valley grows naturally and is tripling every 7.5 years.

   (a) If the initial amount is 10 pu (pollutant units), write a formula for $A(t)$ giving the amount (in pu) present after t years.

    (b)   What will be the amount (in pu) of pollutants present in the valley atmosphere after 5 years?

    (c)   If it will be dangerous to stay in the valley when the amount of pollutants reaches 100 pu, how long will this take?

28. An accident at a nuclear power plant has left the surrounding area polluted with radioactive material that decays naturally. The initial amount of radioactive material present is 15 su (safe units), and 5 months later it is still 10 su.

    (a)   Write a formula giving the amount $A(t)$ of radioactive material (in su) remaining after t months.

    (b)   What amount of radioactive material will remain after 8 months?

    (c)   How long (in total number of months or fraction thereof) will it be until $A = 1$ su, so it is safe for people to return to the area?

29. **(a)**   In 1979 the typical microcomputer contained 29 thousand transistors. Assuming natural growth at the annual rate r, write a formula giving the number $N(t)$ of transistors in a typical micro t years later.

    (b)   In 1993 the typical microcomputer CPU (central processing unit) contained 3.1 million transistors. Find the annual growth rate r in part (a), expressed as a percentage.

    (c)   At this rate, how many months does it take to double the number of transistors in a typical micro?

    (d)   Assuming that this annual rate of increase continues, how many transistors (rounded off accurate to the nearest million) will the typical micro contain in the year 2001?

30. There are now about 3300 different human language families in the whole world. Assume that all these are derived from a single original language and that a language family develops into 1.5 language families every 6000 years. About how long ago was the single original human language spoken?

31. Thousands of years ago ancestors of the American Indians crossed the Bering Strait from Asia and entered the western hemisphere. Since then, they have fanned out across North and South America. The single language that the original Indian settlers spoke has since split into many Indian language families. Assume (as in Problem 30) that the number of these language families has been multiplied by 1.5 every 6000 years. There are now 150 Indian language families in the Americas. About when did the first American Indians arrive?

32. On the April 24, 1999, edition of the Car Talk radio show, Tom and Ray presented a puzzler concerning a fellow who visited a nursery for advice concerning a new lawn. The following scenario is an adaptation of that puzzler. Tam wants to have a lush, new lawn for the Fourth of July. Since it is already May 30, it is too late for grass seed, and sod is too expensive for his budget. Matt, the nursery worker, suggests a new product—a small plug of grass that doubles in size every day. After consulting a diagram of the yard, Matt does some calculations and reports his conclusion. If Tam plants only one plug on June 1, he will have the lawn he desires on June 30. Being a bit nervous, Tam decides to buy two, just to be on the safe side. If Tam plants two grass plugs on June 1, on what day will he have his new lawn?

3.4   FITTING NATURAL GROWTH MODELS TO DATA

In Section 3.3 we discussed briefly the data in the following table, which shows the U.S. population as recorded during the first six census counts—in the decade years 1790, 1800, 1810, 1820, 1830, and 1840.

t	Year	U.S. Census Population (millions)	Change
0	1790	3.9	
10	1800	5.3	1.4
20	1810	7.2	1.9
30	1820	9.6	2.4
40	1830	12.9	3.3
50	1840	17.1	4.2

Looking at the increasing (rather than constant) change figures in the final column, we see immediately that the U.S. population growth during the years 1790–1840 was *not* linear. We therefore want to consider the possibility of fitting the data with either a quadratic model $P(t) = at^2 + bt + c$ or a **natural growth model** of the form

$$P(t) = P_0(1 + r)^t \tag{1}$$

that will have a chance of keeping up with the actual population growth that was observed. Recall from Section 3.3 that (1) describes a population that has initial population P_0 and grows naturally with annual rate of growth r.

Example 1

First, let us fit the population data with an optimal quadratic model, as in Section 2.3. Figures 3.4.1 and 3.4.2 show these data entered in a graphing calculator for analysis. Figure 3.4.3 shows the resulting quadratic model

$$P(t) = 0.004t^2 + 0.086t + 3.986 \tag{2}$$

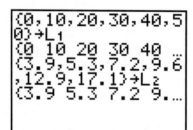

Figure 3.4.1   Storing the 1790–1840 U.S. census data.

Figure 3.4.2   TI-83 **STAT EDIT** screen showing the U.S. population data in table form.

```
QuadReg
y=ax²+bx+c
a=.004
b=.086
c=3.986
```

Figure 3.4.3 Optimal quadratic model resulting from the TI-83 **STAT CALC QuadReg L1, L2, Y1** command.

that best fits the given data. The following table compares the actual population figures with those predicted by this optimal quadratic model.

t	**Actual Population**	**Quadratic $P(t)$**	**Error E**	E^2
0	3.9	3.99	− 0.09	0.0081
10	5.3	5.25	0.05	0.0025
20	7.2	7.31	− 0.11	0.0121
30	9.6	10.17	− 0.57	0.3249
40	12.9	13.83	− 0.93	0.8649
50	17.1	18.29	− 1.19	1.4161

The sum of the squares of the errors shown in the table is

$$\text{SSE} = 0.0081 + 0.0025 + 0.0121 + 0.3249 + 0.8649 + 1.4161 = 2.6286.$$

Since there are $n = 6$ data points, the average error in the optimal model is therefore given by

$$\text{average error} = \sqrt{\frac{\text{SSE}}{n}} = \sqrt{\frac{2.6286}{6}} = \sqrt{0.4381} \approx 0.6619. \qquad (3)$$

Thus the average discrepancy between the actual census population and the population predicted by the quadratic model in (2) is 0.662 million, or 662 thousand persons. Figure 3.4.4 shows a spreadsheet graph comparing the actual and

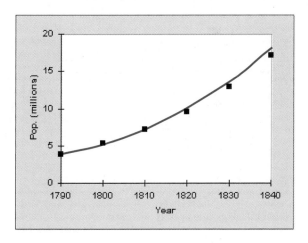

Figure 3.4.4 Comparing the quadratic model (solid curve) and actual U.S. population figures (dots).

predicted figures. The discrepancy between actual and predicted populations, especially for the last three decades, is visually apparent.   ◼

Example 2

Suppose now that we consider fitting the 1790–1840 U.S. population growth with a natural growth model of the form $P(t) = P_0(1 + r)^t$. The spreadsheet charts in Figures 3.4.5, 3.4.6, and 3.4.7 show the results when we take $t = 0$ in 1790,

Figure 3.4.5   Comparing actual U.S. population data (dots) with the natural growth model $P(t) = 3.9 \times 1.028^t$.

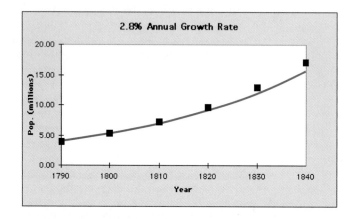

Figure 3.4.6   Comparing actual U.S. population data (dots) with the natural growth model $P(t) = 3.9 \times 1.030^t$.

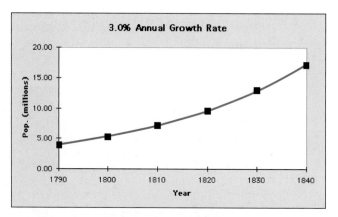

Figure 3.4.7   Comparing actual U.S. population data (dots) with the natural growth model $P(t) = 3.9 \times 1.032^t$.

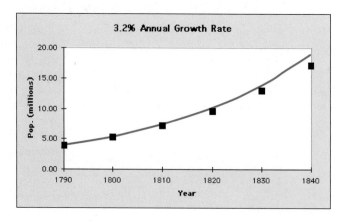

$P_0 = 3.9$ (the actual 1790 population in millions), and try the growth rates $r = 2.8\%, r = 3.0\%$, and $r = 3.2\%$. Comparing the three graphs, it is clear to the naked eye that (among these choices) the U. S. population growth during this half-century is best fitted by natural growth at an annual rate of $r = 0.030 = 3.0\%$, as described by the natural growth model

$$P(t) = 3.9 \times 1.030^t. \tag{4}$$

The following table compares the actual population figures with those predicted by this 3% natural growth model.

t	Actual Population	$P(t) = 3.9 \times 1.030^t$	Error E	E^2
0	3.9	3.90	0.00	0.0000
10	5.3	5.24	0.06	0.0036
20	7.2	7.04	0.16	0.0256
30	9.6	9.47	0.13	0.0169
40	12.9	12.72	0.18	0.0324
50	17.1	17.10	0.00	0.0000

The sum of the squares of the errors shown in the table is

$$\text{SSE} = 0.0000 + 0.0036 + 0.0256 + 0.0169 + 0.0324 + 0.0000 = 0.0785.$$

Since there are $n = 6$ data points, the average error in the optimal model is given by

$$\text{average error} = \sqrt{\frac{\text{SSE}}{n}} = \sqrt{\frac{0.0785}{6}} = \sqrt{0.0131} \approx 0.1144. \tag{5}$$

Thus the average discrepancy between the actual census population and the population predicted by the natural model in (4) is about 0.114 million, or 114 thousand persons. This is less than a fifth of the average error in the optimal quadratic model of Example 1. ◼

Often the question in a given situation is what kind of model best fits the available data. When we compare the results of Examples 1 and 2 in Equations (3) and (5), we see that the actual 1790–1840 U.S. population growth is better fitted by the 3% natural growth model in (4) than by *any* quadratic model.

A common mistake is extrapolation outside the range of accuracy of a mathematical model. Here it would be wrong to assume that the U.S. population continued after 1840 to grow at a constant 3% natural growth rate. Figure 3.4.8 shows a spreadsheet chart comparison of the actual U.S. population growth up to the year 1900, compared with the population growth predicted by the 3% model. The actual population recorded by the 1900 census was 76.2 million, whereas substitution of $t = 110$ in (4) gives a predicted 1900 population of

$$P(110) = 3.9 \times 1.030^{110} \approx 100.7 \text{ million.}$$

Thus the 3% natural growth model, which accurately tracked the actual population growth of the United States during its first half century, considerably overshot the U.S. population growth that occurred during the last half of the nineteenth century.

Figure 3.4.8 Comparing actual 1790–1900 U.S. population data (dots) with the 3% natural growth model $P(t) = 3.9 \times 1.030^t$.

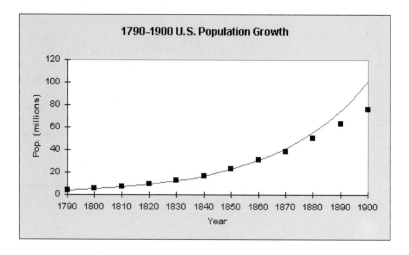

The Average Error in Data Modeling

In this section we discuss the fitting of data by natural growth models. Much of this discussion will parallel the discussion in Sections 1.4 and 2.3 of fitting linear and quadratic models to data. The *general* natural growth model $P(t) = P_0(1 + r)^t$ of Eq. (1) takes the form

$$P(t) = a \cdot b^t \tag{6}$$

if we write a instead of P_0 and b in place of the constant $1 + r$. In the language of Section 3.3, the constant b is the factor by which the population P is multiplied by each year.

With specified numerical values of a and b in (6), we obtain a *particular* natural growth model such as

$$P(t) = 100 \times 1.05^t \text{ with } a = 100 \text{ and } b = 1.05, \text{ or}$$
$$P(t) = 479 \times 1.23^t \text{ with } a = 479 \text{ and } b = 1.23.$$

In a typical data-modeling situation, the numbers a and b in (6) are not known in advance. Indeed the question ordinarily is, What numerical values for a and b yield the best natural growth model for the given data? As before, the optimal model is the one that best fits the actual data, and the better of two different models is the one giving the lesser average error.

The meaning of the term *average error* is also the same as before and has already been illustrated in Examples 1 and 2. More generally, suppose that the **actual populations**

$$P_1, P_2, P_3, \ldots, P_n \tag{7}$$

at the successive times

$$t_1, t_2, t_3, \ldots, t_n \tag{8}$$

have been recorded. If the values a and b have been selected, then Eq. (6) gives the **predicted population**

$$P(t_k) = a \cdot b^{t_k} \tag{9}$$

at time $t = t_k$. The list of times in (8) then gives a list of predicted populations

$$P(t_1), P(t_2), P(t_3), \ldots, P(t_n). \tag{10}$$

The **error** in the kth predicted population $P(t_k)$ is the discrepancy

$$E_k = P_k - P(t_k) \quad (= \text{actual} - \text{predicted population}) \tag{11}$$

between it and the kth actual population P_k. Thus subtraction of the predicted populations in (10) from the actual populations in (7) gives the list

$$E_1, E_2, E_3, \ldots, E_n \tag{12}$$

of the errors in the mathematical model $P(t) = a \cdot b^t$.

Recall that in Section 1.4 we defined the SSE (**sum of squares of errors**) as

$$\text{SSE} = E_1^2 + E_2^2 + E_3^2 + \ldots + E_n^2 \tag{13}$$

and the **average error** as

$$\text{average error} = \sqrt{\frac{\text{SSE}}{n}} \tag{14}$$

where n is the number of original data points.

Tables like those displayed in Examples 1 and 2 are frequently used as an aid in the calculation of average errors.

Example 3

When we look at Figures 3.4.5 through 3.4.7, we see that the 3.0% natural growth model $P(t) = 3.9 \times 1.030^t$ fits the actual 1790–1840 U.S. population growth better than either the 2.8% growth model $P(t) = 3.9 \times 1.028^t$ or the 3.2% growth model $P(t) = 3.9 \times 1.032^t$. But we still can ask which of the latter two models fits the actual growth *best*.

t	Actual Population	$P(t) = 3.9 \times 1.028^t$	Error E	E^2
0	3.9	3.90	0.00	0.0000
10	5.3	5.14	0.16	0.0256
20	7.2	6.78	0.42	0.1764
30	9.6	8.93	0.67	0.4489
40	12.9	11.77	1.13	1.2769
50	17.1	15.51	1.59	2.5281

This table shows the errors (and their squares) in the 2.8% model. The sum of the squares of the errors shown here is

$$\text{SSE} = 0.0000 + 0.0256 + 0.1764 + 0.4489 + 1.2769 + 2.5281 = 4.4559.$$

There being $n = 6$ data points, the average error in the optimal model is therefore given by

$$\text{average error} = \sqrt{\frac{\text{SSE}}{n}} = \sqrt{\frac{4.4559}{6}} = \sqrt{0.7427} \approx 0.8618. \tag{15}$$

Thus the average discrepancy between the actual census population and the population predicted by the 2.8% model $P(t) = 3.9 \times 1.028^t$ is about 0.862 million, or 862 thousand persons.

t	Actual Population	$P(t) = 3.9 \times 1.032^t$	Error E	E^2
0	3.9	3.90	0.00	0.0000
10	5.3	5.34	− 0.04	0.0016
20	7.2	7.32	− 0.12	0.0144
30	9.6	10.03	− 0.43	0.1849
40	12.9	13.75	− 0.85	0.7225
50	17.1	18.84	− 1.74	3.0276

This second table shows the errors (and their squares) in the 3.2% model. The sum of the squares of the errors shown in this table is

$$\text{SSE} = 0.0000 + 0.0016 + 0.0144 + 0.1849 + 0.7225 + 3.0276 = 3.9510.$$

There being $n = 6$ data points, the average error in the optimal model is therefore given by

$$\text{average error} = \sqrt{\frac{\text{SSE}}{n}} = \sqrt{\frac{3.9510}{6}} = \sqrt{0.6585} \approx 0.8115. \tag{16}$$

Thus the average discrepancy between the actual census population and the population predicted by the 3.2% model $P(t) = 3.9 \times 1.032^t$ is about 0.812 million, or 812 thousand persons.

Thus the 3.2% model overestimates the actual population by an average of 0.812 million persons, while the 2.8% model underestimates the actual population by an average of 0.862 million. So the 3.2% model is a better fit than the 2.8% model. But neither fits the actual 1790–1840 U.S. population as well as the quadratic model of Example 1, with its average error of 0.659 million persons. ∎

The Best Fit—The Least Possible Average Error

Once again—as in Sections 1.4 and 2.3—in order to find the model that best fits our data, we want to find the values of the parameters that yield the least possible average error. Here the question is this: What choice of the numerical parameters a and b in the natural growth model $P(t) = a \cdot b^t$ will minimize the average error?

Figure 3.4.1 shows 1790–1840 U.S. population data entered in a calculator. The t-values 0, 10, 20, 30, 40, 50 corresponding to the decade years from 1790 to 1840 are stored as a list **L1,** and the corresponding list of census population figures is stored as a list **L2**. Figure 3.4.2 shows the resulting **STAT EDIT** menu displaying the data in table form.

Figure 3.4.9 shows the calculator's **STAT CALC** menu. Item **0: ExpReg** on this menu (below item 9) is the calculator's so-called exponential regression facility for finding the natural growth (or exponential) curve $y = ab^x$ that best fits the selected data. When we select item **0** on this menu, the **ExpReg** function is entered on the home calculating screen. As shown in Fig. 3.4.10, we must then

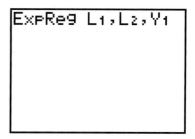

Figure 3.4.9   The TI-83 **STAT CALC** menu.

Figure 3.4.10   Fitting the **X**-data in list **L1** and the **Y**-data in list **L2**.

enter the names of our list **L1** of **X**-coordinates, our list **L2** of **Y**-coordinates, and the name **Y1** of the Y= menu variable where we want the resulting natural growth formula saved.

Figure 3.4.11 shows the display that results when this command is entered. The displayed results say that the natural growth curve best fitting the given data is

$$y = 3.9396 \times 1.0300^x. \tag{17}$$

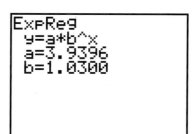

Figure 3.4.11   The optimal natural growth function.

In terms of time t and population P rather than the calculator's variables x and y, this result says that the natural growth function best fitting the actual 1790–1840 U.S. population growth is given by

$$P(t) = 3.9396 \times 1.0300^t. \tag{18}$$

Observe that this optimal population function corresponds to a population that grows at a 3.00% annual rate, starting with an initial population of 3.9396 million when $t = 0$. Note also that this best-fitting initial population, about 3.94 million, is different from the actual initial population of 3.9 million (perhaps rounded off). So when we attempt to best fit a given list of population data, we are free to adjust both the initial population and the rate of growth in order to fit the data as closely as possible.

The **ExpReg L1, L2,Y1** command automatically enters Eq. (17) in the Y= menu, ready for plotting as shown in Fig. 3.4.12. With **Plot 1** turned **On** in the **STAT PLOT** menu (Fig. 3.4.13), **GRAPH** then gives the plot of the best-fitting natural growth curve shown in Fig. 3.4.14, where the original census data points are shown as small squares.

Here we are less interested in the graph than in a table of values that we can use to compute the average error in our optimal fit. Our calculator now provides the table of (rounded off) values of **Y1=3.9396*1.03^X** shown in Fig. 3.4.15. When we combine these values with our original U.S. population data, we get the

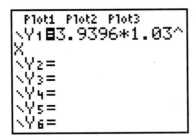

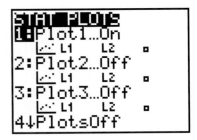

Figure 3.4.12   The best-fitting natural growth function ready to plot or tabulate.

Figure 3.4.13   Preparing to plot the data points together with the optimal natural growth curve.

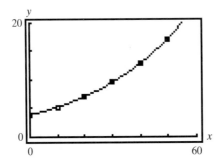

Figure 3.4.14   The optimal natural growth fit.

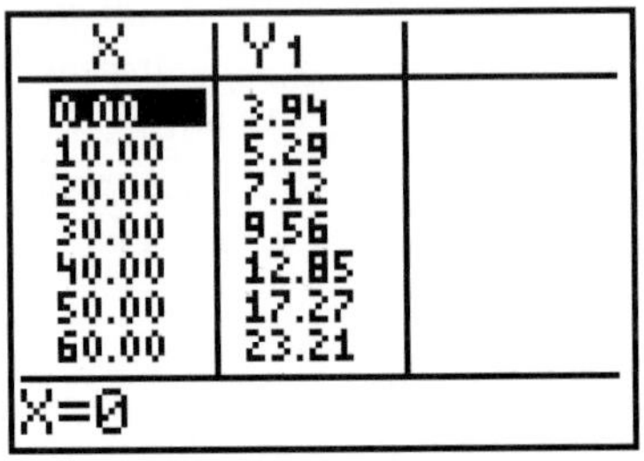

Figure 3.4.15   Values of the optimal natural growth function $P(t) = 3.9396 \times 1.0300^t$.

following table, which compares the original census data with the population figures predicted by the optimal natural growth model $P(t) = 3.9396 \times 1.0300^t$.

t	Actual Population	$P(t) = 3.94 \times 1.03^t$	Error E	E^2
0	3.9	3.94	− 0.04	0.0016
10	5.3	5.29	0.01	0.0001
20	7.2	7.12	0.08	0.0064
30	9.6	9.56	0.04	0.0016
40	12.9	12.85	0.05	0.0025
50	17.1	17.27	− 0.17	0.0289

Example 4

Find the average error in the optimal natural growth model for the U.S. population data.

As usual, the final column shows the *squares* of the errors. Hence the SSE associated with the optimal natural growth model in (18) is

$$\text{SSE} = 0.0016 + 0.0001 + 0.0064 + 0.0016 + 0.0025 + 0.0289 = 0.0411.$$

Since there are $n = 6$ data points, the average error in the optimal model is given by

$$\text{average error} = \sqrt{\frac{\text{SSE}}{n}} = \sqrt{\frac{0.0411}{6}} = \sqrt{0.0069} \approx 0.0828. \qquad (19)$$

Thus the average discrepancy between the actual census population and the population predicted by the natural model in (18) is about 0.083 million, or 83 thousand persons.   ◣

The average error of 83 thousand in the best-fitting exponential model is less than the average error—found in Example 2—of 114 thousand in the 3% natural growth model $P(t) = 3.9 \times 1.03^t$. This latter model is based on the actual 1790 initial U.S. population of 3.9 million rather than on the (hypothetical) initial population of 3.94 million that we see in (18).

Applications of Natural Growth Models

If $a > 0$ and $b > 1$, then the exponential function

$$P(t) = a \cdot b^t \tag{20}$$

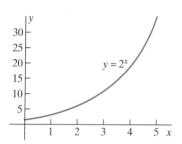

Figure 3.4.16   The natural growth curve $y = 2^x$.

describes a population P that starts with initial value $P(0) = a$ and thereafter *grows* at a steadily *increasing* rate (being multiplied by the factor $b > 1$ during each unit of time). The graph of any such **natural growth function** looks generally like the graph $y = 2^x$ shown in Fig. 3.4.16 and *rises* with *increasing* steepness (from left to right).

However, if $0 < b < 1$, then the same exponential function $P(t) = a \cdot b^t$ describes a population P that starts with initial value $P(0) = a$ and thereafter *declines* (or *decays*) at a steadily *decreasing* rate (being multiplied by the factor $b < 1$ during each unit of time). The graph of any such **natural decay function** looks generally like the graph $y = (\frac{1}{2})^x$ shown in Fig. 3.4.17 and *falls* with *decreasing* steepness (from left to right).

Just as in Section 3.3, we can discuss the natural growth and decline of quantities other than populations. The world is full of quantities that appear either to grow at a steadily increasing rate, or to decline at a steadily decreasing rate. Any such quantity is fair game for modeling by an exponential function as in (20).

Figure 3.4.17   The natural decay curve $y = (\frac{1}{2})^x$.

Definition: Exponential Model

An **exponential model** is a function of the form $P(t) = a \cdot b^t$ that describes either

- a naturally growing quantity (if $b > 1$), or
- a naturally declining quantity (if $0 < b < 1$).

For example, suppose a hot object with initial temperature T_0 is placed in a relatively cool medium with constant temperature A. Thus we might put a hot cake (just out of the oven) in a cool room with air temperature A, or we might put a hot rock in a large water tank with water temperature A. Then **Newton's law of cooling** says that the difference

$$u(t) = T(t) - A \tag{21}$$

between A and the temperature of the object at time t is a naturally declining quantity. That is,

$$u(t) = a \cdot b^t \tag{22}$$

with appropriate values of the positive parameters a and $b < 1$. In the case of the hot cake, for instance, we might measure its falling temperature several times with a thermometer and then attempt to fit the resulting data with the exponential function (22) in order to predict when the cake will be cool enough to serve.

Example 5

Suppose a cake is baked in an oven at 350° (Fahrenheit). At 1 P.M. it is taken out of the oven and placed to cool on a table in a room with air temperature 70°. We plan to slice and serve it as soon as it has cooled to 100°. The temperature of the cake was measured every 15 minutes for the first hour, with the following results.

Time	1:00 P.M.	1:15 P.M.	1:30 P.M.	1:45 P.M.	2:00 P.M.
Temp	350°	265°	214°	166°	143°

When will the cake be cool enough to eat?

To use Newton's law we must replace the cake temperature T with the difference $u = T - 70$ that we see in Eq. (21), with $A = 70$ (room temperature). Measuring time t in hours and subtracting 70 from each temperature entry, the given data takes the form

t	0	0.25	0.5	0.75	1
u	280	195	144	96	73

If we can fit this data with an exponential model $u(t) = a \cdot b^t$, then we should be able to solve graphically for the time when $u = 30$, so $T = 100$ as desired.

We begin by entering the list of t-values as a calculator list **L1** and the list of u-values as a list **L2** (Fig. 3.4.18). Then the **STAT CALC** command **ExpReg L1, L2,Y1** produces the result shown in Fig. 3.4.19, which describes the best-fitting exponential function

$$u(t) = 277.534(0.257)^t \tag{23}$$

(upon replacing **X** with t and **Y** with u). Finally, remembering Eq. (21), we add $A = 70$ (the room temperature) to both sides to obtain the cake's temperature function

$$T(t) = 70 + 277.534(0.257)^t. \tag{24}$$

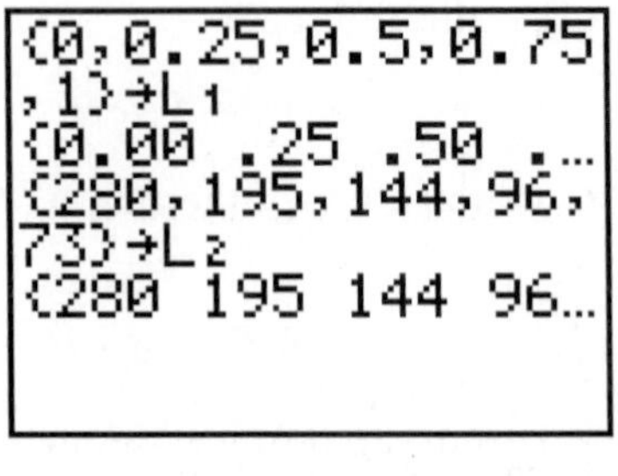

```
{0,0.25,0.5,0.75
,1}→L₁
{0.00 .25 .50 ....
{280,195,144,96,
73}→L₂
{280 195 144 96...
```

```
ExpReg
y=a*b^x
a=277.534
b=.257
```

Figure 3.4.18 Entering the data of Example 5.

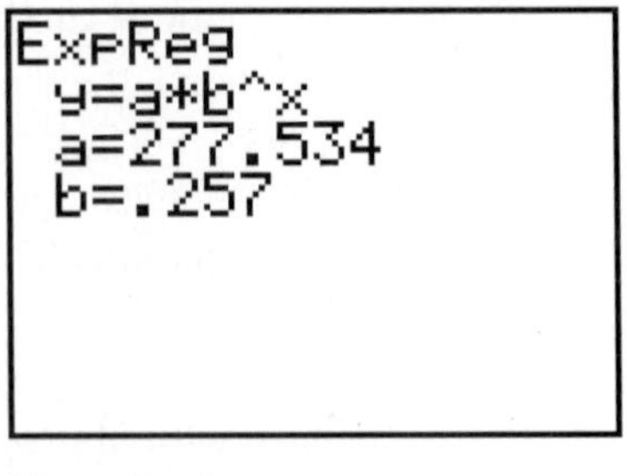

Figure 3.4.19 The best exponential fit $u(t) = 277.534(0.257)^t$.

It's always important to keep your eye on the cake. Here, literally *no one* cares what is the average error in the natural decay function (21). Instead, we all want to know when we can eat our cake. That is, accepting (24) as our mathematical model of the cooling of our cake, for what value of time t is it true that

$$70 + 277.534(0.257)^t = 100? \tag{25}$$

In Fig. 3.4.20 we have graphed the functions **Y1=70+277.534*(0.257)^X** and **Y2=100** and asked for the coordinates of the point of intersection. The x-value of 1.637 tells us that our cake reaches an edible temperature of 100° after 1.637 hours (starting at 1 P.M.). Since $0.637 \times 60 = 38.220$, this means we can slice and eat it at about 2:38 P.M. ◢

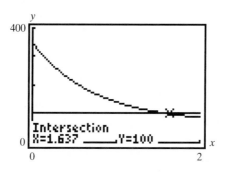

Figure 3.4.20 Solving Eq. (25).

Each of the tables in Problems 1–8 gives data from a function that is exponential. Determine the factor by which y is multiplied by each year, and find a function of the form $y = a \cdot b^x$ that fits these points exactly.

1.

x	0	1	2	3	4
y	10	20	40	80	160

2.

x	0	1	2	3	4
y	5	15	45	135	405

3.

x	0	1	2	3	4
y	80	40	20	10	5

4.

x	0	1	2	3	4
y	100	20	4	0.8	0.16

5.

x	0	2	4	6	8
y	3	9	27	81	243

6.

x	0	3	6	9	12
y	4	8	16	32	64

7.

x	0	4	8	12	16
y	160	80	40	20	10

8.

x	0	5	10	15	20
y	100000	10000	1000	100	10

Each of the tables in Problems 9–16 gives data from a function that is approximately exponential. (a) Find an exponential model of the form $y = a \cdot b^x$ that goes through two of the data points, rounding a and b to three decimal places. Then calculate the average error in this model. (b) Use the exponential regression facility of your calculator to find the exponential model of the form $y = a \cdot b^x$ that best fits these points, rounding a and b to three decimal places. Then calculate the average error in this optimal exponential model.

9.

x	0	1	2	3	4
y	5	7	10	15	23

10.

x	1	2	3	4	5
y	35	75	170	385	865

11.

x	0	2	4	6	8
y	15	30	60	110	220

12.

x	1	1.5	2	2.5	3
y	22	23	24	25	27

13.

x	0	1	2	3	4
y	40	27	17	11	7

14.

x	1	3	5	7	9
y	215	40	7	1	0.1

15.

x	0.5	0.75	1	1.25	1.5
y	80	65	55	45	40

16.

x	0	5	10	15	20
y	1000	775	600	465	360

In each of Problems 17–22, the 1960–1990 population census data for a U.S. city is given. Find the exponential model $P = a \cdot b^t$ (with $t = 0$ in 1950) that best fits this census data, and use it to predict the year 2000 population of this city. Also write this optimal model in the form $P(t) = P_0(1 + r)^t$ in order to determine the city's average annual percentage rate of growth during this 30-year period.

17.   San Diego, CA

Year	1960	1970	1980	1990
Pop. (*thous*)	573	697	876	1111

18.   Phoenix, AZ

Year	1960	1970	1980	1990
Pop. (*thous*)	439	584	790	1008

19.   San Antonio, TX

Year	1960	1970	1980	1990
Pop. (*thous*)	588	654	786	935

20. Cleveland, OH

Year	1960	1970	1980	1990
Pop. (*thous*)	876	751	574	506

21. Buffalo, NY

Year	1960	1970	1980	1990
Pop. (*thous*)	533	463	358	328

22. Raleigh, NC

Year	1960	1970	1980	1990
Pop. (*thous*)	94	123	150	212

In Problems 23–28, use an exponential model to determine the answer to each question. (For problems using calendar years, "reset the clock" so that $t = 0$ in the year for which you first have data.)

23. Suppose a hot cake like the one of Example 5 is taken out of an oven at 175°C and immediately set out on a cool porch where the temperature is 10°C. During the next hour the following temperature readings of the cake are taken.

Time	5 P.M.	5:20 P.M.	5:40 P.M.	6 P.M.
Temp. (°C)	175	125	85	60

The cake will be brought in and served when it has cooled to 35°C. When do you expect this to be?

24. A pitcher of buttermilk initially at 25°C is set out on the 10°C porch of Problem 25. During the next half hour the following temperature readings are taken.

Time	1 P.M.	1:10 P.M.	1:20 P.M.	1:30 P.M.
Temp. (°C)	25	20	17	15

The buttermilk will be brought in and served when it has cooled to 12°C. when do you expect this to be?

25. In a certain lake the intensity I of light beneath the surface is a naturally declining function of the depth x in feet. The following table gives I as a percentage of the intensity of light at the surface.

Depth x (ft)	0	5	10	15
Intensity I (%)	100	60	35	20

How deep would you have to dive in this lake in order that the light intensity there will be 1% of the surface intensity?

26. The atmospheric pressure p (in pounds per square inch) is a naturally declining function of the altitude x above sea level. The following table gives p as a function of x in thousands of feet.

Altitude x (thous ft)	0	4	8	12
Pressure p (lb/in²)	14.7	12.6	10.9	9.3

(a) Suppose that you (like most people) cannot survive without special conditioning at an air pressure of less than 7.5 lb/in². How high could you safely fly in an airplane without pressurization?

(b) During a May 1999 expedition sponsored by the National Geographic Society and the Boston Museum of Science, Sherpas carried Global Positioning System equipment to the summit of Mount Everest. Based on the data they collected, scientists have recalculated the height of Mount Everest as 29,035 feet, rather than the previous height of 29,028 feet, set in 1954 by the Survey of India. Use the new measurement to calculate the air pressure atop Mount Everest.

27. The amount money earned by winning the Kentucky Derby has grown quite a bit since the Derby's first running in 1875. The following table gives the net amount earned by the winner as a function of the year of the race.

Year t	1875	1900	1925	1950	1975
Winnings	$2850	$4850	$52,950	$92,650	$209,600

Source: Churchill Downs Incorporated (www.kentuckyderby.com)

In what year would you expect the prize money to grow to $1,000,000?

28. As cassette tapes and compact discs became more popular, the sales of vinyl singles declined, as shown in the following table.

Year t	1988	1989	1992	1994	1996
Millions of Units s	65.6	36.6	19.8	11.7	10.1

Source: The World Almanac and Book of Facts 1998

Suppose that vinyl singles will be discontinued when their sales fall below 2 million. In what year will this occur?

C H A P T E R   3   R E V I E W

In this chapter, you learned about exponential functions and models. After completing the chapter, you should be able to

- Determine whether a relation described numerically, graphically, or symbolically represents an exponential function.
- Find the output value of an exponential function for a given input value.
- Find the input value of an exponential function for a given output value.
- Solve an equation or inequality involving an exponential function.
- Find an exponential function model that fits given exponential data.
- Find the best-fitting exponential model for data that is approximately exponential.
- Find the annual percent rate of growth or decay for an exponential model.

REVIEW PROBLEMS

In Problems 1–7, the given information (table, graph, or formula) gives y as a function of x. In each case, the functions is linear, quadratic, or exponential. Determine the type of function, and in Problems 1–3, give a symbolic definition of the function.

1.

x	−2	3	4	6	7	10
y	2	4.5	8	18	24.5	50

2.

x	−2	−1	1	3	4	5
y	32	16	4	1	.5	.25

3.

x	−4	−3	−1	2	4	5
y	29	26	20	11	5	2

4.

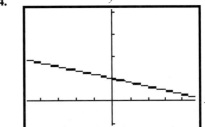

5.

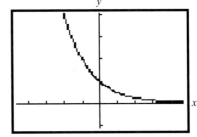

6. $y = 3x^2$

7. $y = 3 \cdot 2^x$

8. Suppose that a child who lost her first tooth in 1998 was left $1.00 by the Tooth Fairy. Let us assume that the Tooth Fairy leaves the same amount for each tooth, if payments are adjusted for inflation. Then, based on the Consumer Price Index, the

Tooth Fairy should have left her mother $0.19 for a tooth in 1963 and given her grandmother $0.09 for a tooth in 1938. Find the best-fitting exponential function for this data, and use it to predict how much the Tooth Fairy should leave for the little girl's daughter if she loses a tooth in 2023. (*Source for conversion factors:* Robert Sahr, Political Science Department, Oregon State University.)

9. An accident at a nuclear power plant has left the surrounding area polluted with a radioactive element that decays naturally. The initial radiation level is 10 times the maximum amount *S* that is safe, and 100 days later it is still 7 times that amount. How long (to the nearest day after the original accident) will it be before it is safe for people to return to the area?

10. Suppose that, as of Jan. 1, 1999, a state's annual Medicaid expenditures are $1 billion and increasing at 6% per year, while its annual Medicaid tax income is $2 billion and is increasing at 3% per year. If these rates continue, during what calendar year will the state's Medicaid budget go into the red (with expenditures exceeding income)?

11. A college professor was hired in 1989 at a yearly salary of $25,600. His yearly salary in 1999 was $49,585. Using an exponential model, find the average annual percent rate of growth of his salary over this time period.

12. The following table gives the gross revenue *R* in millions of dollars for the Broadway season that begins in the indicated year *t*. Find the best-fitting exponential model for this data, and use it to predict the year in which gross revenue will grow to 700 million dollars.

t (*years*)	1957	1967	1976	1988	1995
R (*thous*)	38	59	93	262	436

Source: infoplease.com (from League of American Theatres and Producers)

ACTIVITY

Population Projections for U.S. Cities

In this activity, you will create function models based on U.S. census data for one of the 100 largest cities in the United States.

From the latest census data available, select the *xy*th largest city, where *x* and *y* are the last two digits of your student identification number. This is your city. (For example, if your student ID number ends in 37, you should find the data for the 37th largest city in the United States. If your ID number ends in 00, choose the 100th largest city.) Record the populations for your city in 1950, 1960, 1970, 1980, and 1990.

1. Find the best-fitting linear model for your population data, using years after 1950 as the independent variable. Calculate the SSE for your model, and the average error in the approximation.

2. Find the best-fitting quadratic model for your population data, using the years given in question 1. Calculate the SSE for your model, and the average error in the approximation.

3. Find the best-fitting exponential model for your population data, using the years given in question 1. Calculate the SSE for your model, and the average error in the approximation.

4. On the basis of having the smallest average error, which model is the best predictor of your city's population? Use that model to predict your city's population in the year 2000.

5. Does your answer to question 4 seem to be reasonable? If the 2000 census data is available, check to see how close your prediction is to your city's actual 2000 population.

4

EXPONENTIAL AND LOGARITHMIC MODELS

In 1850 when Horace Greeley said, "Go West, young man," was he starting a trend or merely reporting one? From the beginning of this nation's history, there has been westward expansion. One way to measure this westward expansion is to consider the center of population of the United States. The center of population is determined by regarding the land mass of the United States as a weightless rigid plane—which would balance at that central point if each person were given equal weight and each person's influence on the central point were proportional to his or her distance from it.

The chart in Fig. 4.0.1 shows the westward location of the center of population (in degrees of west longitude). We can see that from 1830 to 1860, the center of population was moving west more rapidly than it was from 1860 to 1900. From 1900 to 1940, the center of population moved west even less rapidly. (From 1950 onward, Alaska and Hawaii are included in the calculation, so later years should be graphed separately.)

This pattern of growth is the opposite of what we observed with the natural growth functions of Chapter 3. Using the data of Fig. 3.0.1, we saw that the growth of the Internet was slow at first, but then increased more rapidly. We saw that this natural growth graph curved upward, while our center of population graph curves downward.

A quantity like the center of population that increases at a decreasing rate suggests a different kind of function to a mathematician, one that is, in some sense, the opposite of a natural growth function.

In this chapter we will study such functions and their relationship to exponential functions.

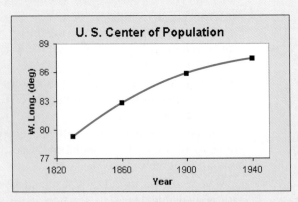

Figure 4.0.1   West longitude location (in degrees) of the U.S. center of population for the years 1830, 1860, 1900, and 1940.

Source: *The World Almanac and Book of Facts 1998.*

4.1   COMPOUND INTEREST AND EXPONENTIAL FUNCTIONS

In Section 3.1 we discussed the growth of the amount in an investment account that earns interest annually. If the amount initially invested is A_0 dollars and the annual interest rate is $r = p\%$, then the amount in the account is multiplied by the factor $(1 + r)$ each year. It follows that the amount A_t the account contains after t years is given by

$$A_t = A_0(1 + r)^t. \tag{1}$$

In particular, the amount in the account after *one* year is

$$A_1 = A_0(1 + r). \tag{2}$$

These formulas describe computations where interest is earned annually; that is, the current amount A in an account is updated *once* each year by the addition of rA in earned interest for the year.

Compounding Interest Semiannually

However, banks often update the amount in an account by the addition of earned interest more frequently than once per year—such as semiannually, quarterly, monthly, weekly, or even daily. This is called *compounding* of interest.

   If the interest period is less than a full year, then less interest is earned during that period. For instance, the interest earned in a half-year would be half the interest rA earned in a full year. If the initial amount is A_0, then the addition of the interest $\frac{1}{2}rA_0$ earned during the first half-year yields the amount

$$A = A_0 + \frac{1}{2}rA_0 = A_0\left(1 + \frac{r}{2}\right)$$

in the account after six months. Thus the addition of interest to an account after a half year corresponds to the multiplication of the amount by the factor $(1 + \frac{r}{2})$—rather than by the annual interest factor $(1 + r)$. At the end of the second half year, the current amount $A_0(1 + \frac{r}{2})$ in the account is again multiplied by the factor $(1 + \frac{r}{2})$. Hence the amount in the account after a full year is

$$A_1 = A_0\left(1 + \frac{r}{2}\right) \cdot \left(1 + \frac{r}{2}\right) = A_0\left(1 + \frac{r}{2}\right)^2. \tag{3}$$

So the addition of interest *twice* per year corresponds to multiplication by the factor $(1 + \frac{r}{2})^2$, the *square* of the factor $(1 + \frac{r}{2})$ corresponding to a single half-year interest period. In t years, the amount in the account is multiplied by this factor t times, that is, by

$$\left(1 + \frac{r}{2}\right)^2 \cdot \left(1 + \frac{r}{2}\right)^2 \cdot \cdots \cdot \left(1 + \frac{r}{2}\right)^2 = \left[\left(1 + \frac{r}{2}\right)^2\right]^t = \left(1 + \frac{r}{2}\right)^{2t}.$$

Consequently, the amount in the account after t years of interest paid semi-annually is

$$A_t = A_0\left(1 + \frac{r}{2}\right)^{2t}. \tag{4}$$

Compare this formula with formula (1). Whereas formula (1) describes the result of interest at the annual rate r, compounded annually, formula (4) describes the result of annual interest r **compounded semiannually.**

Example 1

Compare the results—after 1 year and after 10 years—when $1000 is invested

(a)   At 10% annual interest compounded annually;
(b)   At 10% annual interest compounded semiannually.

(a)   With annual compounding the amount after 1 year is

$$\$1000 \cdot (1 + 0.10) = \$1100,$$

and formula (1), with $r = 10\% = 0.10$ and $t = 10$, gives

$$\$1000 \cdot (1 + 0.10)^{10} = \$2593.74$$

for the amount after 10 years.
(b)   For semiannual compounding with $r = 0.10$ and $t = 1$, formula (3) gives

$$\$1000 \cdot (1 + 0.05)^2 = \$1102.50,$$

after a year if the interest is compounded semiannually. Then formula (4) with $r = 0.10$ and $t = 10$ gives

$$\$1000 \cdot (1 + 0.05)^{20} = \$2653.30$$

for the amount after 10 years.   ◼

Observe that compounding the interest semiannually makes our investment grow more quickly. Semiannual compounding yields $2.50 more than annual compounding in one year, but almost $60 more after 10 years.

Compounding Even More Frequently

Suppose now that interest is compounded quarterly—that is, four times rather than twice per year. Then the interest earned in a quarter would be one-fourth the interest rA earned in a full year. If the amount at the beginning of a quarter is A, then the addition of the interest $\frac{1}{4}rA$ at the end of the quarter yields the amount

$$A + \frac{1}{4}rA = A\left(1 + \frac{r}{4}\right).$$

Thus the amount in the account is multiplied by the factor $\left(1 + \frac{r}{4}\right)$ at the end of each quarter. This happens four times in a full year, so the amount in the account after one year is

$$A_1 = A_0\left(1 + \frac{r}{4}\right)^4. \tag{5}$$

So quarterly compounding of interest corresponds to multiplication of the amount in the account by $\left(1 + \frac{r}{4}\right)^4$ each year. In t years, the amount in the account is multiplied by this factor t times, that is, by

$$\left(1 + \frac{r}{4}\right)^4 \cdot \left(1 + \frac{r}{4}\right)^4 \cdot \,\cdots\, \cdot \left(1 + \frac{r}{4}\right)^4 = \left[\left(1 + \frac{r}{4}\right)^4\right]^t = \left(1 + \frac{r}{4}\right)^{4t}.$$

Consequently, the amount in an account after t years at annual interest rate r **compounded quarterly** is

$$A_t = A_0\left(1 + \frac{r}{4}\right)^{4t}. \tag{6}$$

Example 2

Now find the amount—after 1 year and after 10 years—in the account of Example 1 if the 10% annual interest is compounded quarterly.

With $A_0 = \$1000$ and $r = 0.10$, formula (5) gives

$$\$1000 \cdot (1 + 0.025)^4 = \$1103.81$$

for the amount after 1 year—\$1.31 more than the amount obtained by compounding semiannually. Formula (6), with $r = 10\% = 0.10$ and $t = 10$, gives

$$\$1000 \cdot (1 + 0.025)^{40} = \$2685.06$$

for the amount after 10 years—almost \$32 more than the amount gotten by compounding semiannually. ∎

The general case of compound interest corresponds to compounding $r\%$ interest n times at equal intervals during each year. Then the interest earned in each such interest period is $\frac{rA}{n}$. If the amount at the beginning of the period is A, then the addition of the interest $\frac{rA}{n}$ at the end of the period yields the amount

$$A + \frac{rA}{n} = A\left(1 + \frac{r}{n}\right).$$

Thus the amount in the account is multiplied by the factor $(1 + \frac{r}{n})$ at the end of each interest period. This happens n times in a full year, so the amount in the account after one year is

$$A_1 = A_0\left(1 + \frac{r}{n}\right)^n. \tag{7}$$

It follows that the amount in the account is multiplied by $(1 + \frac{r}{n})^n$ each year. In t years, the amount in the account is multiplied by this factor t times, that is, by

$$\left(1 + \frac{r}{n}\right)^n \cdot \left(1 + \frac{r}{n}\right)^n \cdots \left(1 + \frac{r}{n}\right)^n = \left[\left(1 + \frac{r}{n}\right)^n\right]^t = \left(1 + \frac{r}{n}\right)^{nt}.$$

Consequently, the amount in an account after t years at annual interest rate r **compounded n times annually** is

$$A_t = A_0\left(1 + \frac{r}{n}\right)^{nt}. \tag{8}$$

Observe that each of the previous (numbered) formulas in this section is a special case of formula (8). In particular,

- $n = 1$ gives the formula $A_t = A_0(1 + r)^t$ for interest compounded annually;
- $n = 2$ gives the formula $A_t = A_0(1 + \frac{r}{2})^{2t}$ for interest compounded semiannually; and
- $n = 4$ gives the formula $A_t = A_0(1 + \frac{r}{4})^{4t}$ for interest compounded quarterly.

Example 3

Finally, find the amount—after 1 year and after 10 years—in the account of Example 1 if the 10% annual interest is compounded monthly.

With $A_0 = \$1000$, $r = 0.10$, and $n = 12$, formula (7) gives

$$\$1000 \cdot \left(1 + \frac{0.10}{12}\right)^{12} = \$1104.71$$

for the amount after 1 year—90 cents more than the amount obtained by compounding quarterly. Formula (8), with $n = 12$ and $t = 10$, gives

$$\$1000 \cdot \left(1 + \frac{0.10}{12}\right)^{120} = \$2707.04$$

for the amount after 10 years—almost $22 more than the amount gotten by compounding quarterly. ◼

As Good As It Gets?

Examples 1 through 3 suggest that perhaps we can earn more and more on an investment by insisting that our interest be compounded more and more frequently. The natural question is, How good does it get? For simplicity of investigation, we assume 100% annual interest, so $r = 1$ in the following example.

Example 4

Suppose that the amount $A_0 = 1$ (one dollar) is invested in an account that draws 100% annual interest. Calculate the amount in this account after one year if interest is compounded

(a) monthly   **(d)** hourly
(b) weekly   **(e)** every minute
(c) daily   **(f)** every second

Solution   If we substitute $A_0 = 1$ and $t = 1$ (year) in (8), we find that the amount in the account after one year is given by

$$A_1 = \left(1 + \frac{1}{n}\right)^n \tag{9}$$

if n is the number of times interest is compounded during the year. We need only substitute

- $n = 12$ to compound interest monthly,
- $n = 52$ to compound weekly,
- $n = 365$ to compound daily,
- $n = 365 \times 24 = 8760$ to compound hourly,
- $n = 8760 \times 60 = 525,600$ to compound interest every minute, and
- $n = 525,600 \times 60 = 31,536,000$ to compound every second.

Figure 4.1.1 illustrates an efficient way to substitute these successive values of n into (9).

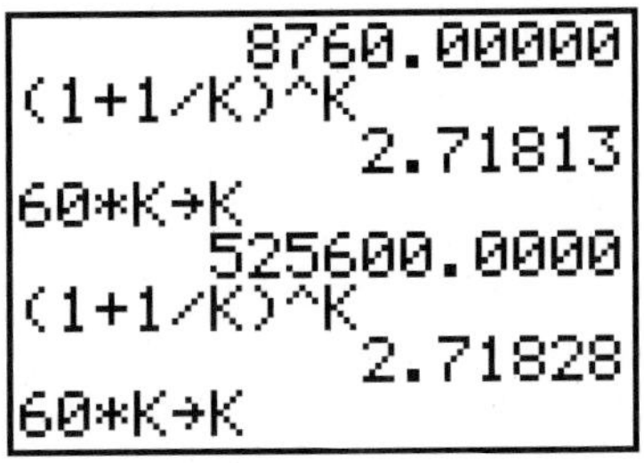

```
             8760.00000
(1+1/K)^K
                2.71813
60*K→K
            525600.0000
(1+1/K)^K
                2.71828
60*K→K
```

Figure 4.1.1   Compounding 100% interest more and more often.

The following table shows the results we obtain in this way.

100% Interest Compounded	Amount After One Year
Monthly	2.61304
Weekly	2.69260
Daily	2.71457
Hourly	2.71813
Each minute	2.71828
Each second	2.71828

In actual practice, of course, the amount in the account will be rounded to 2 decimal places, indicating dollars and cents.   ◣

Apparently we have crept up on a greatest possible "limiting value" of 2.71828 dollars. Indeed, this same 5-decimal-place value results if still larger values of n are used, corresponding to compounding even more than once per second. [However, a typical 9-place calculator encounters round-off error that causes inaccuracies in the 5-place result if values much larger than the 8-digit value $k = 31,536,000$ are substituted in (8).]

In this example, we have started with an investment of $1.00. Hence, if a bank compounds our 100% annual interest every hour, minute, or second—the table says that whichever of these it is makes no difference—then after one year our $1.00 initial investment has grown to $2.72. But if we'd instead invested $1000, then the figures in the second column of the preceding table would be multiplied by 1000. Thus, after one year we'd have $2718.13 if the bank had compounded our interest hourly, $2718.28 (15 cents more) if it had compounded each minute or second. But this is as good as it gets—starting with an investment of $1000, we can earn no more than $2718.28 in a year at 100% interest, even if the bank compounds interest ten (or a hundred, or a thousand) times per second.

Even though ordinary financial computations are unlikely to require such high accuracy, computers can calculate with (for example) 15-place accuracy the limiting value obtained by computing $(1 + \frac{1}{n})^n$ with larger and larger values of n. The result is the number

$$e = 2.7\ 1828\ 1828\ 45\ 90\ 45 \ldots \tag{10}$$

that is generally regarded as the most important special number in mathematics (even more important than the number $\pi = 3.14159\ 26\ 5358\ 9793 \ldots$). In summary, our numerical investigation indicates that

$$\left(1 + \frac{1}{n}\right)^n \approx e \approx 2.71828 \tag{11}$$

if n is sufficiently large.

We henceforth reserve the letter e to denote the number in (10), just as π is universally reserved to denote the famous number pi that we use in calculating areas and perimeters of circles. On a graphing calculator, the number e has its own key—typically the key beneath the π-key (as in Fig. 4.1.2).

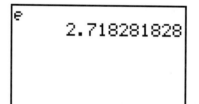

Figure 4.1.2   Pressing the [2nd] [÷] key on a TI-83 calculator yields the number e.

The number e, like π or $\sqrt{2}$, is known to be *irrational*—it cannot be expressed as a terminating or repeating decimal. But can you see how the spaces printed in (10) make it possible for almost anyone, even without a great memory, to remember the first 9 (or even 15) decimal places of e?

Continuously Compounded Interest

Banks sometimes advertise that they compound your interest not quarterly, not monthly or even daily, but *continuously*. The implication is that they thereby pay you "all the interest the law allows." What does this really mean?

As a practical matter it means compounding interest so frequently that compounding it still more frequently would yield no further return on our investment. As we saw in Example 4 and the subsequent discussion, this means that an annual interest rate of $r = 100\%$ would result in our original investment A_0 being multiplied by the special number e each year. According to Section 3.3, multiplication by the constant e each year corresponds to the exponential function with base e. Consequently, the function

$$A(t) = A_0 e^t \qquad (12)$$

gives the amount in the account after t years if 100% annual interest is compounded continuously.

The exponential function e^t in (12), with the special base e, is fundamental and is called **the natural exponential function.** It has its own key (usually denoted by e^x) on any scientific or graphing calculator.

Example 5

Suppose you invest $1000 at 100% interest compounded continuously. What will your account be worth after 5 years?

Substitution of $A_0 = 1000$ and $t = 5$ in (12) gives

$$A(5) = 1000 e^5$$

after 5 years. The e^x-key on our calculator gives the resulting amount $148,413.16 (Fig. 4.1.3). Amazing, but true! This is why nobody's ever going to offer you 100% annual interest compounded continuously. ◥

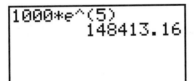

```
1000*e^(5)
          148413.16
```

Figure 4.1.3   Pressing the [e^x] key puts **e^(** on the screen, so we need only type [5][)] and press the [ENTER] key.

So how do we calculate the result of continuous compounding with a more realistic annual interest rate like $r = 6\%$? Suppose that in Example 4 we'd have invested our dollar at annual interest rate r (rather than $100\% = 1$). Then our first step in the solution would have been to write

$$A_1 = \left(1 + \frac{r}{n}\right)^n \qquad (13)$$

for the resulting amount after a year if this interest rate r is compounded n times annually. Since we have seen in (11) that $(1 + \frac{1}{n})^n \approx e$ if n is sufficiently large, it may be reasonable to guess that

$$\left(1 + \frac{r}{n}\right)^n \approx e^r \tag{14}$$

if n is sufficiently large.

Example 6

Verify (14) numerically with $n = 1$ million and $r = 0.1, 0.2, 0.3, \ldots, 1.9, 2.0$.

With x in place of r, we want to verify that

$$\left(1 + \frac{x}{1000000}\right)^{1000000} \approx e^x \tag{15}$$

for $x = 0.1, 0.2, 0.3, \ldots$. Figure 4.1.4 shows the left- and right-hand side functions in (15) defined on a graphing calculator. Figures 4.1.5 and 4.1.6 show the result of tabulating both functions. The agreement we see in these tables can hardly be coincidental. ◪

Plot1 Plot2 Plot3
\Y1=(1+X/1000000)^1000000
\Y2=e^(X)
\Y3=
\Y4=
\Y5=
\Y6=

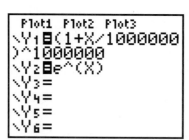

Figure 4.1.4 The functions in (15).

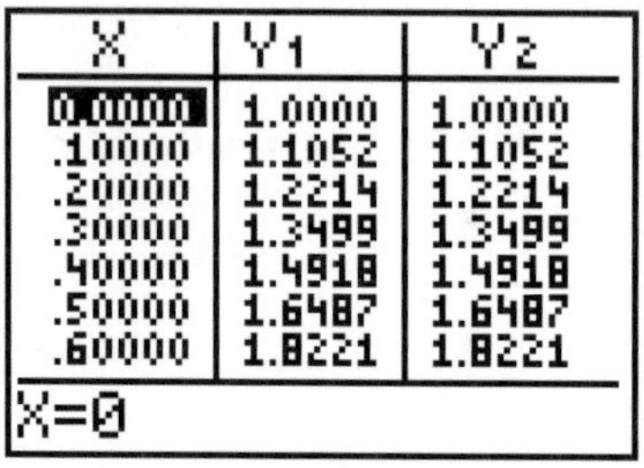
X | Y1 | Y2
0.00000 | 1.0000 | 1.0000
.10000 | 1.1052 | 1.1052
.20000 | 1.2214 | 1.2214
.30000 | 1.3499 | 1.3499
.40000 | 1.4918 | 1.4918
.50000 | 1.6487 | 1.6487
.60000 | 1.8221 | 1.8221
X=0

Figure 4.1.5 Resulting table with **TblStart=0 and ΔTbl=0.1**.

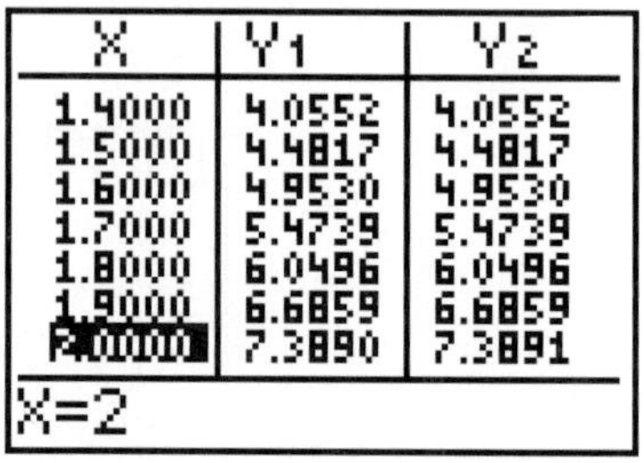
X | Y1 | Y2
1.4000 | 4.0552 | 4.0552
1.5000 | 4.4817 | 4.4817
1.6000 | 4.9530 | 4.9530
1.7000 | 5.4739 | 5.4739
1.8000 | 6.0496 | 6.0496
1.9000 | 6.6859 | 6.6859
2.0000 | 7.3890 | 7.3891
X=2

Figure 4.1.6 Further corroboration of (15).

Equation (14) implies that the 1 dollar grows to e^r dollars in 1 year at interest rate r compounded continuously. Thus a dollar is multiplied by the factor e^r each year, and hence by the factor

$$(e^r)^t = e^{rt}$$

in t years. The following principle tells what happens to an arbitrary initial investment of A_0 dollars.

Principle: **Continuously Compounded Interest**
If the initial amount A_0 is invested at annual interest rate r compounded continuously, then the resulting amount after t years is given by

$$A(t) = A_0 e^{rt}. \tag{16}$$

Thus the natural exponential function (with base e) is the key to all problems involving interest compounded continuously.

Example 7

Suppose you deposit $A_0 = 1000$ dollars in a savings account that draws 5% annual interest compounded continuously. Then Eq. (16) with $r = 0.05$ says that the amount in the account after t years is given by

$$A(t) = 1000 e^{0.05t}. \tag{17}$$

After 5 years this amount is $A(5) = 1000 e^{0.25} \approx 1284.03$ dollars. How much *longer* will you have to wait until you have \$1300 in the account?

In Example 1 of Section 3.2 we found that it takes 5.38 years $\approx$ 5 years, 20 weeks for \$1000 to grow to \$1300 when 5% interest is compounded annually. From (17) we see that we now need to solve the equation

$$1000 e^{0.05t} = 1300 \tag{18}$$

to see how long it takes if the interest is compounded continuously. Let's do this graphically. Figure 4.1.7 shows the graphs of the functions **Y1=1000*e^(0.05*X)** and **Y2=1300** that appear on the two sides of the equation in (18). Obviously, the rising curve is the graph of the exponential function on the left-hand side.

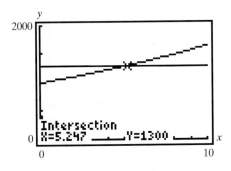

Figure 4.1.7   Solving Eq. (18).

We have already employed our calculator's automatic intersection-finding facility; it yields the solution $x \approx 5.25$. Thus it takes 5.25 years = 5 years, 13 weeks for our original investment to grow to \$1300. This is about 7 weeks less than the time required at 5% interest compounded annually. At any rate (answering the question posed), we must wait 13 weeks *more*—beyond the 5 years originally mentioned.   ◾

Effective Annual Yield

Suppose that you are offered two investment opportunities, one earning 9% interest compounded annually, the other earning 8.75% compounded monthly. How do you decide which of two investments will earn more money? The easiest way is to compute each investment's effective annual yield.

Definition: Effective Annual Yield
The **effective annual yield** for an investment is the percentage rate that would yield the same amount of interest if interest were compounded annually.

Example 8

Find the effective annual yield for an investment paying 8.75% compounded monthly.

According to our compound interest formula (8), after t years the investment will be worth

$$A_t = A_0\left(1 + \frac{0.0875}{12}\right)^{12t}. \tag{19}$$

Recall that the formula for annual compound interest is $A_t = A_0(1 + r)^t$, so in order to determine what annual interest rate r would yield the same interest, we need to rewrite our expression in (19).

$$A_t = A_0\left(1 + \frac{0.0875}{12}\right)^{12t}$$
$$= A_0\left[\left(1 + \frac{0.0875}{12}\right)^{12}\right]^t$$
$$\approx A_0(1 + 0.0911)^t$$

Thus, the effective annual yield for this investment is (approximately) 9.11%. ◼

Our earlier question was, "Which is better, 8.75% compounded monthly, or 9% compounded annually?" We can see, then, that 8.75% compounded monthly yields a bit more than 9% compounded annually, so the interest rate offered is not the whole story.

It is common to refer to the stated rate as the "nominal" rate. (*Nominal* comes from the Latin *nomen,* which means "name.") Note that since determining effective annual yield converts a nominal interest rate to an annual compound rate, the effective annual yield for 9% interest compounded annually is just 9%. In the case of annual compound interest, the nominal rate and the effective annual yield are the same.

Example 9

Determine which is the better investment, 4.75% compounded quarterly, or 4.5% compounded continuously.

In order to determine which investment is better, we will determine the effective annual yield for each.

First, 4.75% compounded quarterly:

$$A_t = A_0\left(1 + \frac{0.0475}{4}\right)^{4t}$$

$$= A_0\left[\left(1 + \frac{0.0475}{4}\right)^4\right]^t$$

$$\approx A_0(1 + 0.0484)^t$$

The effective annual yield is (approximately) 4.84%.

Second, 4.5% compounded continuously:

$$A_t = A_0 e^{0.045t}$$

$$= A_0(e^{0.045})^t$$

$$\approx A_0(1 + 0.0460)^t$$

The effective annual yield is (approximately) 4.60%.

So the better investment is the one with 4.75% interest compounded quarterly. ◨

In this case, the higher interest rate beats the more frequent compounding. When choosing among several different investments, it is important to be "comparing apples to apples." Once you obtain the effective annual yield for each, it is easy to see which offers the best return on your investment.

If you are borrowing money rather than investing it, the actual cost of financing, expressed as a yearly rate, is called the *annual percentage rate* or *APR*. In order for consumers to be able to compare different loans, lenders are required by the Federal Truth in Lending Act to report both the rate that is used to calculate monthly payments and the APR. In the case of a mortgage payment, the APR is generally higher than the advertised interest rate on the loan, because APR takes into account not only interest but also origination fees, points, mortgage insurance, and any other fees. When borrowing money, the lower the APR, the better the deal.

Continuous Growth and Decay

It is not just money that grows at a continuous compound rate. While the mathematical model $A(t) = 100e^{0.03t}$ could represent an investment of $100 that earns interest at an 3% compounded continuously, it could just as easily represent the population of a city of 100,000 people that is growing at a continuous annual rate of 3%, or the growth of a colony of 100 bacteria with a continuous hourly rate of 3%. The mathematics is the same. It is your job to pay attention to how the population is being measured (in thousands or hundreds or single units); to whether the continuous growth is being considered over years, days, or seconds; and to what you are measuring (dollars, people, or bacteria).

Definition: Continuous Growth with Rate r
If the growth of a quantity is described by the function $P(t) = P_0 e^{rt}$, then we say that it **grows continuously** and has **continuous growth rate r.**

In Chapter 3, we saw that the function model $P(t) = P_0(1 + r)^t$ represents **natural growth** if r is positive and **natural decay** if r is negative. Similarly, the function $P(t) = P_0 e^{rt}$ represents **continuous growth** if r is positive and **continuous decay** if r is negative.

Example 10

Carbon-14 is a radioactive substance found in plants, animals, and humans. At death the amount of carbon-14 begins to decrease at a continuous annual rate of (approximately) 0.012%. Determine the percentage of carbon-14 remaining in a mummy that is 5000 years old.

If we let $A_0 = 100$ represent the 100% of the carbon-14 that is present at death, then the percentage remaining after t years is given by

$$A(t) = 100e^{-0.00012t}.$$

After 5000 years, we have $A(5000) = 100e^{-0.00012 \times 5000} \approx 54.88$. Thus, about 55% of the original amount of carbon-14 remains. ◾

4 . 1
PROBLEMS

In Problems 1–6, calculate the amount in an account after t years if A_0 dollars is initially invested and interest at the annual rate r is compounded (a) quarterly, (b) monthly, (c) weekly, (d) daily, (e) continuously.

1. $A_0 = 1000,$ $r = 4\%,$ $t = 1$
2. $A_0 = 2000,$ $r = 8\%,$ $t = 1$
3. $A_0 = 3000,$ $r = 5\%,$ $t = 10$
4. $A_0 = 4000,$ $r = 10\%,$ $t = 5$
5. $A_0 = 5000,$ $r = 2\%,$ $t = 50$
6. $A_0 = 5000,$ $r = 1\%,$ $t = 100$

In Problems 7–10, find how long it takes an amount A_0 initially invested in an account to double in value (a) if interest at the indicated annual rate r is compounded annually, and (b) if this interest is compounded continuously. Calculate each answer both in years (rounded off to 3 decimal places) and in years and weeks (rounded off to the nearest week). (c) Note which answer is closer to the approximation suggested by the *rule of 72* (which says that the product of the time in years and the interest rate in percentage points is approximately 72).

7. $r = 18\%$
8. $r = 9\%$
9. $r = 6\%$
10. $r = 2\%$

In Problems 11–14, find the effective annual yield for each nominal interest rate.

11. 3.5% compounded monthly
12. 4% compounded semiannually
13. 3% compounded continuously
14. 3.75% compounded continuously
15. Which is the better investment—one earning 5% compounded quarterly, or one earning 4.65% compounded continuously?
16. Which is the better investment—one earning 4.5% compounded semiannually, or one earning 4.25% compounded continuously?

In Problems 17–20, solve graphically to find each solution (accurate rounded off to 4 decimal places) of the indicated equation.

17. $e^x = 10$

18. $e^x = 1000$ (What is the relation between the answers to Problems 17 and 18?)

19. $e^x = 2$

20. $e^x = 8$ (What is the relation between the answers to Problems 19 and 20?)

21. If you deposit $3000 in an account earning 3.75% compounded continuously, how long will it take for your money to grow to $10,000?

22. An archaeologist has discovered a mummy and determined that only 65% of the original amount of carbon-14 remains in the mummy. How old, to the nearest year, is the mummy? (Recall from Example 10 that the continuous rate of decay for carbon-14 is 0.012%.)

23. Under certain conditions, the *E. coli* bacteria grows at a continuous hourly rate of about 20%. If a colony of these bacteria initially contains 1000 bacteria, how many bacteria will be present in 6 hours? How long will it take the colony to grow to 5000 bacteria?

Problems 24 and 25 are numeric investigations of the fact that $(1 + \frac{r}{n})^n \approx e^r$ if n is sufficiently large.

24. Calculate the value of $(1 + \frac{2}{n})^n$ (rounded off accurate to 3 decimal places) with $n = 10, 100, 1000, \cdots, 1000000$. Does it appear that $(1 + \frac{2}{n})^n$ approaches the value of e^2 as n gets larger and larger?

25. Calculate the value of $(1 - \frac{1}{n})^n$ (rounded off accurate to 5 decimal places) with $n = 10, 100, 1000, \cdots, 1000000$. Does it appear that $(1 - \frac{1}{n})^n$ approaches the value of $e^{-1} = \frac{1}{e}$ as n gets larger and larger?

26. A credit card for college students advertises an annual percentage rate (APR) of 9.9%, with finance charges calculated using simple interest on the monthly balance. The minimum payment on the credit card is 3% of the outstanding balance or $10, whichever is greater—unless a balance of less than $10 remains, in which case your final payment equals this final balance plus the interest due on it. Now suppose that your credit card balance is $500 on January 1, 2001, and that you make only the minimum payment on the first of each month thereafter. If you make no further purchases on the card, when will you pay off the credit card? How much interest will you have paid over that time period? What continuous annual compound rate of interest will you have paid on this debt? (*Comment:* This problem is typical of real-world applications in that it requires somewhat more extended computations than the preceding problems. You can update your balance each month with a calculator iteration that adds the monthly interest to the preceding month's balance and subtracts your payment. It is also an interesting project to set up a spreadsheet showing columns of successive monthly payments, interest figures, and monthly balances.)

4.2   EXPONENTIAL AND LOGARITHMIC FUNCTIONS

In Section 4.1 we introduced the **natural exponential function** defined by

$$f(x) = e^x \tag{1}$$

using the very special base number $e \approx 2.71828$. In order to investigate this important function, let us recall the following *laws of exponents*.

THEOREM 1   Laws of Exponents with General Base a

If the base number a is positive and x and y are any real numbers, then

$$a^x a^y = a^{x+y} \tag{2}$$

$$a^{-x} = \frac{1}{a^x} \tag{3}$$

$$(a^x)^y = a^{xy}. \tag{4}$$

Also, recall that

$$a^0 = 1. \tag{5}$$

In case you don't remember *why* this is true, observe that

$$
\begin{aligned}
a^0 &= a^{1-1} \\
&= a^1 a^{-1} \quad \text{[using (2)]} \\
&= a \cdot \frac{1}{a} \quad \text{[using (3)]} \\
&= \frac{a}{a} \quad \text{(algebra)} \\
a^0 &= 1
\end{aligned}
$$

using in the final step the fact that division of any nonzero number by itself gives 1. Finally,

$$(ab)^x = a^x b^x \tag{6}$$

if b is a second positive base number.

Example 1

A typical simplification using the laws of exponents is

$$\frac{(2^2)^3 3^{-3}}{(2/3)^{-2}} = \frac{2^6 3^{-3}}{(2^1 3^{-1})^{-2}} = \frac{2^6 3^{-3}}{2^{-2} 3^2} = \frac{2^6 2^2}{3^2 3^3} = \frac{2^8}{3^5} = \frac{256}{243} \approx 1.0535. \qquad ∎$$

Example 2

You probably know that $a^{1/2} = \sqrt{a}$. But do you remember *why* this is so? It's because

$$(a^{1/2})^2 = a^{2 \cdot 1/2} = a^1 = a,$$

using (4). Then taking the square root of each side in $(a^{1/2})^2 = a$ yields $a^{1/2} = \sqrt{a}$. ∎

Example 3

You may (or may not) think it's obvious that $\sqrt{2} \cdot \sqrt{3} = \sqrt{6}$, as indicated in Fig. 4.2.1, where we started with $\sqrt{2} \approx 1.4142$. But it is the exponential law in (6) that implies that this is really so. With $a = 2$ and $b = 3$ we get

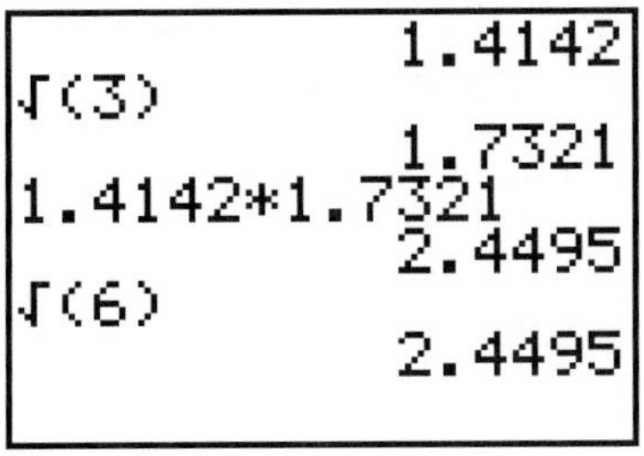

Figure 4.2.1   Checking numerically the fact that $\sqrt{2} \cdot \sqrt{3} = \sqrt{6}$.

$$\sqrt{2} \cdot \sqrt{3} = 2^{1/2}3^{1/2} = (2 \cdot 3)^{1/2} = 6^{1/2} = \sqrt{6}.$$ ◤

It's worthing restating the laws of exponents using the special number $e \approx 2.71828$ as the base a.

THEOREM 2   Laws of Exponents with Base e
If x and y are any real numbers, then

$$e^x e^y = e^{x+y} \tag{7}$$

$$e^{-x} = \frac{1}{e^x} \tag{8}$$

$$(e^x)^y = e^{xy} \tag{9}$$

$$e^0 = 1. \tag{10}$$

Example 4

A typical algebraic simplification using these laws is

$$\sqrt{e^{6x-1}} = (e^{6x-1})^{1/2} = e^{3x-1/2} = \frac{e^{3x}}{\sqrt{e}} \approx \frac{e^{3x}}{1.6487} \approx 0.6065e^{3x}.$$ ◤

Common Logarithms
You may have seen "common" or base 10 logarithms (if only briefly) in a previous mathematics course.

Definition: Common Logarithm
The **common logarithm** of the positive number x is the power to which 10 must be raised in order to obtain the number x. It is denoted by $\log_{10} x$. Thus

$$y = \log_{10} x \quad \text{means that} \quad 10^y = x. \tag{11}$$

Frequently we omit the subscript 10 and simply write $\log x$ for the common logarithm of the positive number x.

The definition of logarithms seems inherently confusing to almost everyone. Sometimes it helps to phrase it as a question. If we ask what is the common logarithm of x, we're asking what number to put in the "question mark" blank:

$$\log x = ? \quad \text{provided that} \quad 10^? = x. \tag{12}$$

This is not so hard to figure out if the given number x is an (integer) power of 10.

Example 5

Some applications of the definition in (11) and (12):

$$\log 100 = 2 \qquad \text{because} \qquad 10^2 = 100$$
$$\log 10{,}000 = 4 \qquad \text{because} \qquad 10^4 = 10{,}000$$
$$\log 10 = 1 \qquad \text{because} \qquad 10^1 = 10$$

$$\log 0.1 = -1 \qquad \text{because} \qquad 10^{-1} = \frac{1}{10} = 0.1$$

$$\log 0.001 = -3 \qquad \text{because} \qquad 10^{-3} = \frac{1}{10^3} = 0.001$$

We can see that in each case the logarithmic and exponential equations are just different versions of the same relationship. ◣

However, we need a calculator to find the value of $\log x$ if x is *not* an integer power of 10. The common logarithm key on a graphing calculator is the one marked ⃞LOG (what else?). However, it is important to realize that calculators use function notation, so the logarithm of x is denoted by **log(x)** with parentheses included. Figure 4.2.2 illustrates the use of a calculator to find some typical logarithms. When we press the log key, the calculator displays **log(** on the screen and waits for us to enter the **x)** with the value of x whose logarithm we want to find.

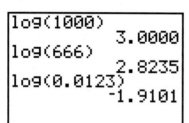

Figure 4.2.2 Some typical common logarithms.

Natural Logarithms

In college mathematics, it is customary to use "natural logarithms" instead of common logarithms. These natural logarithms are defined in a similar way, using powers of the base number $e \approx 2.71828$ rather than powers of the base number 10.

> **Definition: Natural Logarithm**
> The **natural logarithm** of the positive number x is the power to which e must be raised in order to obtain the number x. It is sometimes denoted by $\log_e x$, but more frequently by **ln x** (with l for "log" and n for "natural"). Thus
>
> $$y = \ln x \quad \text{means that} \quad e^y = x. \tag{13}$$

Again, it may help to put it in question mode. If we ask what is the natural logarithm of x, we're asking what number to put in the following "question mark" blank:

$$\ln x = ? \quad \text{provided that} \quad e^? = x. \tag{14}$$

Here, however, there are no really obvious values to anchor our understanding of natural logarithms.

Example 6

Suppose we ask what is the value of ln 10, the natural logarithm of 10. That is, to what power must e be raised in order to obtain 10? Using the $[e^x]$ key, our calculator gives (Fig. 4.2.3)

$$e \approx 2.71828, \quad e^2 \approx 7.38906, \quad e^3 \approx 20.08554.$$

```
e^(1)
            2.71828
e^(2)
            7.38906
e^(3)
            20.08554
```

Figure 4.2.3   Searching for ln 10.

Thus 10 is greater than e^2 but less than e^3, so we need to raise e to higher than the second power, but less than the third power. If our calculator had no $\boxed{\text{LN}}$ key, we could still solve the equation $e^x = 10$ numerically to find the proper exponent x to use. Figure 4.2.4 shows the graph **Y1=e^(X)** of the exponential function and the horizontal line **Y2=10**.

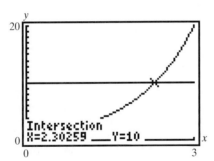

Figure 4.2.4   Finding the value ln 10 ≈ 2.30259.

As indicated, the calculator's intersection-finding facility gives $x \approx 2.30259$ for the x-coordinate of the point where $e^x = 10$. Thus

$$\ln 10 = 2.30259$$

rounded off accurate to 5 decimal places.   ◣

Figure 4.2.5 shows another graph illustrating Example 6. More generally, given a number y, the natural logarithm of y is the x-coordinate of the point $(\ln y, y)$ at height y on the graph $y = e^x$. Note, however, that this makes sense only if $y > 0$, because the curve $y = e^x$ lies entirely above the x-axis. It follows that

Only *positive* numbers have logarithms.

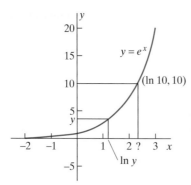

Figure 4.2.5 Finding natural logarithms graphically.

Example 7

Instead of solving graphically for natural logarithms as in Example 6, we can simply use our calculator's [LN] key as indicated in Fig. 4.2.6, where we see that

$$\ln 10 \approx 2.3026, \quad \ln 100 \approx 4.6052, \quad \ln 1000 \approx 6.9078.$$

Here we have deleted the calculator's parentheses—we write ln 10 where the calculator prints ln(10), and so forth.   ◼

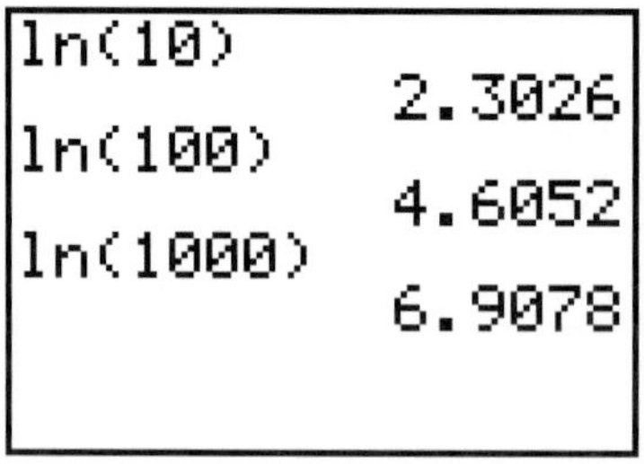

```
ln(10)
              2.3026
ln(100)
              4.6052
ln(1000)
              6.9078
```

Figure 4.2.6 Using the [LN] key to find logarithms.

Can you see that the logarithms in Example 7 fit a certain pattern? If we "chopped" each off to one decimal place—ln 10 ≈ 2.3, ln 100 ≈ 4.6, ln 1000 ≈ 6.9—it would be still more obvious that

$$\ln 100 = 2 \ln 10 \quad \text{and} \quad \ln 1000 = 3 \ln 10.$$

This observation illustrates the following laws for natural logarithms (analogous to the laws for common logarithms that you may have seen before).

THEOREM 3   **Laws of Logarithms**
If x and y are any positive real numbers, then

$$\ln xy = \ln x + \ln y \tag{15}$$

$$\ln \frac{1}{x} = -\ln x \tag{16}$$

$$\ln x^y = y \ln x \tag{17}$$

$$\ln 1 = 0. \tag{18}$$

Some people can learn these laws more readily in words than in symbols:

The logarithm of a product is the sum of the logarithms.
The logarithm of a reciprocal is the negative of the logarithm.
The logarithm of a power is the exponent times the logarithm of the base.
The logarithm of one is zero.

Analyze each statement carefully to make certain you see that it says the same thing as the corresponding symbolic law.

The laws of logarithms in Theorem 3 follow from the laws of exponents in Theorem 2. For instance, consider the last law of exponents, $e^0 = 1$. Thus the power to which e must be raised to obtain 1 is 0. This says that 0 is the natural logarithm of 1. Thus $\ln 1 = 0$, so we have deduced the last law of logarithms from the last law of exponents.

The fact that $\ln 1 = 0$ means that the graph $y = \ln x$ crosses the x-axis at the point $x = 1$, as indicated in Fig. 4.2.7.

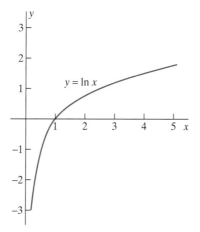

Figure 4.2.7   The graph of the natural logarithm function $\ln x$.

Visualizing this graph is a good way to remember that

- The logarithms of numbers *less than* 1 are **negative,** while
- The logarithms of numbers *greater than* 1 are **positive.**

Example 8

Some typical calculations using the laws of logarithms:

$$\ln 33 = \ln(3 \times 11) = \ln 3 + \ln 11 \approx 1.0986 + 2.3979 = 3.4965$$

$$\ln \frac{1}{66} = -\ln 66 \approx -4.1897$$

$$\ln \frac{29}{13} = \ln\left(29 \times \frac{1}{13}\right) = \ln 29 + \ln \frac{1}{13}$$

$$= \ln 29 - \ln 13 \approx 3.3673 - 2.5649 = 0.8024$$

$$\ln 125 = \ln 5^3 = 3 \ln 5 \approx 3 \times 1.6094 = 4.8282$$

You should verify that in each case the answer matches what you get by using your calculator to evaluate the natural logarithm of the given number.   ◥

Logarithms and Exponentials as Inverse Functions

The definition of the natural logarithm in Eq. (13) says that $e^y = x$ provided that $y = \ln x$. Substitution of the latter equation in the former gives

$$e^{\ln x} = x \tag{19}$$

if the number x is positive (so it *has* a logarithm). That is, if we start with x and apply the logarithm function to get $\ln x$, then use this result as the exponent of e, we get x back. Thus the natural exponential function undoes the result of the natural logarithm function. The reverse is true also—the logarithm function undoes similarly the result of the exponential function:

$$\ln(e^x) = x \tag{20}$$

for any number x.

Equations (19) and (20) say that if you start with x and apply both functions (exponential and logarithm) in succession—in either order—then you're back where you started, with the same number x. Figure 4.2.8 illustrates this fact, regarding each function as an input-output process. If the output of either function is used as the input to the other, the final output is the same as the original input.

Figure 4.2.8 e^x and $\ln x$ as inverse functions.

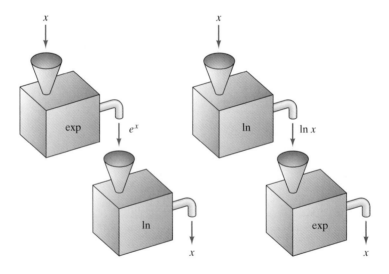

Example 9

Do symbolic expressions in x tend to make your eyes glaze over? If so, think concretely:

$$e^{\ln 2} = 2, \qquad\qquad e^{\ln 7654} = 7654$$
$$\ln(e^{37}) = 37, \qquad\qquad \ln(e^{\pi}) = \pi$$
$$e^{\ln(\text{CAT})} = \text{CAT}, \qquad\qquad \ln(e^{\text{DOG}}) = \text{DOG}.$$

The last line here may seem a bit whimsical, but—assuming that CAT and DOG denote positive numbers—it's just as true as the preceding two lines.   ◼

If f and g are two functions that undo each other either way, meaning that

$$f(g(x)) = x \quad \text{and} \quad g(f(x)) = x, \tag{21}$$

then f and g are called *inverse functions* of each other. Thus (19) and (20) say that the natural exponential and logarithm functions are inverse functions of each other.

Example 10

The concept of inverse functions may seem exotic initially, but there are many common and simple inverse-function pairs:

(a) If $f(x) = 2x$ and $g(x) = \frac{x}{2}$, then $f(g(x)) = 2(\frac{x}{2}) = x$ and $g(f(x)) = \frac{2x}{2} = x$. So the doubling and halving functions are inverses of each other.

(b) If $f(x) = 3x + 1$ and $g(x) = \frac{x-1}{3}$, then $f(g(x)) = 3(\frac{x-1}{3}) + 1 = x$ and $g(f(x)) = \frac{(3x+1)-1}{3} = x$.

(c) If $f(x) = x^3$ and $g(x) = \sqrt[3]{x}$, then $f(g(x)) = (\sqrt[3]{x})^3 = x$ and $g(f(x)) = \sqrt[3]{x^3} = x$. So the cube function and the cube root function are inverses of each other.

(d) If $f(x) = \frac{1}{x}$ and $g(x) = \frac{1}{x}$, then $f(g(x)) = \frac{1}{1/x} = x$ and $g(f(x)) = \frac{1}{1/x} = x$ (as long as $x \neq 0$). So the reciprocal function is its own inverse. ◼

Solving Exponential and Logarithmic Equations

The inverse function relations $e^{\ln x} = x$ and $\ln(e^x) = x$ admittedly have an abstract appearance. However, they are used mainly in very practical situations—in solving equations that involve exponentials and logarithms. We can use each of these two types of functions to "turn the other one inside out." The basic idea is to take natural logarithms of each side of an exponential equation and to "exponentiate" each side of a logarithmic equation.

Example 11

Solve the equation

$$e^{2x-3} = 100.$$

If we take natural logarithms of both sides, we get the equation

$$\ln(e^{2x-3}) = \ln 100.$$

Then the fact that $\ln(e^u) = u$ gives

$$2x - 3 = \ln 100$$

so

$$x = \frac{3 + \ln 100}{2} \approx \frac{3 + 4.6052}{2} = 3.8026. \qquad ◼$$

Example 12

Solve the equation

$$\ln(3x + 4) = 5.$$

Solution   To turn the left-hand side logarithm inside out, we exponentiate this equation—that is, take e to each side of the equation:

$$e^{\ln(3x+4)} = e^5.$$

The fact that $e^{\ln u} = u$ now gives

$$3x + 4 = e^5$$

so

$$x = \frac{e^5 - 4}{3} \approx \frac{148.4132 - 4}{3} \approx 48.1377. \qquad \blacksquare$$

Natural Growth Applications

We can now use exponentials and logarithms to find quick symbolic solutions of population problems that have previously required more time-consuming graphical methods. In Section 3.3 we saw that a natural growth function of the form

$$P(t) = P_0 \cdot b^{t/N} \tag{22}$$

describes a population that is multiplied by the factor b every N years. Now we will see that every natural growth function can be written in the standard form

$$P(t) = P_0 e^{rt}. \tag{23}$$

Example 13

Find the continuous annual growth rate of a population

(a)   of rabbits that doubles every year;

(b)   of people that triples every 25 years.

(a)   The fact that the rabbit population doubles in one year means that

$$P(1) = P_0 e^{r \cdot 1} = 2P_0.$$

Dividing by P_0, we therefore see that

$$e^r = 2,$$
$$\ln(e^r) = \ln 2 \quad \text{(taking logs of both sides),}$$
$$r = \ln 2 \approx 0.6931.$$

Thus its continuous annual growth rate is approximately $r = 0.6931$.

(b)   The fact that the human population triples every 25 years means that

$$P(25) = P_0 e^{r \cdot 25} = 3P_0.$$

Dividing by P_0, we therefore see that

$$e^{25r} = 3,$$
$$\ln(e^{25r}) = \ln 3 \quad \text{(taking logs of both sides),}$$
$$25r = \ln 3$$
$$r = \frac{\ln 3}{25} \approx 0.0439.$$

Thus its continuous annual growth rate is approximately $r = 0.0439$.   ◤

The population of Example 13(b) may be said to grow at the *continuous* annual percentage rate of 4.39%. This use of the word *continuous* is analogous to financial growth with an annual interest rate of 4.39% compounded *continuously*. But we know that this is not the same as 4.39% interest compounded annually. For instance, if the population grew by 4.39% each year, then its population after 25 years would be

$$P_0(1 + 0.0439)^{25} \approx 2.9273 P_0,$$

which is somewhat less than triple the original population.

Example 14

In 1993 the world population had reached 5.5 billion and had a continuous annual growth rate of $r = 0.0166$.

(a) If this growth continues, when will the world population reach 11 billion?
(b) When will the world population reach 50 billion, which some demographers regard as the maximum population for which the planet can provide food?

(a) The world's population is given (in billions, t years after 1993) by

$$P(t) = 5.5 e^{0.0166t}. \tag{24}$$

It will be 11 billion when

$$P(t) = 5.5 e^{0.0166} = 11$$

$$e^{0.0166t} = \frac{11}{5.5} = 2$$

$$\ln(e^{0.0166t}) = \ln 2$$

$$0.0166t = \ln 2$$

$$t = \frac{\ln 2}{0.0166} \approx 41.7559.$$

Thus the world population will reach 11 billion in about 41.76 years (after 1993), that is, in 2034 A.D.

(b) Using (24) similarly, the world population will be 50 billion when

$$P(t) = 5.5 e^{0.0166} = 50$$

$$e^{0.0166t} = \frac{50}{5.5}$$

$$\ln(e^{0.0166t}) = \ln \frac{50}{5.5}$$

$$t = \frac{\ln(50/5.5)}{0.0166} \approx 132.9684.$$

Thus the world population will reach 50 billion in about 132.97 years, that is, in 2125 A.D.   ◤

You might be interested to know that the technique for finding the best fitting exponential function utilizes the inverse relationship between exponential and logarithmic functions. If the original data set consisting of ordered pairs (x, y) is approximately exponential, then the transformed data set $(x, \ln y)$ is approximately linear. Least squares linear regression gives the best fitting linear model for the transformed data as $\ln y = a + bx$.

If we exponentiate both sides of this linear model equation, we get

$$y = e^{a+bx}.$$

Using the laws of exponents to simplify the right side gives

$$y = e^a \cdot e^{bx}.$$

Since a is a constant, e^a is also a constant. Letting $e^a = A$, we have the exponential model $y = A \cdot e^{bx}$ with which we are familiar.

4.2
PROBLEMS

In Problems 1 and 2, use the laws of exponents to simplify the expressions. Write each answer as a base raised to an integer power.

1. **(a)** $2^2 \cdot 2^3$ **(b)** $(2^2)^3$ **(c)** $2^{(2^3)}$
2. **(a)** $3^6 \cdot 3^{-5}$ **(b)** $(3^6)^{1/2}$ **(c)** $9^3 \cdot 3^{-6}$

In Problems 3 and 4, use the laws of exponents to simplify the expressions. Write each answer in the form ce^{kx+p}.

3. **(a)** $\sqrt{e^{4x+6}}$ **(b)** $\sqrt[3]{e^{9x+3}}$ **(c)** $\left(e^{50x+30}\right)^{1/10}$
4. **(a)** $\sqrt{4e^{8-6x}}$ **(b)** $\sqrt[3]{27e^{3-9x}}$ **(c)** $\left(2048e^{22-121x}\right)^{1/11}$

In Problems 5 and 6, use laws of logarithms to express each given natural logarithm in terms of just the three natural logarithms $\ln 2$, $\ln 3$, and $\ln 5$. Use the $\boxed{\text{LN}}$ key on your calculator to check each answer numerically.

5. **(a)** $\ln 6$ **(b)** $\ln 8$ **(c)** $\ln \frac{12}{25}$
6. **(a)** $\ln 15$ **(b)** $\ln 9$ **(c)** $\ln \frac{8}{27}$
7. Which is larger, $2^{(3^4)}$ or $(2^3)^4$?
8. Find (by inspection) two different positive integers such that $x^2 = 2^x$.

In Problems 9 and 10, use the method of Example 6 to find the indicated natural logarithms by solving graphically an equation of the form $e^x = k$ (where k is the number whose natural logarithm is sought).

9. **(a)** $\ln 25$ **(b)** $\ln 1000$
10. **(a)** $\ln \frac{1}{7}$ **(b)** $\ln \frac{3}{17}$

In Problems 11–14, find (by inspection) an inverse function $g(x)$ such that $f(g(x)) = g(f(x)) = x$.

11. $f(x) = 7x$
12. $f(x) = 7x - 5$
13. $f(x) = \sqrt{x+1}$
14. $f(x) = \frac{2}{x}$

Use natural logarithms and exponentials to solve the equations in Problems 15–23.

15. $2^x = 100$
16. $3^x = 70$
17. $5^{-x} = 17$

18. $10^{-2x} = 0.2$

19. $\ln(3x) = 5$

20. $\ln(10x) + 2 = 0$

21. $e^{3x-5} = \frac{1}{7}$

22. $\ln(3x - 5) = \frac{1}{7}$

23. $\ln(2e^{3x} + 4) = 5$

In Section 3.3 you were asked to solve the following applied problems graphically. Now use exponentials and logarithms to solve them.

24. How long does it take a naturally growing bacteria population to triple if it doubles in 1.5 hours?

25. The number of bacteria in a culture increased sixfold in 10 hours. Assuming natural growth, how long did it take their number to double?

26. Suppose a naturally growing rabbit population increases in 3.5 months from an initial population of 4 rabbits to 10 rabbits. How many rabbits will there be after 1 year (starting when there were 4 rabbits)?

27. Suppose a couple plans, upon the birth of their first child, to make a deposit in a savings account guaranteed to continue to pay 6% annual interest. How much should they deposit in order for the account to contain $25,000 when the child is ready to begin college at age 18?

28. A naturally growing bacteria population $P(t)$ numbers 49 at 12 noon.

(a) Write a formula giving $P(t)$ after t hours if there are 294 bacteria at 1 P.M.

(b) How many bacteria are there at 1:40 P.M.?

(c) At what clock time (nearest minute) that afternoon are there 20 thousand bacteria?

29. The English language evolves naturally in such a way that 77% of all words disappear (or are replaced) every 1000 years. Of a basic list of words used by Chaucer in 1400 A.D., what percentage should we expect to find still in use today?

30. The amount $A(t)$ of atmospheric pollutants in a certain mountain valley grows naturally and is tripling every 7.5 years.

(a) If the initial amount is 10 pu (pollutant units), write a formula for $A(t)$ giving the amount (in pu) present after t years.

(b) What will be the amount (in pu) of pollutants present in the valley atmosphere after 5 years?

(c) If it will be dangerous to stay in the valley when the amount of pollutants reaches 100 pu, how long will this take?

31. An accident at a nuclear power plant has left the surrounding area polluted with radioactive material that decays naturally. The initial amount of radioactive material present is 15 su (safe units), and 5 months later it is still 10 su.

(a) Write a formula giving the amount $A(t)$ of radioactive material (in su) remaining after t months.

(b) What amount of radioactive material will remain after 8 months?

(c) How long (in total number of months or fraction thereof) will it be until $A = 1$ su, so it is safe for people to return to the area?

32. (a) In 1979 the typical microcomputer contained 29 thousand transistors. Assuming continuous growth at the annual rate r, write a formula giving the number of transistors in a typical micro t years later.

(b) In 1993 the typical microcomputer CPU contained 3.1 million transistors. Find the annual growth rate r in part (a), expressed as a percentage.

(c) At this rate, how many months does it take to double the number of transistors in a typical micro?

(d) Assuming this annual rate of increase continues, how many transistors (rounded off accurate to the nearest million) will the typical micro contain in the year 2001?

33. There are now about 3300 different human language families in the whole world. Assume that all these are derived from a single original language, and that a language family develops into 1.5 language families every 6 thousand years. About how long ago was the single original human language spoken?

34. Thousands of years ago ancestors of the American Indians crossed the Bering Strait from Asia and entered the western hemisphere. Since then, they have fanned out across North and South America. The single language that the original Indian settlers spoke has since split into many Indian language families. Assume (as in Problem 33) that the number of these language families has been multiplied by 1.5 every 6000 years. There are now 150 Indian language families in the Americas. About when did the first American Indians arrive?

35. In 1998 there were 40 million internet users in the world, and this number was doubling every 100 days. Assuming that this rate of growth continued, how long will it be until all the world's 6 billion human beings are using the internet?

4.3   EXPONENTIAL AND LOGARITHMIC DATA MODELING

In Section 3.4 we analyzed the data in the following table, which shows the U.S. population as recorded during the first six census counts—in the decade years 1790, 1800, 1810, 1820, 1830, and 1840.

t	Year	U.S. Census Population (millions)	Change
0	1790	3.9	
10	1800	5.3	1.4
20	1810	7.2	1.9
30	1820	9.6	2.4
40	1830	12.9	3.3
50	1840	17.1	4.2

Noting the steadily increasing change figures in the final column, we proceeded to fit the recorded data with a **natural growth model** of the form

$$P(t) = a \cdot b^t \tag{1}$$

that will have a better chance (than a linear or quadratic model) of keeping up with the actual population growth that was observed. Now that we know about natural exponentials and logarithms, we can substitute $b = e^{\ln b}$ in (1) and write

$$P(t) = a \cdot (e^{\ln b})^t = a \cdot e^{(\ln b)t}. \tag{2}$$

Thus the natural growth model in (1) is equivalent to the continuous growth model

$$P(t) = a \cdot e^{rt} \tag{3}$$

with growth rate $r = \ln b$. Both the natural growth model (1) and the continuous growth model (3) are referred to as **exponential models,** since the independent variable t appears as the exponent in the algebraic rule for the function.

    We therefore want to revisit here some of the examples in Section 3.4, but from the viewpoint of the continuous growth model in (3). However, we will see that when we fit data with a graphing calculator, we will need to use first the calculator's **ExpReg** feature to find an exponential model of the form in (1), and then use the natural logarithm as in (2) to obtain a final exponential model of the form in (3).

Example 1

In Example 2 of Section 3.4, we compared the U.S. census figures in the preceding table with those predicted by the model

$$P(t) = 3.9 \times 1.030^t, \tag{4}$$

which corresponds to natural growth with a 3% increase each year. If we now write

$$r = \ln(1.030) \approx 0.0296, \quad \text{so } 1.030 \approx e^{0.0296},$$

then (4) can be rewritten in the exponential growth form

$$P(t) = 3.9 \cdot e^{0.0296t}. \tag{5}$$

Thus an increase of 3% annually corresponds to exponential growth with continuous annual growth rate $r = 0.0296$ (rather than the $r = 0.0300$ that might be your first guess). The following table compares the actual population figures with those predicted by this exponential growth model with annual growth rate $r = 0.0296$.

t	Act. Pop.	$P(t) = 3.9 \cdot e^{0.0296t}$	Error E	E^2
0	3.9	3.90	0.00	0.0000
10	5.3	5.24	0.06	0.0036
20	7.2	7.04	0.16	0.0256
30	9.6	9.47	0.13	0.0169
40	12.9	12.72	0.18	0.0324
50	17.1	17.10	0.00	0.0000

    To review the concepts of *sum of squares of errors* and *average error,* note that the sum of the squares of the errors shown in the table is

$$\text{SSE} = 0.0000 + 0.0036 + 0.0256 + 0.0169 + 0.0324 + 0.0000 = 0.0785.$$

There being $n = 6$ data points, the average error in the optimal model is therefore given by

$$\text{average error} = \sqrt{\frac{\text{SSE}}{n}} = \sqrt{\frac{0.0785}{6}} = \sqrt{0.0131} \approx 0.1144.$$

Thus the average discrepancy between the actual census population and the population predicted by the exponential model in (5) is about 0.114 million, or 114 thousand persons.

The Best Exponential Fit

For best fitting, the question is this: What choice of the numerical parameters a and r in the exponential growth model $P(t) = a \cdot e^{rt}$ will minimize the average error

$$\text{average error} = \sqrt{\frac{\text{SSE}}{n}} \tag{6}$$

(where SSE denotes the sum of squares of errors and n is the number of data points)? That is, what values of these two parameters a and r will provide the exponential growth model with the least possible average error? This optimal exponential growth model will be the one that we say best fits the given data.

We now recall briefly how we found the best *natural growth* fit in Section 3.4. Figure 4.3.1 shows the 1790–1840 U.S. population data entered in our graphing calculator. The t-values 0, 10, 20, 30, 40, 50 corresponding to the decade years from 1790 to 1840 are stored as a list **L1**, and the corresponding list of census population figures is stored as a list **L2**. Figure 4.3.2 shows the resulting **STAT EDIT** menu displaying the data in table form.

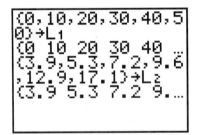

Figure 4.3.1   Storing the 1790–1840 U.S. census data.

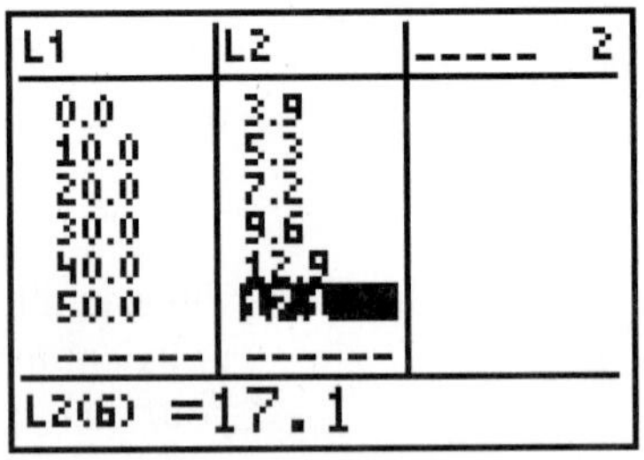

Figure 4.3.2   TI-83 **STAT EDIT** screen showing the U.S. population data in table form.

Figure 4.3.3 shows the calculator's **STAT CALC** menu. When we select item **0** on this menu, the **ExpReg** function is entered on the home calculating screen. As shown in Fig. 4.3.4, we then enter the names of our list **L1** of **X**-coordinates, our list **L2** of **Y**-coordinates, and the name **Y1** of the **Y=** menu variable where we want the resulting natural growth formula saved.

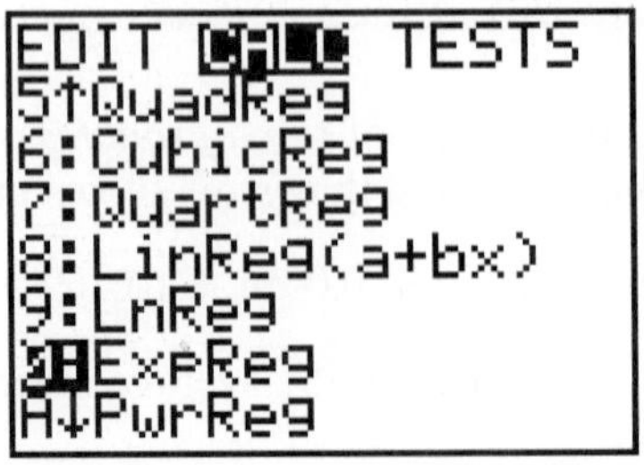

```
EDIT CALC TESTS
5↑QuadReg
6:CubicReg
7:QuartReg
8:LinReg(a+bx)
9:LnReg
0:ExpReg
A↓PwrReg
```

```
ExpReg L₁,L₂,Y₁
```

Figure 4.3.3   The TI-83 **STAT CALC** menu.

Figure 4.3.4   Fitting the **X**-data in list **L1** and the **Y**-data in list **L2**.

Figure 4.3.5 shows the display that results when this command is entered. The displayed results say that the natural growth curve best fitting the given data is

$$y = 3.9396 \times 1.0300^x. \tag{7}$$

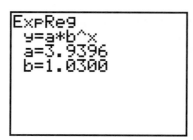

Figure 4.3.5   The optimal natural growth function.

In terms of time t and population P rather than the calculator's variables x and y, this result says that the natural growth function best fitting the actual 1790–1840 U.S. population growth is given by

$$P(t) = 3.9396 \times 1.0300^t. \tag{8}$$

Finally, we convert this natural growth model to an exponential growth model. We substitute $1.0300 = e^{\ln 1.0300} \approx e^{0.029559}$ just as in Example 1—except that we now retain a couple more decimal places for greater accuracy. The result is the exponential growth model

$$P(t) = 3.9396 \cdot e^{0.029559t}. \tag{9}$$

Observe that this optimal population function corresponds to a population that grows exponentially with the same continuous annual growth rate of $r = \ln 1.0300 \approx 0.029559$ as in Example 1, but starting with an initial population of 3.9396 million when $t = 0$. Note also that this best-fitting initial population, about 3.94 million, is different from the actual initial population of 3.9 million (perhaps rounded off). So when we attempt to best fit a given list of population data, we are free to adjust both the initial population and the rate of growth in order to fit the data as closely as possible.

Figure 4.3.6 shows the exponential growth model (9) entered in the **Y=** menu. With **Plot 1** turned **On** in the **STAT PLOT** menu, **GRAPH** then gives the plot of the best-fitting exponential growth curve shown in Fig. 4.3.7, where the original census data points are shown as small squares.

Figure 4.3.6   The best-fitting exponential growth function ready to plot or tabulate.

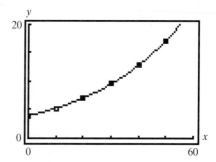

Figure 4.3.7   The optimal exponential growth fit.

Here we are less interested in the graph than in a table of values that we can use to compute the average error in our optimal fit. Our calculator now provides the table of (rounded off) values of **Y1=3.9396*e^(0.029559*X)** shown in Fig. 4.3.8.

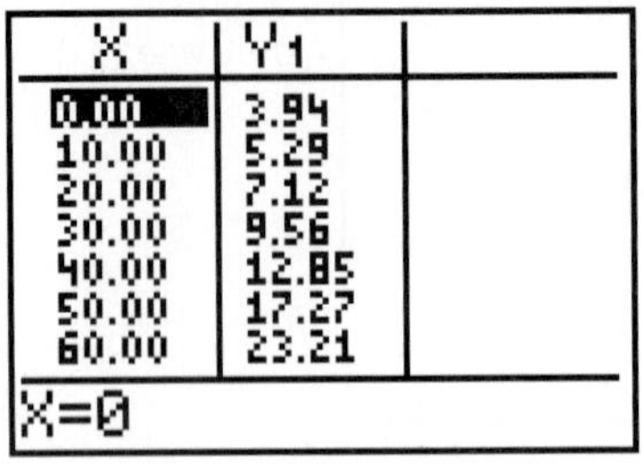

X	Y1	
0.00	3.94	
10.00	5.29	
20.00	7.12	
30.00	9.56	
40.00	12.85	
50.00	17.27	
60.00	23.21	
X=0		

Figure 4.3.8 Values of the optimal exponential growth function $P(t) = 3.9396 \times e^{0.029559t}$.

When we combine these values with our original U.S. population data, we get the following table. It compares the original census data with the population figures predicted by the optimal exponential growth model $P(t) = 3.9396 \cdot e^{0.029559t}$.

t	Act. Pop.	$P(t) = 3.9396 \cdot e^{0.029559t}$	Error E	E^2
0	3.9	3.94	−0.04	0.0016
10	5.3	5.29	0.01	0.0001
20	7.2	7.12	0.08	0.0064
30	9.6	9.56	0.04	0.0016
40	12.9	12.85	0.05	0.0025
50	17.1	17.27	−0.17	0.0289

Example 2

As usual, the final column shows the *squares* of the errors. Hence the SSE associated with the optimal exponential model in (9) is

$$SSE = 0.0016 + 0.0001 + 0.0064 + 0.0016 + 0.0025 + 0.0289 = 0.0411.$$

There being $n = 6$ data points, the average error in the optimal model is therefore given by

$$\text{average error} = \sqrt{\frac{SSE}{n}} = \sqrt{\frac{0.0411}{6}} = \sqrt{0.0069} \approx 0.0828. \qquad (10)$$

Thus the average discrepancy between the actual census population and the population predicted by the exponential model in (9) is about 0.083 million, or 83 thousand persons. ◼

The average error of 83 thousand in the best-fitting exponential model is less than the average error—found in Example 1—of 114 thousand in our original exponential growth model $P(t) = 3.9 \cdot e^{0.0296t}$. This latter model is based on the actual 1790 initial U.S. population of 3.9 million, rather than on the (hypothetical) initial population of 3.9396 million that we see in (9).

Applications of Exponential Models

If $a > 0$ and $r > 0$, then the exponential function

$$P(t) = a \cdot e^{rt} \tag{11}$$

with *positive* exponent (for t positive) describes a population P that starts with initial value $P(0) = a$ and thereafter *grows* at a steadily *increasing* rate (being multiplied by the factor $b = e^r > 1$ during each unit of time). The graph of any such **exponential growth function** looks generally like the graph $y = e^{2t}$ (with $a = 1$ and $r = 2$) shown in Fig. 4.3.9, and *rises* with *increasing* steepness (from left to right).

However, if $r < 0$, then the exponential function

$$P(t) = a \cdot e^{rt} \tag{12}$$

with *negative* exponent (for t positive) describes a population P that starts with initial value $P(0) = a$ and thereafter *declines* (or *decays*) at a steadily *decreasing* rate (being multiplied by the factor $b = e^r < 1$ during each unit of time). The graph of any such **exponential decay function** looks generally like the graph $y = 3e^{-t/2}$ (with $a = 3$ and $r = -\frac{1}{2}$) shown in Fig. 4.3.10, and *falls* with *decreasing* steepness (from left to right).

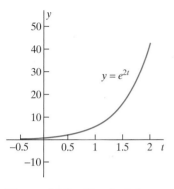

Figure 4.3.9 Graph of the exponential growth function $f(t) = e^{2t}$.

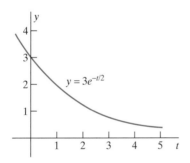

Figure 4.3.10 Graph of the exponential decay function $f(t) = e^{-t/2}$.

Just as in Sections 3.3 and 3.4, we can discuss the continuous growth and decline of quantities other than populations. The world is full of quantities that appear either to grow at a steadily increasing rate, or to decline at a steadily decreasing rate. Any such quantity is fair game for modeling by an exponential function as in (11) or (12).

Definition: Exponential Model

An **exponential model** is one of the form $f(t) = a \cdot e^{rt}$ that describes either

- An exponentially growing quantity (if r is positive), or
- An exponentially declining quantity (if r is negative).

For example, suppose a hot object with initial temperature T_0 is placed in a relatively cool medium with constant temperature A. Thus we might put a hot cake (just out of the oven) in a cool room with air temperature A, or we might put a hot rock in a large water tank with water temperature A. Then recall from Section 3.4 that **Newton's law of cooling** says that the (positive) difference

$$u(t) = T(t) - A \tag{13}$$

between A and the temperature $T(t)$ of the object at time t is a naturally declining quantity. That is,

$$u(t) = a \cdot b^t \tag{14}$$

with appropriate values of the positive parameters a and $b < 1$. We can now rewrite this in the (natural) exponential form

$$u(t) = a \cdot e^{rt} \tag{15}$$

where $r = \ln b < 0$ (because $b < 1$).

The *heating* of an initially cooler body in a warmer medium at temperature A is similar, except we write [instead of (13)] the difference

$$u(t) = A - T(t) \tag{16}$$

(the other way around), so that we're still considering a positive quantity. Then **Newton's law of heating** says that this temperature difference $u(t)$ is—just as in the case of cooling—an exponentially decreasing quantity of the same form as in (15). We use either (13) and (16) depending on whether the body is being cooled or heated.

You should not attempt to memorize the fact that (13) corresponds to cooling and (16) corresponds to heating. The easier way to remember the difference is this—that in either case $u(t)$ is the **positive** difference between the body's temperature $T(t)$ and the constant temperature A of the surrounding medium.

In the case of a roast being cooked in an oven, for instance, we might measure its rising temperature several times with a thermometer, and then attempt to fit the resulting data with the exponential function (15), in order to predict when the roast will be done—that is, hot enough to serve.

Example 3

Suppose a 5-pound roast initially at 50° (Fahrenheit) is placed in a 375° oven at 5 P.M. The temperature of the roast is measured every 15 minutes for the first hour, with the following results.

Time	5:00 P.M.	5:15 P.M.	5:30 P.M.	5:45 P.M.	6:00 P.M.
Temp	50°	67°	82°	96°	110°

When will the roast be 150° and hence ready to serve (medium rare)?

To use Newton's law we must replace the roast temperature T with the difference $u = 375 - T$ that we see in Eq. (16), since the oven temperature is $A = 375°$. Measuring time t in hours after 5:00 and subtracting each temperature entry from 375, the given data takes the form

t	0	0.25	0.5	0.75	1
u	325	308	293	279	265

If we can fit this data with an exponential model $u(t) = a \cdot e^{rt}$, then we should be able to find when the roast will be ready. Since $u(t) = 375 - T(t)$, the temperature of the roast is given by $T(t) = 375 - u(t)$. If we want to serve the roast when it reaches 150°, then we need to solve the equation $375 - u(t) = 150$.

We begin by entering the list of t-values as a calculator list **L1** and the list of u-values as a list **L2** (Fig. 4.3.11). Then the **STAT CALC** command **ExpReg L1, L2,Y1** produces the result shown in Fig. 4.3.12, which describes the best-fitting exponential function

$$u(t) = 324.545 \times 0.816^t \tag{17}$$

(upon replacing **X** with t and **Y** with u).

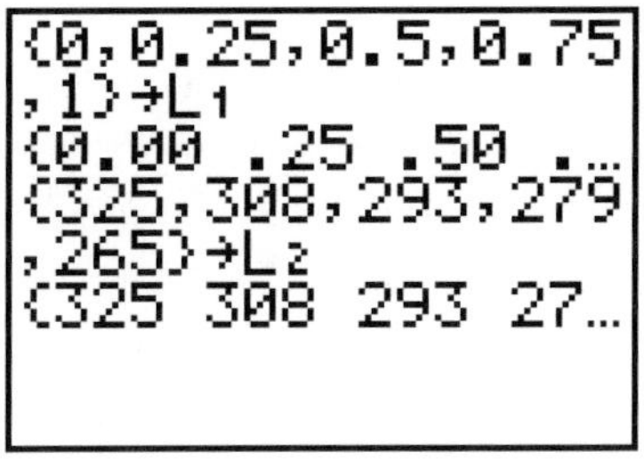

```
{0,0.25,0.5,0.75
,1}→L₁
{0.00 .25 .50 .⋯
{325,308,293,279
,265}→L₂
{325 308 293 27⋯
```

```
ExpReg
y=a*b^x
a=324.545
b=.816
```

Figure 4.3.11   The lists of t- and u-values in Example 3.

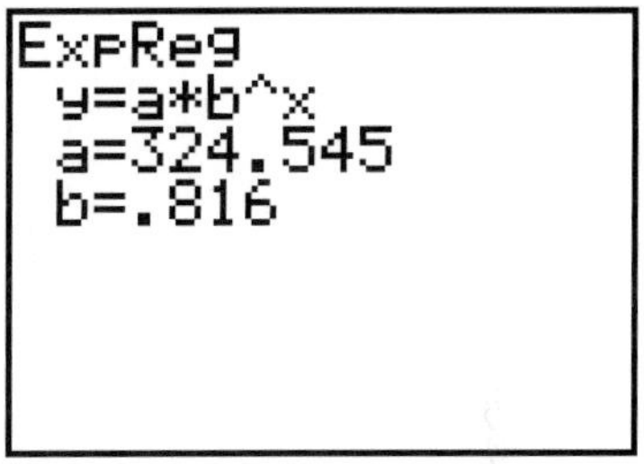

Figure 4.3.12   The best-fitting exponential function $u(t) = 324.545 \times 0.816^t = 324.545e^{-0.203t}$.

Because $\ln 0.816 = -0.203$, this is the same as

$$u(t) = 324.545e^{-0.203t}. \tag{18}$$

Finally, remembering Eq. (17), we subtract $u(t)$ from 375 to obtain the roast's temperature function

$$T(t) = 375 - 324.545e^{-0.203t}. \tag{19}$$

It's always important to keep your eye on the roast (ready to pounce when it's ready). Here, literally *no one* cares what is the average error in the optimal fitting function (21). The only question is when it's ready to eat, that is, when

$$375 - 324.545e^{-0.203t} = 150. \tag{20}$$

So we proceed to solve as follows:

$$324.545e^{-0.203t} = 375 - 150 = 225$$
$$e^{-0.203t} = \frac{225}{324.545}$$
$$-0.203t = \ln \frac{225}{324.545} \quad \text{(taking ln of both sides)}$$
$$t = -\frac{1}{0.203} \ln \frac{225}{324.545} \approx 1.805.$$

So it takes 1.805 hours, or about 1 hour and 48 minutes, for the roast to get done, starting at 5 P.M. So we can take it out of the oven and slice it at about 6:48 P.M. ◼

Fitting Logarithmic Models to Data

Figure 4.3.13 shows both the exponential graph $y = e^x$ and the logarithmic graph $y = \ln x$. Both curves rise (from left to right), so both the exponential function and the logarithmic function increase in value as x increases.

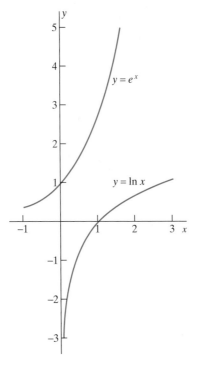

Figure 4.3.13   Logarithmic versus exponential growth.

But the *rates* at which they increase are very different. The exponential graph bends upward and rises ever more steeply, so the exponential function increases more and more *rapidly* as x increases. By contrast, the logarithmic graph bends downward—in the sense that it gets flatter and flatter—so the logarithmic function increases more and more *slowly* as x increases. This contrast often is summarized by saying that

- the exponential function e^x is a rapidly increasing function of x, whereas
- the logarithmic function $\ln x$ is a slowly increasing function of x.

If we have a table of values of either an exponential function or a logarithmic function, we therefore can recognize which it is by looking at the successive differences of the values of the function:

- Differences that are getting larger and larger suggest an exponential function, whereas
- Differences that are getting smaller and smaller suggest a logarithmic function.

If a logarithmic fit is indicated, we can use our calculator's **LnReg** (**l**ogarithmic **reg**ression) command, as illustrated in part (b) of the following example.

Example 4

(a)   Look at the table of values of the function $y = f(x)$.

x	y	change
1	9.74	
2	18.97	9.23
3	36.95	17.98
4	71.96	35.01
5	140.16	68.20
6	272.99	132.83
7	531.71	258.72

You should notice that the y-values almost double from one to the next, as do the changes recorded in the third column. This is a tip-off that we're looking at a table of values of an exponential function. Indeed, the second column consists of 2-decimal place values of the function $y = 5e^{2x/3}$. If you were not told this fact, it would be reasonable to apply the calculator **ExpReg** function (as earlier in this section) to fit the given xy-data. To check this, first enter the data in lists as indicated in Fig. 4.3.14. Then the command **ExpReg L1, L2** should give the result shown in Fig. 4.3.15. Thus

$$y = 5 \times 1.95^x = 5 \cdot e^{(\ln 1.95)x} = 5e^{0.67x},$$

consistent with our claim that $y = 5e^{2x/3}$.

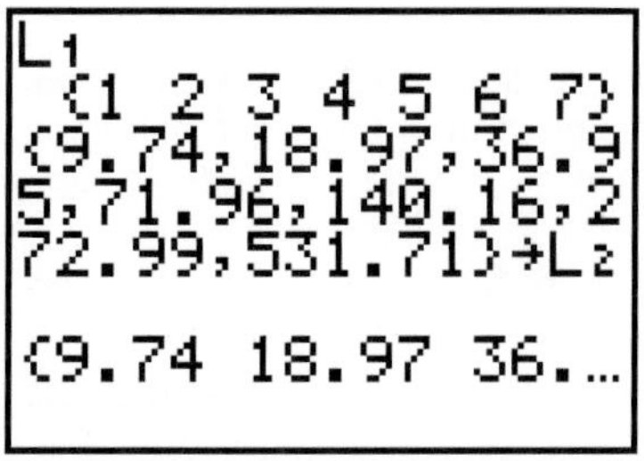

```
L1
 {1 2 3 4 5 6 7}
{9.74,18.97,36.9
5,71.96,140.16,2
72.99,531.71}→L2

{9.74 18.97 36.…
```

```
ExpReg
y=a*b^x
a=5.00
b=1.95
```

Figure 4.3.14   The data of Example 4(a).

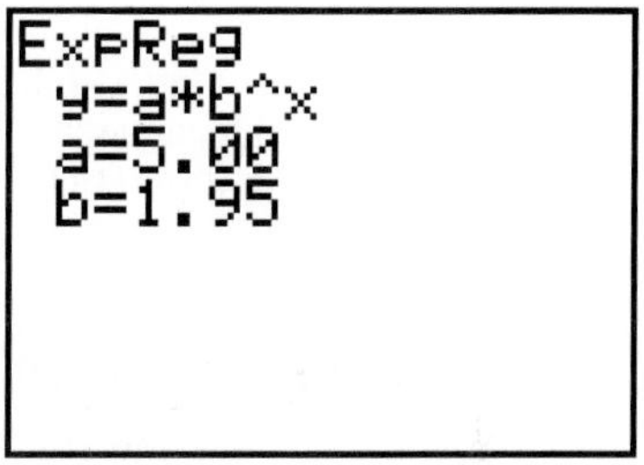

Figure 4.3.15   The exponential function of Example 4(a).

(b)   Look at the table of values of the function $y = f(x)$.

x	y	change
100	18.82	
200	20.89	2.07
300	22.11	1.22
400	22.97	0.86
500	23.64	0.67
600	24.19	0.55
700	24.65	0.46
800	25.05	0.40
900	25.41	0.36

You should notice that the y-values are increasing more and more slowly, perhaps as though they're leveling off. However, the changes recorded in the third column are decreasing more and more slowly. This is a tip-off that we're looking at a table of values of a logarithmic function. Indeed, the second column consists of 2-decimal place values of the function $y = 5 + 3 \ln x$. If you were not told this fact, it would be reasonable to apply the calculator **LnReg** function (Fig. 4.3.16) to fit the given xy-data with a function of the form

$$f(x) = a + b \ln x. \tag{21}$$

To check this, first enter the data in lists **L1** and **L2** as usual. Then the command **LnReg L1, L2** should give the result shown in Fig. 4.3.17. Thus

$$y = 5.01 + 3.00 \ln x,$$

consistent with our claim that $y = 5 + 3 \ln x$ (with slight round-off error in the a-coefficient). ◣

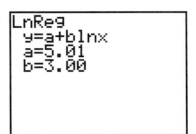

Figure 4.3.16   The **LnReg L1, L2** command fits a function of the form $f(x) = a + b \ln x$.

Figure 4.3.17   The logarithmic function of Example 4(b).

Example 5

When your blood pressure is measured, you receive a result of the form 122/74 (which lies in the normal range for healthy adults). The larger of the two numbers is your *systolic* blood pressure, recorded in millimeters of mercury. The systolic blood pressure p of a healthy child is lower than that of an adult and is known to be essentially of the form

$$p = a + b \ln w, \tag{22}$$

where w is the child's weight in pounds. Use the experimental data

w	41	67	78	93	125
p	89	100	103	107	110

to determine the numerical coefficients a and b in (22). Then calculate the expected systolic blood pressure of a healthy 55-lb child.

Figure 4.3.18 shows the w-data and p-data entered in the usual x-list **L1** and y-list **L2** (respectively). The command **LnReg L1, L2, Y1** then gives the result shown in Fig. 4.3.19.

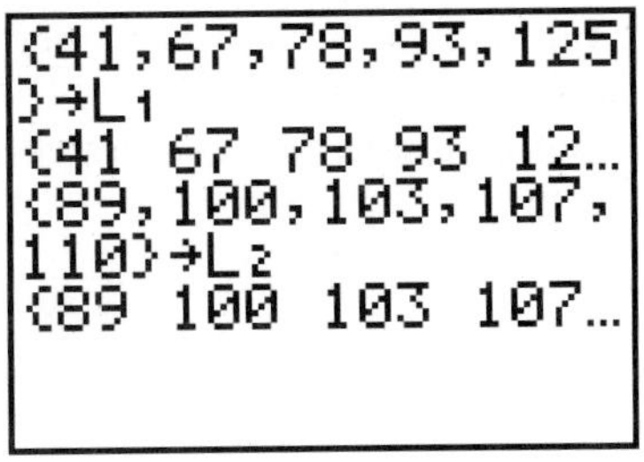

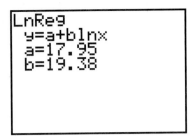

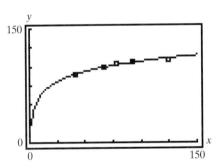

Figure 4.3.18   The weight (x) and blood pressure (y) data of Example 5.

Figure 4.3.19   The optimal logarithmic function $y = 17.95 + 19.38 \ln x$.

Thus our systolic blood pressure function is

$$p = 17.95 + 19.38 \ln w \tag{23}$$

(writing w and p in place of x and y). The graph shown in Fig. 4.3.20 (using the window $0 < x, y < 150$ and with the original data points marked with small squares) indicates that we have a pretty good fit. Substituting $w = 55$ in (23), we therefore get

$$p = 17.95 + 19.38 \ln 55 \approx 95.61 \approx 96$$

for the expected systolic blood pressure of our healthy 55-lb child.   ◼

Figure 4.3.20   Checking our logarithmic fit with the original data.

Fitting Power Functions

Many graphing calculators have a power regression (**PwrReg**) facility that can be used to fit given (x, y) data pairs with a *power function* of the form

$$y = Ax^b. \tag{24}$$

Once the x-data has been stored in the list **L1** and the y-data in the list **L2** as usual, the command

PwrReg L1, L2

generates the values of the constants A and b in (24) that provide the optimal such power function.

In what sense is this the optimal power function model? Recall that in Sec. 4.2, we explained that the best fitting exponential model is obtained by finding the best fitting linear model for the transformed data set of ordered pairs $(x, \ln y)$, and then converting that model to exponential form. To find the best fitting power function model, we proceed in a similar fashion. If the (x, y) data points fit (at least approximately) a power function model, then the transformed data set $(\ln x, \ln y)$ is (approximately) linear.

Using linear regression to find the best fitting linear model for the $(\ln x, \ln y)$ data, we obtain

$$\ln y = a + b \ln x. \tag{25}$$

Exponentiating both sides, we have

$$y = e^{a+b \ln x}.$$

When we simplify the right side using properties of exponents and logarithms, we get

$$y = e^a \cdot e^{b \ln x}$$
$$y = e^a \cdot (e^{\ln x})^b$$
$$y = e^a \cdot x^b.$$

As before, we rename the constant e^a as A to obtain the optimal power model $y = A \cdot x^b$.

Logarithmic regression (using **LnReg**) can also be used to fit a power function. Equation (25) says that the **logarithm** of y—rather than y itself—is a logarithmic function of x. So if we store the logarithm of the original given y-data,

In(L2)→L3

then the command

LnReg L1, L3

produces the values of the coefficients a and b that are optimal in (25). We then simplify as above and substitute $e^a = A$, obtaining

$$y = Ax^b.$$

Thus we again get a power function fitting the given data.

Example 6

Fit a power function $y = Ax^b$ to the data

x	2	3	5	10
y	9.90	12.12	15.65	22.14

As indicated in Fig. 4.3.21, we enter the given x-data and y-data in the lists **L1** and **L2** (respectively), and then enter the $z = \ln y$ data in the list **L3**. Figure 4.3.22 shows the result of the command **PwrReg L1 L2** and corresponds to the power function

$$y = 7.00x^{0.50}$$

that fits optimally the given xy-data.

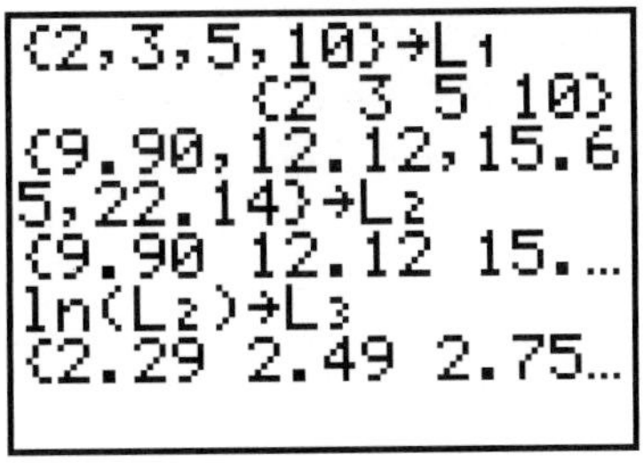

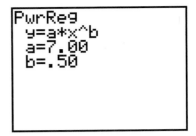

Figure 4.3.21   The data lists in Example 6.

Figure 4.3.22   The optimal power function fit in Example 6.

Alternatively, Fig. 4.3.23 shows the result of the command **LnReg L1 L3** and corresponds to the optimal logarithmic function

$$\ln y = 1.946 + 0.500 \ln x.$$

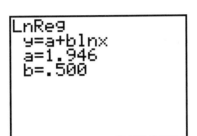

Figure 4.3.23   The optimal logarithmic function fit in Example 6.

With $A = e^{1.946} \approx 7.001$ and $b = 0.500$, our optimal power model is again

$$y = 7.00x^{0.50},$$

if we round the parameters to the 2 decimal places of the original data. Thus our best fit is, more simply, $y = 7\sqrt{x}$.

4.3 PROBLEMS

Problems 1–14 are similar to Problems 1–22 of Section 3.4. However, now you are to find an exponential model of the form $y = a \cdot e^{rx}$ (rather than a natural growth model of the form $y = a \cdot b^x$).

Each of the tables in Problems 1–4 gives several xy-data points that fit (exactly) an exponential model of the form $y = a \cdot e^{rx}$. Find this model, rounding r to three decimal places.

1.

x	0	1	2	3	4
y	5	15	45	135	405

2.

x	0	1	2	3	4
y	80	40	20	10	5

3.

x	0	1	2	3	4
y	100	20	4	0.8	0.16

4.

x	0	2	4	6	8
y	3	9	27	81	243

Each of the tables in Problems 5–8 gives several xy-data points. Use the exponential regression facility of your calculator to find the exponential model of the form $y = a \cdot e^{rx}$ that best fits these points. Find a and r, rounding each to three decimal places.

5.

x	0	2	4	6	8
y	15	30	60	110	220

6.

x	1	1.5	2	2.5	3
y	22	23	24	25	27

7.

x	0.5	0.75	1	1.25	1.5
y	80	65	55	45	40

8.

x	0	5	10	15	20
y	1000	775	600	465	360

In each of Problems 9–14, the 1960–1990 population census data for a U.S. city is given. Find the exponential model $P(t) = P_0 \cdot e^{rt}$ (with $t = 0$ in 1960) that best fits this census data, and use it to predict the year 2000 population of this city.

9. San Diego, CA

Year	1960	1970	1980	1990
Pop. (thous)	573	697	876	1111

10. Phoenix, AZ

Year	1960	1970	1980	1990
Pop. (thous)	439	584	790	1008

11. San Antonio, TX

Year	1960	1970	1980	1990
Pop. (thous)	588	654	786	935

12. Cleveland, OH

Year	1960	1970	1980	1990
Pop. (thous)	876	751	574	506

13. Buffalo, NY

Year	1960	1970	1980	1990
Pop. (thous)	533	463	358	328

14. Raleigh, NC

Year	1960	1970	1980	1990
Pop. (thous)	94	123	150	212

Each of the tables in Problems 15–20 gives several xy-data points. (a) Use the logarithmic regression facility of your calculator to find the logarithmic model of the form $y = a + b \ln x$ that best fits these points, rounding a and b to three decimal places. (b) Calculate the average error in your logarithmic fit.

15.

x	5	10	15	20	25
y	21	28	32	35	37

16.

x	5	10	15	20	25
y	13	10	8	7	6

17.

x	10	20	30	40	50
y	15	10	7	5	4

18.

x	5	15	25	35	45
y	16.0	19.0	20.5	21.5	22.5

19.

x	200	300	400	700	900
y	14.6	15.4	16.0	17.1	17.6

20.

x	500	1000	2000	2500	4000
y	56	23	−11	−22	−45

21. The amount $A(t)$ of atmospheric pollutants in a certain mountain valley grows exponentially and was measured (in pu, pollutant units) as follows during the 1990s:

Year	1991	1993	1995	1997	1999
pu	11.7	16.0	21.9	30.0	41.1

    (a) Find the best fit of the form $A(t) = A_0 \cdot e^{rt}$ with $t = 0$ in 1990.

    (b) Suppose it will be dangerous to stay in the valley when the amount of pollutants reaches 100 pu. When will this occur?

22. An accident at a nuclear power plant occurred on February 1, 2000 and left the surrounding area polluted with radioactive material that decays exponentially. The amount still present (in su, safe units) was measured thereafter at bimonthly intervals, as follows:

Month	April	June	August	October	December
su	12.8	10.8	9.2	7.8	6.7

    (a) Find the best fit of the form $A(t) = A_0 \cdot e^{rt}$ for the amount $A(t)$ of radioactive material (in su) remaining after t months.

(b) Suppose it will not be safe for people to return to the area until $A = 1$ su. In what month of what year will this occur?

23. Suppose the roast of Example 3, initially at 60° (Fahrenheit), is placed in a 350° oven at 11 A.M. The temperature of the roast is measured every 15 minutes for the first hour, with the following results.

Time	11 A.M.	11:15 A.M.	11:30 A.M.	11:45 A.M.	12 noon
Temp	50°	67°	82°	96°	110°

When will the roast be 200° and hence ready to serve (medium)?

24. The temperature inside my freezer is −15°C and the room temperature in my kitchen is a constant 20°C. At 1 P.M. one afternoon the power goes off during an ice storm, and the freezer's internal temperature $T(t)$ rises as follows for the next few hours.

Time	1 P.M.	2 P.M.	3 P.M.	4 P.M.	5 P.M.
Temp	−15.0°	−13.3°	−11.7°	−10.1°	−8.7°

(a) Assuming that $u(t) = 20 - T(t)$ is an exponentially declining function, find the best fit of the form $T(t) = 20 + a \cdot e^{-kt}$.

(b) The food in the freezer will begin to thaw once the temperature hits 0°C. When will this occur?

25. During the winter, the amount of heat the body loses depends on both the actual temperature and the speed of the wind. For example, if the actual temperature is 25°F and the wind is blowing at 15 miles per hour, a person feels as cold as he or she would if the temperature were 2°F with no wind. Meteorologists use the term *wind chill* to describe this phenomenon. The following table relates the wind speed W (in miles per hour) to the wind chill C (in degrees Fahrenheit) when the actual temperature is 15°F.

W	5	10	15	35
C	12	−3	−11	−27

(a) Fit these data with a logarithmic function of the form $C = a + b \ln W$.

(b) Use your model to predict the wind chill when the wind speed is 45 miles per hour. (Since wind speeds greater than 45 miles per hour have little additional chilling effect, this is—at least theoretically—as cold as you can feel when the temperature is 15°F.)

In Problems 26–28 use either power regression or logarithmic regression (as in Example 6) to find the indicated power model.

26. The heart rate R (in beats per minute) and the weight W (in pounds) of various mammals were measured, as follows:

W	25	67	127	175	240	975
R	131	103	88	81	75	53

    (a) Fit these data with a power function model of the form $R = aW^b$.

    (b) What would be the expected heart rate of a 100-lb mammal? of a 300-lb mammal?

27. During the expansion of a certain gas sample, its volume V (in liters) and pressure p (in atmospheres) were measured, as follows:

V	1.46	2.50	3.51	5.73	7.26
p	28.3	13.3	8.3	4.2	3.0

    (a) Fit these data with a power function model of the form $p = aV^b$.

    (b) What would be the expected pressure of the gas when its volume is 3 liters? when it is 6 liters?

28. The orbit of each planet is an ellipse focused at the sun. According to **Kepler's third law of planetary motion,** the semiaxis r of each planet's orbit and its time T of revolution about the sun are related by $T^2 = kr^3$ (so the square of the period is proportional to the cube of the semiaxis). The following table gives the semiaxis (in millions of kilometers) and the period (in Earth days) for six planets including the Earth.

Planet	Mercury	Venus	Earth	Mars	Jupiter	Saturn
r	58	108	149	228	778	1426
T	87.97	224.70	365.26	686.98	4332.59	10759.20

    (a) Fit these data with a power function model of the form $T = ar^b$.

    (b) Is your result consistent with Kepler's third law?

    (c) What is the value of the proportionality constant k?

C H A P T E R   4   R E V I E W

In this chapter, you learned about exponential and logarithmic functions and models. After completing the chapter, you should be able to

- Determine whether a relation described numerically, graphically, or symbolically represents an exponential function or a logarithmic function.
- Find the output value of an exponential or logarithmic function for a given input value.
- Find the input value of an exponential or logarithmic function for a given output value.
- Solve an equation or inequality involving an exponential or logarithmic function.
- Find the exponential or logarithmic model that best fits given data.
- Find the power function model that best fits given data.
- Find the continuous rate of growth or decay for an exponential model.

REVIEW PROBLEMS

In Problems 1–3, the table gives approximate y-values for a function of x. In each case, the function is linear, exponential, or logarithmic. Use the changes in the y-values to determine the type of function.

1.

x	1	2	3	4	5
y	1	1.62	1.99	2.25	2.45

2.

x	1	2	3	4	5
y	1.49	1.98	2.47	2.96	3.45

3.

x	1	2	3	4	5
y	1.14	1.37	2.00	3.73	8.42

In Problems 4–7, identify each function as exponential, logarithmic, or neither.

4.

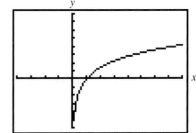

5.

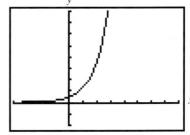

6. $y = 5x^4$

7. $y = 3e^x$

8. The center of U.S. population data discussed in the chapter introduction can be modeled by the function $C(t) = 61.11 + 5.33 \ln t$, where t represents years after 1800. Use your model to approximate the west longitude of the center of population in 1920. According to the model, in what year was the west longitude of the center of population 84 degrees west?

9. An accident at a nuclear power plant has left the surrounding area polluted with a radioactive element that decays naturally. The initial radiation level is 10 times the maximum amount S that is safe, and 100 days later is still 7 times that amount. What is the continuous annual rate of decay for this element?

10. Suppose that, as of Jan. 1, 2000, a state's annual Medicaid expenditures are $1.3 billion and increasing at 6% per year. Find a continuous growth exponential model for the Medicaid expenditures, and use it to predict the Medicaid expenditures in the year 2005.

11. The value of a 1997 Ford Explorer XLT is given by $V(t) = 26{,}400e^{-0.095t}$, where t represents years after 1997. How much is the Explorer worth in 2002? How long will it take for the value to decline to half of its original value?

12. The table below gives the per capita value of money in circulation in the United States t years after 1990.

(a) Find a quadratic function model to fit this data.

(b) Find a logarithmic function model to fit this data.

(c) Find a power function model to fit this data.

(d) Use the average error for each model to determine which model best fits the data.

t (years)	4	5	6	7
R (thous)	1428.37	1531.39	1573.15	1664.58

Source: *World Almanac and Book of Facts 1998*

ACTIVITY

Interest Rates in the Real World—Buying a Used Car

When you buy a car or a house, your monthly payment is calculated by a method called *amortization*. Amortization is the process of paying off a debt by making a given number of equal payments at specified intervals (usually monthly). These payments include the compound interest. With each payment, the amount of interest declines (as the unpaid balance on the loan declines), while the amount paid toward principal increases. If equal payments are made monthly, then the payment amount is calculated according to the following formula:

$$\text{payment} = (\text{loan amount}) \times \frac{\text{interest rate}}{12} \times \frac{1}{1 - (1 + \frac{\text{interest rate}}{12})^{-12t}},$$

where t is the number of years to repay the loan.

The preceding monthly payment formula looks pretty formidable, but if we use some variables and do a little algebra, it begins to look a bit better. Let P represent the amount borrowed (the *principal*), and m represent the *monthly* interest rate (that is, $m =$ interest rate/12). Then your monthly payment is given by

$$\text{payment} = \frac{P \cdot m}{1 - (1 + m)^{-12t}}.$$

Consider an example. Your rich (and generous) uncle agrees to lend you $3000 at the incredibly low interest rate of 3%, amortized over 2 years. Your monthly interest rate is $0.03/12 = 0.0025$, and your monthly payment is

$$\text{payment} = \frac{(3000)(0.0025)}{1 - 1.0025^{-24}} = 128.94 \quad \text{(dollars)}.$$

How do you figure out how much of each payment goes to interest and how much to principal? Each month you must calculate the interest on the current loan balance. If the monthly interest rate is 0.0025 and the initial balance is $3000, then the first month's interest is $7.50. So of the first payment, only $121.44 is applied toward the principal, leaving a new balance of $2878.56.

Using the monthly interest rate of 0.0025 on this new balance gives a second month's interest of $7.20. So $121.74 is applied toward principal, leaving a new balance of $2756.82.

If you continue on in this manner, you can construct an *amortization schedule* for your loan. An amortization schedule gives the amount of each payment that goes to interest, the amount that goes to principal, and the new balance after the payment is made. The following table gives the first four months of the amortization schedule for this loan.

Payment No.	Interest	Principal	New Balance
			$3000.00
1	$7.50	$121.44	$2878.56
2	$7.20	$121.74	$2756.82
3	$6.89	$122.05	$2634.77
4	$6.59	$122.35	$2512.42

By the time you finish making payments, how much interest did you pay on this loan? If you make 24 payments of $128.94, you repay your uncle $3094.56 so you have paid only $94.56 interest on the loan.

Now suppose that you have found a great deal on the used car of your dreams—a four-year-old red Mustang convertible, loaded with options, only 44,000 one-owner miles—for $11,500. You really want to buy this car, and you are hoping that you can afford the payment on a $10,000 loan.

1. If the sales tax in your state is 5%, how much down payment will you need to reduce the loan amount to $10,000?

2. You search the Web to find a car loan and find a rate of 7.8%, amortized over 3 years. Construct an amortization table for the first 12 payments on the loan.

3. What is the total cost of the loan repayment? How much interest will you pay on this loan?

4. After more research, you find two different lenders offering the following loans:

    (a) 8.16% amortized over two years, and

    (b) 8.04% amortized over two and a half years.

    If you can afford a car payment of no more than $375.00, can you borrow the money from either of these lenders?

5. Of the loans you can afford, which one is the better deal? What is the total price (including tax and interest) that you will pay for the car?

5

POLYNOMIAL MODELS AND LINEAR SYSTEMS

"Bring me your tired, your poor,
Your huddled masses yearning to breathe free,
The wretched refuse of your teeming shore,
Send these, the homeless, tempest-tossed, to me,
I lift my lamp beside the golden door!"

The Statue of Liberty, with its inscription by Emma Lazarus, has long been a symbol of freedom and welcome to people from around the world. Unless you are a Native American, either you or your ancestors were born somewhere else. The United States has grown and prospered due to the efforts of those from other lands. Some periods of our history saw many newcomers to our shores; in other times there were fewer. The chart in Fig. 5.0.1 shows the percentage of the U.S. population that was born abroad in the indicated years of the twentieth century.

The dots on the graph represent the actual percentages of foreign-born individuals in the country, while the curve is the graph of a third-degree polynomial function that very closely approximates these percentages.

We see from this chart that the percentage of foreign-born individuals rose from 1900 to 1910, then fell until 1970, and has since been rising. Over the time interval in question, the maximum percentage of foreign-born individuals occurred in 1910, while the minimum occurred in 1970. Notice also

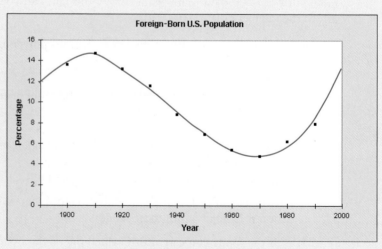

Figure 5.0.1 Percentage of foreign-born U.S. population.

that, at some point near 1930, the graph appears to change from curving downward to curving upward.

This graph does not look like any of the models we have studied so far; rather, with its up-and-down wiggles or bends, it has the distinct characteristics of a higher-degree polynomial graph. In this chapter we will study such polynomial functions, along with systems of linear equations and their real-world applications.

5.1 SOLVING POLYNOMIAL EQUATIONS

In Chapters 1 and 2, we solved problems that involved linear and quadratic equations. We found that a linear (first-degree polynomial) equation $ax + b = 0$ has one real number solution, while a quadratic (second-degree) equation $ax^2 + bx + c = 0$ has at most two (real number) solutions. Further, we noted that the solutions to such a quadratic equation are given by the quadratic formula

$$x = \frac{-b \pm \sqrt{b^2 - 4ac}}{2a}.$$

However, a **cubic** (third-degree) polynomial equation of the form

$$ax^3 + bx^2 + cx + d = 0 \tag{1}$$

can have as many as **three** real number solutions. And a **quartic** (fourth-degree) equation of the form

$$ax^4 + bx^3 + cx^2 + dx + e = 0 \tag{2}$$

can have as many as **four** solutions.

Extremely complicated formulas for the solution of cubic and quartic equations are known. For instance, one of the three solutions of (1) is given by

$$x = \frac{-b + \sqrt[3]{R} + (b^2 - 3ac)/\sqrt[3]{R}}{3a}$$

207

where

$$R = \frac{1}{2}\left(-2b^3 + 9abc - 27a^2d + \sqrt{4(3ac - b^2)^3 + (9abc - 2b^3 - 27a^2d)^2}\right),$$

and the other two solutions can be found using similar formulas. The formulas for the solutions of the quartic equation (2) are still more complicated! Nowadays, these formulas are used only by calculators and computers, and it's a safe bet that no human being alive knows them all by memory. (Certainly, no one *should* use his or her precious memory cells that way!)

So don't let the appearance of the cubic formula intimidate you. Indeed, we quote it only to make you feel grateful for your graphing calculator. Recall the **principle of graphical solution:** The **real solutions** of the equation $f(x) = 0$ are simply the **x-intercepts** of the graph $y = f(x)$. A glance at the graph can therefore reveal the number and approximate locations of the solutions of the equation. We can then zoom in on each solution to approximate it more accurately.

Solving Cubic Equations

As illustrated in Fig. 5.1.1, the graph of a cubic polynomial typically (though not always) has two bends or wiggles as—assuming the leading coefficient a in (1) is positive—it traverses the xy-plane from southwest (lower left) to northeast (upper right).

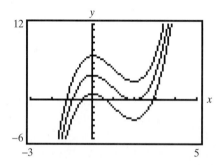

Figure 5.1.1
$y = x^3 - 3x^2 + 7$ (top graph);
$y = x^3 - 3x^2 + 4$ (middle graph);
$y = x^3 - 3x^2 + 1$ (bottom graph).

If your window is big enough to show both these bends, then you should be able to see how many solutions the corresponding cubic equation has. We see in Fig. 5.1.1 that

- The equation $x^3 - 3x^2 + 7 = 0$ has just one solution;
- The equation $x^3 - 3x^2 + 4 = 0$ has two solutions; and
- The equation $x^3 - 3x^2 + 1 = 0$ has three solutions.

A higher-degree polynomial equation can have complex or imaginary solutions in the same way that the quadratic equation $x^2 - 4x + 5 = 0$ has the quadratic formula solutions $x = 2 \pm \sqrt{-1}$ involving the imaginary number $\sqrt{-1}$. Such solutions are not found by graphing. So, here, by *solutions* we mean the "real solutions" of an equation.

Example 1

Looking at the middle graph in Fig. 5.1.1, it appears that the equation

$$x^3 - 3x^2 + 4 = 0 \tag{3}$$

has the two solutions $x = -1$ and $x = 2$. But the graph would probably look the same to the naked eye if the two solutions were, say, $x = -1.0002$ and $x = 1.9997$. We therefore wonder whether the roots actually are integers.

In Fig. 5.1.2 we've applied our calculator's **CALC** zero-finding facility to locate the right-hand solution. The calculator seems to say it's exactly 2, but this still doesn't prove it—if it were actually 2.00000003, then (displaying 4 decimal places) the calculator would round it off to 2. The only way to nail it down is to substitute $x = 2$ in (3) see what happens:

$$(2)^3 - 3(2)^2 + 4 = 8 - 12 + 4 = 0.$$

So $x = 2$ does, indeed, check out as an exact solution—substitution in the left-hand side of Eq. (3) yields exactly 0. You can check similarly that $x = -1$ is also an exact solution. ◼

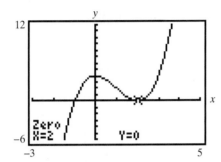

Figure 5.1.2 $y = x^3 - 3x^2 + 4$. It appears that $x = 2$ is a solution.

Example 2

Looking at the bottom graph in Fig. 5.1.1, it appears that the solutions of the equation

$$x^3 - 3x^2 + 1 = 0 \tag{4}$$

are approximately $x \approx -1/2$, $x \approx 1/2$, and $x \approx 3$ (as closely as the eye can see). Are these solutions actually such simple fractions as this? The answer here is no! In Fig. 5.1.3 we have used our calculator's **CALC** zero-finding facility to see that the solution between 0 and 1 actually is $x \approx 0.6527$ (rounded off accurate to 4 decimal places). You should verify similarly that the other two solutions are $x \approx -0.5321$ and $x \approx 2.8794$. Figure 5.1.4 shows that the calculator's **solve** function—entered from the **CATALOG** menu—can be used to find the real

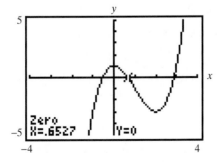

Figure 5.1.3 $y = x^3 - 3x^2 + 1$ and the approximate solution $x = 0.6527$.

Figure 5.1.4   Using **solve** to find all three solutions of **Y$_1$=** $x^3 - 3x^2 + 1 = 0$.

solutions of a cubic equation essentially "all at once" (after having defined **Y₁=X^3–3X²+1** in the **Y=** menu).   ◼

Example 3

Figure 5.1.5 shows the graph $y = 24x^3 + 2x^2 - 227x + 110$ plotted in the window $-5 \le x \le 5, -500 \le y \le 500$, and we see that the cubic equation

$$24x^3 + 2x^2 - 227x + 110 = 0 \qquad (5)$$

has three real solutions. Figures 5.1.5 and 5.1.6 indicate corresponding *approximate* values $x \approx -3.3333$, $x \approx 0.5000$, and $x \approx 2.7500$ of these three solutions. This suggests—but does not prove—that the given equation has the *exact* solutions $x = -3\frac{1}{3}$, $x = \frac{1}{2}$, and $x = 2\frac{3}{4}$. For instance, the different values -3.333317, 0.499985, and 2.750023 would round off to the same 4-decimal-place approximate values.

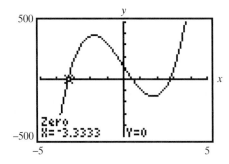

Figure 5.1.5 $y = 24x^3 + 2x^2 - 227x + 110$ and the approximate solution $x = -3.3333$.

Figure 5.1.6   Using **solve** to find all three solutions of $\mathbf{Y_1}=$ $24x^3 + 2x^2 - 227x + 110 = 0$.

However, we can verify by direct substitution that each of these three rational numbers is, indeed, a solution of the given equation. For instance, substitution of $x = -3\frac{1}{3} = -\frac{10}{3}$ gives

$$24\left(-\frac{10}{3}\right)^3 + 2\left(-\frac{10}{3}\right)^2 - 227\left(-\frac{10}{3}\right) + 110$$

$$= -\frac{24000}{27} + \frac{200}{9} + \frac{2270}{3} + 110$$

$$= \frac{-8000 + 200 + 6810 + 990}{9} = \frac{0}{9} = 0.$$

Thus $x = -3\frac{1}{3}$ does, indeed, satisfy Eq. (5). You should verify similarly that $x = \frac{1}{2}$ and $x = 2\frac{3}{4}$ are also exact solutions. Only when we have done so do we actually *know* that $x = -3\frac{1}{3}$, $x = \frac{1}{2}$, and $x = 2\frac{3}{4}$ are exact rather than merely approximate solutions of Eq. (5).   ◼

Example 4   (Popcorn Tray Problem)

Suppose you are a product designer for a consulting firm. Your client is a packaging manufacturer that has acquired cheaply a large surplus of rectangular cardboard sheets of various sizes. This cardboard will be used to make open-topped popcorn trays for sale in movie theaters. Each tray will be constructed by cutting equal squares out of the corners of a cardboard sheet, and then folding up the remaining flaps to form a box (Figure 5.1.7). First an x by x square is to be cut from each corner of the original p by q cardboard rectangle. Then the four flaps are to be folded up to form the vertical sides of the tray.

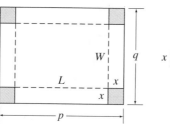 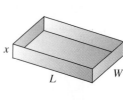

Figure 5.1.7 The popcorn tray construction.

Suppose your specific task is to investigate the way in which the volume V of the resulting tray depends upon the edge length x of the corner squares that are cut out. Looking at the right-hand sketch in Fig. 5.1.7, we see that the resulting tray has height x so its volume is given by

$$V = LWx.$$

Looking at the left-hand sketch in Fig. 5.1.7, we see that

$$L = p - 2x \quad \text{and} \quad W = q - 2x, \tag{6}$$

so it follows that

$$V = x(p - 2x)(q - 2x). \tag{7}$$

This formula tells precisely how the volume V of the box depends on the corner notch size x. ∎

You can use the formula in (7) to determine how to construct a box of a given desired volume. The next example illustrates how to determine the dimensions of a popcorn tray that will hold a half-liter (500 cc) of popcorn.

Example 5

Starting with a 20 cm by 30 cm sheet of cardboard, a popcorn tray is constructed as indicated in Fig. 5.1.7. If its volume is precisely 500 cm^3, what are its dimensions?

To answer this question, we substitute $p = 30$ and $q = 20$ in (7). It follows that the volume V of the tray is described in terms of the size x of the corner notch by the function

$$V(x) = x(30 - 2x)(20 - 2x). \tag{8}$$

(You should verify this volume formula yourself, starting with your own sketch like Fig. 5.1.7, with the cardboard sheet labeled 30×20 rather than $p \times q$.) Then our task is to determine what x should be in order that

$$x(30 - 2x)(20 - 2x) = 500. \tag{9}$$

Without actually expanding the left-hand side, you should be able to see that a *cubic* would result.

If we transpose the right-hand side number 500 and graph **Y₁= X(30–2X)(20–2X)–500** in the window $0 \leq x \leq 20, -1000 \leq y \leq 1000$, we get the cubic graph shown in Fig. 5.1.8. The tick marks on the horizontal axis represent single units, so we see three solutions—very roughly, near $x = 1, x = 8$, and $x = 16$. But the latter one *cannot* be used to make an actual tray from our 30×20 cardboard sheet! Is it obvious to you that the sheet is not big enough to actually cut out four 16×16 squares from its corners?

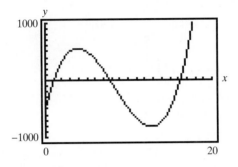

Figure 5.1.8   The graph **Y₁=X(30–2X)(20–2X)–500**, $0 \leq x \leq 20, -1000 \leq y \leq 1000$.

Consequently, we actually need to find only the two smaller solutions that are visible in Fig. 5.1.8. Again using the calculator's **solve** function, we find the real solutions $x \approx 0.9903$ and $x \approx 7.7748$ (Fig. 5.1.9).

```
solve(Y₁,X,1)
             .9903
solve(Y₁,X,8)
            7.7748
```

Figure 5.1.9   Using **solve** to find the two smaller zeros of **Y₁=X(30–2X)(20–2X)–500**.

Thus we have the *two* possible corner notch sizes $x \approx 0.9903$ cm and $x \approx 7.7748$ cm. Substituting these two possibilities into (6), we get

$$L = 30 - 2(0.9903) = 28.0194 \text{ and}$$
$$W = 20 - 2(0.9903) = 18.0194 \text{ with } x = 0.9903$$

and

$$L = 30 - 2(7.7748) = 14.4504 \text{ and}$$
$$W = 20 - 2(7.7748) = 4.4504 \text{ with } x = 7.7748.$$

Thus (rounding off to 2 decimal places) we have the dimensions

28.02 cm by 18.02 cm by 0.99 cm of one possible tray, and

14.45 cm by 4.45 cm by 7.77 cm of another one.

Hence it apparently is possible to make two different "trays" of entirely different shapes from the same size cardboard sheets, each having the desired volume of 500 cm³.

It is important to note that the cubic equation in (9) has three mathematical solutions, but our actual physical question has only two answers.

You should always check your answer to a problem by substituting it in the original equation(s) to make certain they're all satisfied. Here it's a question of whether the dimensions we found actually yield boxes with volume 500 cm³. The calculator multiplications

$$28.0194 \times 18.0194 \times 0.9903 = 499.9953, \text{ and}$$
$$14.4504 \times 4.4504 \times 7.7748 = 499.9979$$

corroborate our results; some round-off inaccuracy is to be expected in computations when we retain only a few decimal places. But any mistake in our solution would likely have produced a clear-cut disparity in this final check.   ◼

Example 5 is fairly typical of applied questions that have polynomial equations like (9) as mathematical models. Not every mathematical solution of the equation necessarily provides a real answer to the applied question. Each mathematical solution must be checked out to see that it actually answers physically the question that was originally posed. In Example 5, each of the two mathematical solutions $x \approx 0.9903$ cm and $x \approx 7.7748$ cm of (9) yields positive tray dimensions with product 500 cm³, but you should check that the third solution $x \approx 16.2349$ would give negative (hence physically impossible) dimensions if substituted in (6).

Solving Quartic Equations

Figure 5.1.10 illustrates the fact that the graph of a *quartic* polynomial $ax^4 + bx^3 + cx^2 + dx + e$ has

- *three* or fewer bends or wiggles and
- *four* or fewer real-number zeros.

If the leading coefficient a is positive, then the graph rises to the northwest on the left and to the northeast on the right. If there are three bends—the largest possible number—and if your window is big enough to show all of these bends, then you should be able to see how many solutions the corresponding quartic equation has. Simply count the number of intersections of the graph with the x-axis. Thus we see in Fig. 5.1.10 that

- The equation $x^4 - 5x^3 + 10x = 0$ has four solutions; but
- The equation $x^4 - 5x^3 + 10x + 15 = 0$ has just two solutions.

Once such a graph is plotted on our calculator screen, we can locate its solutions graphically by zooming in and using our calculator's zero-finding facility. Alternatively, we can simply apply the **solve** function.

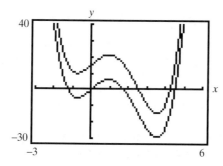

Figure 5.1.10
$y = x^4 - 5x^3 + 10x + 15$ (top graph);
$y = x^4 - 5x^3 + 10x$ (bottom graph).

Example 6

Looking at Fig. 5.1.10, we see that the upper graph $y = x^4 - 5x^3 + 10x + 15$ has one x-intercept between 2 and 3, and the other a bit greater than 4. We therefore use our calculator's **solve** function with initial guesses 2 and 4. Thus we see in Fig. 5.1.11 (with **Y₁=X^4–5X^3+10X+15**) that the *two* real solutions of the equation

$$x^4 - 5x^3 + 10x + 15 = 0$$

are $x \approx 2.5441$ and $x \approx 4.2516$ (rounded off accurate to 4 decimal places).

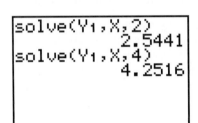

Figure 5.1.11   The two real solutions of the equation $x^4 - 5x^3 + 10x + 15 = 0$.

You should find similarly all *four* real solutions of the equation

$$x^4 - 5x^3 + 10x = 0.$$

Can you see how to alter the constant term in these equations to obtain a quartic equation with *no* real solutions? Verify your guess by graphing your proposed equation.

Example 7

(a)   Explain algebraically why the quartic equation

$$(x^2 + 10)(x - 1)^2 = x^4 - 2x^3 + 11x^2 - 20x + 10 = 0$$

has exactly *one* real solution (as indicated by the graph in Fig. 5.1.12).

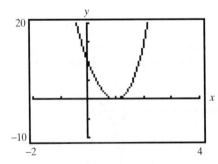

Figure 5.1.12   The graph $y = x^4 - 2x^3 + 11x^2 - 20x + 10$.

Solving the factored form of the equation, we see that since

$$(x^2 + 10)(x - 1)^2 = 0, \text{ then}$$
$$x^2 + 10 = 0 \text{ or } (x - 1)^2 = 0.$$

Since $x^2 + 10 = 0$ has no real solutions, and $(x - 1)^2 = 0$ has only one solution, the quartic equation $(x^2 + 10)(x - 1)^2 = x^4 - 2x^3 + 11x^2 - 20x + 10 = 0$ has only one solution.

(b)   Explain algebraically why the quartic equation

$$(x^2 - 4)(x - 5)^2 = x^4 - 10x^3 + 21x^2 + 40x - 100 = 0$$

has exactly *three* real solutions (as indicated by the graph in Fig. 5.1.13).

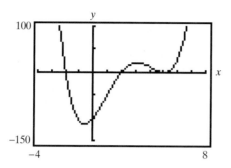

Figure 5.1.13   The graph $y = x^4 - 10x^3 + 21x^2 + 40x - 100$ for $-4 \le x \le 8$.

Again working with the factored form of the equation, we have

$$(x^2 - 4)(x - 5)^2 = 0$$
$$x^2 - 4 = 0 \text{ or } (x - 5)^2 = 0$$
$$(x + 2)(x - 2) = 0 \text{ or } (x - 5)^2 = 0.$$

Thus, we can see that the solutions to the quartic equations are the three real numbers $-2, 2$, and 5.   ◼

Examples 6 and 7 illustrate all the possibilities for a quartic equation. It can have either no (real) solutions, exactly one solution, two (distinct) solutions, three solutions, or four solutions, but it cannot have more than four solutions. Similarly, it cannot have more than three bends. Based on these facts, you ordinarily should be able to tell whether you've graphed a given quartic polynomial in a sufficiently large window to see its essential features. If so, you should be able to see all its x-intercepts, and can therefore proceed to solve for its real zeros.

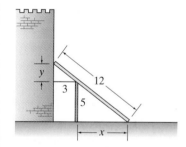

Figure 5.1.14   The leaning ladder of Example 8.

Example 8

Figure 5.1.14 shows a 12-foot ladder that leans across a 5-foot fence and just touches a tall wall standing 3 feet behind the fence. How far (accurate to the nearest eighth of an inch) is the foot of the ladder from the bottom of the fence?

Observe that the figure contains three *similar* (that is, equal-angled) right triangles. The unknown dimension we seek is the base x of one of the two smaller right triangles. The unknown height of the other small right triangle is labeled y. Recall from geometry the equality of base/height ratios,

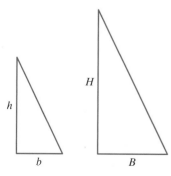

Figure 5.1.15   Similar right triangles with bases b, B and heights h, H.

$$\frac{b}{h} = \frac{B}{H},$$

in similar right triangles—as in Fig. 5.1.15, where we see a small right triangle with base b and height h and a similar but larger triangle with base B and height H.

Applied to the two smaller right triangles in Fig. 5.1.14—with bases 3 and x and with heights y and 5—this fact gives the equation

$$\frac{3}{y} = \frac{x}{5}. \tag{10}$$

The large right triangle in the figure has base $x + 3$, height $y + 5$, and hypotenuse 12. Hence the Pythagorean formula for this triangle is

$$(x + 3)^2 + (y + 5)^2 = 144. \tag{11}$$

Equations (10) and (11) are two equations that the two unknowns x and y must satisfy. The usual first approach to solving two simultaneous equations is to solve one equation for one unknown and substitute the result in the other equation. If we solve (10) for $y = 15/x$ and substitute the result in (11), we get the equation

$$(x + 3)^2 + \left(\frac{15}{x} + 5\right)^2 = 144. \tag{12}$$

Expansion of the two binomials here gives

$$(x^2 + 6x + 9) + \left(\frac{225}{x^2} + \frac{150}{x} + 25\right) = 144. \tag{13}$$

Finally, multiplication by x^2 (to clear fractions),

$$(x^4 + 6x^3 + 9x^2) + (225 + 150x + 25x^2) = 144x^2,$$

and collection of like terms yields the quartic equation

$$x^4 + 6x^3 - 110x^2 + 150x + 225 = 0 \tag{14}$$

that we need to solve for x.

Figure 5.1.16 shows the graph $y = x^4 + 6x^3 - 110x^2 + 150x + 225$ in the standard window $-10 \leq x, y \leq 10$. It appears to show three x-intercepts and hence three solutions. However, the steepness of the graph pieces we see indicates the need for a much wider y-view, which in turn indicates the need for a larger scale on y.

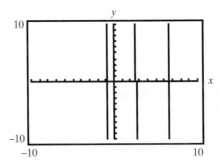

Figure 5.1.16   The graph
$y = x^4 + 6x^3 - 110x^2 + 150x + 225$
for $-10 \leq x, y \leq 10$.

In Figure 5.1.17 we have increased the y-range to $-1000 \leq y \leq 1000$, but we still see only three solutions, rather than the *four* solutions our quartic ought to have. Because we see the graph rising to the northeast as it should, but not to the northwest, we evidently need to look further to the west—in the negative

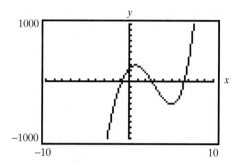

Figure 5.1.17   The graph
$y = x^4 + 6x^3 - 110x^2 + 150x + 225$
for $-10 \leq x \leq 10, -1000 \leq y \leq 1000$.

x-direction—to find the fourth solution. So, finally, the graph in Fig. 5.1.18 for $-20 \leq x \leq 10$ shows all four solutions.

The ticks on the x-axis in Fig. 5.1.18 mark x-intervals of length 5, so it appears that the four solutions of Eq. (14) are, very roughly, near $-14, -1, 3$, and 6. Using these rough approximations as initial guesses, we find the negative solutions shown in Fig. 5.1.19 and the positive solutions shown in 5.1.20.

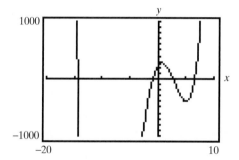

Figure 5.1.18   The graph
$y = x^4 + 6x^3 - 110x^2 + 150x + 225$ for
$-20 \leq x \leq 10, -1000 \leq y \leq 1000$.

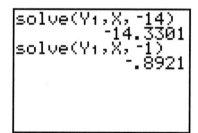

Figure 5.1.19   The two negative solutions of Eq. (14).

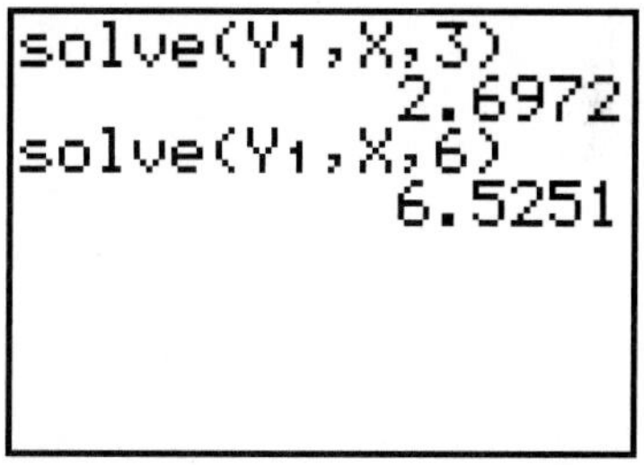

Figure 5.1.20   The two positive solutions of Eq. (14).

Thus our quartic equation has

- two negative solutions $x \approx -14.3301$ and $x \approx -0.8921$, and
- two positive solutions $x \approx 2.6972$ and $x \approx 6.5251$.

But the original question was not how many solutions Eq. (14) has, but where the foot of the ladder should be placed in order to just graze the top of the fence and lean against the wall as shown in Fig. 5.1.14. Our algebraic derivation of Eq. (14) shows that if x is the distance from the foot of the fence to the foot of the ladder, then x must be a solution of the equation, and therefore must be one of the four numbers $-14.3301, -0.8921, 2.6972$, and 6.5251. However, the physical dimension x cannot be negative (why?), so only the two positive solutions qualify. This leaves the two positive solutions 2.6972 and 6.5251 as possibilities.

It remains to round off each possible solution accurate to the nearest eighth of an inch, as desired. Thus

$$x \approx 2.6972 \text{ ft} = 2 \text{ ft} + (0.6972 \times 12 \text{ in}) \approx 2 \text{ ft} + 8.37 \text{ in} \approx 2 \text{ ft } 8\tfrac{3}{8} \text{ in},$$
$$x \approx 6.5251 \text{ ft} = 6 \text{ ft} + (0.5251 \times 12 \text{ in}) \approx 6 \text{ ft} + 6.30 \text{ in} \approx 6 \text{ ft } 6\tfrac{1}{4} \text{ in}.$$

But which of these two values of x is the answer to the original question? Precisely where should the foot of the ladder be placed so that it will lean across the fence and just touch the tall wall behind it?

You might get a ruler to serve as a ladder, make a diagram, and try different placements until you're convinced that this problem has two correct answers! Thus, using Eq. (10), $y = 15/x$, to find the corresponding y-values, we find that

- the smaller positive value $x \approx 2.6972$ ft gives a *high* position of the ladder with $y \approx 15/2.6972 \approx 5.5613$ ft, and
- the larger positive value $x \approx 6.5251$ ft gives a *low* position of the ladder with $y \approx 15/6.5251 \approx 2.2988$ ft (see Fig. 5.1.21).

Figure 5.1.21   The two possible positions of the ladder.

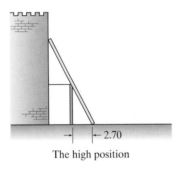

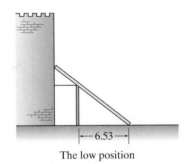

The high position	The low position
—2.70	—6.53—

A final check to assure that both these two xy-pairs work is to verify that they satisfy not only Eq. (10) but also Eq. (11), $(x + 3)^2 + (y + 5)^2 = 144$. Rounding the answers to four decimal places, we find that

$$(2.6972 + 3)^2 + (5.5613 + 5)^2 \approx 143.9991 \approx 144$$

and

$$(6.5251 + 3)^2 + (2.2988 + 5)^2 \approx 144.0000 \approx 144.$$

Thus we do indeed have two physically possible solutions.   ◼

5.1 PROBLEMS

The (exact) solutions of the cubic and quartic equations in Problems 1–12 are all integers or simple fractions (rational numbers). Discover these exact solutions using the approach of Example 2. That is, first find approximate solutions by graphing, and then verify by substitution in the given equation each indicated rational solution.

1. $x^3 - 2x^2 - 5x + 6 = 0$
2. $x^3 - 4x^2 - 11x + 30 = 0$
3. $x^4 - 2x^3 - 13x^2 + 14x + 24 = 0$
4. $x^4 - 37x^2 - 24x + 180 = 0$

5. $6x^3 - 7x^2 - 43x + 30 = 0$

6. $15x^3 - 49x^2 - 104x + 240 = 0$

7. $4x^4 - 8x^3 - 39x^2 + 43x + 70 = 0$

8. $12x^4 + 13x^3 - 188x^2 - 167x + 330 = 0$

9. $40x^3 + 94x^2 - 261x - 468 = 0$

10. $144x^3 - 522x^2 - 757x + 1365 = 0$

11. $120x^4 + 118x^3 - 1859x^2 - 318x + 819 = 0$

12. $576x^4 + 120x^3 - 6650x^2 - 2375x + 6250 = 0$

13. A 2 in $\times$ 4 in $\times$ 7 in iron block is plated with brass so that each of its three dimensions is increased by the same amount x. The volume of the plated block is 50% greater than the volume of the unplated block. What are its dimensions?

14. A 3 in $\times$ 5 in $\times$ 9 in iron block is plated with brass so that each of its three dimensions is increased by the same amount x. The volume of the plated block is exactly twice the volume of the unplated block. What are its dimensions?

In Problems 15 and 16, the edge length p of a square piece of cardboard is given. Find the possible dimensions of an open-topped tray with the given volume V that can be constructed by cutting out square corner notches and turning up the remaining flaps (as indicated in Fig. 5.1.7). Round off these dimensions accurate to the nearest hundredth of an inch.

15. $p = 45$ in and $V = 4500$ in^3

16. $p = 55$ in and $V = 6500$ in^3

In Problems 17 and 18 the length L of a ladder is given. As indicated in Fig. 5.1.14, this ladder is to lean across a fence of the given height p and just touch a tall wall located the given distance q behind the fence. (Thus $L = 12$ ft, $p = 5$ ft, and $q = 3$ ft in Example 8.) First derive a quartic equation [like Eq. (14)] that the distance x from the foot of the ladder to the bottom of the fence must satisfy. Then find the possible physical values of x, rounded off accurate to the nearest tenth of an inch.

17. $L = 17$ ft, $p = 6$ ft, $q = 4$ ft

18. $L = 25$ ft, $p = 8$ ft, $q = 5$ ft

19. A 72-foot tree stands 18 feet from a 10-foot wall. The tree is to be cut at a height of x feet. Then it will be bent—as indicated in Fig. 5.1.22—so that it leans across the wall and its tip just touches the ground on the other side. It can be shown that the height x of the tree cut must satisfy the cubic equation

$$4x^3 - 215x^2 + 3280x - 14400 = 0.$$

This equation has three real solutions. However, only two of these three solutions of the equation give actual ways to cut the tree as indicated in the figure. Express these two in feet and inches, rounded off accurate to the nearest inch.

20. The same as Problem 19, except that an 80-foot tree originally stands 24 feet from a 10-foot wall. Now the cubic equation the cutting height x must satisfy is

$$5x^3 - 282x^2 + 4500x - 20000 = 0.$$

Figure 5.1.22 The bent tree of Problems 19 and 20.

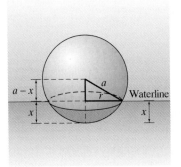

Figure 5.1.23 The floating cork ball of Problems 21–24.

Problems 21–24 refer to a floating cork ball that has a radius of $a = 1$ foot, as illustrated in Figure 5.1.23. The density of the ball is d times the density of water. According to Archimedes, the volume V of the submerged "spherical segment" of the ball is given by

$$V = \frac{\pi x}{6}(3r^2 + x^2) = \frac{4}{3}\pi da^3. \tag{15}$$

The unknowns r and x also satisfy the Pythagorean formula

$$r^2 + (a - x)^2 = a^2 \tag{16}$$

for the right triangle in the figure. In Problems 21–24,

(a) First eliminate r in (15) and (16) with $a = 1$ and the given value of d to obtain a cubic equation in the depth x to which the ball sinks in the water. Write your answer in the form $ax^3 + bx^2 + cx + d = 0$ with integer coefficients a, b, c, and d.

(b) Then find the actual depth x to which the ball sinks in the water, rounded off accurate to the nearest thousandth of an inch.

21. $d = 1/4$

22. $d = 1/5$

23. $d = 2/3$

24. $d = 9/10$

5.2   SOLVING PAIRS OF LINEAR EQUATIONS—LOTS OF WAYS!

In Section 5.1 we talked only about solving *single* equations. Now we talk about solving two equations simultaneously, but both of them must be *linear*. Thus we consider a pair of linear equations of the form

$$\begin{aligned} ax + by &= p \\ cx + dy &= q \end{aligned} \tag{1}$$

where x and y are the unknowns and the coefficients a, b, p in the first equation and c, d, q in the second equation are given constants. A solution of this system is simply a pair (x, y) of numbers that satisfy both of the equations.

Example 1

The numbers $x = 2$, $y = -1$ constitute a solution of the linear system

$$\begin{aligned} 2x - y &= 5 \\ x + 2y &= 0 \end{aligned} \tag{2}$$

because both

$$2 \cdot (2) - (-1) = 5 \quad \text{and} \quad (2) + 2 \cdot (-1) = 0.$$

More briefly, $(2, -1)$ is a solution of the system in (2). By contrast, the values $x = 3$, $y = 1$ satisfy the first equation in (2) but do not satisfy the second one. Thus the pair $(3, 1)$ is not a solution of the system in (2).   ◣

Example 2

The linear system

$$x + y = 1$$
$$2x + 2y = 3 \tag{3}$$

has no solution at all, because if $x + y = 1$, then

$$2x + 2y = 2(x + y) = 2(1) = 2 \neq 3.$$

Thus, if the first equation in (3) is satisfied, then $2x + 2y \neq 3$, so the second equation is not satisfied. Hence, the two equations cannot be satisfied simultaneously. ◼

Graphic Solutions

The graph of each of the equations in (1) is a straight line in the plane—because by transposing the x-term and then dividing by the coefficient of y, either can be written in the form $y = mx + b$. Hence the two equations together define two straight lines L_1 and L_2. The numbers x_0 and y_0 then constitute a solution of the system provided that the point (x_0, y_0) lies on both lines.

From a geometric viewpoint, there are three ways that two lines in the xy-plane can look:

- The two lines intersect at a single point (as in Fig. 5.2.1).
- The two lines are parallel and therefore non-intersecting lines (as in Fig. 5.2.2).
- The two lines coincide—they actually are the same line (see Fig. 5.2.3).

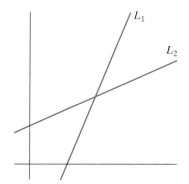

Figure 5.2.1 Two intersecting lines—exactly one solution.

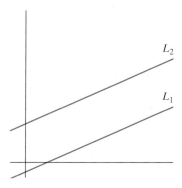

Figure 5.2.2 Two parallel lines—no solution.

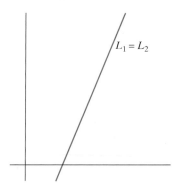

Figure 5.2.3 Two coincident lines—infinitely many solutions.

It follows that there are just three possibilities for the solution of a linear pair of equations:

- Exactly one solution;
- No solution; or
- Infinitely many solutions.

Example 3

Obviously, the two equations

$$2x + 2y = 6$$
$$4x + 4y = 12 \tag{4}$$

are both equivalent to the single equation $x + y = 3$ (that is, $y = 3 - x$), which is obtained upon division of the first equation by 2 and the second equation by 4. Hence *every* point (x, y) on this line—for instance, $(1, 2)$ or $(3, 0)$ or $(7, -4)$—provides a solution of the system in (4). ◼

In the typical applied problem we are interested mainly in the case of exactly one solution. One way to find this single solution is to graph both equations and locate the point of intersection of their straight line graphs.

Example 4

Solve the linear system

$$2x - y = 2$$
$$4x + 2y = 10. \tag{5}$$

First we solve each equation for y in terms of x:

$$y = 2x - 2$$
$$y = 5 - 2x. \tag{6}$$

We can now graph $Y_1=2X-2$ and $Y_2=5-2X$, with the result shown in Fig. 5.2.4. We have already used our calculator's intersection-finding facility to locate the point $(1.75, 1.5)$ of intersection of these two lines.

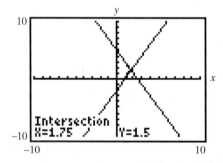

Figure 5.2.4 Solving the equations $2x - y = 2, 4x + 2y = 10$ of Example 4.

We naturally wonder whether this means that $x = 7/4$, $y = 3/2$ is the exact solution of the original system in (5). We should always verify an apparent graphical solution by direct substitution in the original system:

$$2\left(\frac{7}{4}\right) - \left(\frac{3}{2}\right) = \frac{7}{2} - \frac{3}{2} = \frac{4}{2} = 2, \quad 4\left(\frac{7}{4}\right) + 2\left(\frac{3}{2}\right) = 7 + 3 = 10.$$

Thus both equations in (5) are satisfied, so $x = 7/4$, $y = 3/2$ is indeed the solution.

We can also solve two linear equations numerically. Figure 5.2.5 shows a tabulation of the functions $Y_1=2X-2$ and $Y_2=5-2X$ in (6), and we see again that

X	Y₁	Y₂
1.6000	1.2000	1.8000
1.6500	1.3000	1.7000
1.7000	1.4000	1.6000
1.7500	1.5000	1.5000
1.8000	1.6000	1.4000
1.8500	1.7000	1.3000
1.9000	1.8000	1.2000

X=1.75

Figure 5.2.5   Two intersecting lines—exactly one solution. Solving the same two equations numerically.

Y_1 and Y_2 have the same value $y = 1.5 = 3/2$ when $x = 1.75 = 7/4$, thereby showing again that $(7/4, 3/2)$ is the solution.   ◪

Algebraic Solutions

In elementary algebra we learn the symbolic **method of elimination** for solution of pairs of linear equations. The method is implemented like this: First we add an appropriate constant multiple of the first equation to the second equation. The idea is to choose the constant multiple that serves to eliminate the variable x from the second equation. We can then solve readily the resulting equation for the remaining variable y. Finally, knowing y, we find the value of x by substitution of this value of y into the original first equation.

Example 5

Let's consider again the same system

$$2x - y = 2$$
$$4x + 2y = 10 \tag{7}$$

as in Example 4. We note that the coefficient of x in the second equation is twice the coefficient of x in the first equation. Hence we can eliminate x by subtracting two times the first equation from the second equation. We do this by subtracting twice the left-hand side from the left-hand side, and twice the right-hand side from the right-hand side:

$$(4x + 2y) - 2 \cdot (2x - y) = 10 - 2 \cdot (2).$$

The result is the simpler equation

$$4y = 6,$$

which immediately gives $y = 6/4 = 3/2$. Substitution of this value of y into the first equation in (7) gives

$$2x - (3/2) = 2,$$

so

$$2x = 2 + \frac{3}{2} = \frac{4}{2} + \frac{3}{2} = \frac{7}{2}.$$

Hence $x = 7/4$, and we have found algebraically the same solution $(7/4, 3/2)$ that we discovered graphically (and then verified numerically) in Example 4.   ◪

The method of Example 5 is not as easy to apply if neither coefficient of x in one equation is an integer multiple of the coefficient of x in the other equation. The next example illustrates an elimination technique that always suffices to eliminate x from a linear pair of equations. We multiply the first equation by the coefficient of x in the second equation, and we multiply the second equation by the coefficient of x in the first equation. Then we subtract one of the resulting equations from the other. This gives the desired equation involving only y.

Example 6

The linear pair

$$7x + 6y = 202$$
$$11x + 9y = 245 \tag{8}$$

looks pretty formidable. But let's multiply the first equation by 11 and the second one by 7. This gives the pair

$$77x + 66y = 11 \times 202 = 2222$$
$$77x + 63y = 7 \times 245 = 1715 \tag{9}$$

in which the coefficients of x are the same. Hence subtraction of the second equation in (9) from the first one gives

$$3y = 2222 - 1715 = 507,$$

so

$$y = \frac{507}{3} = 169.$$

Finally, substitution of this value of y into the original first equation gives

$$7x + 6(169) = 202,$$
$$7x = 202 - 6(169) = -812$$
$$x = \frac{-812}{7} = -116.$$

Thus we have found the solution $(-116, 169)$ of the system in (8).   ◪

Symbolic Solutions

We can derive a formula solution by applying the method of Example 6 to the general pair

$$ax + by = p$$
$$cx + dy = q \tag{10}$$

of linear equations in the two unknowns x and y. Multiplication of the first equation by c and multiplication of the second equation by a yields the new pair

$$acx + bcy = pc$$
$$acx + ady = qa.$$

Then subtraction of the first equation here from the second one gives

$$(ad - bc)y = qa - pc,$$

so

$$y = \frac{qa - pc}{ad - bc} \tag{11}$$

Instead of substituting this value of y into (10) and solving for x, it's simpler to start afresh and multiply the first equation in (10) by d and the second one by b:

$$adx + bdy = pd$$
$$bcx + bdy = qb.$$

Subtraction of the second equation here from the first one yields

$$(ad - bc)x = pd - qb,$$

so

$$x = \frac{pd - qb}{ad - bc}. \tag{12}$$

One can then solve any linear pair of equations by plugging the coefficients a, b, c, d, p, q into the formulas in (11) and (12).

Example 7

Starting once more with the system

$$2x - y = 2$$
$$4x + 2y = 10 \tag{13}$$

of Examples 4 and 5, we have

$$a = 2, \quad b = -1, \quad p = 2,$$
$$c = 4, \quad d = 2, \quad q = 10. \tag{14}$$

[Observe that, if the literal symbols and the equal signs are removed in (13) and in (14), then the same array of 6 numbers remains.] Then the formulas in (12) and (11) give

$$x = \frac{2 \cdot 2 - 10 \cdot (-1)}{2 \cdot 2 - (-1) \cdot 4} = \frac{14}{8} = \frac{7}{4}, \quad y = \frac{10 \cdot 2 - 2 \cdot 4}{2 \cdot 2 - (-1) \cdot 4} = \frac{12}{8} = \frac{3}{2},$$

the same solution found previously. ◣

Determinants

Although it's virtually automatic, the method of solution illustrated in Example 7 surely seems useless as a practical matter, because you could never remember formulas (11) and (12) when you need them. Or could you?

Observe that the fractions giving x and y in (11) and (12) have the same denominator $ad - bc$. This is the value of the 2-by-2 (or 2×2) *determinant* defined by

$$\Delta = \begin{vmatrix} a & b \\ c & d \end{vmatrix} = ad - cb, \tag{15}$$

where Δ is the upper-case Greek letter delta.

Note that the value $ad - bc$ is the product of the (left-to-right) downward diagonal elements a and d, minus the product of the upward diagonal elements c and b. For instance,

$$\begin{vmatrix} 5 & 3 \\ 21 & 17 \end{vmatrix} = (5)(17) - (21)(3) = 85 - 63 = 22.$$

You should teach your "fingers to do the walking"—from upper left to lower right, then from lower left to upper right.

The particular determinant in (15) is called the **coefficient determinant** of the linear system

$$\begin{aligned} ax + by &= p \\ cx + dy &= q, \end{aligned} \tag{16}$$

because the numbers a, b, c, d appear as the same array—both in the determinant [on the left in (15)] and as the coefficients of the unknowns on the left in (16).

Now let's look at the numerators in (11) and (12). The numerator in the expression for x is

$$\begin{vmatrix} p & b \\ q & d \end{vmatrix} = pd - qb,$$

while the numerator in the expression for y is

$$\begin{vmatrix} a & p \\ c & q \end{vmatrix} = aq - cp.$$

Therefore, Eqs. (11) and (12) say that

$$x = \frac{\begin{vmatrix} p & b \\ q & d \end{vmatrix}}{\begin{vmatrix} a & b \\ c & d \end{vmatrix}} \quad \text{and} \quad y = \frac{\begin{vmatrix} a & p \\ c & q \end{vmatrix}}{\begin{vmatrix} a & b \\ c & d \end{vmatrix}}. \tag{17}$$

Finally, the point is that—unlike Eqs. (11) and (12)—these formulas for x and y are easy to remember! But how, and why? It's because the numerator determinant for x is obtained from the coefficient determinant upon replacing the coefficients $\begin{bmatrix} a \\ c \end{bmatrix}$ of x in (16) by the constants $\begin{bmatrix} p \\ q \end{bmatrix}$. Similarly, the numerator determinant for y is obtained from the coefficient determinant upon replacing the coefficients $\begin{bmatrix} b \\ d \end{bmatrix}$ of y by the same constants $\begin{bmatrix} p \\ q \end{bmatrix}$. In short, when setting up the numerator determinant to solve for either unknown x or y, its coefficients are replaced by the constants on the other side in the pair of equations.

It is important to remember that in order to divide by it, the coefficient appearing in the denominators in (17) must be *nonzero*. If $\Delta = 0$, then it turns out that the system has *either*

- infinitely many different solutions (because the two equations have the same straight line graph), *or*
- no solution at all (because the two equations have parallel nonintersecting straight line graphs).

However, we need not be concerned here with these exceptional cases.

Example 8

To solve once more the system

$$2x - y = 2$$
$$4x + 2y = 10$$

of Example 7, we start by calculating its coefficient determinant

$$\begin{vmatrix} 2 & -1 \\ 4 & 2 \end{vmatrix} = (2)(2) - (4)(-1) = 4 - (-4) = 8$$

that appears in both denominators in (17). Then

$$x = \frac{\begin{vmatrix} 2 & -1 \\ 10 & 2 \end{vmatrix}}{8} = \frac{(2)(2) - (10)(-1)}{8} = \frac{4 + 10}{8} = \frac{14}{8} = \frac{7}{4},$$

$$y = \frac{\begin{vmatrix} 2 & 2 \\ 4 & 10 \end{vmatrix}}{8} = \frac{(2)(10) - (4)(2)}{8} = \frac{20 - 8}{8} = \frac{12}{8} = \frac{3}{2}.$$

As we expect, we once again get the same solution $\left(\frac{7}{4}, \frac{3}{2}\right)$ to our system of linear equations. ◼

Example 9

To solve again the system

$$7x + 6y = 202$$
$$11x + 9y = 245$$

of Example 6, we start by calculating its coefficient determinant

$$\begin{vmatrix} 7 & 6 \\ 11 & 9 \end{vmatrix} = (7)(9) - (11)(6) = 63 - 66 = -3$$

that appears in both denominators in (17). Then

$$x = \frac{\begin{vmatrix} 202 & 6 \\ 245 & 9 \end{vmatrix}}{-3} = \frac{(202)(9) - (245)(6)}{-3} = \frac{1818 - 1470}{-3} = \frac{348}{-3} = -116,$$

$$y = \frac{\begin{vmatrix} 7 & 202 \\ 11 & 245 \end{vmatrix}}{-3} = \frac{(7)(245) - (11)(202)}{-3} = \frac{1715 - 2222}{-3} = \frac{-507}{-3} = 169. ◼$$

The bottom line is this: Whereas it may seem that the solution of a pair of linear equations by elimination involves some ingenuity, the solution using determinants is a fail-safe matter. Just "plug and chug"—substitute in the determinant formulas and calculate.

Using Matrices

A *matrix* is simply a rectangular array—that is, a rectangular pattern—of numbers. For instance, the determinant formulas in (17) suggest that the solutions of the linear system

$$ax + by = p$$
$$cx + dy = q \tag{16 again}$$

are determined by its matrix

$$\mathbf{A} = \begin{bmatrix} a & b \\ c & d \end{bmatrix} \tag{18}$$

of left-hand side coefficients (of the unknowns) and its matrix

$$\mathbf{B} = \begin{bmatrix} p \\ q \end{bmatrix} \tag{19}$$

of right-hand side constants. The letters **A** and **B** simply represent the indicated arrays in (18) and (19).

The **coefficient matrix A** in (18) is called a 2×2 (or 2-by-2) matrix, for obvious reasons—it has the two *horizontal* **rows**

$$\begin{bmatrix} a & b \end{bmatrix}$$
and
$$\begin{bmatrix} c & d \end{bmatrix},$$

as well as the two *vertical* **columns**

$$\begin{bmatrix} a \\ c \end{bmatrix} \quad \text{and} \quad \begin{bmatrix} b \\ d \end{bmatrix}.$$

The **constant matrix B** in (19) is a 2×1 matrix because it has the two rows $[p]$ and $[q]$ but just one vertical column.

In terms of its coefficient and constant matrices, the linear system in (16) can be abbreviated by writing

$$\begin{bmatrix} a & b \\ c & d \end{bmatrix} \begin{bmatrix} x \\ y \end{bmatrix} = \begin{bmatrix} p \\ q \end{bmatrix},$$

or simply

$$\mathbf{A} \begin{bmatrix} x \\ y \end{bmatrix} = \mathbf{B}, \tag{20}$$

where

$$\begin{bmatrix} x \\ y \end{bmatrix}$$

is a 2×1 *unknown matrix* consisting of the two unknown numbers x and y.

In some ways, matrices can be used symbolically like other algebraic symbols. For instance, think of the fact that the solution of the single equation

$$Ax = B \tag{21}$$

(where *A*, *B*, and *x* represent ordinary numbers) can be written in the form

$$x = \frac{B}{A} = A^{-1}B. \tag{22}$$

There is an obvious analogy between (20) and (21)—in each we see a coefficient number or matrix, an unknown number or matrix, and a constant number or matrix. In analogy with (22) we can symbolically write

$$\begin{bmatrix} x \\ y \end{bmatrix} = \mathbf{A}^{-1}\mathbf{B} \tag{23}$$

to represent the solution matrix for the original linear system in (16).

The amazing thing is that an algebra of matrices has been devised so that (23) actually makes sense! That is, the "inverse matrix" $\mathbf{A}^{-1}$ can be calculated as a 2×2 matrix, and then the product of the matrices $\mathbf{A}^{-1}$ and $\mathbf{B}$ can be calculated, so that the result is the 2×1 **solution matrix** $\begin{bmatrix} x \\ y \end{bmatrix}$ consisting of the two unknown values *x* and *y*. Indeed, our graphing calculator can do this!

Example 10

Consider again the linear system

$$7x + 6y = 202$$
$$11x + 9y = 245$$

with coefficient matrix and constant matrix given by

$$\mathbf{A} = \begin{bmatrix} 7 & 6 \\ 11 & 9 \end{bmatrix} \quad \text{and} \quad \mathbf{B} = \begin{bmatrix} 202 \\ 245 \end{bmatrix}.$$

We enter these matrices in our calculator using the **MATRX EDIT** menu (Fig. 5.2.6), where available matrices are denoted by **[A]**, **[B]**, **[C]**, and so forth. If we select matrix **[A]** and enter 2×2 we see a 2-by-2 array ready to receive our entries (Fig. 5.2.7).

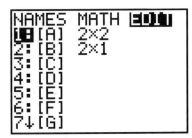

Figure 5.2.6   The **MATRX EDIT** menu.

Figure 5.2.7   The matrix **[A]** before entry of the coefficients in our system.

We can now enter the coefficients in our linear system one at a time, first those on the first row, then those on the second row (Fig. 5.2.8). Next we enter similarly our system's 2×1 constant matrix **[B]** (Fig. 5.2.9).

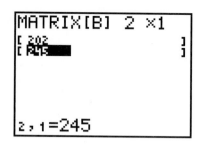

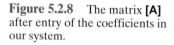

Figure 5.2.8   The matrix **[A]** after entry of the coefficients in our system.

Figure 5.2.9   Our system's constant matrix **[B]**.

Now we're ready! We need only enter **[A]**$^{-1}$**[B]** [as in Eq. (23)]—using the **MATRX NAMES** menu—to calculate the solution (Fig. 5.2.10).

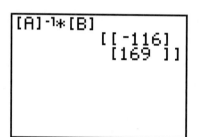

Figure 5.2.10   Calculating the solution matrix $\begin{bmatrix} x \\ y \end{bmatrix}$.

The result

$$\begin{bmatrix} x \\ y \end{bmatrix} = \begin{bmatrix} -116 \\ 169 \end{bmatrix}$$

tells us that the solution of our system is given by $x = -116$, $y = 169$.   ◣

To solve any other linear system of two equations in two unknowns, we need only reenter the elements of the coefficient and constant matrices **[A]** and **[B]** for our new system, then recalculate the solution matrix **[A]**$^{-1}$**[B]**.

Applications

Algebra textbooks usually contain several types of word problems—such as coin problems, mixture problems, and the like—that may seem unrelated but actually fit a single pattern. Such a problem typically deals with the unknown numbers x and y of two different items, such as widgets and wodgets. The total number N of widgets and wodgets is given, so we know that

$$x + y = N.$$

We also know that the value of each widget is c, and the value of each wodget is d. Finally, the total value V of the all the widgets and wodgets is given, so we also know that

$$cx + dy = V.$$

We can therefore find the number x of widgets and the number y of wodgets by solving the linear system

$$x + y = N$$
$$cx + dy = V. \tag{24}$$

These equations provide a common mathematical model for a wide range of value problems. Except for inflation, the following example is like a coin problem, in which one typically is asked to find the numbers of nickels and dimes in a bag of coins.

Example 11

You are walking down the street minding your own business when you spot a thick envelope lying on the sidewalk. It turns out to contain fives and twenties, a total of 61 bills with a total value of $875. How many of each type of bill is there?
    If there are x fives and y twenties, then

$$x + y = 61 \qquad \textbf{(total number)},$$
$$5x + 20y = 875 \quad \textbf{(total value)} \tag{25}$$

because each of the x fives is worth 5 dollars, and each of the y twenties is worth 20 dollars. Using the determinant method in Eq. (17), we find that

$$x = \frac{\begin{vmatrix} 61 & 1 \\ 875 & 20 \end{vmatrix}}{\begin{vmatrix} 1 & 1 \\ 5 & 20 \end{vmatrix}} = \frac{1220 - 875}{20 - 5} = \frac{345}{15} = 23$$

and

$$y = \frac{\begin{vmatrix} 1 & 61 \\ 5 & 875 \end{vmatrix}}{\begin{vmatrix} 1 & 1 \\ 5 & 20 \end{vmatrix}} = \frac{875 - 305}{20 - 5} = \frac{570}{15} = 38.$$

Thus our lucky envelope contained 23 fives and 38 twenties.   ◤

    The denominator determinant in this example is 15, however many fives and twenties there are. Can you see if both the total number of bills and their total value are multiples of 15, then x and y are both *integers*? For instance, if your bonanza had consisted of $77 \times 15 = 1155$ bills adding up to $777 \times 15 = 11655$ dollars, then you would have found that there were 763 fives and 392 twenties. (Pick a pair of multiples of 15 to try out for yourself.)
    The following example is a mixture problem. We can regard it as a value problem modeled by Eqs. (24) by regarding the water in an alcohol-water solution as worthless. Then the value of the solution is measured by the amount of alcohol it contains.

Example 12

Suppose large quantities of both a 7% alcohol solution and a 17% alcohol solution are available. How many gallons of each must be mixed in order to get 42 gallons of a 13% alcohol solution?

Suppose we mix x gallons of the 7% solution with y gallons of the 17% solution. We must have

$$x + y = 42$$

in order to get 42 gallons of the mixed 13% solution. Now

$$\begin{pmatrix} \text{alcohol in the} \\ \text{7\% solution} \end{pmatrix} + \begin{pmatrix} \text{alcohol in the} \\ \text{17\% solution} \end{pmatrix} = \begin{pmatrix} \text{alcohol in the} \\ \text{13\% solution} \end{pmatrix},$$

that is,

$$(7\% \text{ of } x) + (17\% \text{ of } y) = (13\% \text{ of } 42),$$

so

$$0.07x + 0.17y = 0.13 \times 42 = 5.46.$$

This last equation is of the form of the second equation in (24), with $c = 0.07$, $d = 0.17$, and $V = 5.46$. Thus we can find x and y by solving the two equations

$$\begin{aligned} x + y &= 42 \\ 0.07x + 0.17y &= 5.46. \end{aligned} \tag{26}$$

Using the determinant method in Eq. (17), we find that

$$x = \frac{\begin{vmatrix} 42 & 1 \\ 5.46 & 0.17 \end{vmatrix}}{\begin{vmatrix} 1 & 1 \\ 0.07 & 0.17 \end{vmatrix}} = \frac{42 \times 0.17 - 5.46 \times 1}{0.17 - 0.07} = \frac{1.68}{0.1} = 16.8$$

and

$$y = \frac{\begin{vmatrix} 1 & 42 \\ 0.07 & 5.46 \end{vmatrix}}{\begin{vmatrix} 1 & 1 \\ 0.07 & 0.17 \end{vmatrix}} = \frac{1 \times 5.46 - 0.07 \times 42}{0.17 - 0.07} = \frac{2.52}{0.1} = 25.2.$$

Thus we should mix 16.8 gallons of a 7% solution with 25.2 gallons of a 17% solution in order to get 42 gallons of a 13% solution.   ◼

Summary

In this section you have seen five different methods of solving two linear equations in two unknowns:

- Graphic—as in Example 4;
- Elimination—as in Examples 5 and 6;
- Symbolic formulas—as in Example 7;
- Determinants—as in Examples 8 and 9; and
- Matrices—as in Example 10.

Each of these methods yields its own insights, but in applications like Examples 11 and 12 the determinant method is likely to yield the quickest and most routine calculation. The matrix method is used mainly for larger linear systems (as in Section 5.3).

**5.2
PROBLEMS**

Solve the linear systems in Problems 1–10 using a variety of the methods listed in the Summary for this section. Each x- and y-value is an integer or a simple fraction whose denominator is not greater than 10. Verify that the values you obtain actually satisfy the given equations exactly.

1. $7x + 4y = 26$
   $5x + 3y = 19$

2. $5x + 2y = 26$
   $7x + 3y = 37$

3. $3x + 6y = 11$
   $2x + 2y = 9$

4. $5x + 9y = 26$
   $3x + 6y = 20$

5. $5x + 5y = 3$
   $7x + 8y = 5$

6. $8x + 8y = 15$
   $9x + 10y = 19$

7. $7x - 3y = 14$
   $-9x + 4y = -19$

8. $11x - 7y = -28$
   $13x - 6y = 51$

9. $3859x - 6691y = 5645$
   $5751x - 9976y = 1628$

10. $779x - 691y = 4129$
    $751x - 666y = 4642$

11. You have a bag of 77 nickels and dimes worth 5 dollars. How many coins of each type do you have?

12. You have a bag of 666 nickels and dimes worth 60 dollars. How many coins of each type do you have?

13. You have a bag of 49 dimes and quarters worth 10 dollars. How many coins of each type do you have?

14. You have a bag of 555 dimes and quarters worth 90 dollars. How many coins of each type do you have?

15. You buy 2 dozen hamburgers and cheeseburgers for a small party and pay a total of $19.80. If hamburgers cost 75 cents each and cheeseburgers cost 95 cents each (including tax), how many of each did you buy?

16. You buy 100 dozen chicken and beef sandwiches for a big class reception and pay a total of $1604.60. If chicken sandwiches cost $1.25 cents each and beef sandwiches cost $1.45 cents each (including tax), how many of each did you buy?

17. A package store sold 696 bottles of wine and liquor during a single day, with total receipts of $5298. If the price of wine was $5.75 per bottle and the price of liquor was $11.75 per bottle, how many bottles of each were sold that day?

18. A automobile dealer sold 47 cars one month for a total of $718,500. Some were small cars that sold for $13,500 each, and some were large cars that sold for $18,750 each. How many of each were sold that month?

19. Suppose both a 6% alcohol solution and a 12% alcohol solution are available. How many gallons of each must be mixed in order to get 30 gallons of a 10% alcohol solution?

20. Suppose both a 4% alcohol solution and a 14% alcohol solution are available. How many gallons of each must be mixed in order to get 50 gallons of a 7% alcohol solution?

For Problems 21 and 22 you need to know that 24-karat gold is pure gold, that 12-karat gold is an alloy that is half gold, that 17-karat gold is an alloy that consists of 17 parts gold and 7 parts of another metal, and so on.

21. Suppose that both pure gold and 14-karat gold are available. How many grams of each must be mixed to get 120 grams of 17-karat gold?

22. Suppose that both 8-karat gold and 16-karat gold are available. How many grams of each must be mixed to get 120 grams of 13-karat gold?

For Problems 23 and 24 you need to know that brass is an alloy of copper and zinc. For instance, 75% brass is 75% copper and 25% zinc; 90% brass is 90% copper and 10% zinc; and so on.

23. Suppose that both 75% brass and 90% brass are available. How many pounds of each must be mixed to get 150 pounds of 87% brass?

24. Suppose that both 65% brass and 95% brass are available. How many pounds of each must be mixed to get 90 pounds of 77% brass?

25. You are trying to match the blue-green paint in your basement, which is a mixture of 37% blue and 63% green paint. You have available cans of light blue-green paint that is 25% blue and 75% green, and also cans of dark blue-green paint that is 35% green and 65% blue paint. How many gallons of each must you mix in order to get 3 gallons of the right paint for your basement?

5.3   LINEAR SYSTEMS OF EQUATIONS

In Section 5.2 we talked about solving two linear equations in two unknowns. Now we talk about solving three or more linear equations in the same number of unknowns. For instance, three linear equations in the three unknowns x, y, z take the form

$$
\begin{aligned}
ax + by + cz &= p \\
dx + ey + fz &= q \\
gx + hy + kz &= r
\end{aligned}
\tag{1}
$$

where the coefficients on the left-hand sides and the constants on the right-hand sides are given numbers. A **solution** of this system is simply a triple x, y, z of numbers that satisfy all three of the equations.

In this section we discuss methods of solving the system in (1) that are analogous to the methods of Section 5.2 for pairs of linear equations:

- The method of elimination,
- The use of determinants, and
- The use of matrices.

Graphic and numeric tabulation methods are not as useful for three or more equations as they are for two equations in two unknowns. One reason is that the graph of a single linear equation in three variables is a *plane* in space (rather than a line in the plane). Therefore, a solution of the system in (1) is a common point of intersection of three planes in space, and this situation is too complicated to represent effectively with a simple graphing calculator.

The Method of Elimination

The three equations in (1) constitute three *pairs* of equations—the first and second equations, the first and third equations, and the second and third equations. If we eliminate x in two of these pairs, we are left with two equations in the two unknowns y and z that can be solved using any one of the methods discussed in Section 5.2. We can then substitute the values of y and z that are found into one of the original equations to solve finally for the value of x.

Example 1

Let's apply this method of elimination to the system

$$x + 2y + z = 4$$
$$3x + 8y + 7z = 20 \tag{2}$$
$$2x + 7y + 9z = 23.$$

First, we observe that we can eliminate x by subtracting three times the first equation from the second equation:

$$(3x + 8y + 7z) - 3 \cdot (x + 2y + z) = 20 - 3 \cdot (4).$$

The result is the equation

$$2y + 4z = 8. \tag{3}$$

Next, we eliminate x again by subtracting two times the first equation from the third equation:

$$(2x + 7y + 9z) - 2 \cdot (x + 2y + z) = 23 - 2 \cdot (4).$$

This gives

$$3y + 7z = 15. \tag{4}$$

Equations (3) and (4) constitute a linear system

$$2y + 4z = 8$$
$$3y + 7z = 15 \tag{5}$$

in the two unknowns y and z. We might ordinarily use 2×2 determinants to solve this system. However, note that the first equation here can be divided by 2 and then solved for

$$y = 4 - 2z. \tag{6}$$

Substitution in the second equation in (5) then gives

$$3(4 - 2z) + 7z = 15,$$
$$12 - 6z + 7z = 15,$$
$$z = 3.$$

Substitution of $z = 3$ in (6) gives

$$y = 4 - 2(3) = -2.$$

Now that we know the values $y = -2$ and $z = 3$, substitution in the first equation in (2) yields

$$x + 2 \cdot (-2) + (3) = 4$$
$$x - 4 + 3 = 4,$$
$$x = 5.$$

Consequently, we have found the solution $x = 5$, $y = -2$, $z = 3$ of the original system (2).

We just substituted the values of y and z we found into the original first equation to find the value of x. It is therefore a good check to verify that our three values $x = 5$, $y = -2$, $z = 3$ satisfy the other two equations in (2):

$$3(5) + 8(-2) + 7(3) = 15 - 16 + 21 = 20$$
$$2(5) + 7(-2) + 9(3) = 10 - 14 + 27 = 23.$$

Thus all is well.   ◪

The precise steps in the solution of Example 1 should *not* be memorized. Instead, carry out the basic approach for three equations in three unknowns however you wish, along the following lines:

- First, eliminate one of the unknowns from some pair of the given equations.
- Then, eliminate the same unknown from another pair of the given equations.
- Solve the resulting pair of equations in two unknowns.
- Finally, substitute the values found into one of the original equations to find the value of the unknown that was eliminated.

In short, you start with the idea of eliminating one of the unknowns and then solving the equations that remain. As for the details, just hammer it out as you go, any which way you can.

In principle, the method of elimination can be applied to systems of four linear equations in four unknowns, to five linear equations in five unknowns, etc. But in practice it is usually easier and quicker for systems larger than 3×3 to use the determinant and matrix methods that we discuss next.

The Determinant Method

Although it would be extremely tedious, one could carry out the method of elimination with the general 3×3 linear system in (1) to solve for the values of the 3 unknowns x, y, z in terms of the coefficients and constants that appear in the three equations. The resulting formulas are best expressed in terms of 3×3 determinants.

The *coefficient determinant* of the system in (1) is defined by

$$\Delta = \begin{vmatrix} a & b & c \\ d & e & f \\ g & h & k \end{vmatrix} = +a \begin{vmatrix} e & f \\ h & k \end{vmatrix} - b \begin{vmatrix} d & f \\ g & k \end{vmatrix} + c \begin{vmatrix} d & e \\ g & h \end{vmatrix}. \tag{7}$$

It remains to evaluate the three 2×2 determinants to get the value of Δ. Observe both

- the $+ - +$ pattern of signs on the right-hand side in (7), and that
- each element of the first row of the 3×3 determinant is multiplied by the 2×2 "subdeterminant" that remains when that element's row and column are deleted.

Example 2

The value of the coefficient determinant of the system

$$x + 2y + z = 4$$
$$3x + 8y + 7z = 20 \tag{8}$$
$$2x + 7y + 9z = 23$$

of Example 1 is

$$\Delta = \begin{vmatrix} 1 & 2 & 1 \\ 3 & 8 & 7 \\ 2 & 7 & 9 \end{vmatrix} = +(1)\begin{vmatrix} 8 & 7 \\ 7 & 9 \end{vmatrix} - (2)\begin{vmatrix} 3 & 7 \\ 2 & 9 \end{vmatrix} + (1)\begin{vmatrix} 3 & 8 \\ 2 & 7 \end{vmatrix}$$

$$= +(72 - 49) - 2(27 - 14) + (21 - 16)$$
$$= +23 - 2(13) + 5$$
$$= 23 - 26 + 5$$

so $\Delta = 2$.   ◣

Here we have expanded the determinant along its first row, but a 3×3 determinant can be expanded along any row or column. We need only remember the checkerboard pattern

$$\begin{vmatrix} + & - & + \\ - & + & - \\ + & - & + \end{vmatrix} \tag{9}$$

of signs that must be attached to the particular row or column elements we use as coefficients of the corresponding three 2×2 subdeterminants. For instance, to expand the coefficient determinant of Example 2 along its second column (instead of along its first row), we attach the signs that appear in the second column in (9). This gives

$$\Delta = \begin{vmatrix} 1 & 2 & 1 \\ 3 & 8 & 7 \\ 2 & 7 & 9 \end{vmatrix} = -(2)\begin{vmatrix} 3 & 7 \\ 2 & 9 \end{vmatrix} + (8)\begin{vmatrix} 1 & 1 \\ 2 & 9 \end{vmatrix} - (7)\begin{vmatrix} 1 & 1 \\ 3 & 7 \end{vmatrix}$$

$$= -2(27 - 14) + 8(9 - 2) - 7(7 - 3)$$
$$= -2(13) + 8(7) - 7(4)$$
$$= -26 + 56 - 28 = 2$$

so we get the same value $\Delta = 2$ of Example 2 by an entirely different calculation. You should check this value by calculating it still another way—by expanding along the first column or along the third row, for instance.

The **determinant formulas** for solution of the 3×3 linear system

$$\begin{aligned} ax + by + cz &= p \\ dx + ey + fz &= q \\ gx + hy + kz &= r \end{aligned} \tag{10}$$

are

$$x = \frac{\begin{vmatrix} p & b & c \\ q & e & f \\ r & h & k \end{vmatrix}}{\Delta}, \quad y = \frac{\begin{vmatrix} a & p & c \\ d & q & f \\ g & r & k \end{vmatrix}}{\Delta}, \quad z = \frac{\begin{vmatrix} a & b & p \\ d & e & q \\ g & h & r \end{vmatrix}}{\Delta}. \tag{11}$$

The way to remember these formulas is the same as with the 2×2 determinant formulas in Section 5.2. We observe that—in solving for any one of the unknowns—*that* unknown's column of coefficients are replaced (in its numerator determinant) by the right-hand-side constants in the system (10). Thus

- the numerator determinant for x is gotten from the coefficient determinant upon replacing the first-column coefficients a, d, g by $p, q, r;$
- the numerator determinant for y is gotten from the coefficient determinant upon replacing the second-column coefficients b, e, h by $p, q, r;$
- the numerator determinant for z is gotten from the coefficient determinant upon replacing the third-column coefficients c, f, k by $p, q, r.$

Consequently, there is no need to remember the particular letters that appear in (11). Instead, we think solely of replacing columns of left-hand-side coefficients with the column of right-hand-side constants.

Recall that the coefficient determinant Δ must be nonzero in order to divide by it in (11). If $\Delta = 0$, then it turns out that the system has *either* infinitely many different solutions *or* no solution at all. In the applications we consider, we need not be concerned with these exceptional cases.

Determinant calculations by hand are particularly error prone, so it's good practice to calculate each one two different ways (by expanding along different rows and columns). This can be tedious, so the use of a calculator is an attractive alternative. In this case, the accurate entry of each determinant is crucial, because the entry of the nine elements of a 3×3 determinant is itself somewhat error prone. We will illustrate the use of the calculator to evaluate the determinants in the next example.

Example 3

Solve the system

$$x + 2y + z = 4$$
$$3x + 8y + 7z = 20 \qquad (12)$$
$$2x + 7y + 9z = 23$$

using determinants.

Unnecessary labor—and additional possibility of keystroke errors—can be avoided by an efficient approach to entry of the four determinants that are needed for the solution of a 3×3 system. Figure 5.3.1 shows the entry of the 3×3 array or matrix **[D]** of coefficients in the 3×3 system (12). (The available calculator names for matrices are selected from the **MATRX NAMES** menu and are automatically enclosed with square brackets.)

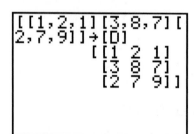

Figure 5.3.1   The coefficient matrix of the 3×3 system in (12).

Instead of entering separately the three numerator matrices in (11), we first make three separate copies **[A]**, **[B]**, and **[C]** of the coefficient matrix (Fig. 5.3.2).

Then we need only edit each of these matrices, adjusting the appropriate column of each to get the numerator matrices required for the *x, y,* and *z* determinant formulas. For instance, Fig. 5.3.3 shows the original first column of **[A]** replaced with the column of right-hand-side constants in (12).

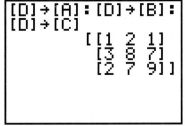

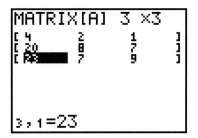

Figure 5.3.2   Making three copies of the coefficient matrix.

Figure 5.3.3   The numerator matrix **[A]** for *x.*

Figures 5.3.4 and 5.3.5 show the numerator matrices for *y* and *z.* Editing the three matrices is much quicker than entering them from scratch.

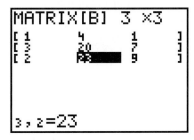

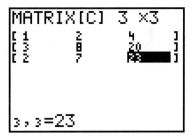

Figure 5.3.4   The numerator matrix **[B]** for *y.*

Figure 5.3.5   The numerator matrix **[C]** for *z.*

Once they're entered, we divide out the determinants in (11) to calculate the desired values of the unknowns *x, y,* and *z.* Since the numerator matrices **[A], [B], [C]** correspond to the unknowns *x, y, z,* and the denominator matrix is **[D]**, the determinant formulas in (11) take the calculator forms

$$x = \frac{\det(\mathbf{[A]})}{\det(\mathbf{[D]})}, \quad y = \frac{\det(\mathbf{[B]})}{\det(\mathbf{[D]})}, \quad z = \frac{\det(\mathbf{[C]})}{\det(\mathbf{[D]})},$$

that we see in Fig. 5.3.6.

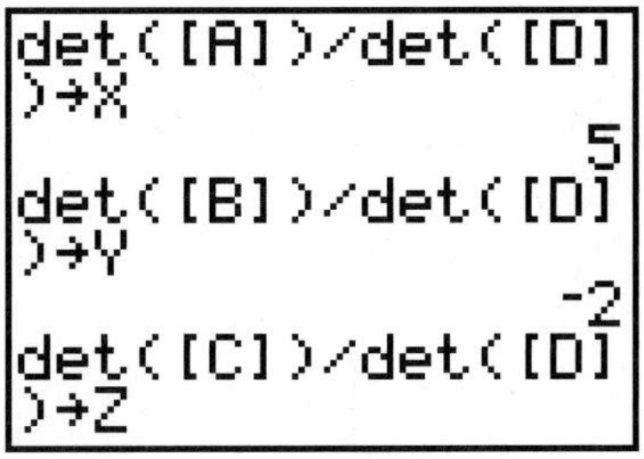

```
det([A])/det([D]
)→X
                 5
det([B])/det([D]
)→Y
                -2
det([C])/det([D]
)→Z
```

Figure 5.3.6   Finally, calculating the unknowns *x, y,* and *z.*

Thus, the solution to the linear system is the triple *x* = 5, *y* = −2, *z* = 3, the same solution we got when we solved the system by elimination.

The key to making math easy often lies in making the notation work for us (rather than the other way around). Surely it's easy to remember that the numerator matrices **[A], [B], [C]** correspond to the unknowns x, y, z, and that the denominator matrix is **[D]**.

As before, the bottom line is this: While solving a system of three linear equations by elimination may require some ingenuity, the solution using determinants is straightforward. Just substitute in the determinant formulas and calculate (either by hand or by calculator).

Using Matrices

Figures 5.3.1 through 5.3.6 illustrate the calculator entry and manipulation of 3×3 arrays or *matrices*. In general, matrices are used to solve linear systems of three or more equations in the same way as with two equations in two unknowns (Section 5.2). The solution of the 3×3 system

$$
\begin{aligned}
ax + by + cz &= p \\
dx + ey + fz &= q \\
gx + hy + kz &= r
\end{aligned}
\tag{13}
$$

is determined by its 3×3 **coefficient matrix**

$$
\mathbf{A} = \begin{bmatrix} a & b & c \\ d & e & f \\ g & h & k \end{bmatrix}
\tag{14}
$$

and its 3×1 matrix

$$
\mathbf{B} = \begin{bmatrix} p \\ q \\ r \end{bmatrix}
\tag{15}
$$

of right-hand-side constants. Observe that the three *rows*

$$
\begin{bmatrix} a & b & c \end{bmatrix}, \\
\begin{bmatrix} d & e & f \end{bmatrix}, \\
\begin{bmatrix} g & h & k \end{bmatrix}
$$

of the coefficient matrix **A** contain (respectively) the coefficients of the unknowns in the three separate equations in (13). The three *columns*

$$
\begin{bmatrix} a \\ d \\ g \end{bmatrix}, \begin{bmatrix} b \\ e \\ h \end{bmatrix}, \begin{bmatrix} c \\ f \\ k \end{bmatrix}
$$

of **A** are (respectively) the coefficients of x, the coefficients of y, and the coefficients of z in the equations.

In terms of its coefficient and constant matrices, the linear system in (16) can be abbreviated by writing

$$
\begin{bmatrix} a & b & c \\ d & e & f \\ g & h & k \end{bmatrix} \begin{bmatrix} x \\ y \\ z \end{bmatrix} = \begin{bmatrix} p \\ q \\ r \end{bmatrix},
$$

or simply

$$A \begin{bmatrix} x \\ y \\ z \end{bmatrix} = \mathbf{B}, \tag{16}$$

where

$$\begin{bmatrix} x \\ y \\ z \end{bmatrix}$$

is a 3×1 *unknown matrix* consisting of the three unknown numbers x, y, and z. Just as the solution of the single equation

$$Ax = B \tag{17}$$

(where A, B, and x represent ordinary numbers) can be written in the form

$$x = \frac{B}{A} = A^{-1}B, \tag{18}$$

we can symbolically write

$$\begin{bmatrix} x \\ y \\ z \end{bmatrix} = \mathbf{A}^{-1}\mathbf{B} \tag{19}$$

to represent the solution matrix for the 3×3 linear system in (13).

After the coefficient matrix $\mathbf{A}$ has been entered, our calculator can find the 3×3 inverse matrix $\mathbf{A}^{-1}$. Then the product of the matrices $\mathbf{A}^{-1}$ and $\mathbf{B}$ can be calculated, so that the result is the 3×1 **solution matrix** $\begin{bmatrix} x \\ y \\ z \end{bmatrix}$ consisting of the three unknown values x, y, and z.

Example 4

Consider again the linear system

$$\begin{aligned} x + 2y + z &= 4 \\ 3x + 8y + 7z &= 20 \\ 2x + 7y + 9z &= 23 \end{aligned}$$

with coefficient matrix and constant matrix given by

$$\mathbf{A} = \begin{bmatrix} 1 & 2 & 1 \\ 3 & 8 & 7 \\ 2 & 7 & 9 \end{bmatrix} \quad \text{and} \quad \mathbf{B} = \begin{bmatrix} 4 \\ 20 \\ 23 \end{bmatrix}.$$

Figures 5.3.7 and 5.3.8 show the calculator entry of these two matrices. Note that we enter the elements of a matrix (of whatever size) one row at a time, with each row enclosed within square brackets, and with the list of rows enclosed within

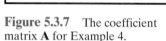

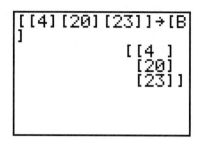

Figure 5.3.7   The coefficient matrix **A** for Example 4.

Figure 5.3.8   The matrix **B** of constants for Example 4.

another pair of square brackets, like **[[· · ·][· · ·][· · ·]]** (where each ... denotes the elements of a separate row).

Once the matrices **A** and **B** have been entered, we need only enter **[A]⁻¹∗[B]** [as in Eq. (19)]—using the **MATRX NAMES** menu—to calculate the solution (Fig. 5.3.9). The result

$$\begin{bmatrix} x \\ y \\ z \end{bmatrix} = \begin{bmatrix} 5 \\ -2 \\ 3 \end{bmatrix}$$

tells us that the solution of our system is given by $x = 5$, $y = -2$, and $z = 3$.   ∎

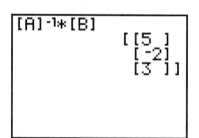

Figure 5.3.9   Calculating the values $x = 5$, $y = -2$, $z = 3$ of the three unknowns in Example 4.

To solve any other linear system of three equations in three unknowns, we need only reenter the elements of the coefficient and constant matrices **[A]** and **[B]** for our new system, then recalculate the solution matrix **[A]⁻¹∗[B]**. In fact, we can solve in exactly the same way a system of four equations in four unknowns, or a system of five or more equations in the same number of unknowns.

Example 5

To solve the system

$$\begin{aligned} 3w - 2x + 7y + 5z &= 505 \\ 2w + 4x - y + 6z &= 435 \\ 5w + x + 7y - 3z &= 286 \\ 4w - 6x - 8y + 9z &= 445 \end{aligned}$$

of four equations in the four unknowns w, x, y, z, we enter the coefficient matrix **A** and the constant matrix **B**, then calculate **A⁻¹∗B** as indicated in Figs. 5.3.10–5.3.12. Thus we find that $w = 59$, $x = 13$, $y = 17$, $z = 47$.   ∎

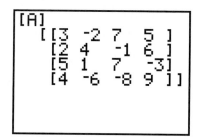

Figure 5.3.10   The 4×4 coefficient matrix **A** in Example 5.

Figure 5.3.11   The 4×1 matrix **B** of contents in Example 5.

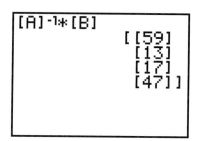

Figure 5.3.12   Finding the solution values in Example 5.

Applications

In Section 5.2 we discussed word problems that lead to two linear equations in two unknowns. If you're armed with a powerful calculator, word problems with three unknowns are essentially the same. The only difference is that you must continue writing relations between the three unknowns until you have three equations to solve.

Example 6

You are walking down the street minding your own business when you spot a small but heavy leather bag lying on the sidewalk. It turns out to contain U.S. Mint American Eagle gold coins of the following types:

- One-half ounce gold coins that sell for \$285 each,
- One-quarter ounce gold coins that sell for \$150 each, and
- One-tenth ounce gold coins that sell for \$70 each.

A bank receipt found in the bag certifies that it contains 258 such coins with a total weight of 67 ounces and a total value of exactly \$40,145. How many coins of each type are there?

If x is the number of half-ounce coins, y is the number of quarter-ounce coins, and z is the number of tenth-ounce coins in the bag, then the fact that there are 258 coins in all means that

$$x + y + z = 258.$$

If we multiply the number of coins of each type by its weight in ounces and add up these weights, we get the equation

$$\frac{1}{2}x + \frac{1}{4}y + \frac{1}{10}z = 67,$$

because we know that the coins weigh 67 ounces. Finally, we add up the dollar values of the coins of each type and get the equation

$$285x + 150y + 70z = 40145.$$

This system of three equations in three unknowns has coefficient and constant matrices

$$\mathbf{A} = \begin{bmatrix} 1 & 1 & 1 \\ \frac{1}{2} & \frac{1}{4} & \frac{1}{10} \\ 285 & 150 & 70 \end{bmatrix} \quad \text{and} \quad \mathbf{B} = \begin{bmatrix} 258 \\ 67 \\ 40145 \end{bmatrix}.$$

Once we have entered these two matrices, the usual calculation (Fig. 5.3.13) reveals that our bounty consists of 67 half-ounce gold coins, 96 quarter-ounce gold coins, and 95 tenth-ounce gold coins. ◼

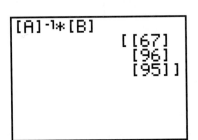

Figure 5.3.13 The numbers of gold bullion coins in Example 6.

As an example of a mixing problem involving three equations in three unknowns, let's consider a paint store that prepares whatever color of paint the customer orders by mixing appropriate amounts of pure red paint, pure green paint, and pure blue paint.

Example 7

A commercial customer orders 81 gallons of paint that contains equal amounts of red paint, green paint, and blue paint—and hence could be prepared by mixing 27 gallons of each. However, the store wishes to prepare this order by mixing three types of paint that are already available in large quantity:

- a *reddish* paint that is a mixture of 50% red, 25% green, and 25% blue paint;
- a *greenish* paint that is 12.5% red, 75% green, and 12.5% blue paint; and
- a *bluish* paint that is 20% red, 20% green, and 60% blue paint.

How many gallons of each are needed to prepare the customer's order?

If x gallons of reddish paint, y gallons of greenish paint, and z gallons of bluish paint are mixed, then the resulting mixture contains

- $0.5x$ gallons of pure red paint, because reddish paint is 50% red; plus
- $0.125y$ gallons of pure red paint, because greenish paint is 12.5% red; plus
- $0.2z$ gallons of pure red paint, because bluish paint is 20% red.

These three amounts must add up to the 27 gallons of pure red paint needed for the customer's desired mixture, so it follows that x, y, and z must satisfy the equation

$$0.5x + 0.125y + 0.2z = 27.$$

Similarly, the amounts $0.25x$ gallons of pure green paint in the reddish paint, $0.75y$ gallons of pure green paint in the greenish paint, and the $0.2z$ gallons of pure green paint in the bluish paint must add up to the 27 gallons of pure green paint that is needed for the desired mixture. Thus x, y, and z must satisfy the second equation

$$0.25x + 0.75y + 0.2z = 27.$$

Finally, the amounts $0.25x$ gallons of pure blue paint in the reddish paint, $0.125y$ gallons of pure blue paint in the greenish paint, and the $0.6z$ gallons of pure blue paint in the bluish paint must add up to the 27 gallons of pure blue paint that is needed for the desired mixture. Thus x, y, and z must satisfy the third equation

$$0.25x + 0.125y + 0.6z = 27.$$

These three equations comprise a 3×3 system with coefficient and constant matrices

$$\mathbf{A} = \begin{bmatrix} 0.5 & 0.125 & 0.2 \\ 0.25 & 0.75 & 0.2 \\ 0.25 & 0.125 & 0.6 \end{bmatrix} \quad \text{and} \quad \mathbf{B} = \begin{bmatrix} 27 \\ 27 \\ 27 \end{bmatrix}.$$

As indicated in Figs. 5.3.14 and 5.3.15, a calculator solution gives the amounts $x = 40$ gallons of reddish paint, $y = 16$ gallons of greenish paint, and $z = 25$ gallons of bluish paint that must be mixed to prepare the customer's 81 gallons of equally mixed red/green/blue paint. ◣

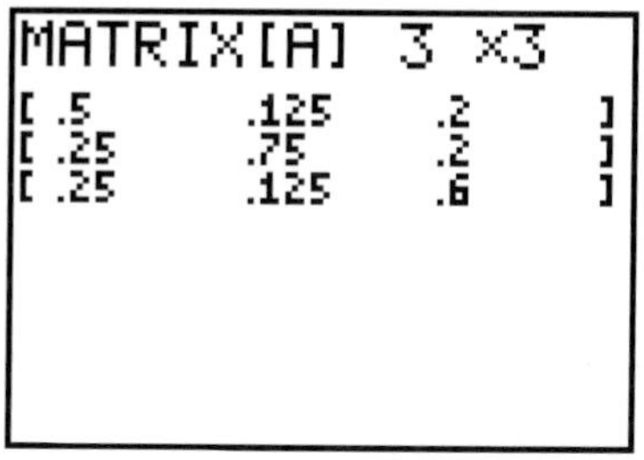

Figure 5.3.14 The coefficient matrix **A** in Example 7.

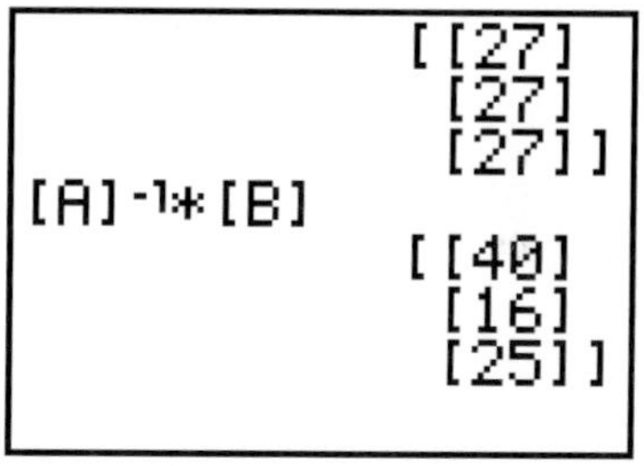

Figure 5.3.15 The constant and solution matrices in Example 7.

**5.3
PROBLEMS**

Each of the determinants in Problems 1–4 is most easily evaluated by expansion along a carefully chosen row or column. Do so.

1. $\begin{vmatrix} 0 & 3 & -2 \\ -3 & 11 & 17 \\ 0 & 5 & 7 \end{vmatrix}$

2. $\begin{vmatrix} 5 & 4 & 10 \\ 4 & 5 & 20 \\ 0 & 0 & 5 \end{vmatrix}$

3. $\begin{vmatrix} 5 & 77 & 4 \\ 0 & 3 & 0 \\ 4 & 99 & 5 \end{vmatrix}$

4. $\begin{vmatrix} 21 & 31 & 5 \\ 11 & 10 & 0 \\ 12 & 11 & 0 \end{vmatrix}$

Each of the linear systems in Problems 5–10 is especially easy to solve by elimination, because a single operation combining a carefully selected pair of equations suffices to reduce the given 3×3 system to a 2×2 system. Solve each system in this manner.

5. $x + 4y - z = 5$
    $x + 3y + z = 8$
    $2y + z = 4$

6. $2x - 3y + z = 7$
    $3y + 2z = 11$
    $2x + 2y + z = 12$

7. $7x + 3y + z = 39$
    $5x + 3y + 2z = 36$
    $2x + 3z = 23$

8. $7x + 5y + 3z = 18$
    $4x + 2z = 14$
    $2x + 5y + 6z = 17$

9. $4x + 7y = 5$
    $6x + 5y + 4z = -5$
    $8x + 3y + 4z = 25$

10. $15x + 17y + 11z = 22$
    $13x + 16y + 11z = 23$
    $29x + 9y = 13$

Use either determinants or matrix inverses (with your calculator) to solve the systems in Problems 11–16.

11. $17x + 42y - 36z = 213$
    $13x + 45y - 34z = 226$
    $12x + 47y - 35z = 197$

12. $32x + 57y - 41z = 713$
    $23x + 43y - 37z = 130$
    $42x - 61y + 39z = 221$

13. $231x + 157y - 241z = 420$
    $323x + 181y - 375z = 412$
    $542x + 161y - 759z = 419$

14. $837x + 667y - 729z = 1659$
    $152x - 179y - 975z = 1630$
    $542x + 328y - 759z = 1645$

15. $81w - 97x + 67y - 19z = 50$
    $12w - 15x - 79y - 82z = 102$
    $42w - 54x + 14y - 29z = 78$
    $13w + 27x + 63y + 25z = 74$

16. $64w - 57x + 97y - 67z = 485$
    $92w + 77x - 34y - 37z = 486$
    $44w - 34x + 53y - 34z = 465$
    $27w + 57x - 69y + 29z = 464$

17. Suppose you find a smaller bag of U.S. American Eagle half-ounce, quarter-ounce, and tenth-ounce gold coins valued as in Example 6. If this bag contains a total of 58 coins with a total weight of 17 ounces and a total value of $10,065, how many gold coins of each type are there?

18. Now you really strike it rich! You find a bag containing one-ounce U.S. American Eagle gold coins valued at $550 each, together with half-ounce and quarter-ounce coins valued as in Example 6. If this bag contains a total of 365 coins with a total weight of exactly 11 pounds and a total value of $100,130, how many gold coins of each type are there?

19. A commercial customer orders 51 gallons of paint that contains equal amounts of red paint, green paint, and blue paint—and hence could be prepared by mixing 17 gallons of each pure color of paint. However, the store wishes to prepare this order by mixing three types of already mixed paint that are available in large quantity—the reddish paint and the bluish paint of Example 7, and a greenish paint that is one-sixth red, two-thirds green, and one-sixth blue paint. How many gallons of each are needed?

20. Now the paint store receives a really big order—for 244 gallons of paint that is one-half red paint, one-quarter green paint, and one-quarter blue paint. The store has three already-mixed types of paint available in large quantity—the greenish paint and the bluish paint of Example 7, plus a reddish paint that is two-thirds red paint, one-sixth green paint, and one-sixth blue paint. How many gallons of each must be mixed in order to fill this order?

21. A tour busload of 45 people attended two Florida theme parks on successive days. On Day 1 the entrance fee was $15 per adult, $8 per child, $12 per senior citizen and the total charge was $558. On Day 2 the entrance fee was $20 per adult, $12 per child, $17 per senior citizen and the total charge was $771. How many adults, children, and senior citizens were on this tour bus?

22. For some crazy reason, the lunches bought at the first theme park were totaled separately for the adults, children, and seniors. The adults ordered 34 hot dogs, 15 French fries, and 24 soft drinks for a total bill of $70.85. The children ordered 20 hot dogs, 14 French fries, and 15 soft drinks for a total bill of $46.65. The senior citizens ordered 11 hot dogs, 10 French fries, and 12 soft drinks for a total bill of $30.05. What were the prices of a hot dog, an order of French fries, and a soft drink?

23. Carter has a weekend business selling Beanie Babies at flea markets in Missouri. She keeps very close track of the changing prices of these popular collectibles. In April a customer spilled coffee on a page of her records, and information on Happy the hippo, Hippity the bunny, and Hoot the owl was lost. The following table gives the numbers of each Beanie Baby sold and the total receipts from three different markets. How much did Carter charge in April for each of these Beanie Babies?

	Happy	Hippity	Hoot	Receipts
Jefferson City	5	8	6	$488
Columbia	4	9	10	$653
Cape Girardeau	8	6	8	$562

24. An office supply company with four locations sells TI-82, TI-83, TI-85, and TI-86 calculators. During the month of August, the stores reported the following sales.

	TI-82	TI-83	TI-85	TI-86	Receipts
Store 1	4	94	10	32	$14,130
Store 2	8	80	3	29	$12,100
Store 3	6	50	2	4	$ 5970
Store 4	5	63	7	21	$ 9655

At what price did the company sell each model calculator?

25. A fast food restaurant sells four types of sandwiches—hamburgers, cheeseburgers, roast beef, and chicken—and has four cash registers. At the end of each day, each cash register tallies the number of each type of sandwich sold and the total sandwich receipts for the day. The four cash register operators work at different speeds, and one day's totals were as follows:

	Hamburgers	Cheeseburgers	Roast Beef	Chicken	Receipts
Register 1	37	44	17	23	$232.99
Register 2	28	35	13	17	$178.97
Register 3	32	39	19	21	$215.99
Register 4	47	51	25	29	$294.38

What was the price of each of the four types of sandwiches?

26. The fast food restaurant of Problem 29 adds a ham sandwich to its menu, and due to increased business it also adds a fifth cash register and reduces prices. After this expansion, one day's totals were as follows:

	Hamburgers	Cheeseburgers	Roast Beef	Chicken	Ham	Total
Register 1	41	49	22	26	19	$292.79
Register 2	34	39	18	20	16	$236.73
Register 3	36	43	23	24	18	$270.70
Register 4	49	52	26	31	24	$340.19
Register 5	52	55	24	28	25	$341.64

What were the new prices of the five types of sandwiches?

5.4   POLYNOMIAL DATA MODELING

The following table shows the total world population (in billions) at 5-year intervals. Actual world populations are shown for the years 1960–1995. The figures listed for the years 2000–2025 are future populations predicted by the United

Nations on the basis of detailed demographic analysis of population trends on a country-by-country basis throughout the world.

Year	World Population (billions)	Percent Growth
1960	3.039	
1965	3.345	1.94%
1970	3.707	2.08%
1975	4.086	1.97%
1980	4.454	1.74%
1985	4.851	1.72%
1990	5.279	1.71%
1995	5.688	1.50%
2000	6.083	1.35%
2005	6.468	1.23%
2010	6.849	1.15%
2015	7.227	1.08%
2020	7.585	0.97%
2025	7.923	0.88%

Each entry in the third column of this table gives the average annual percentage growth rate during the preceding 5-year period. For instance, to find the average growth rate r from 1960 to 1965, we solved the equation

$$3.345 = 3.039(1 + r)^5$$

for

$$r = \left(\frac{3.345}{3.039}\right)^{1/5} - 1 \approx 0.01937 \approx 1.94\%.$$

We see that the world population grew at an annual rate of about 2% during the 1960s, but the rate of growth has slowed since then, and it is expected to slow even more during the early decades of the twenty-first century.

Thus the growth of the world population at present is *not* natural or exponential in character. In this section we explore the possibility of fitting world population data with polynomial models that might be used to predict future populations.

Linear and Quadratic Models

First, recall from Section 1.2 that two data points determine a linear function whose graph is a straight line. Thus, given any two year-population pairs (t_1, P_1) and (t_2, P_2), there exists a linear function

$$P(t) = a + bt \tag{1}$$

such that $P(t_1) = P_1$ and $P(t_2) = P_2$. As in the following example, we need to solve two linear equations in two unknowns to find the values of the coefficients a and b in (1).

Example 1

Let's fit a linear function to the 1980 and 1990 world population values. If we substitute first the data point $(1980, 4.454)$ and then the data point $(1990, 5.279)$ into (1), we get the two equations

$$4.454 = a + 1980b$$
$$5.279 = a + 1990b. \tag{2}$$

We note that the a-terms cancel if we subtract the first equation from the second one. The result is $10b = 5.279 - 4.454 = 0.825$, so $b = 0.0825$. Substitution of this value in the first equation in (2) then gives

$$a = 4.454 - 1980(0.0825) = -158.896.$$

With these coefficients, our linear population model (1) is

$$P(t) = -158.896 + 0.0825t. \tag{3}$$

You should always check your solution of a system of equations. The way we found a appears to guarantee that the first equation in (2) is satisfied, and

$$-158.896 + 0.0825(1990) = 5.279,$$

so the second one is satisfied also. (The first time we ourselves worked Example 1, a numerical error in recording the value of b was revealed when we performed this check.)
Substitution of $t = 2000$ in (3) gives

$$P(2000) = -158.896 + 0.0825(2000) = 6.104$$

billion as our linear extrapolation for the world population in the year 2000. This is a bit more than the U.N. prediction of 6.083 billion. (This is being written late in 1999, but by the time you read it, you should be able to find the actual year 2000 world population by consulting the Web site www.census.gov.) ◣

Just as two data points determine a linear function whose graph is a straight line, three given data points determine a quadratic function with parabolic graph (as in Chapter 2). Thus, given any three year-population pairs (t_1, P_1), (t_2, P_2), and (t_3, P_3), there exists a quadratic function

$$P(t) = a + bt + ct^2 \tag{4}$$

such that $P(t_1) = P_1$, $P(t_2) = P_2$, and $P(t_3) = P_3$. As in the following example, we need only solve three linear equations in three unknowns to find the values of the coefficients a, b, and c in (4).

Example 2

Now let's fit a quadratic function to the 1970, 1980, and 1990 world population values. If we substitute the three data points $(1970, 3.707)$, $(1980, 4.454)$, and $(1990, 5.279)$ into (4), we get the three equations

$$3.707 = a + 1970b + 1970^2c$$
$$4.454 = a + 1980b + 1980^2c \tag{5}$$
$$5.279 = a + 1990b + 1990^2c.$$

This is a linear system of equations with the 3×1 unknown and constant matrices

$$\mathbf{X} = \begin{bmatrix} a \\ b \\ c \end{bmatrix} \quad \text{and} \quad \mathbf{B} = \begin{bmatrix} 3.707 \\ 4.454 \\ 5.279 \end{bmatrix}$$

and with the 3×3 coefficient matrix

$$\mathbf{A} = \begin{bmatrix} 1 & 1970 & 1970^2 \\ 1 & 1980 & 1980^2 \\ 1 & 1990 & 1990^2 \end{bmatrix}.$$

Figures 5.4.1 and 5.4.2 show the calculator entry of **A** and **B,** and Fig. 5.4.3 then shows the solution for the unknown matrix **X** (which we save as **[G]** because our calculator allows for saving only the 10 matrices **[A]** through **[J]**, and hence has no matrix **[X]**).

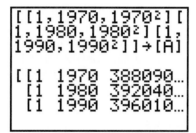

Figure 5.4.1   The coefficient matrix **A** of the 3×3 system in (5).

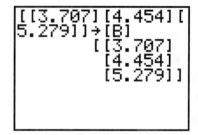

Figure 5.4.2   The constant matrix **B** of the 3×3 system in (5).

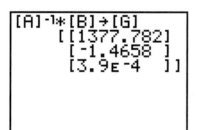

Figure 5.4.3   Calculating the coefficients in (5).

We see that the components of **X=[G]** are $a = 1377.782$, $b = -1.4658$, and $c = 0.00039$. Substituting these coefficient values in (4), we get the quadratic population model

$$P(t) = 1377.782 - 1.4658t + 0.00039t^2. \tag{6}$$

To facilitate checking our solution of the equations in (5), we first save the coefficient values $a = 1377.782$, $b = -1.4658$, and $c = 0.00039$ as the calculator values A, B, and C. Then we can quickly check the equations individually as indicated in Fig. 5.4.4. Alternatively, we can check the system all at once by matrix multiplication as indicated in Fig. 5.4.5 (where the formal matrix product **AX** is entered in calculator notation as **[A]*[G]**).

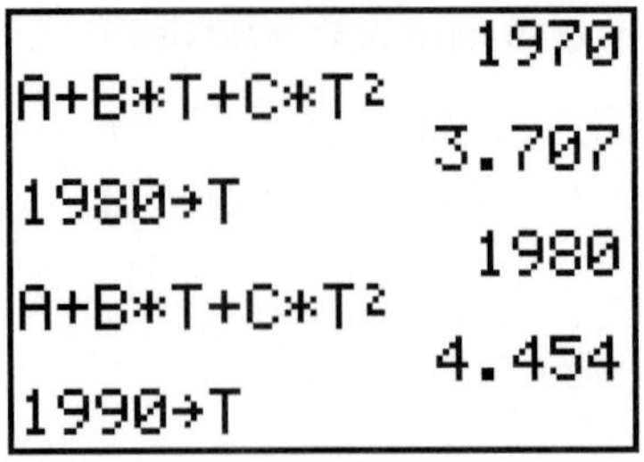

```
                        1970
A+B*T+C*T²
                       3.707
1980→T
                        1980
A+B*T+C*T²
                       4.454
1990→T
```

```
[A]*[G]
              [[3.707]
               [4.454]
               [5.279]]
```

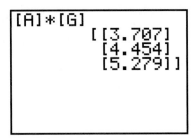

Figure 5.4.4 Checking our solution of the equations in (5).

Figure 5.4.5 Matrix check of our solution of system (5).

If we substitute $t = 2000$ in (6) the result is

$$P(2000) = 1377.782 - 1.4658(2000) + 0.00039(2000)^2 = 6.182$$

billion. If we regard the U.N. prediction of 6.083 billion as the correct figure for the year 2000, then we see that our quadratic prediction of 6.182 billion (Example 2) is a *worse* approximation than our linear prediction (Example 1) of 6.104 billion. This contradicts the common belief that a higher-degree approximation is always better. This is not always true. One reason that Example 2 did not yield a better approximation may be that we used more ancient data—going back to 1970—than in Example 1, where we went back only to 1980. In Problems 1 and 2 we ask you to see whether the use of more recent 1980–1985–1990 or 1985–1990–1995 data yields more accurate predictions for the world population in the year 2000. ◼

Higher-Degree Models

Just as three data points determine a quadratic function, four given data points determine a cubic function, and five given data points determine a quartic function. For instance, given any four year-population pairs (t_1, P_1), (t_2, P_2), (t_3, P_3), and (t_4, P_4), there exists a cubic function

$$P(t) = a + bt + ct^2 + dt^3 \tag{7}$$

such that $P(t_1) = P_1$, $P(t_2) = P_2$, $P(t_3) = P_3$, and $P(t_4) = P_4$. Note that the number of coefficients is always one greater than the degree of the polynomial function. So the method in higher-degree cases is the same as in Examples 1 and 2. However many data points we start with, we set up a polynomial of degree *one less* than the number of given data points. Then substitution of the given data yields a linear system with the right number of equations to solve for the coefficients in our polynomial.

Example 3

Now let's fit a cubic function to the 1980, 1985, 1990, and 1995 world population values. If we substitute the four data points (1980, 4.454), (1985, 4.851), (1990, 5.279), and (1995, 5.688) into (7), we get the four equations

$$
\begin{aligned}
4.454 &= a + 1980b + 1980^2c + 1980^3d \\
4.851 &= a + 1985b + 1985^2c + 1985^3d \\
5.279 &= a + 1990b + 1990^2c + 1990^3d \\
5.688 &= a + 1995b + 1995^2c + 1995^3d.
\end{aligned}
\tag{8}
$$

This is a 4×1 linear system $\mathbf{AX} = \mathbf{B}$ with

$$\mathbf{A} = \begin{bmatrix} 1 & 1980 & 1980^2 & 1980^3 \\ 1 & 1985 & 1985^2 & 1985^3 \\ 1 & 1990 & 1990^2 & 1990^3 \\ 1 & 1995 & 1995^2 & 1995^3 \end{bmatrix} \quad \text{and} \quad \mathbf{B} = \begin{bmatrix} 4.454 \\ 4.851 \\ 5.279 \\ 5.688 \end{bmatrix}$$

and with the 4×1 unknown matrix $\mathbf{X}$ comprised of the coefficients a, b, c, and d in (7).

The matrices $\mathbf{A}$ and $\mathbf{B}$ can be entered in the direct home-screen manner of Example 2, but the use of the calculator's matrix editor is often more efficient with larger matrices. Then the matrix computation shown in Fig. 5.4.6 stores the coefficient values $a = 523703.828$, $b = -790.42223$, $c = 0.39762$, and $d = -0.00006666666667$ (copying all digits shown to get the greatest possible accuracy) as elements of the 4×1 calculator matrix **[G]**.

```
[A]-1*[B]→[G]
[[523703.828    …
 [ -790.4222333 …
 [.39762        …
 [ -6.666666667E…
```

Figure 5.4.6   Calculating the coefficients in (7).

Thus our cubic population model is

$$P(t) = 523703.828 - 790.42223t + 0.39762t^2 - 0.0000666666667t^3. \quad (9)$$

Just as in Fig. 5.4.5, we can (and should) readily check all at once that the cubic function in (9) fits the 1980–1985–1990–1995 data with which we started.

It is quite tedious—as well as error prone—to retype numerical solutions. Figure 5.4.7 shows a much more efficient way to store the numerical values of the coefficients in (9)—by "picking out" the appropriate elements of the solution matrix **[G]**. Figure 5.4.8 then shows the result

$$P(2000) = 523703.828 - 790.42223(2000) \\ + 0.39762(2000)^2 - 0.0000666666667(2000)^3 \approx 6.028$$

billion people, obtained by substituting $t = 2000$ in (9).

```
[G](1,1)→A
          523703.828
[G](2,1)→B
          -790.4222333
[G](3,1)→C
                 .39762
[G](4,1)→D
```

Figure 5.4.7   Storing the coefficients in the cubic model (9).

```
2000→T
                 2000
A+B*T+C*T²+D*T^3
               6.027998
```

Figure 5.4.8   Cubic polynomial prediction of the year 2000 world population.

The following table compares our linear, quadratic, and cubic predictions with the "correct" United Nations prediction for the year 2000. It also includes the prediction of the quartic polynomial in Example 4. Each "error" in the third column of this table is the amount by which the corresponding prediction under-shoots (positive error) or overshoots (negative error) the U.N. prediction. We see that the cubic prediction is better than the quadratic prediction but worse than the linear prediction. The quartic prediction is even worse. Thus there apparently is no correlation between the degree of the polynomial model and the accuracy of its predictions.

	Year 2000 Prediction	Error
Linear	6.104	−0.021
Quadratic	6.182	−0.099
Cubic	6.028	+0.055
Quartic	5.976	+0.107
United Nations	6.083	

Example 4

In order to fit a fourth-degree population model of the form

$$P(t) = a + bt + ct^2 + dt^3 + et^4 \tag{10}$$

to the 1975–1980–1985–1990–1995 world population data, we need to solve the linear system

$$\begin{bmatrix} 1 & 1975 & 1975^2 & 1975^3 & 1975^4 \\ 1 & 1980 & 1980^2 & 1980^3 & 1980^4 \\ 1 & 1985 & 1985^2 & 1985^3 & 1985^4 \\ 1 & 1990 & 1990^2 & 1990^3 & 1990^4 \\ 1 & 1995 & 1995^2 & 1995^3 & 1995^4 \end{bmatrix} \begin{bmatrix} a \\ b \\ c \\ d \\ e \end{bmatrix} = \begin{bmatrix} 4.086 \\ 4.454 \\ 4.851 \\ 5.279 \\ 5.688 \end{bmatrix} \tag{11}$$

to find the values of the coefficients a, b, c, d, and e in (10). Some of the entries in this matrix are so large ($1995^4 = 15{,}840{,}599{,}000{,}625$) that your calculator is un-able to solve the system. Using mathematical software capable of storing more digits, we find that

$$P(t) = -53{,}568{,}386.224 + 108{,}075.0227667t - 81.76541333333t^2$$
$$+ 0.02749333333333t^3 - 0.000003466666666667t^4. \tag{12} \blacksquare$$

Figure 5.4.9 shows the U.N. world population data points for the years 1960 through 2025, together with the plots of the linear, quadratic, cubic, and quartic population functions of Examples 1 through 4. It looks as though, the more work we do to find a polynomial fitting selected data points, the less we get for our effort. It certainly is true in this figure that—outside the interval from 1975 to 1995—the higher the degree of the polynomial, the worse it appears to fit the given data points. The issue here is the difference between

- *interpolating* data points *within* the interval of given points being fitted, and
- *extrapolating* data points *outside* this interval.

Figure 5.4.9 Plot of world population data points and the interpolating polynomials of degrees $n = 1$ through $n = 4$.

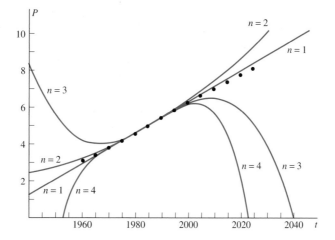

All four of our polynomials appear to do a good job of interpolation but, somewhat paradoxically, the higher is the degree the worse is the apparent accuracy of extrapolation. The highly questionable accuracy of data extrapolation outside the interval of interpolation has significant implications. For instance, consider a news report that when a certain alleged carcinogen was fed to mice in sufficient amounts to kill an elephant, the mice got cancer. It is then argued that moderate amounts of this carcinogen may cause cancer in humans. Or that if 1 part per billion of this carcinogen in the environment kills 1 person, then 1 part per million (a thousand times as much) will kill 1000 people. Such arguments are common, but who knows? They may well be cases of extrapolation beyond the range of accuracy. The bottom line is that interpolation is fairly safe—though hardly fail safe—but extrapolation is risky.

Geometric Applications

In contrast with population prediction, there are situations where curve fitting is exact. For instance, the fact that two points determine a line in the plane means that, when we fit the linear function $y = a + bx$ to a given pair of points, we get precisely the one and only straight line in the plane that passes through these points. Similarly, three points determine a circle, meaning that there is one and only one circle in the plane that passes through three given noncollinear points. In order to find this particular circle, we need to recall that the equation of a circle with center (h, k) and radius r is

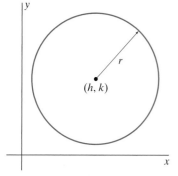

Figure 5.4.10 The circle with radius r and center (h, k).

$$(x - h)^2 + (y - k)^2 = r^2 \quad \text{(Fig. 5.4.10).} \tag{13}$$

Example 5

Find the equation of the circle that is determined by the points $P(-1, 5)$, $Q(5, -3)$, and $R(6, 4)$.

Substitution of the xy-coordinates of each of the three points P, Q, and R into (13) gives the three equations

$$\begin{aligned}
(-1 - h)^2 + (5 - k)^2 &= r^2 \\
(5 - h)^2 + (-3 - k)^2 &= r^2 \\
(6 - h)^2 + (4 - k)^2 &= r^2.
\end{aligned} \tag{14}$$

Expansion and collection of coefficients in these three equations gives

$$h^2 + k^2 + 2h - 10k + 26 = r^2$$
$$h^2 + k^2 - 10h + 6k + 34 = r^2 \qquad (15)$$
$$h^2 + k^2 - 12h - 8k + 52 = r^2.$$

These equations may at first look a bit formidable because of the three square terms in each. However, subtraction of any two of them eliminates all these square terms! Thus subtraction of the second and third equations in (15) from the first one yields the linear system

$$12h - 16k - 8 = 0$$
$$14h - 2k - 26 = 0$$

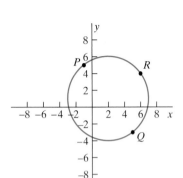

Figure 5.4.11   The circle through the three points of Example 5.

of just two equations in the two unknowns h and k. Just two equations should seem easy by now; we get $h = 2$ and $k = 1$. Substitution of these two values into the first equation in (14) now gives $r^2 = (-3)^2 + (4)^2 = 25$, so $r = 5$. Thus our circle has center $(2, 1)$ and radius 5 (Fig. 5.4.11). ◼

Three points in the plane also determine a **central conic** with equation of the form

$$ax^2 + bxy + cy^2 = 1. \qquad (16)$$

A typical central conic is an ellipse (or "flattened circle") that has been rotated about the origin.

Example 6

Find the central conic that passes through the same three points $P(-1, 5)$, $Q(5, -3)$, and $R(6, 4)$ of Example 5.

Substitution of the xy-coordinates of each of the three points P, Q, and R into (16) gives the linear system of three equations

$$a - 5b + 25c = 1$$
$$25a - 15b + 9c = 1 \qquad (17)$$
$$36a + 24b + 16c = 1$$

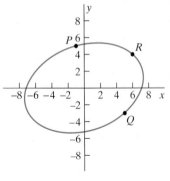

Figure 5.4.12   The central conic through the three points of Example 6.

in the three unknowns a, b, and c. In Problem 3 we ask you to solve this system by the method of elimination to obtain fractions (rather than decimal numbers) for the coefficients. You should obtain the values

$$a = \frac{277}{14{,}212}, \quad b = -\frac{172}{14{,}212}, \quad \text{and } c = \frac{523}{14{,}212}.$$

If we substitute these coefficient values in (16) and multiply the result by 14,212, we get the desired equation

$$277x^2 - 172xy + 523y^2 = 14{,}212 \qquad (18)$$

of our central conic. The computer plot in Fig. 5.4.12 verifies that this rotated ellipse does, indeed, pass through all three points P, Q, and R. ◼

Least Squares Polynomials

In Section 2.3 we discussed the use of a graphing calculator's quadratic regression facility to find the quadratic model $P(t) = P_0 + at + bt^2$ that best fits a given table of *tP*-data. Here we describe similarly the use of the cubic regression and quartic regression facilities provided by the **CubicReg** and **QuartReg** functions listed in the **STAT CALC** menu of Fig. 5.4.13.

Figure 5.4.13 Graphing calculator regression functions.

Given a list **L₁** of *x*-data and a corresponding list **L₂** of *y*-data, the command **CubicReg L₁, L₂, Y₃** finds the *cubic* polynomial $y = ax^3 + bx^2 + cx + d$ that best fits the given data—meaning that it minimizes the sum of the squares of the errors or discrepancies between actual and predicted values. This best-fitting cubic polynomial is stored as the **Y=** menu function **Y₃**. Similarly, the command **QuartReg L₁, L₂, Y₄** finds the *quartic* polynomial $y = ax^4 + bx^3 + cx^2 + dx + e$ that best fits the given data, and saves this polynomial as the **Y=** menu function **Y₄**.

For greatest accuracy of fit, the calculator should be set (using the ⌈MODE⌉ menu) to display 9 significant digits, because only the displayed decimal places are stored in the *a, b, c,* ... coefficient values in the **Y=** menu functions.

The given data lists **L₁** and **L₂** must contain at least four data points to use **CubicReg**, and at least five data points to use **QuartReg**. In the case of exactly four data points **CubicReg** calculates the cubic polynomial that *interpolates* these points (and hence has average error 0), while in the case of exactly five data points **QuartReg** calculates the quartic polynomial that interpolates these points. With more than four (or five) given data points, **CubicReg** (or **QuartReg**) finds the polynomial of the indicated degree that *best fits* these points, and hence has least possible average error.

Example 7

Find the quadratic, cubic, and quartic polynomials that best fit the 1960–1990 world population data listed in the table at the beginning of this section.

For variety we choose $t = 0$ in 1950, so the years 1960, 1965, . . . , 1985, 1990 correspond to the values $t = 10, 15, . . . , 35, 40$. As indicated in Fig. 5.4.14, we store these *t*-values in the list **L₁** and the corresponding world population values in the list **L₂**.

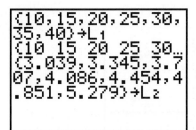

Figure 5.4.14 Storing the 1960–1990 world population data.

Then Figs. 5.4.15–5.4.17 show the results of the successive commands

QuadReg L$_1$, L$_2$, Y$_2$
CubicReg L$_1$, L$_2$, Y$_3$
QuartReg L$_1$, L$_2$, Y$_4$

that save the optimal quadratic polynomial as **Y$_2$**, the optimal cubic polynomial as **Y$_3$**, and the optimal quartic polynomial as **Y$_4$** (with 9-place accuracy selected as suggested previously).

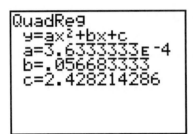

Figure 5.4.15   The best-fitting quadratic polynomial **Y$_2$**.

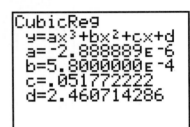

Figure 5.4.16   The best-fitting cubic polynomial **Y$_3$**.

Figure 5.4.17   The best-fitting quartic polynomial **Y$_4$**.

We see the optimal quadratic polynomial

$$P_2(t) = 0.00036333333t^2 + 0.056683333t + 2.428214286, \tag{19}$$

the optimal cubic polynomial

$$P_3(t) = -0.000002888889t^3 + 0.00058t^2 + 0.051772222t + 2.460714286, \tag{20}$$

and the optimal quartic polynomial

$$P_4(t) = 0.000001569697t^4 - 0.0001598586t^3 + 0.006090758t^2 \\ - 0.027553535t + 2.849214286. \tag{21} \blacksquare$$

Figure 5.4.18 shows the resulting table of values of **Y$_2$** and **Y$_3$**—that is, $P_2(t)$ and $P_3(t)$. Upon scrolling this calculator screen to the right we get the table of

X	Y2	Y3
10.000	3.031	3.034
15.000	3.360	3.358
20.000	3.707	3.705
25.000	4.072	4.072
30.000	4.456	4.458
35.000	4.857	4.859
40.000	5.277	5.275

X=10

Figure 5.4.18   Quadratic **(Y$_2$)** and cubic **(Y$_3$)** polynomial values.

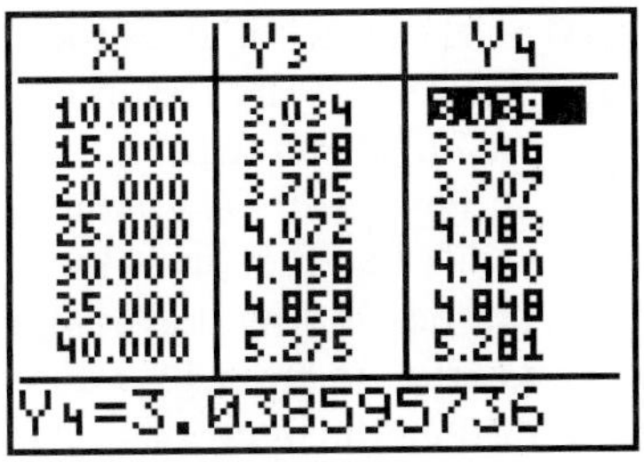

X	Y3	Y4
10.000	3.034	3.039
15.000	3.358	3.346
20.000	3.705	3.707
25.000	4.072	4.083
30.000	4.458	4.460
35.000	4.859	4.848
40.000	5.275	5.281

Y4=3.038595736

Figure 5.4.19   Cubic (**Y₃**) and quartic (**Y₄**) polynomial values.

values of **Y₃** and **Y₄**—that is, $P_3(t)$ and $P_4(t)$—shown in Fig. 5.4.19. The following table assembles these results.

Year	t	Actual Pop.	Quadratic	Cubic	Quartic
1960	10	3.039	3.031	3.034	3.039
1965	15	3.345	3.360	3.358	3.346
1970	20	3.707	3.707	3.705	3.707
1975	25	4.086	4.072	4.072	4.083
1980	30	4.454	4.456	4.458	4.460
1985	35	4.851	4.857	4.859	4.848
1990	40	5.279	5.277	5.275	5.281

Comparing the quadratic, cubic, and quartic predictions with the actual populations for the years 1960–1990, we calculate the sums of squares of errors

$$SSE_2 = (0.008)^2 + (-0.015)^2 + (0.000)^2 + (0.014)^2 + (-0.002)^2$$
$$+ (-0.006)^2 + (0.002)^2 = 0.000529,$$
$$SSE_3 = (0.005)^2 + (-0.013)^2 + (0.002)^2 + (0.014)^2 + (-0.004)^2$$
$$+ (-0.008)^2 + (0.004)^2 = 0.000490,$$

and

$$SSE_4 = (0.000)^2 + (-0.001)^2 + (0.000)^2 + (0.003)^2 + (-0.006)^2$$
$$+ (0.003)^2 + (-0.002)^2 = 0.000059$$

in the quadratic, cubic, and quartic fits (respectively). The resulting average errors are

$$\text{quadratic ave. error} = \sqrt{\frac{0.000529}{7}} = 0.009$$

$$\text{cubic ave. error} = \sqrt{\frac{0.000490}{7}} = 0.008,$$

and

$$\text{quartic ave. error} = \sqrt{\frac{0.000059}{7}} = 0.003.$$

We appear to have excellent fits. The predicted year 2000 populations are

$$P_2(50) = 6.171, P_3(50) = 6.138, \text{ and } P_4(50) = 6.527$$

as compared with the United Nation's predicted year 2000 population of 6.083 billion. There is a lesson in the fact that the quartic polynomial gives the worst extrapolation to 2000, even though it gives the best fit (that is, the least average error) for the years 1960–1990. (The lesson is that, when extrapolating outside the region of best fit, you never can tell.)

Finally, we show in Fig. 5.4.20 the graphs of our quadratic, cubic, and quartic best-fitting polynomials together with the U.N. data points for 1960–2025. Compare these graphs of best-fitting polynomials with the graphs of interpolating polynomials shown earlier in Fig. 5.4.9. Evidently the best-fitting polynomials extrapolate much better than the interpolating polynomials. This is reasonable to expect, given that best-fitting polynomials are determined by "more than enough" points, while interpolating polynomials are determined by "just enough" points.

Figure 5.4.20   Plot of world population data points and the optimal polynomials of degrees $n = 2$ through $n = 4$.

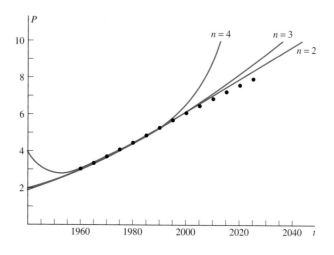

5.4
PROBLEMS

1. Use the world population data from 1980, 1985, and 1990 to determine a quadratic model for world population growth. Then use your model to predict the world population in the year 2000. Is this prediction closer to the U.N. prediction of 6.083 billion than the one we found in Example 2 by using the data from 1970, 1980, and 1990?

2. Use the world population data from 1985, 1990, and 1995 to determine a quadratic model for world population growth. Then use your model to predict the world population in the year 2000. Is this prediction closer to the U.N. prediction of 6.083 billion than the one we found in Example 2 by using the data from 1970, 1980, and 1990?

3. Use the method of elimination to solve the linear system indicated in Example 6, using fractions rather than decimal numbers. Verify that the coefficients you obtain are the same as those shown in the example.

Most of the following problems are based on the U.S. census data in the following table, listed in millions for the census years 1900–1990, by national region described roughly as follows:

- Northeast—from Maine to Pennsylvania and New Jersey
- Midwest—from Ohio to North Dakota to Kansas
- South—from Delaware to Kentucky to Oklahoma and Texas to Florida
- West—from Montana to New Mexico to Hawaii and Alaska

See www.census.gov/population/www/censusdata for further details.

	1900	1910	1920	1930	1940	1950	1960	1970	1980	1990
Northeast	21.047	25.869	29.662	34.427	35.977	39.478	44.678	49.061	49.137	50.809
Midwest	26.333	29.889	34.020	38.594	40.143	44.461	51.619	56.590	58.867	59.669
South	24.524	29.389	33.126	37.858	41.666	47.197	54.973	62.813	75.367	85.446
West	4.309	7.082	9.214	12.324	14.379	20.190	28.053	34.838	43.171	52.786
U.S.	76.212	92.228	106.022	123.203	132.165	151.326	179.323	203.302	226.542	248.710

In Problems 4–8, fit (as in Example 1) a linear function to the 1980 and 1990 population values for the indicated region.

4. The Northeast

5. The Midwest

6. The South

7. The West

8. The whole United States

In Problems 9–13, fit (as in Example 2) a quadratic function to the 1970, 1980, and 1990 population values for the indicated region.

9. The Northeast

10. The Midwest

11. The South

12. The West

13. The whole United States

In Problems 14–18, fit (as in Example 3) a cubic polynomial to the 1960, 1970, 1980, and 1990 population data for the indicated region.

14. The Northeast

15. The Midwest

16. The South

17. The West

18. The whole United States

In Problems 19–23, find the cubic polynomial that best fits the 1910, 1930, 1950, 1970, and 1990 population data for the indicated region, and calculate the average error in this optimal cubic.

19. The Northeast

20. The Midwest

21. The South

22. The West

23. The whole United States

In Problems 24–28, find the quartic polynomial that best fits the 1900–1990 (all decades) population data for the indicated region, and calculate the average error in this optimal quartic.

24. The Northeast

25. The Midwest

26. The South

27. The West

28. The whole United States

In Problems 29–32, find (as in Example 5) the center and radius of the circle in the xy-plane that passes through the three given points P, Q, and R.

29. $P(4, 2), Q(5, 1), R(-2, -6)$

30. $P(-7, 15), Q(0, 22), R(17, 15)$

31. $P(3, 5), Q(10, -2), R(-20, -18)$

32. $P(43, 41), Q(33, 51), R(-37, -19)$

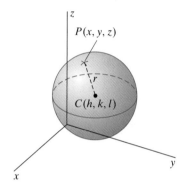

A sphere in space with **center** (h, k, l) and **radius** r (Fig. 5.4.21) has equation

$$(x - h)^2 + (y - k)^2 + (z - l)^2 = r^2.$$

Four given noncoplanar points in space suffice to determine the values of h, k, l, and r. In Problems 33 and 34, find the center and radius of the sphere that passes through the four given points P, Q, R, and S. (*Hint:* Substitute each given triple of coordinates into the sphere equation to obtain four equations that h, k, l, and r must satisfy. To solve these equations, first subtract the first one from each of the other three. How many unknowns are left in the three equations that result?)

33. $P(4, 6, 15), Q(13, 5, 7), R(5, 14, 6), S(5, 5, -9)$

Figure 5.4.21 The sphere with center (h, k, l) and radius r.

34. $P(11, 17, 17), Q(29, 1, 15), R(13, -1, 33), S(-19, -13, 1)$

C H A P T E R   5   R E V I E W

In this chapter, you learned about polynomial functions and models and linear systems of equations. After completing the chapter, you should be able to

- Determine whether a function described graphically or symbolically represents a polynomial function, an exponential function, or a logarithmic function.
- Find the output value of a polynomial function for a given input value.
- Find the input values(s) of a polynomial function for a given output value.
- Solve an equation or inequality involving a polynomial function.

- Solve a system of two linear equations in two unknowns by the method of elimination.
- Solve a system of two or more linear equations in the same number of unknowns by determinant or matrix inverse methods.
- Use linear system methods to find a cubic or quartic interpolating polynomial that fits given data points.
- Use regression methods to find a best-fitting cubic or quartic model for given data.

REVIEW PROBLEMS

In Problems 1–6, match each graph both with the most appropriate function model in A–F and with the type of function it represents I–III. (Choices from I–III may be used more than once.)

A. $f(x) = ax + b$
B. $f(x) = ax^2 + bx + c$
C. $f(x) = ax^3 + bx^2 + cx + d$
D. $f(x) = ax^4 + bx^3 + cx^2 + dx + e$
E. $f(x) = ae^{bx}$
F. $f(x) = z \ln(bx)$

I.   polynomial
II. exponential
III. logarithmic

1.

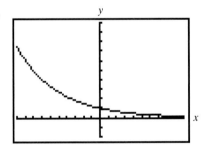

2.

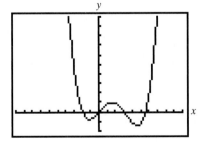

3.

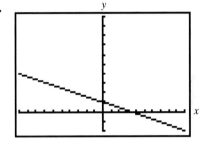

4.

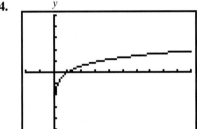

5.

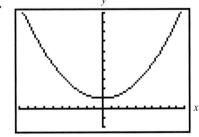

6.

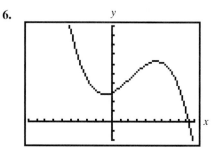

The exact solutions to Problems 7 and 8 are all integers or simple rational numbers. Approximate the solutions by graphing, then verify the apparent exact solution by substituting the appropriate value in the given equation.

7. $15x^3 - 49x^2 - 104x + 240 = 0$
8. $576x^4 + 120x^3 - 6650x^2 - 2375x + 6250 = 0$
9. The data on the foreign-born population in the United States discussed in the chapter introduction can be modeled by the function

$$F(t) = 0.000075t^3 - 0.008713t^2 + 0.110004t + 13.906853,$$

where t represents the number of years after 1900.
   (a) Use this model to approximate the percentage of the U.S. population that was foreign born in 2000.
   (b) According to the model, during what years of the twentieth century was less than 10% of the U.S. population foreign born?
10. During fall registration, the student government association sold hot dogs, chips and soft drinks to raise money for a scholarship fund. The following table gives the numbers of each item sold and the total receipts for each day.

	Hot Dogs	Chips	Soft Drinks	Receipts
Wednesday	54	32	80	$177.00
Thursday	64	50	95	$216.00
Friday	45	22	50	$128.50

If a student purchased two hot dogs, one bag of chips, and a soft drink, how much was she charged?

11. The following data give percentage of all music sold (recorded music and music video) that was rap music in the given years.

Year t	1992	1993	1994	1995	1996
Percentage rap music R	8.6	9.2	7.9	6.7	8.9

Source: *World Almanac and Book of Facts 1998*

   (a) Use linear system methods to determine the interpolating quartic polynomial for this data.
   (b) Use your model to predict the percentage of all music sold that was rap music in 1999. Do you believe that this is a good model to predict rap music sales? Why or why not?
12. The following data indicate the total U.S. lead emissions E in short tons for the indicated years.

Year x	1986	1987	1988	1989	1990
Days E	7296	6857	6513	6034	5666

Year x	1991	1992	1993	1994	1995
Days E	5280	4862	4945	5028	4986

Source: *World Almanac and Book of Facts 1998*

   (a) Use the data to determine the best-fitting cubic polynomial model $E_3(x)$, where x is given in years after 1986.
   (b) Use the data to determine a best-fitting quartic polynomial model $E_4(x)$, where x is given in years after 1986.
   (c) Both of these models fit the data very well. Which model would you use if you wanted to argue for stronger pollution control laws? Give an extrapolation point using each model to support your answer.

A C T I V I T Y

Cost Curves and Minimum Average Cost

When a company manufactures a product, it incurs two basic types of cost. The first type of cost is *fixed cost,* which is frequently referred to as "overhead." Fixed cost might include such things as rent or mortgage payment, insurance, telephone, or business license. This cost remains the same no matter how many items are produced. The second type of cost is called *variable cost* because it depends on the number of items produced. Variable cost could include the cost of materials, workers' salaries, and electricity.

When we speak of the total cost function, we mean the sum of the fixed cost function and the variable cost function. That is,

total cost = total fixed cost + total variable cost,

or, in the notation used in economics, TC = TFC + TVC. (We use the word *total* in these cases to distinguish between these costs and others we will discuss later, and refer to graphs of these cost functions as *cost curves.*)

Total cost curves are often modeled by cubic polynomials, such as the one whose graph is shown in Fig. 5.R.1.

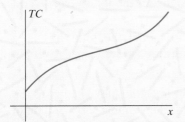

Figure 5.R.1 A cubic total cost curve.

Let's think about the features of this kind of curve that make it useful in representing cost:

- First, the *y*-intercept of this curve is positive. The *y*-intercept corresponds to the cost for zero output, that is, the fixed cost.
- Second, the function represented by the graph is increasing; in general, as output increases, so does cost.
- Third, the graph first curves downward, then curves upward. For small values of the output *x,* the curve becomes less steep as *x* increases, while for large values of *x,* the curve becomes steeper as *x* increases. At small production levels, it is relatively easy to increase production efficiently, making costs increase less rapidly. At a certain point, however, in order to increase output, the company requires more labor and more materials, and costs begin to increase more rapidly.

Brian has decided to turn his hobby of making birdhouses into a small home business, BJD Designer Birdhouses. He has determined his short-run daily cost schedules as indicated in the accompanying table.

Output	Fixed Cost	Variable Cost
0	7	0
1	7	11.75
2	7	22.25
3	7	31.75
4	7	40.00
5	7	47.80
6	7	55.30
7	7	63.05
8	7	71.15
9	7	79.75
10	7	89.25

(1) Find the total fixed cost function $TFC(x)$ in terms of the output level x for BJD Designer Birdhouses.

(2) Find a cubic polynomial function $TVC(x)$ to model the total variable cost as a function of the output x.

(3) Find a cubic polynomial function $TC(x)$ to model the total cost as a function of the output x. What is the relationship among your answers to (1), (2), and (3)?

There are two other cost curves that are important in economics. The first is the average variable cost (AVC). The average variable cost is the variable cost per item of all the items being produced and is calculated by dividing the total variable cost by the output. That is,

$$AVC(x) = \frac{TVC(x)}{x}.$$

For example, $AVC(8) = \dfrac{TVC(8)}{8} = \dfrac{71.15}{8} \approx \$8.89.$

(4) Use the total variable cost function you found in (2) to find a function for the average variable cost $AVC(x)$. (You might be interested to know that the average variable cost function is an example of a *rational* function, which is the quotient of two polynomial functions.)

The most important cost curve to an economist is the marginal cost (MC), which is the increase in total cost that results from producing one more item (one more birdhouse, in this case). The easiest way to determine marginal cost is to find the change in cost required to produce each additional unit.

(5)   Complete the following table to determine a marginal cost schedule for the birdhouse company.

Output	Variable Cost	Marginal Cost
0	0	11.75
1	11.75	10.50
2	22.25	
3	31.75	
4	40.00	
5	47.80	
6	55.30	
7	63.05	
8	71.15	
9	79.75	
10	89.25	—

(6)   Find a quadratic function model $MC(x)$ that represents the marginal cost as a function of the output x.

(7)   It is a law of economics that the marginal cost curve rises to intersect the average total cost curve at the lowest point of the average cost curve. Graph the average total cost curve and the marginal cost curve and find their point of intersection. If Brian wants to minimize his average cost per birdhouse, how many birdhouses should he produce per day?

6

TRIGONOMETRIC MODELS

Do you know the difference between weather and climate? *Weather* generally refers to the state of the atmosphere at a given time, with regard to such characteristics as temperature, humidity, barometric pressure, and cloudiness. *Climate* refers to a long-term view of weather—that is, climate consists of the composite of the weather conditions of a region, averaged over a number of years. Thus, while scientists expect the weather to change daily, the climate of a certain place remains essentially the same. One of the controversies associated with the issue of global warming is whether (or by how much) climates are gradually changing over a period of time.

The chart in Fig. 6.0.1 shows climate data for Topeka, Kansas—specifically, the average maximum temperature over a 24-month period beginning and ending in January. You can see that the graph consists of two annual cycles of the same average monthly high temperatures.

As we would expect, the lowest average temperature occurs in the winter (in January) and the highest average temperature occurs in the summer (in July). Because this graph represents temperature averages over many years, the same pattern of values (rounded to the nearest degree) would repeat over and over again as we add more and more months to the data. A function such as this—repeating the same pattern of values over and over again—is called a *periodic function*.

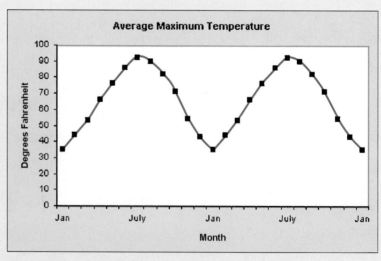

Figure 6.0.1 Average maximum temperatures in Topeka.

Source: American Automobile Association.

Trigonometric functions are typical examples of periodic functions. In this chapter you will study the use of trigonometric functions to model periodic phenomena in the real world.

6.1 PERIODIC PHENOMENA AND TRIGONOMETRIC FUNCTIONS

Many of the phenomena that take place in the world around us fall into one of two broad categories:

- Either they involve quantities that increase or decline steadily; or
- They involve quantities that oscillate up and down periodically.

In Chapters 3 and 4 we studied exponential functions that describe processes of (steady) natural growth or decay. In this section we discuss the trigonometric functions that describe oscillatory phenomena and data.

Trigonometric Functions

The following table shows the average temperature (°F) in suburban Atlanta for each of the 12 months of the year.

Month	Ave. Temp.
January	41
February	45
March	54
April	62
May	69
June	76
July	79
August	78
September	73
October	62
November	53
December	45

In Fig. 6.1.1 we have plotted these average temperatures month-by-month for a period of two years. They vary each year up and down from a low of 41°F in January to a high of 79°F in July. This up-and-down repetitive pattern is quite unlike the steadily rising or steadily falling behavior of an exponential function. A new type of function is needed to model temperature oscillations.

Figure 6.1.1 Monthly average temperatures in Atlanta.

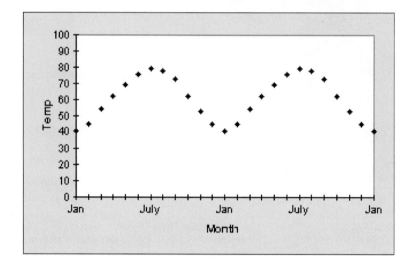

Let's take $t = 0$ in January and measure time by the month, so the successive times $t = 1, 2, \ldots, 11$ correspond to the successive months February, March, $\ldots$, December. Then $t = 12$ brings us back to January (of the next year), and thereafter the familiar cycle of months repeats in correspondence with the monthly times $t = 12, 13, \ldots, 23$. As time passes,

- The values $t = 0, 12, 24, \ldots$ correspond to January;
- The values $t = 1, 13, 25, \ldots$ correspond to February;
- The values $t = 2, 14, 26, \ldots$ correspond to March; and so forth,

with the values $t = 11, 23, 35, \ldots$ corresponding to December in succeeding years. Whenever we need to be more precise, we'll assume that $t = 0$ means mid-January and $t = 11$ means mid-December.

Example 1

Later in this section we will see how to fit our Atlanta monthly average temperature data with a *trigonometric function*

$$f(t) = 18.54 \sin(0.52t - 1.57) + 61.33 \tag{1}$$

involving the *sine function*, which we will introduce shortly. In Section 6.2 we'll describe how one might *find* such a trigonometric fitting function. In this example, we'll just describe the way the function given in (1) fits the Atlanta monthly average temperature data.

The following table compares the monthly temperatures predicted by this function with the actual monthly average temperatures. We see that (rounded off to the nearest degree) the discrepancy is no more than a couple of degrees in any month.

t	Ave. Temp.	$f(t)$	Error
0	41	42.8	−1.8
1	45	45.2	−0.2
2	54	52.0	2.0
3	62	61.1	0.9
4	69	70.4	−1.4
5	76	77.2	−1.2
6	79	79.9	−0.9
7	78	77.6	0.4
8	73	71.0	2.0
9	62	61.9	0.1
10	53	52.6	0.4
11	45	45.6	−0.6

Figure 6.1.2 shows that the smooth curve $y = f(t)$ appears visually to fit the actual data (dots) quite well. Note that the temperature predicted by (1) overestimates the average temperature for six months, and underestimates it for the other six months of the year.

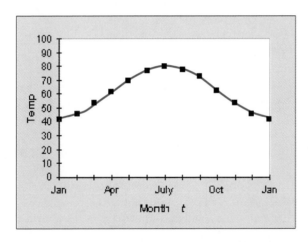

Figure 6.1.2   Monthly average temperatures (dots) in Atlanta fitted with the (curve) graph $f(t) = 61.33 + 18.54 \sin(0.52t − 1.57)$.

The sum of the squares of the errors shown in the final column is

$$\text{SSE} = (-1.8)^2 + (-0.2)^2 + (2.0)^2 + \ldots + (0.1)^2 + (0.4)^2 + (-0.6)^2 = 16.99,$$

so the average error in the trigonometric approximation is

$$\text{Average error} = \sqrt{\frac{\text{SSE}}{n}} = \sqrt{\frac{16.99}{12}} \approx 1.19.$$

Thus the formula in (1) predicts each month's temperature, on average, to within about a degree. ◤

Equation (1) involves the *sine function,* which—together with its relative the *cosine function*—is needed to describe the oscillations of temperature and other periodic phenomena in nature. The basic trigonometric functions of an angle θ in a right triangle are defined as ratios between pairs of sides of the triangle. As in

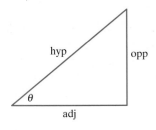

Figure 6.1.3 The sides and angle θ of a right triangle.

Fig. 6.1.3—where "adj" stands for adjacent, "opp" for opposite, and "hyp" for hypotenuse—the sine and cosine of the angle θ are defined by

$$\cos \theta = \frac{\text{adj}}{\text{hyp}}, \quad \sin \theta = \frac{\text{opp}}{\text{hyp}}. \tag{2}$$

There are four other trigonometric functions (tan, cot, sec, csc), but here we need only discuss the sine and cosine.

Example 2

Figure 6.1.4 shows the common 30°-60°-90° and 45°-45°-90° triangles, and we see that (2) gives

$$\cos 30° = \frac{\sqrt{3}}{2}, \quad \sin 30° = \frac{1}{2}, \quad \cos 45° = \sin 45° = \frac{1}{\sqrt{2}}. \tag{3} ∎$$

Figure 6.1.4 The 30°-60°-90° and 45°-45°-90° triangles.

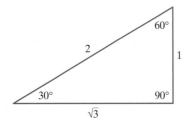

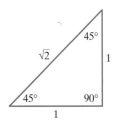

The triangle definitions in (2) apply only to angles less than 90°, but there are circle definitions that apply to angles of any size. Suppose that the initial side of the angle θ is the positive x-axis, so its vertex is located at the origin (Fig. 6.1.5).

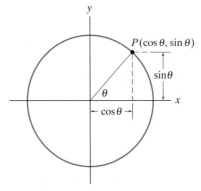

Figure 6.1.5 The circle definitions of the sine and cosine.

The angle of rotation (for a positive angle) is then *counterclockwise* from the initial side to the terminal side of the angle. (Negative angles are measured clockwise.) If $P(x, y)$ is the point at which the terminal side of θ intersects the unit circle (of radius 1), then we define

$$\cos \theta = x, \quad \sin \theta = y. \tag{4}$$

Because x is the adjacent side and y the opposite side of a right triangle whose hypotenuse is the radius 1 of the unit circle, it follows that the definitions in (4) agree with those in (2) for an *acute* angle less than 90°.

Radian Measure

In elementary mathematics, angles usually are measured in *degrees*, with 90° in a right angle. However, the trigonometric functions on calculators and computers frequently are based on **radian measure** of angles. Just as miles and meters are different units of length, with 1 mile = 1609.344 meters, degrees and radians are different units of angular measure. The relation between degrees and radians is given by

$$\pi \text{ radians} = 180 \text{ degrees.} \tag{5}$$

Division of both sides by π (and abbreviation of radians to rad, degrees to deg) yields

$$1 \text{ rad} = \frac{180}{\pi} \text{ deg} \approx 57.2958 \text{ deg,} \tag{5$'$}$$

while division of both sides in (5) by 180 gives

$$1 \text{ deg} = \frac{\pi}{180} \text{ rad} \approx 0.01745 \text{ rad.} \tag{5$''$}$$

The following table gives degree–radian equivalents and cosines and sines for the common angles of the triangles in Fig. 6.1.4.

Degrees	Radians	Cosine	Sine
0	0	1	0
30	$\pi/6$	$\sqrt{3}/2$	$1/2$
45	$\pi/4$	$1/\sqrt{2}$	$1/\sqrt{2}$
60	$\pi/3$	$1/2$	$\sqrt{3}/2$
90	$\pi/2$	0	1

For other angles, you should rely *only* upon memory of the fundamental relation in (5), dividing as necessary as in (5$'$) and (5$''$). To recall quickly whether to use $180/\pi$ or $\pi/180$, it helps to remember that a radian is a relatively large angle—almost 60°—while a degree is a quite small angle in terms of radians.

Example 3

$$25° = 25 \times \frac{\pi}{180} \text{ rad} \approx 0.4363 \text{ rad,}$$

$$0.25 \text{ rad} = 0.25 \times \frac{180}{\pi} \text{ deg} \approx 14.32° \qquad ◼$$

Example 4

Figure 6.1.6 shows some trig calculations with a graphing calculator set in **radian mode**. Because $1/\sqrt{2} \approx 0.7071$ and $\sqrt{3}/2 \approx 0.8660$, we see that these results agree with the familiar values obtained from the right triangles of Fig. 6.1.7.

```
cos(π/4)
              .7071
sin(π/3)
              .8660
cos(1.25)
              .3153
sin(3.86)
```

Figure 6.1.6   Some trig function calculations.

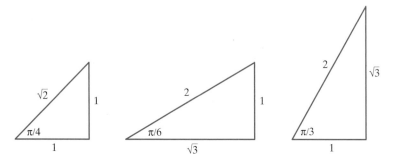

Figure 6.1.7   Familiar right triangles.

Figure 6.1.8 shows some more trig calculations, illustrating the fact that we can ask for the sine of any real number (of radians). Observe that the calculator uses the parentheses associated with standard functional notation—cos(x) and sin(x).   ◤

```
sin(3.86)
             -.6582
cos(-0.73)
              .7452
sin(3/4)
              .6816
cos(-5/8)
```

Figure 6.1.8   Some more trig calculations.

Whenever we use this functional notation with parentheses, it is understood that x is measured in radians. The argument (independent variable) is measured in degrees only when we use the degree symbol explicitly, as in writing sin $x°$.

Most of us think more naturally of angles in degrees because that's what we first learned in school and what we commonly use in real life. However, for the purposes of college mathematics you should keep your calculator set in radian mode (rather than degree mode). Whenever you want to check quickly the trig mode of your calculator, just remember (from the 30°-60°-90° triangle of Fig. 6.1.4) that the sine of an angle of 30° = $\pi/6$ rad is 1/2:

$$\sin 30° = \sin\left(\frac{\pi}{6}\right) = \frac{1}{2}.$$

So we just calculate the sine of 30 to see whether our calculator is in radian mode or in degree mode. If the calculator's in *degree* mode, then it'll give 1/2.

sin(30)

0.5000   (It's in degree mode.)

sin(30)

-0.9880   (It's in radian mode.)

But if it's in *radian* mode then it'll give $1/2$ when we calculate the sine of $\pi/6$.

sin(π/6)

0.5000   (It's in radian mode.)

sin(π/6)

0.0091   (It's in degree mode.)

Try all four possibilities with your own calculator—switching trig modes as necessary—to duplicate the results just shown. Because it is easy to type in the degree symbol (using the **ANGLE** menu of your calculator) when you need it, it is a good idea to leave your calculator in radian mode.

Trigonometric Graphs and Periodicity

An angle of 2π radians corresponds to one full revolution around the unit circle. Therefore the circle definition in (4) implies that the (radian-based) sine and cosine functions repeat themselves in each new interval of length 2π. In more precise language, these functions have *period* 2π, meaning that

$$\cos(x + 2\pi) = \cos(x), \quad \sin(x + 2\pi) = \sin(x) \tag{6}$$

for every x. **Thus addition of 2π to x does *not* change the value of either the sine or the cosine of x.** Can you see why it follows that addition of any *even* multiple of π to x leaves both the sine and the cosine unchanged? That is,

$$\cos(x + 2n\pi) = \cos(x), \quad \sin(x + 2n\pi) = \sin(x)$$

for any integer n. This periodicity of the sine and cosine functions is evident in the repetitive character of their graphs (Fig. 6.1.9), where we see each repeatedly varying between the values -1 and $+1$.

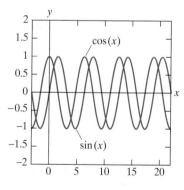

Figure 6.1.9   The sine and cosine graphs.

Note also that these graphs are consistent with the facts that

$$\cos(-x) = \cos(x), \quad \sin(-x) = -\sin(x) \tag{7}$$

for all x. [It is therefore said that cos (x) is an *even* function of x, while $\sin(x)$ is an *odd* function of x— in analogy with the fact that an even power of a negative number is positive, while an odd power of a negative number is negative.] A related useful property of these functions is that

$$\cos(x \pm \pi) = -\cos(x), \quad \sin(x \pm \pi) = -\sin(x). \tag{8}$$

We can summarize (6) and (8) by saying that **whereas changing x by 2π does not change the value of either the sine and cosine, changing x by π changes (only) the *sign* of each.**

Example 5

$$\cos(2\pi) = \cos(0) = 1$$

$$\sin\left(\frac{3\pi}{2}\right) = \sin\left(2\pi - \frac{\pi}{2}\right) = \sin\left(-\frac{\pi}{2}\right) = -\sin\left(\frac{\pi}{2}\right) = -1$$

$$\sin\left(\frac{3\pi}{4}\right) = \sin\left(-\frac{\pi}{4} + \pi\right) = -\sin\left(-\frac{\pi}{4}\right) = \sin\left(\frac{\pi}{4}\right) \approx 0.7071$$

$$\cos\left(\frac{7\pi}{6}\right) = \cos\left(\frac{\pi}{6} + \pi\right) = -\cos\left(\frac{\pi}{6}\right) \approx -0.8660$$

Example 6

If you define **Y1=cos(X)** and **Y2=sin(X)** on your graphing calculator (in radian mode, as always) and then enter

Xmin=−2π   **Ymin=−2**
Xmax=2π   **Ymax=2**

to define the viewing window, the resulting graph (Fig. 6.1.10) resembles the artist's sketch in Fig. 6.1.9. Is it clear to you which curve in Fig. 6.1.10 is the graph $y = \cos x$ and which is the graph $y = \sin x$?

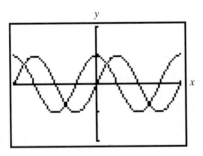

Figure 6.1.10   Which is the sine graph, which the cosine graph?

Example 7

Because

$$\frac{\pi}{6} \approx 0.5236 \approx 0.52 \quad \text{and} \quad \frac{\pi}{2} \approx 1.5708 \approx 1.57$$

the Atlanta monthly average temperature model in (1) is equivalent (with 2-place accuracy) to

$$f(t) = 61.33 + 18.54 \sin\left(\frac{\pi t}{6} - \frac{\pi}{2}\right). \qquad (9)$$

It is worth verifying that this alleged temperature function is, indeed, *periodic* with a *period* of 12 months—meaning that it predicts the same temperature at time t and at time $t + 12$ twelve months hence. Upon replacing t with $t + 12$ in (9) we get

$$f(t + 12) = 61.33 + 18.54 \sin\left(\frac{\pi(t + 12)}{6} - \frac{\pi}{2}\right)$$

$$= 61.33 + 18.54 \sin\left(\frac{\pi t + 12\pi}{6} - \frac{\pi}{2}\right)$$

$$= 61.33 + 18.54 \sin\left(\frac{\pi t}{6} + 2\pi - \frac{\pi}{2}\right)$$

$$= 61.33 + 18.54 \sin\left(\left(\frac{\pi t}{6} - \frac{\pi}{2}\right) + 2\pi\right)$$

$$= 61.33 + 18.54 \sin\left(\frac{\pi t}{6} - \frac{\pi}{2}\right) = f(t).$$

In the last line here we have applied the 2π-periodicity of the sine function—the fact that $\sin(x + 2\pi) = \sin(x)$, using $x = \pi t/6 - \pi/2$. ∎

Thus we have verified that $f(t + 12) = f(t)$, so the predicted average temperature one year (12 months) from now is the same as this month's average temperature. To construct your own graph of this function, you must remember that the typical graphing calculator requires use of x as the independent variable and y as the independent variable. Thus the function in (9) is entered as shown in Fig. 6.1.11 [where the original version in (1) is also entered]. How must the viewing window be specified to get the graph in Fig. 6.1.12 (similar to Fig. 6.1.2)?

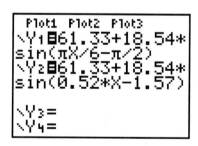

Figure 6.1.11   Atlanta's montly average temperature function.

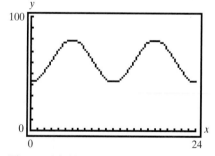

Figure 6.1.12   How many 12-month periods of $f(t)$ are shown?

Solving Trigonometric Equations

In previous chapters we have frequently used graphing calculator facilities to solve equations numerically or graphically. The approach is no different when trigonometric functions are involved.

Example 8

In Figure 6.1.13 we have plotted the graphs $y = x$ and $y = \cos x$. The single point of intersection indicates that the equation

$$x = \cos x \tag{10}$$

has only a single solution. Indeed, Fig. 6.1.14 indicates that we have used our calculator's **CALC intersect** facility to find that this solution of Eq. (10) is $x = 0.7391$, accurate to 4 decimal places.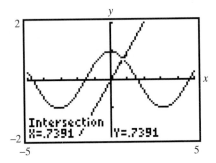

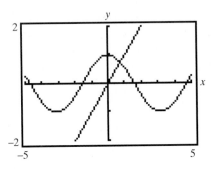

Figure 6.1.13　The graphs $y = x$ and $y = \cos x$.

Figure 6.1.14　Solving the equation $x = \cos x$ of Example 8.

Example 9

In Fig. 6.1.15 we have plotted the graphs $y = 1 - x$ and $y = 3 \cos x$. Now three points of intersection are visible, so we see that the equation

$$1 - x = 3 \cos x \tag{11}$$

has *three* different solutions. You should use your calculator's **CALC intersect** facility to verify that these three solutions are $x \approx -0.8895$, $x \approx 1.8624$, and $x \approx 3.6380$.

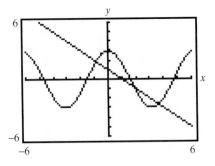

Figure 6.1.15　The graphs $y = 1 - x$ and $y = 3 \cos x$ of Example 9.

Example 10

Suppose we ask when—that is, in which month(s)—during the year the Atlanta monthly average temperature is 70°. According to Eq. (9) we need to solve the equation

$$61.33 + 18.54 \sin\left(\frac{\pi t}{6} - \frac{\pi}{2}\right) = 70, \tag{12}$$

recalling (from our initial discussion of Atlanta temperatures at the beginning of this section) that $t = 0$ in mid-January and $t = 11$ in mid-December.

In Fig. 6.1.16 we have graphed the left-hand and right-hand sides in Eq. (12) for $0 \le t \le 12$, and we see two points of intersection. We have used our calculator's intersection-finding facility to find that the first intersection is $t = 3.93 \approx 4$, and you can show similarly that the second intersection is $t = 8.07 \approx 8$. Thus the average temperature is 70° near the middle of the fourth month after January—that is, in May—and again near the middle of the eighth month after January—that is, in September. More precisely, since $\frac{7}{100}$ of a month is close to 2 days, we conclude that the approximate dates are May 13 and September 17 (why?). ◼

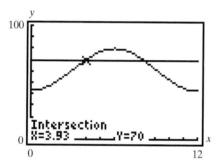

Figure 6.1.16   Solving Eq. (12) in Example 10.

Composition—New Functions from Old Ones

In this book you have seen many types of functions, including linear functions, polynomials, exponential and logarithmic functions, and now trigonometric functions. Still more varied and complex functions can be put together by using these as building-block functions. In addition to adding, subtracting, multiplying, and dividing two given functions, we can also combine functions by letting one function act on the output of the other.

Definition: Composition of functions
The **composition** of the two functions f and g is the new function $h = f \circ g$ defined by

$$h(x) = f(g(x)). \tag{13}$$

The domain of h consists of all points x for which the right-hand side in (13) is meaningful—that is, x is in the domain of g and $u = g(x)$ is in the domain of f. [The right-hand side in (13) is read "f of g of x".]

Thus the output $u = g(x)$ of the function g is used as the input to the function f (Fig. 6.1.17). We sometimes refer to g as the inner function and to f as the outer function in Eq. (13).

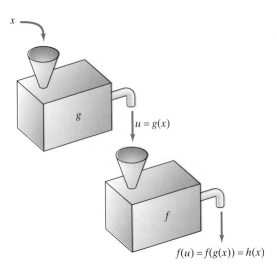

Figure 6.1.17   The composition $h = f \circ g$.

Example 11

If $f(x) = \sqrt{x}$ and $g(x) = 1 - x^2$, then

$$f(g(x)) = \sqrt{1 - x^2} \quad \text{for } |x| \leq 1,$$

whereas

$$g(f(x)) = 1 - (\sqrt{x})^2 = 1 - x \quad \text{for } x \geq 0. \qquad \blacksquare$$

The $f(g(x))$ notation for compositions is most commonly used in ordinary computations, but the $f \circ g$ notation emphasizes that the composition may be regarded as a new kind of combination of the functions f and g. But Example 11 shows that $f \circ g$ is quite unlike the ordinary product $f \cdot g$ of the two functions f and g. For $f \circ g \neq g \circ f$, whereas $f \cdot g = g \cdot f$ [because $f(x) \cdot g(x) = g(x) \cdot f(x)$ whenever $f(x)$ and $g(x)$ are both defined]. So remember that composition is quite different in character from ordinary multiplication of functions.

Example 12

If

$$f(x) = x^2 \quad \text{and} \quad g(x) = \cos x,$$

then the functions

$$f(x) \cdot g(x) = x^2 \cos x,$$
$$f(g(x)) = (\cos x)^2 = \cos^2 x, \text{and}$$
$$g(f(x)) = \cos(x^2) = \cos x^2$$

are defined for all x. But Figs. 6.1.18–6.1.20 illustrate vividly how different these three functions are.

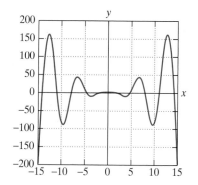

Figure 6.1.18 $y = x^2 \cos x$.

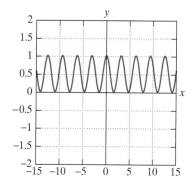

Figure 6.1.19 $y = \cos^2 x$.

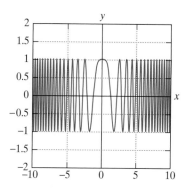

Figure 6.1.20 $y = \cos x^2$.

Example 13

Given the function $h(x) = (x^2 + 4)^{3/2}$, find two functions f and g such that $f(g(x))$.

It is technically correct—but useless—simply to let $g(x) = x$ and $f(u) = (u^2 + 4)^{3/2}$. We seek a nontrivial answer here. To calculate $(x^2 + 4)^{3/2}$, we must *first* calculate $x^2 + 4$. So we choose $g(x) = x^2 + 4$ as the *inner* function. The *last* step is to raise $u = g(x)$ to the power $3/2$, so we take $f(u) = u^{3/2}$ as the *outer* function. Thus if

$$f(x) = x^{3/2} \quad \text{and} \quad g(x) = x^2 + 4,$$

then $f(g(x)) = f(x^2 + 4) = (x^2 + 4)^{3/2} = h(x)$, as desired.

Example 13 illustrates a useful approach to recognizing a given function $h(x)$ as a composition $f(g(x))$. Instead of just looking at $h(x)$, think of *actually doing it*—that is, calculating $h(x)$ with a calculator. If, starting with a number x, just two calculator functions need to be applied in succession to calculate $h(x)$, then the *first* function applied is the *inner* function g, and the *last* function applied is the *outer* function g.

In this section we have discussed trigonometric functions that oscillate periodically as time goes by. The following example exhibits a function that combines the steady decrease of a (negative-exponent) exponential function with the oscillation of a trigonometric function.

Example 14

Think of the up-and-down vibrations of a car with very poor shock absorbers. These vibrations might be described by the function

$$y(t) = 3 \cdot 2^{-t} \cos(4\pi t) \tag{14}$$

that gives the car's height y (in inches above or below its normal position) t seconds after it hits a deep pothole. Observe that

- $y(0) = 3$, so the car's *initial* bounce is 3 inches;
- $y(1) = \frac{3}{2}$, $y(2) = \frac{3}{4}$, $y(3) = \frac{3}{8}$, and so forth, to the amplitude of the car's up-and-down oscillations *halves* every second; and
- $4\pi t = 2\pi$ when $t = \frac{1}{2}$, so the period of the factor $\cos(4\pi t)$ in (14) is a half second, and hence the car undergoes *two* up-and-down oscillations per second.

Figure 6.1.21 shows the graph of $y(t)$. The curve described in (14) oscillates up and down between the *two* curves $y(t) = \pm 3 \cdot 2^{-t}$. It appears that the car's vibrations die out and are negligible after 7 or 8 seconds. ◼

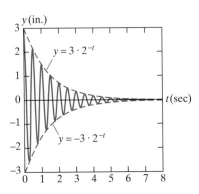

Figure 6.1.21 $y = 3 \cdot 2^{-t} \cos(4\pi t)$.

Express in radian measure each of the angles given in Problems 1–4.

1. (a) 30°   (b) 150°   (c) 210°
2. (a) 20°   (b) 160°   (c) 340°
3. (a) 135°   (b) 225°   (c) 315°
4. (a) 120°   (b) 240°   (c) 300°

Each of the angles in Problems 5–8 is given in radians. Convert it to degrees.

5. (a) $\pi/10$ (b) $\pi/9$ (c) $\pi/5$
6. (a) $2\pi/9$ (b) $2\pi/5$ (c) $5\pi/6$
7. (a) $3\pi/10$ (b) $4\pi/9$ (c) $7\pi/5$
8. (a) $4\pi/15$ (b) $11\pi/18$ (c) $17\pi/36$

In Problems 9–12, use the method of Example 5 to find the indicated value.

9.   (a) $\sin\left(\frac{5\pi}{6}\right)$ (b) $\sin\left(\frac{7\pi}{6}\right)$ (c) $\sin\left(\frac{11\pi}{6}\right)$
10. (a) $\sin\left(\frac{3\pi}{4}\right)$ (b) $\sin\left(\frac{5\pi}{4}\right)$ (c) $\sin\left(\frac{7\pi}{4}\right)$
11. (a) $\cos\left(\frac{4\pi}{3}\right)$ (b) $\cos\left(\frac{4\pi}{3}\right)$ (c) $\cos\left(\frac{5\pi}{3}\right)$
12. (a) $\sin(\pi)$ (b) $\cos\left(\frac{3\pi}{2}\right)$ (c) $\sin\left(\frac{5\pi}{2}\right)$

In Problems 13–20, match the given function with its graph among those shown in Figs. 6.1.22 through 6.1.29. Try to do this without turning on your graphing calculator or computer.

13. $f(x) = 2^x - 1$
14. $f(x) = 2 - 3^{-x}$

15. $f(x) = 1 + \cos x$

16. $f(x) = 2 - 2 \sin x$

17. $f(x) = 1 + 2 \cos x$

18. $f(x) = 2 - \sin x$

19. $f(x) = 2^{-x} \sin(10x)$

20. $f(x) = \dfrac{1 + \cos 6x}{1 + x^2}$

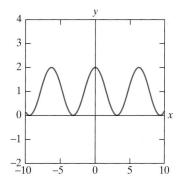

Figure 6.1.22

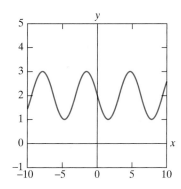

Figure 6.1.23

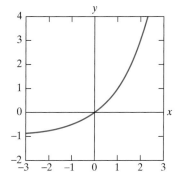

Figure 6.1.24

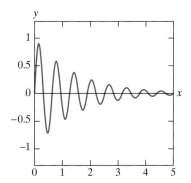

Figure 6.1.25

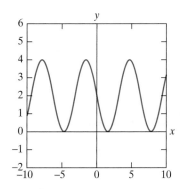

Figure 6.1.26

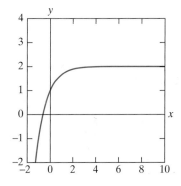

Figure 6.1.27

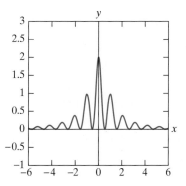

Figure 6.1.28

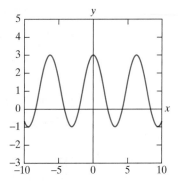

Figure 6.1.29

In Problems 21–30, find both $f(g(x))$ and $g(f(x))$. Then compare the graphs of these two compositions.

21. $f(x) = 1 - x^2$ and $g(x) = 2x + 3$

22. $f(x) = -17$ and $g(x) = |x|$

23. $f(x) = \sqrt{x^2 - 3}$ and $g(x) = x^2 + 3$

24. $f(x) = x^2 + 1$ and $g(x) = \dfrac{1}{x^2 + 1}$

25. $f(x) = x^3 - 4$ and $g(x) = \sqrt[3]{x + 4}$

26. $f(x) = \sqrt{x}$ and $g(x) = \cos x$

27. $f(x) = \sin x$ and $g(x) = x^3$

28. $f(x) = \sin 2x$ and $g(x) = \cos 3x$

29. $f(x) = 2^x$ and $g(x) = x^2$

30. $f(x) = x^{1/3}$ and $g(x) = 3^{-x}$

Use a graphing calculator to find (accurate to 4 decimal places) each solution of the equations in Problems 31–38.

31. $2x = \cos x$

32. $x + 1 = 3 \cos x$

33. $x - 1 = 3 \cos x$

34. $x = 5 \cos x$

35. $x = 7 \cos x$

36. $x^2 = 10 \cos x$

37. $x^2 = 100 \sin x$

38. $\cos 3x = x^3 - 3x^2 + 1$

6.2   TRIGONOMETRIC MODELS AND PERIODIC DATA

When we look at the Atlanta monthly average temperature function

$$f(t) = 61.33 + 18.54 \sin\left(\frac{\pi t}{6} - \frac{\pi}{2}\right) \tag{1}$$

discussed in Section 6.1, we see that

- The constant term 61.33 is the year-round average temperature, while
- The coefficient 18.54 is the maximal variation up and down from this average.

More generally, the function

$$f(t) = A + B \sin\left(\frac{\pi t}{6} - \frac{\pi}{2}\right) \tag{2}$$

describes a 12-month variation with a year-round average of A and a maximal variation of B up and down from this average.

Example 1

With $A = 49$ and $B = 17$ in (2) we obtain the monthly average temperature function

$$f(t) = 49 + 17 \sin\left(\frac{\pi t}{6} - \frac{\pi}{2}\right) \qquad (3)$$

of a more temperate locale with a year-round average of 49°, a minimal (January) average temperature of $(49 - 17 =) 32°$, and a maximal (July) average of $(49 + 17 =) 66°$. Substituting $t = 4$, we get the average May temperature of

$$f(4) = 49 + 17 \sin\left(\frac{4\pi}{6} - \frac{\pi}{2}\right) = 49 + 17 \sin\left(\frac{\pi}{6}\right) = 49 + 17 \cdot \frac{1}{2} = 57.5$$

in this locale. ◣

The annual average temperature function in (3) can be rewritten in the form

$$f(t) = 49 + 17 \sin\left(\frac{2\pi(t - 3)}{12}\right). \qquad (4)$$

The number 12 in the denominator is the *period* in months—12 months in a year. The number 3 subtracted from t in the numerator is the *delay* (in months) between time $t = 0$ (January) and the time $t = 3$ (April) when the temperature reaches its yearly average of 49—since $f(3) = 49 + 17 \sin(0) = 49 + 17 \cdot 0 = 49$. The formula in (4) illustrates the way a typical periodic function is constructed.

Definition: The General Periodic Function
The formula

$$f(t) = A + B \sin\left(\frac{2\pi(t - D)}{P}\right) \qquad (5)$$

defines a periodic function where

- A = the **average value** of the function;
- B = the **amplitude** of its oscillation—meaning the amount by which it oscillates above and below its average;
- P = the **period** during which its value makes a complete cycle and returns to its original value; and
- D = the **delay** between time $t = 0$ and the next time when the function reaches its average value. (So if the average value occurs at time $t = 0$, then $D = 0$.)

The meanings of the average A, amplitude B, period P, and delay D of a periodic function are illustrated graphically in Fig. 6.2.1. We can use (5) to construct a mathematical model for a periodically varying quantity if we know the values of these four parameters. In particular, observe that the period P can be described either as the time between successive maximum values or as the time between successive minimum values.

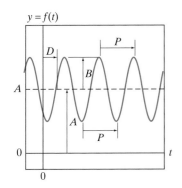

Figure 6.2.1 The graph of the periodic function $f(t) = A + B \sin\left(\frac{2\pi(t - D)}{P}\right)$.

Example 2

The temperature during a typical late July day in Atlanta varies periodically between a minimum of 70° at 4 A.M. and a maximum of 90° at 4 P.M.

(a) Write a formula giving the temperature t hours past midnight (when $t = 0$).
(b) Use this formula to predict the temperatures at midnight and at noon during the day.
(c) Find when during the afternoon the temperature is exactly 87.5°.

(a) The *period* during which the temperature repeats itself daily is $P = 24$ hours. Given that the temperature varies up and down between 70 and 90, we see that the *average* temperature during a day is $A = 80$, with an *amplitude* of variation of $B = 10$. Finally, we reason that the average temperature of 80 occurs halfway between the minimum at 4 A.M. and the maximum at 4 P.M., and hence at 10 A.M. Hence the *delay* between time $t = 0$ (midnight) and the time 10 A.M. of average temperature is $D = 10$ hours. When we substitute these four values in (5), we get the mathematical model

$$f(t) = 80 + 10 \sin\left(\frac{2\pi(t - 10)}{24}\right) \qquad (6)$$

giving the temperature at time t during the 24-hour day.
(b) Thus

- the temperature at midnight is

$$f(0) = 80 + 10 \sin\left(\frac{2\pi(0 - 10)}{24}\right) = 80 + 10 \sin\left(\frac{-20\pi}{24}\right) = 75°, \text{ and}$$

- the temperature at noon is

$$f(12) = 80 + 10 \sin\left(\frac{2\pi(12 - 10)}{24}\right) = 80 + 10 \sin\left(\frac{4\pi}{24}\right) = 85°.$$

(c) To find when the temperature is 87.5°, we need to solve the equation

$$80 + 10 \sin\left(\frac{2\pi(t - 10)}{24}\right) = 87.5.$$

It would be good practice for you to do this graphically, but let's proceed symbolically. Upon transposing 80 and then dividing by 10, we find that

$$\sin\left(\frac{2\pi(t - 10)}{24}\right) = 0.75.$$

Now by using the inverse sine ("the angle whose sine is") key on our calculator, we get

$$\frac{2\pi(t - 10)}{24} = \sin^{-1}(0.75) \approx 0.8481.$$

Solving this equation for t, we find that

$$t \approx \frac{24 \times 0.8481}{2\pi} + 10 = 13.2395 \text{ hours after midnight.}$$

Since 0.2395 hours is about 14.37 minutes (since $0.2395 \times 60 \approx 14.37$), the temperature is exactly 87.5° at a bit after 1:14 P.M. ◨

Fitting Periodic Data

We now discuss the use of a graphing calculator's sine regression function to fit given data with a periodic function. For this purpose, let's rewrite the formula for a general periodic function in the form

$$y = a\sin(bx + c) + d \tag{7}$$

(with x instead of t as the independent variable) that a graphing calculator ordinarily uses. The coefficients in (7) are given in terms of those in (5) by

$$a = B, \quad b = \frac{2\pi}{P}, \quad c = -\frac{2\pi D}{P}, \quad d = A. \tag{8}$$

You should check that—when these relations are turned inside out to express the coefficients in (5) in terms of those in (7)—the result is

$$A = d, \quad B = a, \quad P = \frac{2\pi}{b}, \quad D = -\frac{Pc}{2\pi} = -\frac{c}{b}. \tag{9}$$

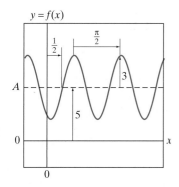

$y = f(x)$

Figure 6.2.2 The graph $y = 3\sin(4x - 2) + 5$ in Example 3.

Example 3

Find the average value A, the amplitude B of oscillation, the period P, and the delay D of the periodic function

$$y = 3\sin(4x - 2) + 5. \tag{10}$$

Comparing (10) and (7), we have $a = 3$, $b = 4$, $c = -2$, $d = 5$. Then the relations in (9) give

$$A = 5, \quad B = 3, \quad P = \frac{2\pi}{4} \approx 1.57, \quad D = -\frac{-2}{4} = 0.5.$$

The graph of (10) is shown in Fig. 6.2.2. ∎

The TI-83 **SinReg** (**Sin**e **Reg**ression) function (on the **STAT CALC** menu) fits a periodic function $y = a\sin(bx + c) + d$ to given x- and y-lists $\mathbf{L_1}$ and $\mathbf{L_2}$ of numerical data. We must decide in advance what the period P of the desired function is to be. Then the command **SinReg $\mathbf{L_1}$, $\mathbf{L_2}$, P, $\mathbf{Y_1}$** calculates the coefficients a, b, c, d and stores the resulting periodic function as $\mathbf{Y_1}$. The period P to enter may be determined either

- By inspection (perhaps graphical) of the given data, or
- By the situation being modeled.

The next two examples illustrate these two possibilities.

Example 4

Fit a periodic function to the data in the following table, and determine its average value, amplitude, period, and delay.

x	0	$\pi/12$	$\pi/4$	$5\pi/12$	$\pi/2$
y	3	5	7	5	3

We first enter this data as shown in Fig. 6.2.3. The graph (Fig. 6.2.4) of this data in the window $-\pi \le x \le \pi, 0 \le y \le 10$ appears to correspond to *one* of the two arches of a sine function.

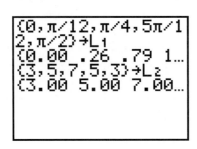

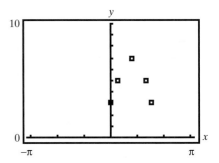

Figure 6.2.3   Entering the data of Example 4.

Figure 6.2.4   Graph of the Example 4 data.

Hence the x-range $\pi/2$ of this data is *half* of the period P of the corresponding periodic function. We therefore choose $P = \pi$ and enter the command **SinReg L₁, L₂, π, Y₁**. The results shown in Fig. 6.2.5—$a = 4$, $b = 2$, $c = 0$, $d = 3$—yield the periodic function

$$y = 4\sin(2x) + 3 \tag{11}$$

whose graph fitting the original data points is shown in Fig. 6.2.6. Indeed, you can check that this function fits the given data *exactly,* not just approximately. Finally, the relations in (9) give us the average value $A = 3$, amplitude $B = 4$, period $P = 2\pi/2 = \pi$, and the delay $D = 0$. ◼

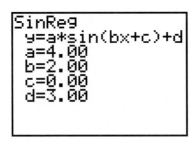

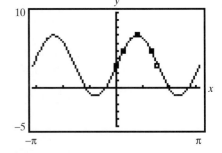

Figure 6.2.5   The resulting periodic function $y = 4\sin(2x) + 3$.

Figure 6.2.6   The graph $y = 4\sin(2x) + 3$.

Example 5

Find a periodic function fitting the Atlanta monthly average temperature data given at the beginning of Section 6.1.

With the 12 months January through December numbered $t = 0$ through $t = 11$, we enter the given data as indicated in Fig. 6.2.7. The command **SinReg** **L₁, L₂, 12, Y₁** (seeking a function of period $P = 12$) yields the results shown in Fig. 6.2.8—$a = 19.42, b = 0.48, c = -1.35, d = 59.79$—and thus gives the periodic function

$$f(t) = 19.42 \sin(0.48t - 1.35) + 59.79. \tag{12}$$

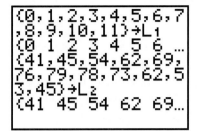

Figure 6.2.7   The Atlanta monthly temperature data.

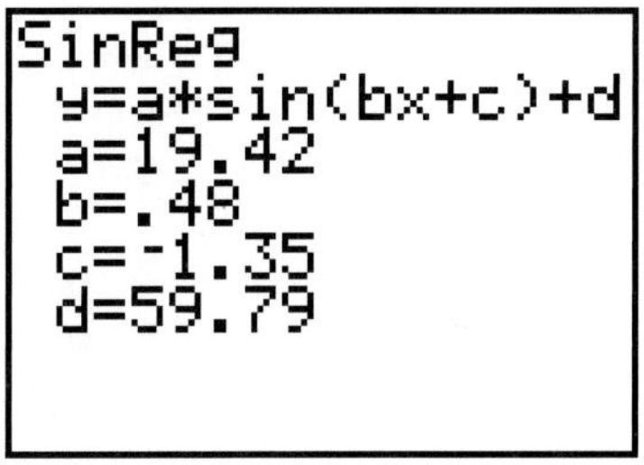

Figure 6.2.8   Fitting the monthly temperature data.

The plot shown in Fig. 6.2.9 indicates that this function approximates the given data quite well. However, do you see that something about this picture is not quite right? Although we asked for a function of period 12, it appears that the period of $f(t)$—which is the distance between successive minima—is larger than 12. Indeed, the P-relation in (9) gives

$$P = \frac{2\pi}{b} = \frac{2\pi}{0.48} \approx 13.09$$

(months) instead of 12. The reason is this: The periodic function of the form in (7)—the one that best approximates the data—simply does not have period 12. Sometimes you've got to take what you get.

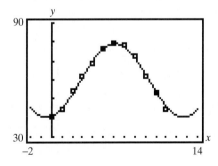

Figure 6.2.9   The periodic approximation $f(t) = 19.42 \sin(0.48t - 1.35) + 59.79.$

It's sometimes said that trigonometric data modeling is more art than science. We would like to have an approximating function that really does have period 12. A trick by which we can attempt to force this to happen is to enter *two years'* rather than a single year's worth of data, as indicated in Fig. 6.2.10. We have already entered {0,1,2,3,...,21,22,23}→**L₃** to count two full years of months. Then the command **SinReg L₃, L₄, 12, Y₁** yields the results shown in Fig. 6.2.11—$a = 18.54, b = 0.52, c = -1.57, d = 61.33$—and thus gives the periodic function

$$f(t) = 18.54 \sin(0.52t - 1.57) + 61.33. \tag{13}$$

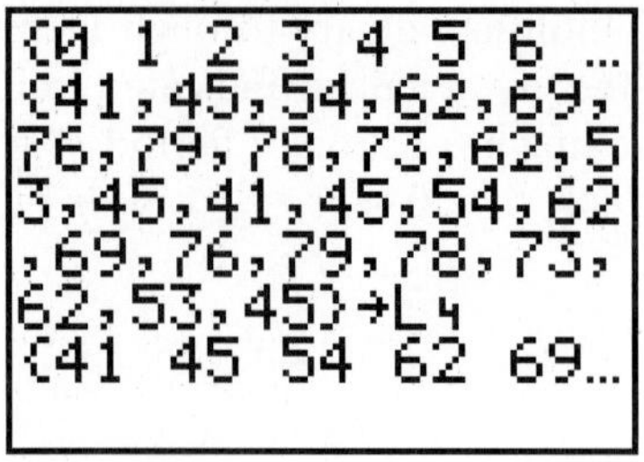

```
(0 1 2 3 4 5 6 ...
(41,45,54,62,69,
76,79,78,73,62,5
3,45,41,45,54,62
,69,76,79,78,73,
62,53,45)→L4
(41 45 54 62 69...
```

```
SinReg
 y=a*sin(bx+c)+d
 a=18.54
 b=.52
 c=-1.57
 d=61.33
```

Figure 6.2.10   Two years worth of temperature data.

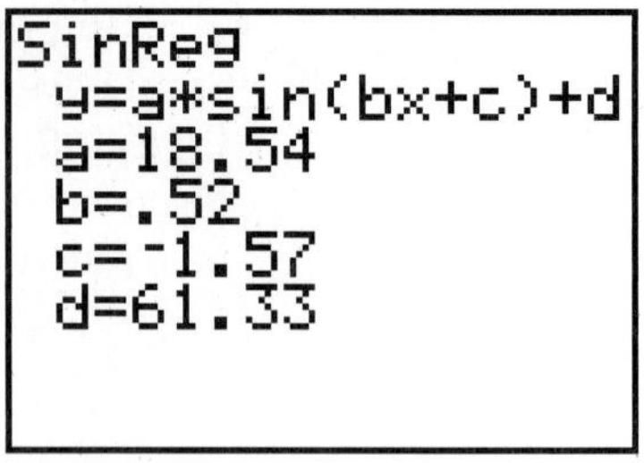

Figure 6.2.11   The new periodic approximation $f(t) = 18.54 \sin(0.52t - 1.57) + 61.33$.

The plot shown in Fig. 6.2.12 indicates that this function approximates the given data quite well. Moreover, the *P*-relation in (9) now gives

$$P = \frac{2\pi}{b} = \frac{2\pi}{0.52} \approx 12.08,$$

much closer to the ideal 12-month period we sought. Finally, (13) is the periodic approximation with which we began in Example 1 of Section 6.1.   ◼

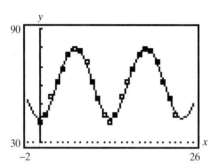

Figure 6.2.12   The new periodic approximation $f(t) = 18.54 \sin(0.52t - 1.57) + 61.33$.

6.2
PROBLEMS

In Problems 1–4, the average value *A*, the amplitude *B*, the period *P*, and the delay *D* of a periodic function are given. Sketch the graph of this function, and label *A*, *B*, *P*, and *D* on this graph. Use your graphing calculator only if you must.

1. $A = 5,$	$B = 2,$	$P = 1,$	$D = 0$
2. $A = 3,$	$B = 5,$	$P = 2,$	$D = 0$
3. $A = 4,$	$B = 3,$	$P = 2,$	$D = 1$
4. $A = 10,$	$B = 5,$	$P = 4,$	$D = 3$

Find the average value *A*, the amplitude *B*, the period *P*, and the delay *D* of each of the periodic functions given in Problems 5–10.

5. $f(x) = 3 \sin(x) + 7$
6. $f(x) = 7 \sin(\pi x) + 3$
7. $f(x) = 3 \sin(x - 2) + 5$
8. $f(x) = 5 \sin(2\pi x - \pi) + 3$
9. $f(x) = 10 \sin(4x - 2) + 5$
10. $f(x) = 15 \sin(\frac{\pi x}{3} - \frac{2\pi}{3}) + 10$

11. The average temperature during a year in a certain location is given by a function of the form

$$f(t) = A + B\sin(kt).$$

(a) Determine the values of the coefficients A and B so that the average temperature here varies during a year between a minimum of $36°$ and a maximum of $72°$. *Hint:* What are the largest and smallest possible values of $\sin(kt)$?

(b) Determine the value of the coefficient k so that the period of this temperature is 12 months. *Hint:* One oscillation of $\sin(kt)$ is complete when $kt = 2\pi$.

12. The temperature during a single July day in a certain location is given by a function of the form

$$f(t) = A + B\cos(kt).$$

(a) Determine the values of the coefficients A and B so that the temperature varies during a day between a minimum of $64°$ and a maximum of $79°$. *Hint:* What are the largest and smallest possible values of $\cos(kt)$?

(b) Determine the value of the coefficient k so that the period of this temperature is 24 hours. *Hint:* One oscillation of $\cos(kt)$ is complete when $kt = 2\pi$.

In each of Problems 13–18, use either inspection or the method of Example 4 to fit a periodic function $y = a\sin(bx) + d$ to the data given in the table. Determine the average value, amplitude, period, and delay of this periodic function.

13.

x	0	$\pi/2$	π	$3\pi/2$	2π
y	4	7	4	1	4

14.

x	0	$\pi/6$	$\pi/2$	$5\pi/6$	π
y	5	6	7	6	5

15.

x	0	1	2	3	4
y	3	7	3	-1	3

16.

x	0	4	12	20	24
y	7	12	17	12	7

17.

x	0	1	3	5	6
y	5	11	17	11	5

18.

x	0	5	15	25	30
y	13	17	21	17	13

In each of Problems 19–22, the monthly average temperatures of a U.S. city are given. Use the method of Example 5 to find a periodic function with period $P \approx 12$ that models these temperatures.

19.   Boston, MA

Jan	Feb	Mar	Apr	May	June	July	Aug	Sept	Oct	Nov	Dec
29°	30°	39°	48°	58°	68°	74°	72°	65°	55°	45°	34°

20.   Minneapolis, MN

Jan	Feb	Mar	Apr	May	June	July	Aug	Sept	Oct	Nov	Dec
12°	18°	31°	46°	59°	68°	74°	71°	61°	49°	33°	18°

21.   Houston, TX

Jan	Feb	Mar	Apr	May	June	July	Aug	Sept	Oct	Nov	Dec
50°	54°	61°	68°	75°	80°	83°	82°	78°	70°	61°	54°

22.   Seattle, WA

Jan	Feb	Mar	Apr	May	June	July	Aug	Sept	Oct	Nov	Dec
41°	44°	47°	50°	56°	61°	65°	66°	61°	54°	46°	42°

At the equator (0° latitude), the length of each day (measuring from sunrise to sunset) is always the same (a little bit more than 12 hours per day). In each of Problems 23–26, the number of hours between sunrise and sunset on the fifteenth of each month at a certain latitude is given. Use the method of Example 5 to find a periodic function with period $P \approx 12$ that models these data.

23. 10° latitude

Jan	Feb	Mar	Apr	May	June	July	Aug	Sept	Oct	Nov	Dec
11.58	11.82	12.07	12.35	12.57	12.70	12.67	12.47	12.30	11.92	11.67	11.53

24. 20° latitude

Jan	Feb	Mar	Apr	May	June	July	Aug	Sept	Oct	Nov	Dec
11.03	11.35	12.00	12.60	13.07	13.33	13.27	12.83	12.28	11.70	11.20	10.93

25. 40° latitude

Jan	Feb	Mar	Apr	May	June	July	Aug	Sept	Oct	Nov	Dec
9.62	10.70	11.88	13.23	14.37	15.00	14.82	13.80	12.52	11.17	10.02	9.33

26. 60° latitude

Jan	Feb	Mar	Apr	May	June	July	Aug	Sept	Oct	Nov	Dec
6.63	9.18	11.68	14.52	17.07	18.82	17.52	15.77	13.00	10.18	7.62	5.90

27. Refer to Problems 23–26. What happens to the pattern of the length of days as you move farther from the equator? Which parameter in your mathematical model describes this phenomenon?

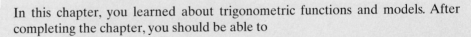

C H A P T E R   6   R E V I E W

In this chapter, you learned about trigonometric functions and models. After completing the chapter, you should be able to

- Determine whether a relation described numercially, graphically, or symbolically represents a trigonometric function.
- Find the output value of a trigonometric function for a given input value.
- Find the input value(s) of a trigonometric function for a given output value.
- Solve an equation or inequality involving a trigonometric function.
- Determine the amplitude, the period, and the delay of a trigonometric function.
- Find the sine function model that best fits given data.

REVIEW PROBLEMS

In Problems 1–6, the given information (table, graph, or formula) gives y as a function of x. In each case, the function is quadratic, trigonometric, or neither. Determine the type of function.

1.

x	-5	-3	-2	-1	0	1	2
y	-2.5	2.5	0	-2.5	0	2.5	0

2.

x	-2	-1	0	1	2	4
y	4	2.5	2	2.5	4	6.5

3.

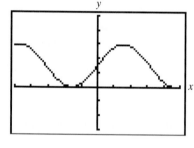

4.

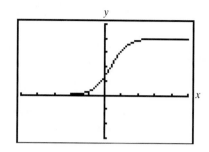

5. $y = 0.4(x - 1)^2 + 3$

6. $y = 0.4\cos(x - 1) + 3$

7. Find $\sin\left(\frac{4\pi}{3}\right)$ and $\cos\left(\frac{5\pi}{6}\right)$.

8. Find two values of x for which $\cos x = \frac{1}{2}$.

9. Find numerically all solutions of the equation $3\cos 2x = 2x^2$.

10. The accompanying table gives the monthly average minimum temperature for Columbia, Missouri. Find a trigonometric function with period $P \approx 12$ that models these temperatures.

Jan	Feb	Mar	Apr	May	June
21°	24°	32°	44°	54°	64°

July	Aug	Sept	Oct	Nov	Dec
68°	66°	58°	47°	33°	25°

ACTIVITY

Are U.S. Cities Getting Warmer?

In this activity, you will create function models based on temperature data for one of the 100 largest cities in the United States.

From the latest census data available, select the xyth largest city, where x and y are the last two digits of your student identification number. This is your city. (For example, if your student ID number ends in 37, you should find the data for the 37th largest city in the United States. If your ID number ends in 00, choose the 100th largest city.)

Find the historical temperature data for your city for the years 1950, 1970, and 1990. Record the maximum and minimum temperatures for each month during those years.

(1) Find the best-fitting trigonometric model for the monthly maximum temperatures for each of the years 1950, 1970, and 1990. Compare your models with respect to amplitude and average value.

(2) Find the best-fitting trigonometric model for the monthly minimum temperatures for each year. Compare your models with respect to amplitude and average value.

(3) Do your models provide evidence to support the theory of global warming? Why or why not?

7 BOUNDED GROWTH MODELS

How do you know when a certain disease reaches epidemic proportions? For the layperson, a disease appears to be an epidemic when it is either already widespread or spreading at an alarming rate. Since the 1980s, you have probably heard references to the "AIDS epidemic" and comments about deaths from AIDS increasing "exponentially." But is this indeed the case?

The chart in Fig. 7.0.1 shows the cumulative deaths from HIV (the virus that causes AIDS) for the years 1987 through 1997. We can see from this chart that from 1987 to about 1994, deaths from HIV were increasing at an increasing rate. This portion of the graph displays the upward curving shape typical of an exponential function. But after about 1994, while the total number of deaths was still increasing, it was increasing at a decreasing rate and may appear to be leveling off. This portion of the graph curves downward and looks more logarithmic than exponential.

Because this data represents cumulative deaths, the function modeling the data can never be decreasing. Thus, the graph cannot have the peaks and valleys usually associated with polynomial functions. This data provides a good example of a bounded growth function, the type of function and model we will study in this chapter.

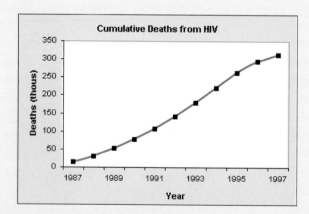

Figure 7.0.1   Cumulative HIV deaths.

Source: National Center for Health Statistics.

7.1	Limited Populations
7.2	Fitting Logistic Models to Data
7.3	Discrete Models and Chaos

7.1   LIMITED POPULATIONS

A pristine forest habitat was initially stocked with 10 rabbits. Over the next three years the rabbit population in this forest was monitored carefully, with the results shown in the following table.

t months	P rabbits	t months	P rabbits
0	10		
3	21	21	98
6	40	24	99
9	62	27	100
12	80	30	100
15	91	33	100
18	96	36	100

We see from the first two columns that the rabbits immediately began to reproduce rapidly, as is typical of rabbits. After 6 months the initial population of 10 rabbits had quadrupled to 40 rabbits. In the second 6-month period the rabbit population doubled, from 40 rabbits to 80 rabbits. But then the rate of growth of the population slowed noticeably—only 16 more rabbits were added to the population during the first half of the second year. And we see from the last two columns of the table that the population leveled off at 100 rabbits during the third year.

A possible explanation for this phenomenon is that the forest habitat may contain only enough food to sustain a maximum population of 100 rabbits. At any rate, our rabbits provide an example of a population that is **bounded** or **limited.** Instead of increasing indefinitely as time goes on, it levels off at a finite **limiting population.**

297

Another example of a limited population would be a population of fruit flies in a closed container that can support only so many flies. Similarly, a lake may provide enough food only for a limited population of fish. And we will see that many human populations also are limited—for instance, by the area of a country or by the food products it can provide.

The spreadsheet chart in Fig. 7.1.1 shows a plot of the rabbit population data in the preceding table. It is apparent at a glance that this graph does not resemble any seen in previous chapters. Polynomial, exponential, and logarithmic graphs ultimately continue either to rise or to fall indefinitely; they do not level off.

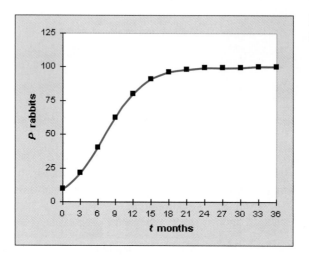

Figure 7.1.1   Plot of rabbit population data.

Thus we need some new type of mathematical function that can serve to model a limited population. The logistic functions we now define are useful for this purpose.

Definition: Logistic Function
A **logistic function** is one of the form

$$f(x) = \frac{c}{1 + ae^{-bx}} \qquad (1)$$

where a, b, c are positive constants (while $e \approx 2.71828$ denotes as usual the famous natural base number of Chapter 4). Figure 7.1.2 shows this general logistic function defined with a graphing calculator.

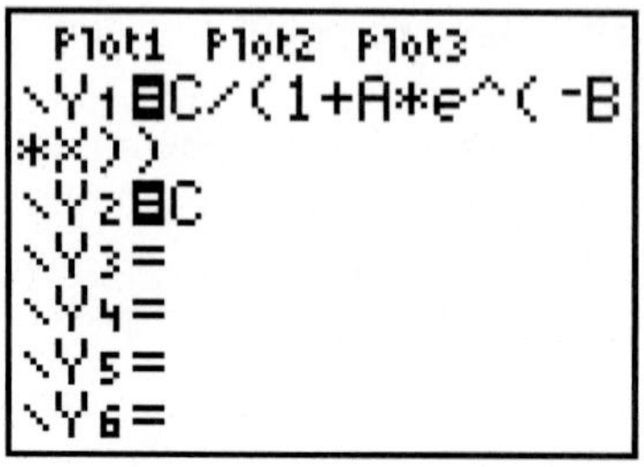

Figure 7.1.2   The logistic function $f(x) = \dfrac{c}{1 + ae^{-bx}}$ and its limiting value $y = c$.

Example 1

With $a = 3, b = 1,$ and $c = 12$ in (1) we get the logistic function

$$f(x) = \frac{12}{1 + 3e^{-x}}. \tag{2}$$

Upon entering these parameters as in Fig. 7.1.3 we are prepared to plot or tabulate this function. Figure 7.1.4 shows the resulting graph-table (**G-T** calculator mode) split screen. The logistic function in (2) is plotted on the left in the window $0 < x < 8, 0 < y < 20,$ together with the line $y = 12$ (which is plotted also because we defined $Y_2 = C$ as in Fig. 7.1.2). Evidently, our logistic function levels off at the height $c = 12.$ This is still more obvious in the table on the right in Fig. 7.1.4, where we see that $f(x)$ has reached the approximate value $11.9984 \approx c$ when $x = 10.$ ◼

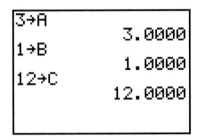

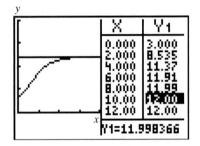

Figure 7.1.3   Parameters for the logistic function $f(x) = \dfrac{12}{1 + 3e^{-x}}.$

Figure 7.1.4   Calculator graph and table of values of the logistic function $f(x) = \dfrac{12}{1 + 3e^{-x}}.$

Example 2

The smooth curve interpolating the data points in Fig. 7.1.1 is the graph of the logistic function

$$P(t) = \frac{100}{1 + 9e^{-0.3t}} \tag{3}$$

that we obtain with the parameter values $a = 9, b = 0.3,$ and $c = 100.$ Upon

- entering these new parameter values in the manner of Fig. 7.1.3;
- defining the new viewing window $0 < x < 36, 0 < y < 150;$ and
- specifying **ΔTbl=6** in the table setup menu

we get the split screen shown in Fig. 7.1.5. [Of course, the calculator is using **X** in place of the independent variable t in (3), and **Y** in place of the dependent variable $P.$] On the left we see the graph apparently leveling off at the height $c = 100,$ and on the right we see that $P(t)$ has actually reached the approximate value $99.9816 \approx c$ when $t = 36$ (months). ◼

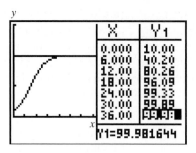

Figure 7.1.5 Graph and table for the logistic population model $P(t) = \dfrac{100}{1 + 9e^{-0.3t}}$ of Example 2.

As in Example 1 where $c = 12$, and in Example 2 where $c = 100$, the value $f(x) = c/(1 + ae^{-bx})$ of a logistic function always approaches the fixed value of the numerator constant c as x gets larger and larger. The reason is that the denominator

$$1 + ae^{-bx} = 1 + \frac{a}{e^{bx}}$$

approaches the value 1 as x increases. This, in turn, is so because the exponential $e^{-bx} = 1/e^{bx}$ with negative exponent approaches the value 0 as x gets larger and larger. Thus if x is very large in value, then

$$f(x) = \frac{c}{1 + ae^{-bx}} = \frac{c}{1 + \text{very small}} \approx \frac{c}{1} = c.$$

Hence if the number x is sufficiently large, then the values of $f(x)$ and c are indistinguishable as decimal numbers with a fixed number of decimal places.

This means geometrically that, as illustrated in Figs. 7.1.4 and 7.1.5, the curve $y = f(x)$ approaches the horizontal line $y = c$ as it moves further and further to the right (in the direction of increasing values of x). When x is sufficiently large the logistic curve and the line are visually indistinguishable. As illustrated in the following example, the value of the parameter b in (1) affects how rapidly the value $f(x)$ approaches the fixed number c.

Example 3

The functions

$$f(x) = \frac{1}{1 + 10e^{-100x}} \quad \text{and} \quad g(x) = \frac{1}{1 + 10e^{-0.01x}} \tag{4}$$

are both logistic functions with $a = 10$ and $c = 1$. But $b = 100$ for $f(x)$ and $b = 0.01 = \frac{1}{100}$ for $g(x)$. The graphs of these two functions are shown in Figs. 7.1.6

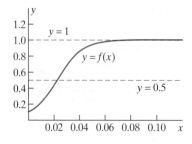

Figure 7.1.6 Graph of $f(x) = \dfrac{1}{1 + 10e^{-100x}}$.

and 7.1.7. These two graphs may look the same at first glance. Both $f(x)$ and $g(x)$ approach the same value 1 as x increases. However, look at the different scales on the x-axes. Evidently, $f(x) \approx 1$ when $x \geq 0.1$, while $g(x) \approx 1$ when $x \geq 1000$. Because 1000 equals ten thousand times 0.1, we might say that $f(x)$ (with $b = 100$) approaches 1 ten thousand times faster than $g(x)$ (with $b = 0.01$) approaches 1. ◼

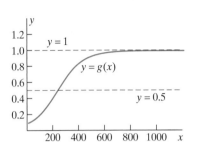

Figure 7.1.7   Graph of $g(x) = \dfrac{1}{1 + 10e^{-0.01x}}$.

Example 4

The line $y = 0.5$ is also shown in Figs. 7.1.6 and 7.1.7. Find the points where the logistic curves $y = f(x)$ and $y = g(x)$ cross this horizontal line. That is, find x_1 and x_2 such that $f(x_1) = 0.5$ and $g(x_2) = 0.5$.

The desired values can be found either graphically or symbolically. We illustrate the two approaches by finding x_1 graphically and x_2 symbolically.

Graphic Approach: Figure 7.1.8 shows the graphs $y = 1/(1 + 10e^{-100x})$ and $y = 0.5$ in the viewing window $0 \leq x \leq 0.1, 0 \leq y \leq 1.25$. We have used our calculator's intersection-finding facility to locate the intersection of the two graphs. We see that they intersect where $x_1 \approx 0.023$.

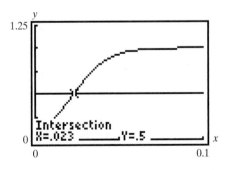

Figure 7.1.8   The intersection of the curve $y = \dfrac{1}{1 + 10e^{-100x}}$ and the line $y = 0.5$.

Symbolic Approach: We use the natural logarithms of Section 4.2 to find x_2 by solving the equation $g(x) = 0.5$, that is,

$$\frac{1}{1 + 10e^{-0.01x}} = 0.5.$$

If we multiply both sides of the equation by $\dfrac{1 + 10e^{-0.01x}}{0.5}$, we get

$$2 = 1 + 10e^{-0.01x}.$$

Upon subtracting 1 and then dividing by 10, we get

$$0.1 = e^{-0.01x} \quad \text{or} \quad e^{-0.01x} = 0.1.$$

Now we take natural logarithms of both sides. Because $\ln(e^{-0.01x}) = -0.01x$ (remembering that the natural exponential and logarithm functions undo each other), this gives

$$-0.01x = \ln(0.1)$$

so finally (after multiplying by -100) our calculator gives the desired value

$$x_2 = -100 \ln(0.01) \approx 230.26.$$

In summary, we see that

- the logistic function $f(x)$ with the larger value $b = 100$ starts with $f(0) = \frac{1}{11}$ and reaches the value $\frac{1}{2}$ when $x \approx 0.023$, while
- the logistic function $g(x)$ with the smaller value $b = 0.01$ starts with $g(0) = \frac{1}{11}$ and doesn't reach the value $\frac{1}{2}$ until $x \approx 230$. ◨

It would be good practice for you to reverse our procedure; that is, to find x_1 symbolically and x_2 graphically. Of course, you should get the same numerical results.

Example 4 illustrates the important principle that

The larger is the parameter b in the logistic function $f(x) = \dfrac{c}{1 + ae^{-bx}}$, the faster $f(x)$ approaches the limiting value c as x increases.

Logistic Population Models

In Fig. 7.1.1 the markers indicate the actual rabbit population data points given by our initial data, while the smooth curve is the graph of the logistic function

$$P(t) = \frac{100}{1 + 9e^{-0.3t}}$$

of Example 2. Hence this function is a **logistic model** that closely approximates the actual rabbit population in Example 2.

In the case of the general logistic population model

$$P(t) = \frac{c}{1 + ae^{-bt}} \tag{5}$$

it is customary to write $M = c$ for the limiting population that $P(t)$ approaches, so

$$P(t) = \frac{M}{1 + ae^{-bt}}. \tag{6}$$

If $P(0) = P_0$ denotes the initial population, then substitution of $t = 0$ gives

$$P_0 = \frac{M}{1 + a}$$

(because $e^0 = 1$). If we solve this last equation for

$$a = \frac{M}{P_0} - 1 = \frac{M - P_0}{P_0}$$

and substitute in (6), we get

$$P(t) = \frac{M}{1 + \dfrac{M - P_0}{P_0}e^{-bt}}.$$

Multiplication of numerator and denominator by P_0 finally gives the formula in (7).

Definition: Logistic Population Model
The **logistic population model** with limiting population M, initial population P_0, and rate constant b is

$$P(t) = \frac{MP_0}{P_0 + (M - P_0)e^{-bt}}. \tag{7}$$

In the case of a population occupying a specific habitat, the limiting population M is sometimes called the **carrying capacity** of this environment. It is the maximal population that the environment has the capacity to support (or "carry").
   We can check our derivation of this model first by substituting $t = 0$ to obtain

$$P(0) = \frac{MP_0}{P_0 + (M - P_0) \cdot 1} = \frac{MP_0}{M} = P_0,$$

so the model does, indeed, correspond to an initial population of P_0. Second, when t is so large that $e^{-bt} \approx 0$, we see that

$$P(t) \approx \frac{MP_0}{P_0 + (M - P_0) \cdot 0} = \frac{MP_0}{P_0} = M.$$

Thus the model does, indeed, correspond to a limiting population of M.
   If the initial and limiting populations P_0 and M are given, then a knowledge of the population at some single future time suffices to determine the value of the rate constant b in (7).

Example 5

You own a small lake with a carrying capacity of 300 fish. You initially stock it with 50 fish, and plan to permit fishing to begin when the lake contains 200 fish. After 1 year there are 100 fish in the lake. Assuming a logistic fish population, how long must you wait to begin fishing?
   We are given the initial and limiting population values. But we must find the value of the rate constant b in (7) before we can proceed to answer the question asked. Thus there are two steps to the solution—first finding b, and then finding when $P(t) = 200$.

Step 1   Substitution of $M = 300$ and $P_0 = 50$ in the general logistic population model (7) gives

$$P(t) = \frac{15000}{50 + 250e^{-bt}}. \tag{8}$$

In order to have a complete population model that we can use for predictive purposes, we obviously need also the value of b. But we are given that $P(12) = 100$, so substitution of $t = 12$ in (8) yields the equation

$$\frac{15000}{50 + 250e^{-12b}} = 100 \tag{9}$$

the rate constant b must satisfy. Figure 7.1.9 shows a graphing calculator set up to solve this equation graphically, using **X** as the independent variable b and **Y** as the dependent variable.

Figure 7.1.9   A graphing calculator set up to solve Eq. (9).

Some experimentation is required to determine an appropriate viewing window. We are talking about populations in the hundreds, so the y-scale should be measured in hundreds. But it turns out that the desired value of $b = x$ is quite small (in particular, smaller than 1). Figure 7.1.10 shows the resulting plot in the window $0 \leq x \leq 1, 0 \leq y \leq 400$. The calculator's intersection-finding facility has been applied, and we see that $b = 0.0764$ (rounded off to 4 decimal places). Substitution of this value of b in (8) yields the logistic model

$$P(t) = \frac{15000}{50 + 250e^{-0.0764t}} \tag{10}$$

for our fish population.

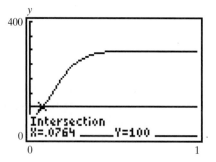

Figure 7.1.10   Solving the equation
$$\frac{15000}{50 + 250e^{-12b}} = 100.$$

Step 2   In order to find when $P(t) = 200$, we need to solve the equation

$$\frac{15000}{50 + 250e^{-0.0764t}} = 200. \tag{11}$$

We could do this graphically (much as in Step 1), but let's do this step symbolically. Cross multiplication gives

$$15,000 = 200(50 + 250e^{-0.0764t}) = 10,000 + 50,000e^{-0.0764t},$$

that is,

$$3 = 2 + 10e^{-0.0764t} \quad \text{(upon division by 5000), or}$$
$$10e^{-0.0764t} = 1.$$

Hence

$$e^{-0.0764t} = \tfrac{1}{10},$$
$$-0.0764t = \ln\left(\tfrac{1}{10}\right),$$
$$t = -\frac{\ln(0.1)}{0.0764} \approx 30.1385$$

(in months). Consequently, we must wait just over $2\frac{1}{2}$ years (after initial stocking) before beginning to fish our lake. ◼

For variety, you might rework Example 5—solving Eq. (9) symbolically in Step 1, and solving Eq. (11) graphically in Step 2.

There's nothing to prevent us from stocking the lake of Example 5 with an initial fish population greater than its carrying capacity of $M = 300$ fish. If we substitute $M = 300$ and $b = 0.0764$ in (7), we get the logistic population function

$$P(t) = \frac{300P_0}{P_0 + (300 - P_0)e^{-0.0764t}}, \tag{12}$$

which models the fish population of the lake if it is stocked initially with P_0 fish. Figure 7.1.11 shows the resulting population graphs with a variety of initial populations ranging from 25 to 600 fish when $t = 0$. We see that, whatever is the initial population P_0—either less than or greater than the carrying capacity $M = 300$—the fish population levels off at the lake's carrying capacity of 300 fish. If there are too many fish initially, then the fish population $P(t)$ decreases in order to approach M, while it increases in order to approach M if there are too few fish initially. In short, nature compensates for any initial imbalance.

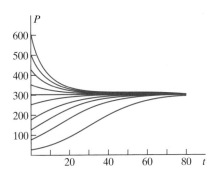

Figure 7.1.11   The logistic population $P(t) = \dfrac{300P_0}{P_0 + (300 - P_0)e^{-0.0764t}}$ with different initial population values P_0.

This behavior is characteristic of all logistic populations. Whatever is the initial population $P_0 > 0$, the resulting population $P(t)$ approaches the same limiting population M as t increases.

Example 6

Suppose the lake of Example 5 is stocked initially with 500 fish. Under natural conditions—that is, with no fishing taking place—how long will it be until the lake contains only 350 fish?

With $M = 300$, $P_0 = 500$, and $b = 0.0764$ in Eq. (7), we find that the fish population after t months is given by

$$P(t) = \frac{150000}{500 - 200e^{-0.0764t}}. \tag{13}$$

Substitution of $P = 350$ then yields the equation

$$\frac{150000}{500 - 200e^{-0.0764t}} = 350, \tag{14}$$

which we need to solve for t. Figure 7.1.12 shows the graph—in the window $0 \leq x \leq 36, 0 \leq y \leq 600$—of the logistic function on the left-hand side and the horizontal line defined by the right-hand side of this equation. We have used our calculator's intersection-finding facility and see that the 4-decimal-place solution of Eq. (14) is $t = 13.4767$. Thus it's about $13\frac{1}{2}$ months until only 350 fish are left in the lake. ◼

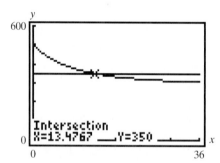

Figure 7.1.12   Solving the equation $\dfrac{150000}{500 - 200e^{-0.0764t}} = 350$.

Summary

This section contains just two basic formulas—the formula

$$f(x) = \frac{c}{1 + ae^{-bx}} \tag{1}$$

for a purely mathematical *logistic function* with limiting value c, and the formula

$$P(t) = \frac{MP_0}{P_0 + (M - P_0)e^{-bt}} \tag{7}$$

for a *logistic population model* with limiting value M, initial population P_0, and rate constant b. It is neither necessary nor desirable that you remember the relationship between the parameters a, b, c in (1) and those in (7). It is important that you know how to

- fit the logistic population model (7) to given population information—as in Step 1 of Example 5, and
- find when a given value of a logistic function or population is attained—as in Examples 4 and 6, or in Step 2 of Example 5.

7.1

PROBLEMS

The following problems can be solved either graphically or symbolically. For each of the logistic functions given in Problems 1–4, find x such that $f(x)$ is 75% of the limiting value c that $f(x)$ approaches as x increases.

1. $f(x) = \dfrac{200}{1 + 2e^{-0.1x}}$

2. $f(x) = \dfrac{300}{1 + 4e^{-0.05x}}$

3. $f(x) = \dfrac{4}{1 + 0.5e^{-2x}}$

4. $f(x) = \dfrac{10000}{1 + 7e^{-17x}}$

In each of Problems 5–10, find a formula—of the form in Eq. (7)—for the logistic population model that has the given limiting population M, the given initial population P_0, and satisfies the additional population condition that is given.

5. $M = 250$, $P_0 = 50$, and $P(10) = 150$

6. $M = 1000$, $P_0 = 200$, and $P(25) = 400$

7. $M = 7$, $P_0 = 1$, and $P(1) = 5$

8. $M = 17$, $P_0 = 3$, and $P(100) = 5$

9. $M = 100$, $P_0 = 300$, and $P(10) = 200$

10. $M = 2000$, $P_0 = 5000$, and $P(50) = 4000$

11–14. For each population described in Problems 5–8 (respectively), determine when $P(t) = \frac{1}{2}M$.

15–16. For each population described in Problems 9 and 10 (respectively), determine when $P(t) = \frac{3}{2}M$.

17. A lake has a carrying capacity of 500 fish. On July 1, 2000 the lake is stocked with 50 fish. Six months later there are 100 fish in the lake. Assuming a logistic fish population, in what month of what year will there be 350 fish in the lake?

18. A large game preserve has a carrying capacity of 300 foxes. On July 1, 2000 the preserve is stocked with 20 foxes. A year later there are 50 foxes in the preserve. Assuming a logistic fox population, in what month of what year will there be 150 foxes in the game preserve?

Problems 19 and 20 deal with the spread of an incurable contagious disease in a city with given constant population M. Let $P(t)$ be the population of infected individuals at time t. Assume that $P(t)$ is a logistic population with limiting population M (meaning that everyone in the city eventually gets it).

19. The city has a constant population of 240 thousand people. On July 1, 2000 the infected population numbers 25 thousand, and on January 1, 2001 it numbers 40 thousand. In what month of what year will half of the city's population be infected?

20. The city has a constant population of 600 thousand people. On July 1, 2000 a quarter of the people are infected, and five months later a third are infected. In what month of what year will three-quarters of the city's population be infected?

Problems 21 and 22 deal with the spread of a rumor in a city with a constant population M. The rumor spreads just like an incurable infectious disease. The population $P(t)$ of those who have heard it at time t is logistic, and eventually everyone in the city hears it.

21. Two people start a rumor in a city with a population of 20 thousand people. After four weeks a thousand people have heard this rumor. How many weeks (since its inception) will it take for half the people in the city to have heard this rumor?

22. On February 1, 2000 a tenth of the people in a city of 120 thousand people have heard a certain rumor, and four months later a quarter of the city's people have heard it. In what month of what year will 90% of the city's population have heard this rumor?

Problems 23 and 24 deal with advertising. The spread of knowledge of a new product is similar to the spread of a rumor. Assume that the number $P(t)$ of people who've heard of the product at time t is a logistic population, and that if the advertising campaign continues indefinitely, then eventually everyone hears of it.

23. An advertising campaign starts when only 5% of the people in the United States (population 270 million) have heard of an all-new washing detergent. After 4 weeks of advertising, 15% of the people know about this new detergent. The soap company plans to advertise it until 35% of the people have heard of it. How many weeks will this take?

24. Now it's a new presidential candidate that's being advertised. Initially, only 1% of the people in the United States recognize his name. After 6 weeks of political advertising, 10% of the people have heard of him. How many *more* weeks will it take for 60% of the people to have heard of this candidate?

7.2 FITTING LOGISTIC MODELS TO DATA

The following table shows the population of Albuquerque, New Mexico, as recorded in the census counts of 1960, 1970, 1980, and 1990.

t	Year	Population P (thousands)	10-Year Change	Ave. Annual Change (thous/yr)
0	1960	201		
10	1970	245	44	4.4
20	1980	333	88	8.8
30	1990	385	52	5.2

We see that the population of Albuquerque increased more rapidly during the decade of the 1970s than in either the preceding decade of the 1960s or in the succeeding decade of the 1980s. Obviously, the growth is not linear, and it also seems pointless to fit this population with a natural (exponential) growth model, which would predict growth at an ever-increasing rate. Similarly, we would not expect a quadratic model to fit Albuquerque's population well. (Can you explain why not?)

Figures 7.2.1 and 7.2.2 show the Albuquerque tP-population data entered in a graphing calculator for analysis.

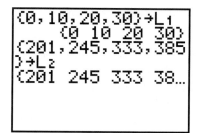

Figure 7.2.1 Storing the 1960–1990 Albuquerque population data.

Figure 7.2.2 **STAT EDIT** calculator screen showing the Albuquerque population data in table form.

Figure 7.2.3 shows an **xyline Stat Plot** of these data. Do you see some resemblance with the logistic function graphs of Section 7.1? There's at least a hint of a leveling off that suggests trying a logistic population model of the form

$$P(t) = \frac{c}{1 + ae^{-bt}}. \tag{1}$$

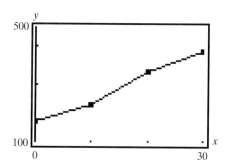

Figure 7.2.3 **xyline Stat Plot** of the Albuquerque population data.

Example 1

Let's proceed to fit the Albuquerque population data with an optimal logistic model. Fortunately, we see a **Logistic** selection among the choices on the **Stat Calc** menu of our graphing calculator. Having stored the t-data as list L_1 and the P-data for Albuquerque as list L_2 as shown in Fig. 7.2.2, the command **Logistic L_1, L_2, Y_1** produces the result shown in Fig. 7.2.4. Of course, the calculator uses x instead of t for the independent variable and y instead of P for the dependent variable.

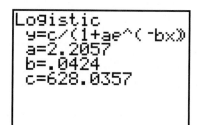

Figure 7.2.4 Optimal logistic model resulting from the TI-83 **STAT CALC Logistic L_1, L_2, Y_1** command.

Thus we obtain the logistic model

$$P(t) = \frac{628.0357}{1 + 2.2057e^{-0.0424t}}. \tag{2}$$

The logistic model in (2) predicts that the population of Albuquerque will not continue to grow indefinitely, but will eventually level off with a limiting population of about 628 thousand people (because $c = 628.0357$ and P is measured in thousands). The **Logistic** command also stores the optimal logistic function as Y_1, so we can immediately generate the graph shown in Fig. 7.2.5, with the window $0 \le t \le 140, 0 \le P \le 700$ corresponding to the period from 1960 to 2100. We see that the population of Albuquerque continues to increase noticeably until about the middle of the twenty-first century, but then levels off conspicuously during the second half of the century. The table of population values pictured in Fig. 7.2.6 shows that the population in the year 2050 (when $t = 90$) is just under 600 thousand, and that by the end of the twenty-first century the population has reached 624 thousand (just 4 thousand short of the limiting population).   ◼

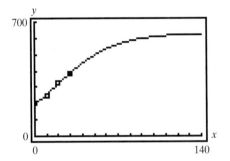

Figure 7.2.5 Graph of the optimal logistic model in (2).

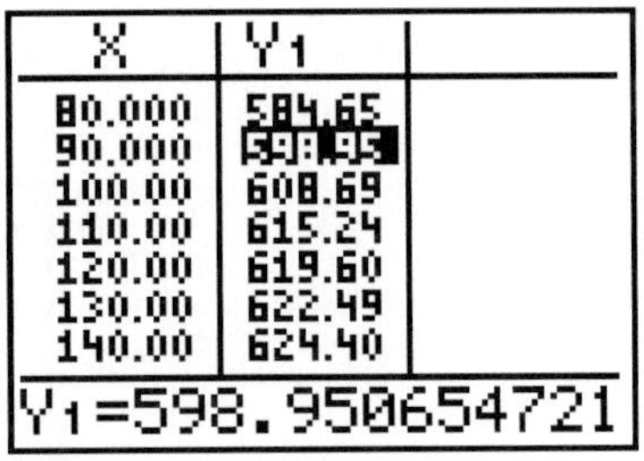

Figure 7.2.6 Table of logistic population values.

Would you bet real money that the population of Albuquerque will never reach 630 thousand? This would certainly be unwise! Real confidence in any such mathematical prediction is unwarranted, because the population function in (2) is merely a least squares model based on our limited 1960–1990 population data. Almost anything could actually happen in the next century—ranging from a vast increase in the population due to immigration to a decimation of the population by war or disease.

Example 2

Find the average error in the 1960–1990 population figures predicted by the logistic model in (2).

t	Act. Pop.	Logistic $P(t)$	Error E
0	201	196	5
10	245	257	−12
20	333	323	10
30	385	388	−3

The preceding table compares the actual and predicted Albuquerque population (in thousands) for the years 1960–1990 (that is, for $t = 0$ to $t = 30$). The sum of the squares of the errors shown in the table is

$$\text{SSE} = (5)^2 + (-12)^2 + (10)^2 + (-3)^2 = 278.$$

There being $n = 4$ data points, the average error in the optimal model is therefore given by

$$\text{average error} = \sqrt{\frac{\text{SSE}}{n}} = \sqrt{\frac{278}{4}} = \sqrt{69.5} \approx 8.337.$$

Thus the average error in the predicted population is over 8 thousand people. Can you see that this is about 3% for the range of populations involved?   ◣

Example 3

When should the city planners of Albuquerque anticipate a population of a half million?

For a graphical solution we need only define $Y_2 = 500$ [Y_1 was already defined as the logistic function in (2)]. This gives the plot shown in Fig. 7.2.7. As indicated there, the calculator's intersecting-finding facility gives $t = 50.786$ when $P = 500$ (thousand). Adding 50.8 years to the starting date of Jan. 1, 1960, we get 2010 for the year in which the predicted population hits a half million.   ◣

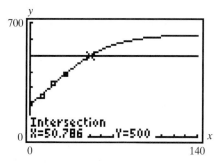

Figure 7.2.7   Finding graphically when the predicted population of Albuquerque is 500 thousand.

Political Modeling

We turn next to a political modeling example. Political campaigning is a form of advertising—in this case, advertising the candidate. The same general principle—that only bounded growth in approval is possible—applies to advertising any product, be it a new improved detergent or a new line of jeans.

In politics, it is commonly observed that—when an attractive candidate starts campaigning with only limited initial voter approval—the percentage $P(t)$ of voters favoring this candidate at first increases steadily with time t as his or her name recognition spreads. However, this percentage certainly can never exceed 100%. Consequently, neither a linear nor an exponential nor any kind of polynomial model for $P(t)$ is plausible. Of the different types of mathematical models we've encountered, only a (bounded growth) logistic model for the candidate's voter approval percentage $P(t)$ makes sense.

Months	0	1	2	3	4
Voters	10%	13%	17%	22%	27%

Example 4

The preceding table summarizes voter approval of a gubernatorial candidate who begins the campaign as the favorite of only 10% of the voters in the state. After the first month of campaigning, polling indicates that 13% of the voters favor this candidate, and after four months 27% of them favor him. It looks like voter approval is taking off, but eventually it must level off. Assuming a logistic model for the percentage $P(t)$ of voters favoring this candidate after t months, determine whether it is possible for this candidate to win the election. If so, how long must the campaign last in order for him to gain majority voter approval?

To find the optimal logistic model, we first enter (as in Fig. 7.2.8) the polling data shown in the preceding table. We use percentage points rather than decimal percentages to record voter approval. Then the command **Logistic L₁, L₂, Y₁** produces the results shown in Fig. 7.2.9.

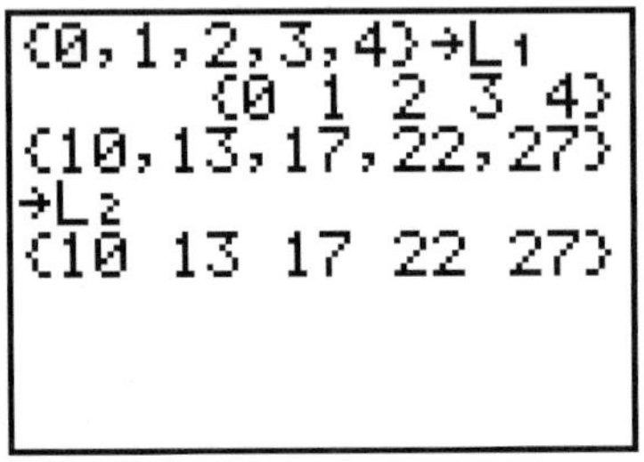

Figure 7.2.8 Entering the polling data of Example 4.

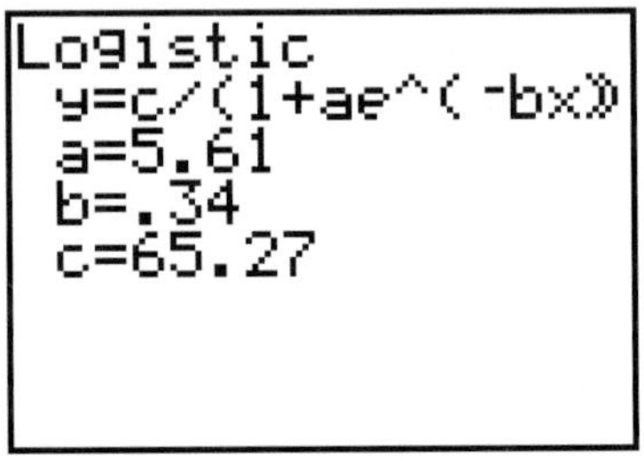

Figure 7.2.9 Logistic model for voter approval percent $P(t)$.

Thus our optimal logistic model is

$$P(t) = \frac{65.27}{1 + 5.61e^{-0.34t}}. \tag{3}$$

It follows that—if the campaign lasts long enough—then our candidate can win election in a landslide with 65% of the vote.

Since the logistic function in (3) is automatically entered as **Y₁**, we can immediately tabulate values to follow the progress of the campaign. The table in Fig. 7.2.10—where we have scrolled down far enough to see values leveling off—indicates that a 65% landslide could take 3 years, and we can certainly hope that no state political campaign will last that long.

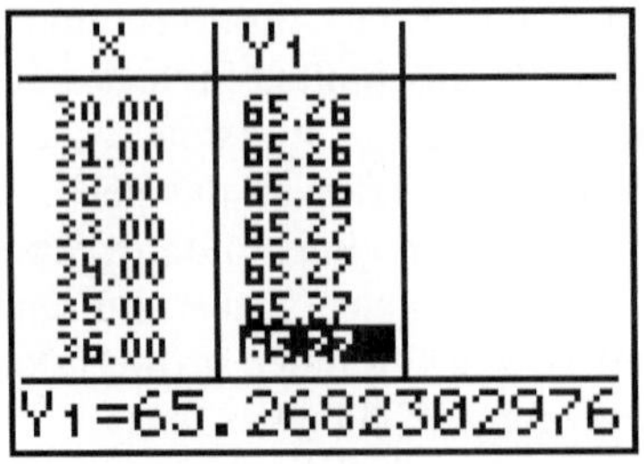

Figure 7.2.10 In a 3-year campaign our candidate wins with over 65% of the vote.

However, the practical question is how long the campaign must last in order for the candidate to garner over 50% of the vote. To answer this question, we need only scroll back up in our table to see when **Y₁**= $P(t)$ first exceeds 50 (percent). Figure 7.2.11 shows that this occurs after only 9 months. ∎

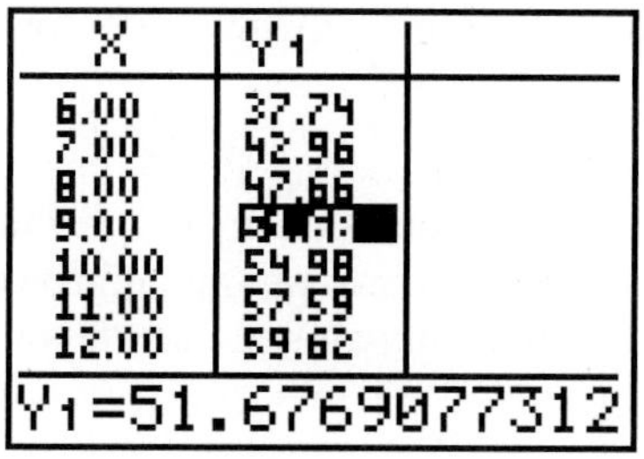

X	Y1	
6.00	37.74	
7.00	42.96	
8.00	47.66	
9.00	▓▓▓▓	
10.00	54.98	
11.00	57.59	
12.00	59.62	

Y1=51.6769077312

Figure 7.2.11   But it only takes 9 months of campaigning for him to gain a majority of the vote.

U.S. Population Projections

Logistic functions were first used to model human population growth (around 1840) by the Belgian mathematician and demographer P. F. Verhulst. He sought to use U.S. census population data for the first half of the nineteenth century to predict the future growth of the United States.

Here we will use census data for the last half of the nineteenth century to attempt to project U.S. population growth during the twentieth century. The following table lists population figures for the 1850–1890 period.

Year	U.S. Pop. (millions)
1850	23.192
1860	31.443
1870	38.558
1880	50.189
1890	62.980

We will try several different fits to the population data shown here and compare the goodness of fit in terms of average errors.

Example 5

For a simplest model of U.S. population growth during the late nineteenth century, let's fit the exponential growth model $P(t) = P_0 e^{rt}$ to just the 1850 and 1890 figures. If we take $t = 0$ in 1850, then $P_0 = P_0 e^0 = P(0) = 23.192$ so

$$P(t) = 23.192 e^{rt}.$$

Substitution of $P(40) = 62.980$ gives the equation

$$23.192 e^{40r} = 62.980.$$

When we divide by 23.192 and take natural logarithms we get

$$e^{40r} = \frac{62.980}{23.192} = 2.7156,$$

$$40r = \ln(e^{40r}) = \ln(2.7156) = 0.9990,$$

$$r = \frac{0.9990}{40} = 0.0250.$$

Consequently, our first natural growth model for U.S. population growth is

$$P(t) = 23.192e^{0.0250t}. \tag{4}$$

In each year the population in (4) is multiplied by the factor $e^{0.0250} = 1.0253$. Thus this model predicts an annual growth of 2.53% in the U.S. population. The following table compares the actual and natural growth figures for the 1850–1890 period.

Year	Actual U.S. Pop.	Natural Growth Model	Error E	E^2
1850	23.192	23.192	0.000	0.000
1860	31.443	29.779	1.664	2.769
1870	38.558	38.237	0.321	0.103
1880	50.189	49.097	1.092	1.191
1890	62.980	63.042	−0.062	0.004

The slight discrepancy in the actual and predicted 1890 populations results from calculator round-off error in the computations leading to (4). At any rate, the sum of the $n = 5$ squared errors in the final column is SSE $= 4.067$, so the average error is given by

$$\text{average error} = \sqrt{\frac{\text{SSE}}{n}} = \sqrt{\frac{4.067}{5}} \approx 0.902 \text{ million.} \qquad ∎$$

Example 6

Next we try a best-fitting exponential model. Figure 7.2.12 shows the calculator entry of the actual 1850–1890 U.S. population data at 10-year intervals. The command **ExpReg L₁, L₂, Y₁** then produces the results shown in Fig. 7.2.13.

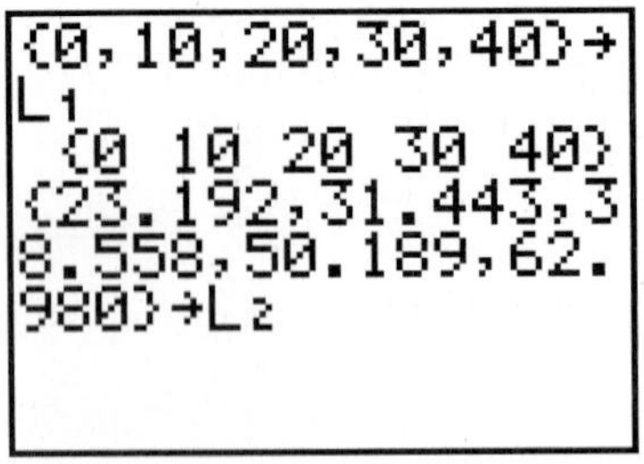

Figure 7.2.12   Entry of 1850–1890 U.S. population figures.

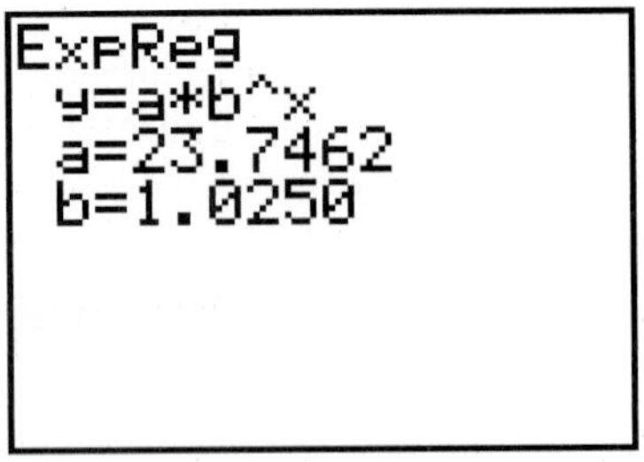

Figure 7.2.13   The optimal exponential growth model.

Thus our least squares natural growth model is

$$P(t) = 23.7462 \times 1.0250^t,$$

that is [since $\ln(1.0250) = 0.0247$],

$$P(t) = 23.7462e^{0.0247t}. \tag{5}$$

As compared with the natural growth model in (4), the optimal model in (5) has the slightly larger initial population $P_0 = 23.7462$ and the slightly smaller annual growth rate of 2.50%. The following table compares the actual and the optimal natural growth figures for the 1850–1890 period.

Year	Actual U.S. Pop.	Optimal Exponential Model	Error E	E^2
1850	23.192	23.746	−0.554	0.307
1860	31.443	30.399	1.044	1.090
1870	38.558	38.917	−0.579	0.335
1880	50.189	49.820	0.369	0.136
1890	62.980	63.779	−0.779	0.638

The sum of the $n = 5$ squared errors in the final column is SSE $= 2.506$, so the average error is given by

$$\text{average error} = \sqrt{\frac{\text{SSE}}{n}} = \sqrt{\frac{2.506}{5}} \approx 0.708 \text{ million}$$

(as compared with the previous average error of 0.902 million).   ◣

Example 7

With the actual 1850–1890 data still stored in the lists **L₁** and **L₂**, the command **Logistic L₁, L₂, Y₁** produces the result shown in Fig. 7.2.14.

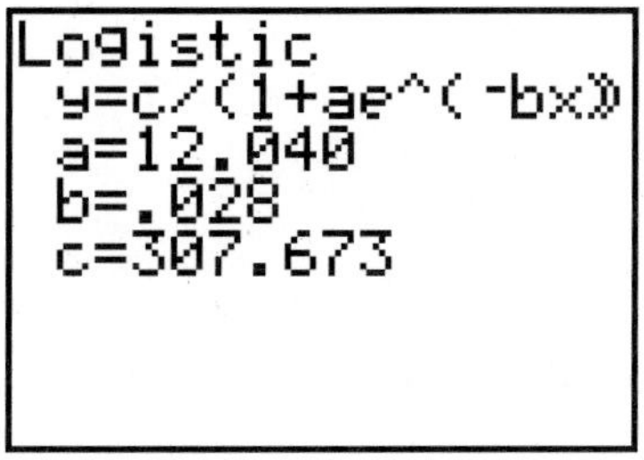

```
Logistic
 y=c/(1+ae^(-bx))
 a=12.040
 b=.028
 c=307.673
```

Figure 7.2.14   The optimal logistic population model.

Thus the optimal logistic model for U.S. population growth during the 1850–1890 period is

$$P(t) = \frac{307.673}{1 + 12.040e^{-0.028t}}. \tag{6}$$

The following table compares the actual and the optimal logistic growth figures for the 1850–1890 period.

Year	Actual U.S. Pop.	Optimal Logistic Model	Error E	E^2
1850	23.192	23.595	−0.403	0.162
1860	31.443	30.464	0.979	0.959
1870	38.558	39.058	−0.500	0.250
1880	50.189	49.642	0.547	0.299
1890	62.980	62.428	0.552	0.305

The sum of the $n = 5$ squared errors in the final column is SSE $= 1.975$, so the average error is given by

$$\text{average error} = \sqrt{\frac{\text{SSE}}{n}} = \sqrt{\frac{1.974}{5}} \approx 0.628 \text{ million.}$$

This is only a small improvement over the optimal exponential average error of 0.678 million, but there is nevertheless a vast difference between our exponential and logistic models for the U.S. population. The optimal exponential model in (5) predicts a never-ending increase in the U.S. population, whereas the optimal logistic model in (6) predicts that this population will eventually level off at about 307 million people. ◣

The following table compares the actual population figures with the optimal exponential and logistic population model figures for the United States during the twentieth century.

Year	Actual U.S. Pop.	Exponential Growth Model	Logistic Model
1900	76.212	81.648	77.518
1910	92.228	104.525	94.845
1920	106.022	133.810	114.125
1930	123.203	171.301	134.840
1940	132.165	219.296	156.280
1950	151.326	280.738	177.625
1960	179.323	359.395	198.071
1970	203.302	460.090	216.944
1980	226.542	588.998	233.780
1990	248.710	754.023	248.346

Undoubtedly, it is something of a fortuitous coincidence that—after the passage of a century—the logistic population model predicts the 1990 U.S. population right on the nose at 248+ million people. Indeed, you can verify that the average error in the ten logistic population figures in this table is about 14 million (nowhere near as good as the final figure suggests). But the exponential model prediction for 1990 is a U.S. population of over three-quarters of a billion, way off the chart. The spreadsheet chart in Fig. 7.2.15 compares these actual, exponential model, and logistic model figures visually.

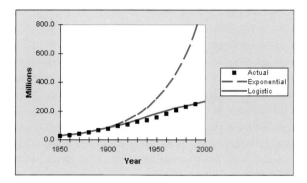

Figure 7.2.15 Comparing the actual, exponential, and logistic populations.

Example 8

When does the logistic model predict that the U.S. population will hit 300 million?

The logistic model in (6) is still stored as **Y₁**, so we need only proceed to plot **Y₁** and **Y₂** = 300 (Fig. 7.2.16, with the window $0 \leq x, y \leq 400$). We see from the intersection found in Fig. 7.2.17 that the predicted U.S. population hits 300 million 219.797 years after 1850, that is—adding 219 to 1850—during the year 2069. Remember that all this comes from the original five original data points marked by the small squares in the lower left of Fig. 7.2.16. ∎

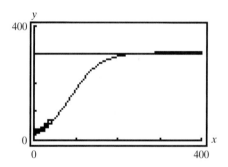

Figure 7.2.16 Graph of the optimal logistic population model.

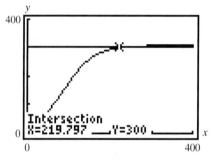

Figure 7.2.17 Finding when the predicted U.S. population is 300 million.

7.2

PROBLEMS

In each of Problems 1–6, use the logistic regression facility of your calculator to find the logistic function of the form $f(x) = c/(1 + ae^{-bx})$ that best fits the given data (with a, b, and c rounded off accurate to 3 decimal places), and find the average error in the fit.

1.

x	3	4	6
y	4	5	6

2.

x	20	40	60
y	18	30	40

3.

x	1	2	3	4
y	9	12	14	15

4.

x	15	30	50	80
y	19	50	124	201

5.

x	1	5	6	7	13
y	8	20	23	26	35

6.

x	5	20	40	60	70
y	43	107	294	543	637

Each of the tables in Problems 7–12 gives the 1960–1990 census data for a U.S. city.

(a) Use the logistic regression facility of your calculator to find the logistic model of the form $P(t) = c/(1 + ae^{-bt})$ that best fits the given data (with a, b, and c rounded off accurate to 3 decimal places). Take $t = 0$ in 1960.

(b) Predict the population of the city in the year 2025.

(c) Find the city's limiting population, and determine when its population will be 90% of its limiting population.

7. Oklahoma City, OK

Year	1960	1970	1980	1990
Pop. (thous)	324	368	404	445

8. Tuscon, AZ

Year	1960	1970	1980	1990
Pop. (thous)	213	263	331	405

9. Anchorage, AK

Year	1960	1970	1980	1990
Pop. (thous)	44.2	48.1	174	226

10.   Lexington, KY

Year	1960	1970	1980	1990
Pop. (thous)	62.8	108	204	225

11.   Aurora, CO

Year	1960	1970	1980	1990
Pop. (thous)	48.5	75.0	159	222

12.   Tulsa, OK

Year	1960	1970	1980	1990
Pop. (thous)	262	330	361	367

13.   The following table summarizes voter approval—after a given number of weeks of campaigning—of a mayoral candidate who begins the campaign as the favorite of only 12% of the voters in the city. Assuming a logistic model for the percentage $P(t)$ of voters favoring this candidate after t weeks, determine whether it is possible for this candidate to win the election. If so, how long must the campaign last in order for him to gain majority voter approval?

Weeks	0	1	2	3	4
Voters	12%	15.5%	19.5%	24%	29%

14.   The following table summarizes voter approval—after a given number of months of campaigning—of a presidential candidate who begins the campaign as the favorite of only 5% of the voters in the country. Assuming a logistic model for the percentage $P(t)$ of voters favoring this candidate after t months, determine whether it is possible for this candidate to win the election. If so, how long must the campaign last in order for him to gain majority voter approval?

Months	0	3	6	9	12
Voters	5%	8.5%	13.7%	20.7%	28.8%

In Problems 15 and 16 a lake is initially stocked with fish, and thereafter the fish population grows logistically. The given table lists the number of fish in the lake as recorded by careful count during the first year. Fit the data logistically in order to predict the lake's limiting population of fish. How long will it take for the number of fish to reach 80% of the limiting population?

15.

Months	0	3	6	9	12
Fish	30	39	49	60	70

16.

Months	0	3	6	9	12
Fish	50	73	103	137	173

In Problems 17 and 18 a contagious disease begins spreading among the people in a city. The given table lists the percentage of diseased people as monitored during the first month. Fit the data logistically in order to predict the limiting percentage of people who eventually will suffer this disease. How long will it take for the percentage of diseased people to reach 95% of the limiting percentage?

17.

Weeks	0	1	2	3	4
Diseased	4%	7%	12%	18%	24%

18.

Weeks	0	1	2	3	4
Diseased	2.0%	2.5%	3.2%	4.0%	4.9%

In Problems 19 and 20,
(a) First fit a logistic population model to the given U.S. population data.
(b) What limiting population does this model predict?
(c) In what year does it predict the U.S. population will hit 400 million?

19.

Year	1900	1920	1940	1960	1980
Millions	76.2	106.0	132.2	179.3	226.5

20.

Year	1950	1960	1970	1980	1990
Millions	151.3	179.3	203.3	226.5	248.7

21. The following table gives 1950–1990 population data for China. Fit a logistic model in order to determine the limiting population of this most populous country in the world. When does your model predict the population of China will hit 2 billion?

Year	1950	1960	1970	1980	1990
Millions	563	651	820	985	1139

In Problems 22 and 23,
(a) First fit a logistic population model to the given world population data.
(b) What limiting population does this model predict?
(c) In what year does it predict the world population will hit 10 billion?

22.

Year	1950	1960	1970	1980	1990
Billions	2.556	3.039	3.707	4.454	5.277

23.

Year	1975	1980	1985	1990	1995
Billions	4.086	4.454	4.851	5.277	5.682

7.3   DISCRETE MODELS AND CHAOS

In Section 7.1 we introduced the logistic model

$$P(t) = \frac{MP_0}{P_0 + (M - P_0)e^{-bt}}. \tag{1}$$

This model describes a bounded population P that begins with $P(0) = P_0$ and varies smoothly and continuously as a function of time t. Ultimately it approaches the limiting population M.

Let's consider now a rodent population in a fixed environment that has a short annual breeding season, so that births occur only once per year. Suppose also that deaths of the rodents occur only during the breeding season (perhaps due to exhaustion). Such a rodent population would *not* vary smoothly and continuously like the model in (1). Instead, it would vary by a sequence of annual discrete jumps:

- From P_0 to the population P_1 after 1 year; then
- From P_1 to the population P_2 after 2 years; then
- From P_2 to the population P_3 after 3 years; and so on.

Thus the growth of the rodent population in succeeding years could be described by listing a sequence of populations

$$P_0, P_1, P_2, P_3, \ldots, P_n, P_{n+1}, \ldots \tag{2}$$

where P_n denotes the number of rodents after n years.

Note that each of the populations P_n appearing in (2) would be an *integer*—the precise number of rodents after n years. This is so because the typical happy rodent couple has exactly one or two (or perhaps five) baby rodents each year, but never the 2.7 children of the mythical average rural human family. The resulting discrete population values contrast with the fractional values that the logistic model in (1) typically predicts.

In the case of a discrete population it is useful to focus on the change

$$\Delta P_n = P_{n+1} - P_n \tag{3}$$

in the population from year n to year $n + 1$. Thus ΔP_n is the net number of births minus deaths that occur in the rodent population during the nth year's breeding season.

Because a larger number of births occur in a larger population, it is reasonable to expect the change ΔP_n to be proportional to the population P_n itself. On the other hand, if the population is to approach the finite limiting population M, then the number of births must decrease as the population nears M. This would happen if the change ΔP_n were also proportional to the difference $M - P_n$, which is small when P_n is close to M. The assumption that ΔP_n is proportional to both P_n and $M - P_n$ means that

$$\Delta P_n = kP_n(M - P_n) \tag{4}$$

where the proportionality constant k depends on the characteristics of the specific population and its supporting environment.

If we write Eq. (3) in the form

$$P_{n+1} = P_n + \Delta P_n \tag{5}$$

and then substitute (4), we get the *discrete population model*

$$P_{n+1} = P_n + kP_n(M - P_n). \tag{6}$$

The constant k in (6) is sometimes called the *growth rate parameter* for the population. Note that—once the values of the constants k and M are known—this discrete model gives each succeeding population P_{n+1} not in terms of the time variable, but rather in terms of the preceding population P_n.

The initial population P_0 must be given, so that (6) with $n = 0$ then yields

$$P_1 = P_0 + kP_0(M - P_0).$$

Now that we know P_1, Eq. (6) with $n = 1$ gives

$$P_2 = P_1 + kP_1(M - P_1).$$

Substituting $n = 2$ in (6), we next calculate

$$P_3 = P_2 + kP_2(M - P_2).$$

Obviously, we can continue in this way to calculate successive population values, one at a time. For instance, once we have calculated $P_0, P_1, P_2, P_3, \ldots, P_{10}$, we can substitute $n = 10$ in (6) and write

$$P_{11} = P_{10} + kP_{10}(M - P_{10}).$$

The sequence of successive population values we obtain depends upon the initial population P_0 we start with, so when its value is known we specify the initial population as a part of the discrete model, as in (7).

Example 1

If we start with $P_0 = 5$ rodents in a forest environment that will support $M = 100$ rodents, then $k = 0.005$ in (6) gives the discrete population model

$$P_0 = 5, \quad P_{n+1} = P_n + 0.005P_n(100 - P_n). \tag{7}$$

Starting with $P_0 = 5$, we can calculate the successive predicted population values

$$P_1 = 5 + 0.005(5)(100 - 5) \approx 7.375,$$
$$P_2 = 7.375 + 0.005(7.375)(100 - 7.375) \approx 10.791,$$
$$P_3 = 10.791 + 0.005(10.791)(100 - 10.791) \approx 15.604,$$
$$\vdots$$

one at a time.

However, it is much faster and more efficient to set up an iteration using our calculator. Figure 7.3.1 shows the initial setup, with the values $k = 0.005$, $M = 100$, and $P_0 = 5$. The first line shown in Fig. 7.3.2 implements the formula in (7). When this line is entered, the value of P_1 is calculated and stored as the variable **P**. If the ENTER key is pressed again, then this command is reexecuted, so that the value of P_2 is calculated and now stored as the variable **P**. Each successive press of the ENTER key calculates another population value. Figure 7.3.2 shows the first six resulting population values $P_1, P_2, P_3, P_4, P_5, P_6$.

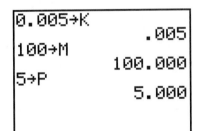

Figure 7.3.1   Initial setup for Example 1.

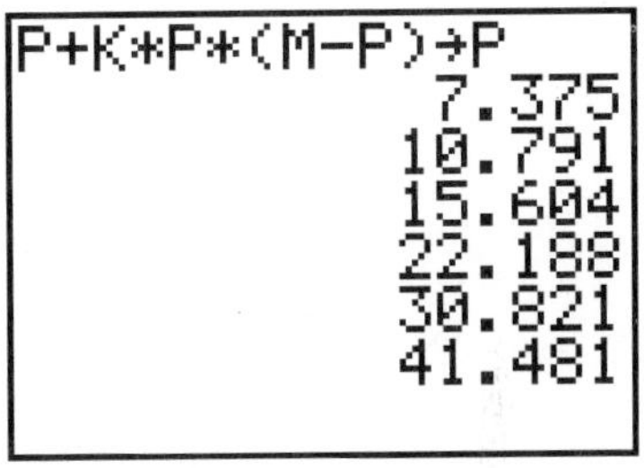

Figure 7.3.2   The first 6 population values, $P_1, P_2, P_3, P_4, P_5, P_6$.

Even though we're discussing a discrete population, our model still predicts nonintegral decimal population values. Rounding off, we conclude that our population numbers

- 7 rodents after 1 year;
- 11 rodents after 2 years;
- 16 rodents after 3 years;
- 22 rodents after 4 years;
- 31 rodents after 5 years;
- 41 rodents after 6 years.

We count key presses carefully, one at a time, and continue to reexecute our population update command. Figure 7.3.3 shows the populations $P_{14}, P_{15}, P_{16}, P_{17}, P_{18}, P_{19}, P_{20}$ that are visible after 20 executions. We see that after 20 years the populations predicted by the discrete model in (7) are, indeed, leveling off at the limiting population of 100 rodents.

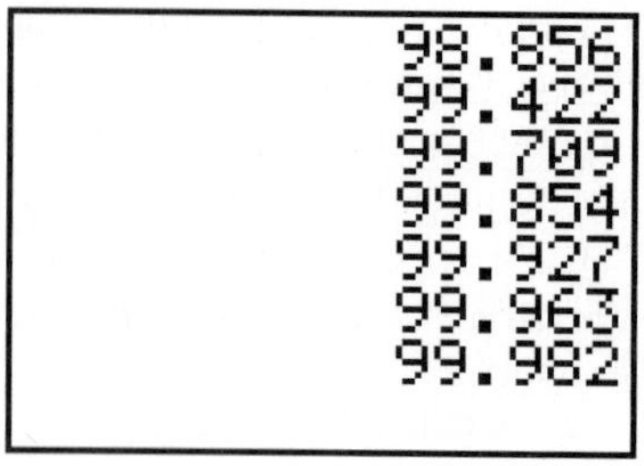

```
98.856
99.422
99.709
99.854
99.927
99.963
99.982
```

Figure 7.3.3 The last 7 population values, P_{14}, P_{15}, P_{16}, P_{17}, P_{18}, P_{19}, P_{20}.

The model in (6) actually is discrete in that it provides for the calculation of a discrete sequence of predicted populations, not that these predicted population values are necessarily integers. Sometimes the discrete model and the logistic model in (1) are distinguished by calling

$$P(t) = \frac{MP_0}{P_0 + (M - P_0)e^{-bt}}$$

a *continuous* logistic model, and

$$P_{n+1} = P_n + kP_n(M - P_n)$$

a *discrete* logistic model. The following example indicates that continuous and discrete logistic models can predict comparable results.

Example 2

The following table compares the populations predicted by the discrete model

$$P_0 = 5, \quad P_{n+1} = P_n + 0.005P_n(100 - P_n) \tag{7}$$

of Example 1 and by the continuous model

$$P(t) = \frac{500}{5 + 95e^{-0.45t}}. \tag{8}$$

The latter model was obtained by substituting $M = 100$ and $P_0 = 5$ in (1), then adjusting the value of b to obtain the greatest correspondence (as measured by the sum of squares of differences) between the populations predicted by the two models. We have rounded all data off to integers to facilitate visual comparison.

Time, $n = t$	Discrete model (7)	Continuous model (8)	Time, $n = t$	Discrete model (7)	Continuous model (8)
0	5	5			
1	7	8	11	92	88
2	11	11	12	96	92
3	16	17	13	98	95
4	22	24	14	99	97
5	31	33	15	99	98
6	41	44	16	100	99
7	54	55	17	100	99
8	66	66	18	100	99
9	77	75	19	100	100
10	86	83	20	100	100

Careful examination of the data in this table shows that 16 of the 21 pairs of population predictions differ by only 1 or 2 rodents, with the remaining 5 pairs of predictions differing by 3 or 4 rodents. The spreadsheet chart shown in Fig. 7.3.4 shows that the discrete model data points exhibit the same "sigmoid plot" shape that is associated with a logistic population curve. In particular, the population first increases at an increasing rate, then increases at a decreasing rate as it levels off to approach the limiting population.   ◣

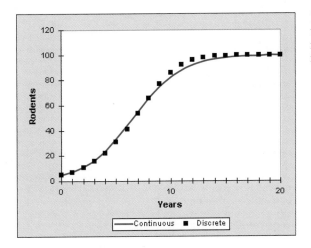

Figure 7.3.4 Comparing the discrete and continuous model population predictions in Example 2.

Example 3

If $P_0 = 15$, $M = 120$, and $k = 0.015$, then Eq. (6) gives the discrete population model

$$P_0 = 15, \quad P_{n+1} = P_n + 0.015P_n(120 - P_n). \tag{9}$$

A calculator calculation as in Example 1 now yields the data shown in the following table.

Year n	Discrete model (9)	Year n	Discrete model (9)
0	15		
1	39	11	122
2	86	12	119
3	130	13	121
4	111	14	119
5	126	15	121
6	115	16	119
7	124	17	120
8	117	18	120
9	123	19	120
10	118	20	120

Here we see a different phenomenon than a population that simply increases toward and gradually levels off as it approaches its limiting population. In this case, the population quickly shoots up to a population of 130 rodents after 3 years—10 rodents more than the limiting population of 120 rodents. It then oscillates back and forth, over and under the limiting population before leveling off and approaching it. This oscillation is charted in Fig. 7.3.5. ◪

Figure 7.3.5 The oscillating discrete population of Example 3.

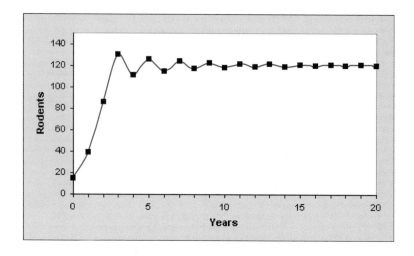

Period Doubling and Chaos

The following example shows that a discrete bounded population may *never* level off.

Example 4

Suppose our rodents have the same limiting population $M = 100$ as in Example 1, the initial population $P_0 = 25$, and the larger growth rate parameter $k = 0.021$ indicated in the calculator setup of Fig. 7.3.6, corresponding to the discrete population model

$$P_0 = 25, \quad P_{n+1} = P_n + 0.021P_n(100 - P_n). \tag{10}$$

If we carry out 50 successive iterations, we wind up with the population values $P_{44}, P_{45}, P_{46}, P_{47}, P_{48}, P_{49}, P_{50}$ shown in Fig. 7.3.7 and charted in Fig. 7.3.8.

```
0.021→K
                .021
100→M
             100.000
25→P
              25.000
P+K*P*(M-P)→P
```

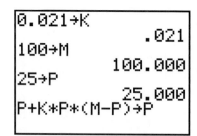

Figure 7.3.6 Initial setup for Example 4.

```
              112.86
               82.37
              112.86
               82.37
              112.86
               82.37
              112.86
```

Figure 7.3.7 The last 7 population values, $P_{44}, P_{45}, P_{46}, P_{47}, P_{48}, P_{49}, P_{50}$ in Example 4.

We see that these predicted population values do not level off and approach the limiting population value $M = 100$. Instead, we have

$$P_{45} = P_{47} = P_{49} = \cdots = 82.37 \approx 82$$

and

$$P_{46} = P_{48} = P_{50} = \cdots = 112.86 \approx 113.$$

Thus the discrete model in (10) ultimately predicts a population of 82 rodents in each odd-numbered year, but a population of 113 rodents in each even-numbered year!   ◤

Figure 7.3.8 The oscillating discrete population of Example 4.

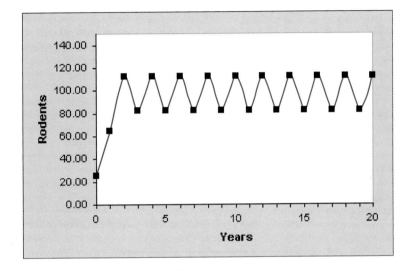

We describe the situation in Example 4 by saying that the population ultimately oscillates between 82 rodents and 113 rodents with a period of 2 years. The *period* of a population oscillation is simply the number of generations—two in this case—that it takes for each population value to be repeated.

Now that we know about oscillating populations, it is better to think of the limiting population M as the maximum *stable* population that the environment can support. It simplifies further discussion to rewrite the logistic iteration (6) as follows. First we write

$$\begin{aligned} P_{n+1} &= P_n + kP_n(M - P_n) \\ &= (1 + kM)P_n - kP_n^2 \\ P_{n+1} &= rP_n - kP_n^2 \end{aligned}$$

where $r = 1 + kM$. If we substitute

$$P_n = \frac{r}{k}x_n \quad \text{and} \quad P_{n+1} = \frac{r}{k}x_{n+1}$$

in the last equation, we get

$$\frac{r}{k}x_{n+1} = r\left(\frac{r}{k}x_n\right) - k\left(\frac{r}{k}x_n\right)^2 = \frac{r^2}{k}(x_n - x_n^2).$$

Finally, division by the common factor r/k yields the simple-looking iteration

$$x_{n+1} = rx_n(1 - x_n). \tag{11}$$

From here on, we focus our attention on the final iterative formula in (11). It is, in essence, an idealized version of our original discrete population model. Beginning with a given initial value x_0 and a *growth parameter r*, we can use (11) to generate as usual a sequence of values

$$x_0, x_1, x_2, x_3, \cdots, x_n, x_{n+1}, \cdots. \tag{12}$$

The *n*th value x_n is commonly interpreted as a *fractional population*—that is, as a fraction of the maximum possible stable population. For instance, if $x_n = 0.5$, then the *n*th population is half of the maximum stable population M. In effect, we're measuring populations in terms of a unit that corresponds to the maximum stable population M that the environment can support.

We therefore call (11) a **discrete fractional population model with growth parameter r**. Because we substituted $r = 1 + kM > 1$ along the way in deriving (11), only values of r greater than 1 are pertinent to discrete fractional population models.

Example 5

Starting with the initial value $x_0 = 0.5$, verify that if $r = 1.5$, then x_n approaches the limiting value $1/3$.

We set up our calculator as indicated in Fig. 7.3.9 to carry out the iteration $x_{n+1} = rx_n(1 - x_n)$ and display 3 decimal places.

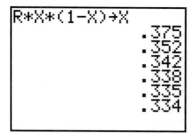

Figure 7.3.9   Calculator setup for the iteration $x_{n+1} = rx_n(1 - x_n)$.

Figures 7.3.10 and 7.3.11 show the first 13 iterates, and we can see that (correct to three decimal places) we have reached the limiting value of $1/3$. ◼

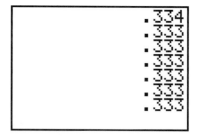

Figure 7.3.10   The first 6 iterates in Example 5.

Figure 7.3.11   The next 7 iterates.

When using our continuous logistic model, we found that the limiting value did not depend on the initial value. Might the same situation occur with our discrete model? The next example investigates this question.

Example 6

Using the initial values $x_0 = 0.1$ and $x_0 = 0.99$, determine the limiting value for the discrete fractional population model in Example 5.

Setting up our calculator as we did in Example 5, with 0.1 stored as our initial x, Fig. 7.3.12 shows iterates x_7 through x_{13}. We see that we are again reaching the limiting value $1/3$.

Now, using 0.99 as our initial x, Fig. 7.3.13 shows iterates x_{17} through x_{23}. Once again, we seem to be approaching the same limiting value of $1/3$.   ◣

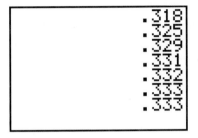

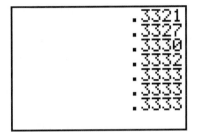

Figure 7.3.12 Iterates x_7 through x_{13} with $x_0 = 0.1$.

Figure 7.3.13 Iterates x_{17} through x_{23} with $x_0 = 0.99$.

Thus, when using the iteration $x_{n+1} = rx_n(1 - x_n)$, you apparently can begin with any initial value between 0 and 1. In our examples we will use the initial value $x_0 = 0.5$.

What happens if you change the value of r? It turns out that changing the value of r has quite an impact on the iterates. In Problem 13, you will see that, as long as r is between 1 and 3, x_n eventually approaches a single limiting value. (If r is close to 1 or 3, you have to be very patient and continue iterating long enough to see the limiting value.)

If the value of the growth parameter is greater than 3, then oscillation sets in. If $r = 3.25$, then x_n ultimately oscillates between the two values 0.4953 and 0.8124. This period 2 oscillation is illustrated in Fig. 7.3.14, where we have carried out a thousand iterations but show only the last dozen.

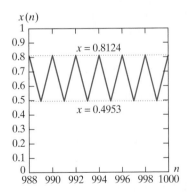

Figure 7.3.14 Graph of $x(n) = x_n$ showing the period 2 oscillations obtained with $r = 3.25$.

With still larger values of r something even stranger occurs. When the growth rate is increased to $r = 3.5$, the fractional population x_n ultimately cycles repeatedly through the *four* distinct values 0.501, 0.875, 0.383, and 0.827 (Fig. 7.3.15). In Problem 14, you will verify that if $r = 3.55$, then the fractional

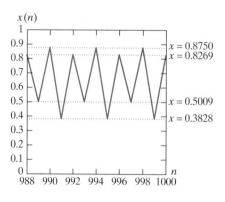

Figure 7.3.15   Graph of $x(n) = x_n$ showing the period 4 cycle of iterates obtained with $r = 3.5$.

population x_n ultimately cycles repeatedly through the *eight* distinct values 0.506, 0.887, 0.355, 0.813, 0.541, 0.882, 0.370, and 0.828.

Obviously, things now are changing quite rapidly as the growth parameter r increases. This is the phenomenon of **period doubling**—from a period 2 oscillation to a period 4 oscillation to a period 8 oscillation—for which the innocuous-looking iteration $x_{n+1} = rx_n(1 - x_n)$ has become famous in recent years.

As the growth parameter is increased beyond $r = 3.56$, period doubling (from period 16 to period 32 to period 64, and so on) occurs so rapidly that utter chaos appears to break out somewhere near $r = 3.57$ (Fig. 7.3.16). However many successive iterates with $r = 3.57$ you look at, no periodic oscillations are evident. The earlier periodicity seems to have disappeared, and the population appears to be changing (from one year to the next) in some essentially random fashion, with no apparent pattern. Indeed, the deterministic and predictable population growth that is observed with smaller growth parameters now seems to have degenerated into a nondeterministic and nonpredictable process of seemingly random change from one year to the next.

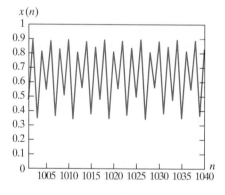

Figure 7.3.16   With $r = 3.57$: Chaos!

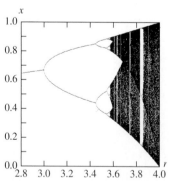

Figure 7.3.17   The pitchfork diagram.

This is the famous phenomenon of **chaos** that not only mathematics students but also ordinary TV viewers and newspaper readers have heard about. Although chaos was first discovered (around 1970) in connection with seemingly simple population growth problems, it is now known that the world around us is full of complex chaotic phenomena, ranging (for instance) from the weather to the stock market.

Figure 7.3.17 illustrates the phenomenon of period doubling toward chaos that occurs with the iteration $x_{n+1} = rx_n(1 - x_n)$ as the growth parameter r is increased. It provides a visual representation of the way in which the behavior of the iteration depends upon the value of the growth parameter. For each value in the range $2.8 \le r \le 4.0$ a computer was programmed to first carry out 1000 iterations to achieve stability. Then the next 250 values of x generated by the iteration were plotted on the vertical axis. That is, the computer screen pixel at the point (r, x) was turned on (and printed black in the figure).

The descriptively named pitchfork diagram that results then shows at a glance whether a given value of r corresponds to an oscillation or to chaos. If the resolution in the picture suffices to make it clear that only finitely many values of x are plotted above a given value of r, then we see that an oscillation through finitely many fractional population values eventually occurs for the specified value of the growth parameter.

For instance, as we scan Fig. 7.3.17 from left to right, we see a single limiting population until $r \approx 3$, then a period 2 oscillation until $r \approx 3.45$, then an oscillation of period 4, then one of period 8, and so forth, rapidly approaching the darkness of chaos. But note the vertical bands of white space that first appear in the diagram between $r = 3.6$ and $r = 3.7$, and then again between $r = 3.8$ and $r = 3.9$. These bands represent regions where (periodic) order returns from the preceding chaos, only to again degenerate into chaos as r increases further.

The Mandelbrot Set

The pitchfork diagram of Fig. 7.3.17 is one of two chaos/fractal pictures that are so emblematic of our era that they sometimes appear in elaborately printed and expensive picture books that are displayed on decorative reception room tables. The other is based on the innocuous-looking iteration

$$x_0 = 0, \quad x_{n+1} = x_n^2 + c \tag{13}$$

where c is a constant. We describe later how this iteration leads ultimately to the construction of perhaps the most complicated and fascinating geometric object that has yet appeared in the long history of mathematics. The famous Mandelbrot set was discovered in 1980 by the French-born mathematician Benoit Mandelbrot, who was then working at the IBM Watson Research Center in New York.

Example 7

The first five iterates defined by (13) are

$$x_1 = c$$
$$x_2 = c^2 + c$$
$$x_3 = (c^2 + c)^2 + c$$
$$x_4 = ((c^2 + c)^2 + c)^2 + c$$
$$x_5 = (((c^2 + c)^2 + c)^2 + c)^2 + c.$$

∎

Obviously, you want to use a calculator rather than pencil and paper to calculate further iterates using (13). Figure 7.3.18 shows a calculator setup for this kind of iteration when $c = -2$.

```
0→X
              0.000
-2→C
             -2.000
X²+C→X
             -2.000
              2.000
```

Figure 7.3.18   Calculator setup for the iteration $x_0 = 0, x_{n+1} = x_n^2 + c$.

You will see in Problem 17 that there is no clear pattern to what happens to the iterates as c changes. Sometimes the value of x_n gets larger and larger, sometimes the successive iterates approach a limiting value, sometimes the iterates oscillate, and sometimes they are exactly the same value. But it turns out that the important question is this: For what values of the constant c in (13) do the resulting iterates get larger and larger, and for what values do they remain bounded?

The answer, which you will discover, is that the iterates remain bounded if and only if the constant c is in the range $-2 \le c \le 0.25$. This result is interesting, though perhaps not exciting. The real excitement stemmed from Mandelbrot's idea to let c be a *complex* constant, and to replace (13) with the iteration

$$z_0 = 0, \quad z_{n+1} = z_n^2 + c, \tag{14}$$

which generates a sequence $z_1, z_2, z_3, \cdots, z_n, z_{n+1}, \ldots$ of complex numbers. Recall that a complex number is one of the form $z = x + yi$ where $i = \sqrt{-1}$. Complex numbers are added and multiplied in the usual way of algebra, collecting real and imaginary terms separately and using the fact that $i^2 = -1$. For instance,

$$(3 + 7i) + (8 - 2i) = (3 + 8) + (7i - 2i) = 11 + 5i,$$
$$(3 + 7i) \cdot (8 - 2i) = 3(8 - 2i) + (7i)(8 - 2i)$$
$$= (24 - 6i) + (56i - 14i^2)$$
$$= 24 - 6i + 56i + 14 = 38 + 50i.$$

Example 8

If $c = 1 + i$, then the iteration (14) yields

$$z_1 = (0)^2 + (1 + i) = 1 + i,$$
$$z_2 = (1 + i)^2 + (1 + i) = 1 + 3i,$$
$$z_3 = (1 + 3i)^2 + (1 + i) = -7 + 7i,$$
$$z_4 = (-7 + 7i)^2 + (1 + i) = 1 - 97i,$$
$$z_5 = (1 - 97i)^2 + (1 + i) = -9407 - 193i. \qquad \blacksquare$$

In general, if the nth iterate defined by (14) is denoted by

$$z_n = x_n + iy_n$$

and the complex constant c is given by

$$c = a + bi$$

then the next iterate is given by

$$z_{n+1} = z_n^2 + c$$
$$= (x_n + iy_n)^2 + (a + bi)$$
$$= (x_n^2 + 2ix_ny_n - y_n^2) + (a + bi)$$
$$z_{n+1} = (x_n^2 - y_n^2 + a) + i(2x_ny_n + b).$$

Thus the real and imaginary parts of z_{n+1} are given by $x_{n+1} = x_n^2 - y_n^2 + a$ and $y_{n+1} = 2x_ny_n + b$.

We can therefore describe the **complex Mandelbrot iteration** by forgetting about all these complex numbers and simply starting with the origin $z_0 = (0, 0)$ and a fixed point $c = (a, b)$ in the xy-plane. We then use the iteration

$$x_{n+1} = x_n^2 - y_n^2 + a, \quad y_{n+1} = 2x_ny_n + b \tag{15}$$

to generate a sequence

$$(x_1, y_1), (x_2, y_2), (x_3, y_3), \cdots, (x_n, y_n), \cdots$$

of points in the plane.

Some advanced graphing calculators can carry out the complex Mandelbrot iteration directly. Figure 7.3.19 shows a TI-86 calculator set up to carry out the iteration with $c = (0, 0.5)$. After 50 entries (Fig. 7.3.20) we see that the iterates are approaching the point $(-0.1360, 0.3931)$.

```
(0,0.5)→C
          (0.0000,.5000)
(0,0)→Z
          (0.0000,0.0000)
Z²+C→Z
          (0.0000,.5000)
          (-.2500,.5000)
```

```
(-.1360,.3930)
(-.1360,.3931)
(-.1361,.3931)
(-.1360,.3930)
(-.1360,.3931)
(-.1360,.3931)
(-.1360,.3931)
```

Figure 7.3.19   TI-86 calculator setup for the complex Mandelbrot iteration.

Figure 7.3.20   With $c = (0, 0.5)$ the iterates approach the point $(-0.1360, 0.3931)$.

We now ask the question as to what happens for a given constant point $c = (a, b)$ in the plane. Does the resulting sequence of iteration points generated using (15) diverge further and further from the origin—as appears may be the case in Example 8—or does it remain bounded and stay fairly close to the origin (as in Fig. 7.3.20)? It turns out that the sequence of iterates either stays inside the circle $x^2 + y^2 = 4$ of radius 2, or it goes off to infinity.

The famous Mandelbrot set is the set of all those points $c = (a, b)$ in the xy-plane for which the resulting sequence of iteration points *does* stay within the circle of radius 2. We programmed a computer to divide the xy-square $-1.75 \leq x \leq 0.75, 1.25 \leq y \leq 1.25$ into a 500 by 500 grid of tiny square pixels. For each of these pixels, its midpoint $c = (a, b)$ was selected, and the iteration in (15) carried out for several hundred steps starting each time afresh with $z_0 = (0, 0)$. If the resulting iterates remained inside the circle of radius 2, then the pixel was colored black; otherwise it was colored white.

Figure 7.3.21 shows the picture of the Mandelbrot set that we obtained in this way. A characteristic feature of the set is that balls protrude from the central

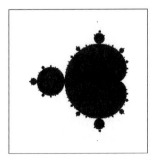

Figure 7.3.21   The Mandelbrot set.

Figure 7.3.22 The
Mandelbrot set in the
viewing window
$-0.65 \leq x \leq -0.40$,
$0.45 \leq y \leq 0.70$.

heart-shaped figure. From these balls protrude smaller balls, from which protrude still smaller balls, and so on ad infinitum. The Mandelbrot set is the best-known example of a **fractal**—a figure in which similar patterns are replicated at higher and higher levels of magnification. Figure 7.3.22 is a magnification of one of the original balls protruding from the central figure.

Higher resolution is required to do justice to the extraordinary complexity and beauty of the Mandelbrot set. For truly marvelous full-color pictures of the Mandelbrot set with repeated magnifications to show its incredible self-replicating detail at higher and higher resolutions, it is well worth a trip to the library to see H.-O. Peitgen and P. H. Richter, *The Beauty of Fractals* (Springer-Verlag, 1986).

7 . 3

P R O B L E M S

In Problems 1–6, use a discrete logistic model to construct a table of predicted populations as in Example 3. Carry out sufficiently many iterations to see that the rounded off predicted population approaches the limiting population. Determine whether the predicted populations steadily increase toward the limiting population (as in Examples 1 and 2) or oscillate about it (as in Example 3).

1. $P_0 = 50, M = 200$, and $k = 0.005$

2. $P_0 = 100, M = 300$, and $k = 0.001$

3. $P_0 = 100, M = 500$, and $k = 0.0005$

4. $P_0 = 100, M = 200$, and $k = 0.008$

5. $P_0 = 100, M = 300$, and $k = 0.006$

6. $P_0 = 200, M = 500$, and $k = 0.0037$

In Problems 7–10, use a discrete logistic model to construct a table of predicted populations. Carry out sufficiently many iterations to see that the rounded off predicted population oscillates with a period of 2. What are the two values (rounded off accurate to 2 decimal places) between which the predicted population ultimately oscillates?

7. $P_0 = 50, M = 200$, and $k = 0.011$

8. $P_0 = 100, M = 300$, and $k = 0.0071$

9. $P_0 = 100, M = 500$, and $k = 0.005$

10. $P_0 = 100, M = 500$, and $k = 0.0047$

Problems 11–16 deal with the iteration $x_{n+1} = rx_n(1 - x_n)$ in Eq. (11) of this section.

11. Starting with the initial value $x_0 = 0.5$, verify that
  (a) If $r = 2$, then x_n approaches the limiting value $1/2$;
  (b) If $r = 2.5$, then x_n approaches the limiting value $3/5$.

12. Verify that you still get the same limiting value in each part of Problem 11 if you use different initial values between 0 and 1, such as $x_0 = 0.1$ and $x_0 = 0.9$.

13. Starting with the initial value $x_0 = 0.5$, try several other values of the growth parameter in the range $1 < r < 3$. How many iterations did it take for your calculator to get to a (three decimal place) limiting value?

14. Verify that if $r = 3.55$, then the fractional population x_n ultimately cycles repeatedly through the *eight* distinct values 0.506, 0.887, 0.355, 0.813, 0.541, 0.882, 0.370, and 0.828.

15. Verify that if $r = 3.83$, then the fractional population x_n ultimately cyles repeatedly through the *three* distinct values 0.156, 0.505, and 0.957.

16. Can you find a value of the growth parameter just greater than $r = 3.84$ where a period 6 oscillation occurs?

17. For the Mandelbrot iteration $x_{n+1} = x_n^2 + c$, show that
    (a) If $x_0 = 0$ and $c = -3$, then the value of x_n gets larger and larger. For instance, $x_6 = 1390967848446$, and thereafter the iterates get *really* big.
    (b) If $x_0 = 0$ and $c = -2$, then $x_2 = x_3 = x_4 = \cdots = 2$.
    (c) If $x_0 = 0$ and $c = -1$, then successive iterates oscillate between -1 and 0.
    (d) If $x_0 = 0$ and $c = -0.5$, then successive iterates approach the number -0.3660.
    (e) If $x_0 = 0$ and $c = 0.2$, then successive iterates approach the number 0.2764.
    (f) If $x_0 = 0$ and $c = 0.5$, then the value of x_n gets larger and larger.

18. Try enough values of c to corroborate the fact that the Mandelbrot iterates remain bounded if and only if the constant c is in the range $-2 \le c \le 0.25$.

19. Use the equations in (15) directly to verify the results stated in Example 8.

20. If $c = (0, 1)$, show that after a couple of iterations of (15) the point (x_n, y_n) oscillates between $(0, -1)$ and $(-1, 1)$.

C H A P T E R   7   R E V I E W

In this chapter, you learned about bounded growth function models. After completing the chapter, you should be able to

- Determine whether a relation described graphically or symbolically represents a logistic function.
- Find the output value of a logistic function for a given input value.
- Find the input value of a logistic function for a given output value.
- Solve an equation or inequality involving a logistic function.
- Find a logistic function that best fits given data.
- Use a discrete logistic model to construct a table of function values.

REVIEW PROBLEMS

In Problems 1–4, match each graph with the most appropriate function rule in A–D and the type of function it represents in I–IV.

A. $f(x) = ax^3 + bx^2 + cx + d$ I.   polynomial
B. $f(x) = a \ln(bx)$ II. exponential

C. $f(x) = \dfrac{c}{1 + ae^{-bx}}$ III. logarithmic

D. $f(x) = ae^{bx}$ IV. logistic

1.

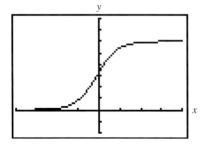

2.

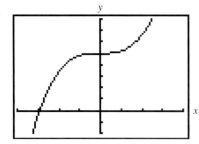

3.

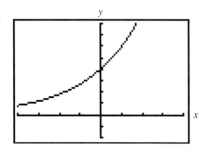

4.

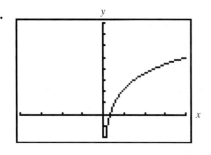

5. Given $f(x) = \dfrac{16}{1 + 1.5e^{-4x}}$, find **(a)** $f(10)$ and **(b)** x so that $f(x) = 10$.

6. A lake has a carrying capacity of 800 fish. On July 1, 2000 the lake is stocked with 100 fish. Six months later there are 180 fish in the lake. Assuming a logistic fish population, in what month of what year will there be 600 fish in the lake?

7. Ripley is Sandee House's Rhodesian Ridgeback puppy. The following table gives Ripley's weight in pounds at 2-week intervals.

Age in weeks	8	10	12	14	16	18
Weight in pounds	14	19	28	46	56	60

Source: Sandee House

(a) Find a best-fitting logistic function to model Ripley's weight as a function of her age in weeks.

(b) Use your model to predict Ripley's weight at 30 weeks of age.

(c) An adult female Rhodesian Ridgeback typically weights about 75 pounds. Based on your model, will Ripley be heavier or lighter than the typical female?

8. Use a discrete logistic model to construct a table of predicted populations for a population with initial value 60, limiting population 180, and growth rate parameter 0.0062. Determine whether the predicted populations steadily increase toward the limiting population or oscillate about it. Give either the limiting value or the values between which it oscillates.

Sierpinski, Pascal, and Chaos

While many fractals are difficult to construct, there are some that are easy to produce (at least in theory) by repeating simple geometric procedures. In this activity, we will look at fractals based on triangles. It is important to remember that what we generate here are "snapshots" at particular points in the process. It is not possible for us to produce the real fractal, because it is the result of repeating these procedures indefinitely—a job we could never complete in a finite amount of time.

Taking Away Triangles

We will begin our investigation by drawing an isosceles triangle (one with two equal sides) as illustrated in Figure 7.R.1, although you can do this with any shape triangle you like. Then we draw lines connecting the midpoints of the triangle's three sides, creating four smaller triangles that are similar to the large one. We "remove" the middle triangle by coloring it black (Fig. 7.R.2), leaving us with what we call a "stage 1 polygon" consisting of three white triangles.

1. Make an enlarged copy of the stage 1 polygon, and continue this process through three more stages. At each stage, divide each white triangle into four similar triangles and color the "middle" triangle of each set of four (to remove it). Fig. 7.R.3 shows the stage 2 polygon consiting of the remaining white triangles at stage 2. How many triangles did you color in stage 3? In stage 4? The white triangles left after stage 1 (Fig. 7.R.2) comprise 3/4 of the original white area of the triangle. How much of this original area is left after stage 2? After stage 3?

Figure 7.R.1   **Figure 7.R.2**   **Figure 7.R.3**

If you continued this process indefinitely, you would end up with the fractal known as the Sierpinski Triangle. If you magnify each white triangle in a Sierpinski Triangle, you will see a copy of the whole triangle. (Actually, what you have created is the negative image of how the Sierpinski Triangle is usually pictured. That is, the "removed" triangles are usually white, and the ones remaining are colored.)

A Triangle of a Different Sort?

Earlier in your study of mathematics, you may have encountered a somewhat different triangle—Pascal's triangle. While Pascal's triangle has many interesting applications, we frequently use it to help us determine the coefficients in expansions resulting when the binomial $x + y$ is raised to whole number powers. Recalling that

- $(x + y)^0 = 1$
- $(x + y)^1 = x + y$
- $(x + y)^2 = x^2 + 2xy + y^2$
- $(x + y)^3 = x^3 + 3x^2y + 3xy^2 + y^3$,

we arrange the coefficients of these terms in a triangular-shaped table, proceeding by descending powers of x and ascending powers of y.

$$
\begin{array}{ccccccc}
 & & & 1 & & & \\
 & & 1 & & 1 & & \\
 & 1 & & 2 & & 1 & \\
1 & & 3 & & 3 & & 1
\end{array}
$$

We can obtain successive rows by carrying the 1's down the diagonals at the beginning and ending of each row, and calculating each of the middle coefficients by adding the numbers directly to the left and right in the row above. Thus, the next row of Pascal's triangle would be

$$
\begin{array}{ccccc}
1 & 1+3 & 3+3 & 3+1 & 1
\end{array}
$$

or

$$
\begin{array}{ccccc}
1 & 4 & 6 & 4 & 1.
\end{array}
$$

2. Carefully write out the first 16 rows of Pascal's triangle, using different colors to write odd and even numbers in the table. What pattern seems to be emerging?

The Chaos Game

Fractals can arise in many surprising ways. Even a random process can be used to produce a highly structured figure. One way to do this is to play what Michael Barnsley, a pioneer in fractal applications, calls the Chaos Game.

We again begin with an isosceles triangle, and label its vertices A, B, and C. We mark a point inside the triangle as our starting point, and move it by rolling a die. We will associate each of the numbers (1 to 6) on the die with one vertex. It doesn't matter which numbers go with which vertex, so for our purposes, we will say 1 and 5 move the point toward A, 2 and 3 move it toward B, and 4 and 6 move it toward C.

Once we roll the die, and determine toward which vertex we are to move, we mark the point halfway (on the straight line) between the starting point and the vertex selected. This is our new starting point. We roll again, and mark the point halfway between the second point and the vertex indicated by the die. Continuing on in this fashion, we mark a series of distinct points inside the triangle.

3. Copy the original white triangle we used to make Sierpinski's triangle. Play 5 rounds of the Chaos Game, marking a total of six points inside the triangle. Does it appear that a pattern is developing?

As we indicated previously, creating a fractal requires repeating procedures indefinitely. It would be quite cumbersome to play the Chaos Game by hand long enough to see the fractal develop. The accompanying program, adapted from a program developed by Texas Instruments for their graphing calculators, allows us to speed up the process a great deal.

The program defines the vertices of the triangle as $A = (0,0)$, $B = (0.5,1)$, and $C = (1,0)$. You will be asked by the program to select the coordinates of your initial point. You should choose an x-coordinate between 0 and 1 and a y-coordinate between 0 and 1. (It is entirely possible that the starting point that you select is outside the triangle, but eventually, one of the points will move inside and the fractal pattern will begin to develop.)

The program uses a random number generator rather than a die to determine toward which vertex to move. A whole number between 1 and 6 is chosen at random. As before, if the number is 1 or 5, then the next point is halfway toward the vertex A $(0, 0)$. If the number is 2 or 3, then the next point is halfway toward the vertex B $(0.5, 1)$. Finally, if the number is 4 or 6, then the next point is halfway toward the vertex C $(1, 0)$. The program uses the formula for the midpoint of a line segment to find the new points.

Notice that, just as in the game using the die, (roughly) one-third of the time the point is moved toward each vertex. The advantage of using the calculator is that it can perform the calculations very quickly and plot the points without needing a ruler. It can play many rounds of the game in the time it would take us to do just a few.

4. Use the calculator program listed below to generate an image. Can you see the fractal pattern clearly when you do 100 iterations? Edit your program to do more iterations by replacing 100 with 500 in the line that says "**:For(K, 1, 100)**". Then try 1000 and 2000 iterations. (If you wish to save each of the intermediate fractal pictures, you will need to change the picture number in the last line of the program when you change the number of iterations.) Be patient when you run the program—even your calculator is a bit slow with that many iterations. What pattern do you see developing?

There are many interesting fractal Web sites you might wish to explore. Another fractal that can be generated using triangles is called the Koch snowflake. You might enjoy developing that one, too.

Fractal Program

(Note that → indicates the STO▶ key on the calculator.)

```
FnOff:ClrDraw                      If N=2 or N=3
PlotsOff:AxesOff                   Then
0→Xmin:1→Xmax                      .5(.5+X)→X
0→Ymin:1→Ymax                      .5(1+Y)→Y
Disp "CHOOSE 0<X<1"                End
Input X                            If N=4 or N=6
Disp "CHOOSE 0<Y<1"                Then
Input Y                            .5(1+X)→X
For(K, 1, 100)                     .5Y→Y
randInt(1,6)→N                     End
If N=1 or N=5                      Pt-On(X,Y)
Then                               End
.5X→X                              StorePic Pic1
.5Y→Y
End
```

8

OPTIMIZATION

"Buy low, sell high" is the goal of those who invest in the stock market. But how does an investor know when the highs and lows will occur? The chart in Fig. 8.0.1 shows the closing Dow Jones Industrial Average on the first 17 Tuesdays of 1998.

Looking at this graph now, it is easy to spot the highs and lows. If you had bought a stock reflected in this index in the second week, and sold it in the tenth week, you would have made a tidy profit, if not a killing. However, if you had bought in the sixteenth week, expecting prices to continue to rise, and needed to sell in the seventeenth week, you would have lost money.

Wouldn't it be nice if you could know ahead of time when the stock market would go up and when it would go down? Stock analysts sometimes use formulas to fit market data like that plotted in Fig. 8.0.1. Given a function modeling the Dow Jones average, we can find the high and low points on the graph of this function, and thereby hope to estimate the maximum and minimum values of the Dow Jones average itself.

In this chapter, we will study techniques for finding maximum and minimum values for such functions and models.

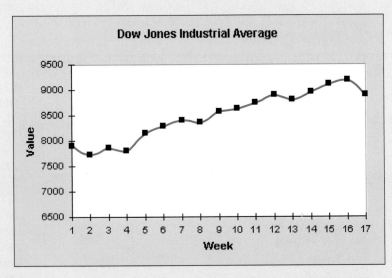

Figure 8.0.1   The Dow Jones average on the first 17 Tuesdays in 1998.

8.1	Highs and Lows
8.2	Applied Maxima and Minima I
8.3	Applied Maxima and Minima II

8.1 HIGHS AND LOWS

Both people and functions have highs and lows, and in either case it can be important to know when and where they occur.

By looking at the graph $y = f(x)$ on an **interval** $a \le x \le b$ of x-values, we can usually spot its highest or lowest point visually. In this chapter we'll see that this simple idea has a surprising range of practical applications in the real world. But first we illustrate the use of a graphing calculator to locate high and low points in purely graphical examples.

Example 1

Find the lowest point on the parabola $y = x^2 - 6x + 7$.

Figure 8.1.1 shows the graph $y = x^2 - 6x^2 + 7$ plotted in the standard window $-10 \le x, y \le 10$. The parabola opens upward from the low point that's visible. So it's just a matter of zooming in to see exactly where this low point lies. At first glance, it looks near the point $(3, -2)$. Figure 8.1.2 shows the graph in the

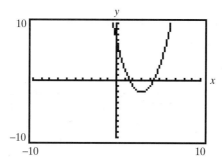

Figure 8.1.1 The parabola $y = x^2 - 6x + 7$ in the window $-10 \le x, y \le 10$.

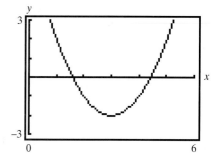

Figure 8.1.2 The parabola in the window $0 \le x \le 6, -3 \le y \le 3$ where it looks like the low point is $(3, -2)$.

window $0 \le x \le 6, -3 \le y \le 3$ and now it looks like it really is *exactly* the point $(3, -2)$.

But how can we be sure the low point is not $(3.002, -2.001)$ instead? Such a tiny difference from $(3, -2)$ might not be visible on a graph. In a case like this, in which we have a quadratic function, we could algebraically determine the low point by completing the square to find the vertex of the parabola.

In the case of more complicated functions, algebraic techniques will not do; the exact coordinates of high and low points are determined using the methods of calculus. For these functions (as well as quadratic ones), the **CALC** menu on our calculator offers **minimum** and **maximum** functions that will give us a better approximation than we can get visually.

If we enter this selection, then we are prompted to provide first a *left bound,* then a *right bound,* and finally a *guess.* We move the cursor just to the left of the apparent low point and press **ENTER** to record our left bound (Fig. 8.1.3), then just to the right to record our right bound similarly, then back to the low point itself. When we enter our guess, the calculator screen in Fig. 8.1.4 results, indicating that $(3, -2)$ is, indeed, the best guess for the low point on the parabola.   ◼

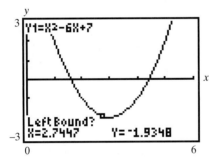

Figure 8.1.3   Entering a left bound.

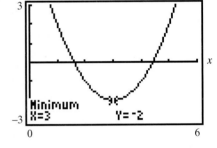

Figure 8.1.4   The low point on the graph has coordinates $x = 3$ and $y = -2$.

When, as in Fig. 8.1.4, your calculator reports integer values for the coordinates of your maximum or minimum point, it is a reasonable bet that you have found the exact answer. If your calculator reports coordinates like $x = 2.9999993$ and $y = -2.0000001$, you may have found approximate answers. To be on the safe side, however, you should consider the answers found by the **maximum** and **minimum** functions to be very good approximations but not necessarily exact values.

The result found in Example 1 can be stated in a couple of different ways:

- The *lowest point* on the parabola $y = x^2 - 6x + 7$ is the point $(3, -2)$;
- The *minimum value* of the function $f(x) = x^2 - 6x + 7$ is the number $f(3) = -2$.

Thus we distinguish between the minimum value of the function $f(x)$ and the lowest point on the graph $y = f(x)$. The **minimum value** of the function is the y-coordinate of the low point, and the x-coordinate of the low point is the value of x that gives the minimum value of the function.

The parabola in Figure 8.1.1 has a lowest point, but because it opens upward it obviously does *not* have a highest point. On the other hand, a parabola that opened downward would have a highest point but not a lowest point.

Frequently we need to know the maximum or minimum value attained by a given function $f(x)$ for values of x in a *given interval* $a \leq x \leq b$. As illustrated in Example 2, each of these extreme values must occur *either*

- At an **interior point** x of the interval where $a < x < b$, *or*
- At one of the interval's **endpoints** $x = a$ and $x = b$.

If we graph the function on the given interval, we can

- Spot visually an extreme value that occurs at an endpoint of the interval, and
- Use the calculator's maximum or minimum function to find an extreme value that occurs at an interior point.

Example 2

Find the maximum and minimum values of the function $f(x) = 5 + 12x - 4x^2$ on the interval $0 \leq x \leq 4$.

Figure 8.1.5 shows the graph $y = 5 + 12x - 4x^2$ plotted on the given interval $0 \leq x \leq 4$. Now we have a parabola that opens downward. There is therefore no lowest point on the whole parabola, but we are concerned only with the portion that corresponds to the interval $0 \leq x \leq 4$. Evidently, the minimum value of the function $f(x)$ occurs at the right-hand endpoint $x = 4$ of the interval. Thus the minimum is the value

$$f(4) = 5 + 12(4) - 4(4)^2 = -11.$$

It is equally obvious in Fig. 8.1.5 that the maximum value of the function occurs at an interior point of the interval, and the **CALC maximum** screen in Fig. 8.1.6 tells us that this maximum value is $f(1.5) = 14$.   ◨

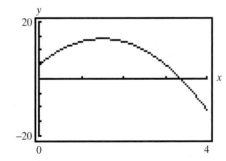

Figure 8.1.5   The graph $y = 5 + 12x - 4x^2$ with low point at the right-hand endpoint and high point in the interior of the interval $0 \leq x \leq 4$.

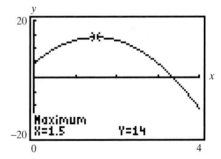

Figure 8.1.6   The high point on the graph has coordinates $x = 1.5$ and $y = 14$.

Example 3

Find the highest and lowest points on the graph of the function

$$f(x) = 2x^3 - 3x^2 - 36x + 25 \quad \text{for} \quad -4 \leq x \leq 4.$$

Figure 8.1.7 shows the graph $y = 2x^3 - 3x^2 - 36x + 25$ in the window $-6 \le x \le 6, -100 \le y \le 100$, and we see the two bends that are typical of a cubic curve. Evidently, the highest and lowest points of this curve are its two end-points. But we want to find the highest and lowest points of the graph on the interval $-4 \le x \le 4$ rather than on the interval $-6 \le x \le 6$.

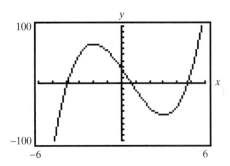

Figure 8.1.7 $y = 2x^3 - 3x^2 - 36x + 25$ for $-6 \le x \le 6$.

Looking more carefully at Fig. 8.1.7 (where each x-axis tick mark represents one unit), we see that the highest and lowest points of the graph on this interval occur at the two bend points, apparently near $x = -2$ and $x = 3$. Indeed, the **CALC maximum** and **CALC minimum** screens in Figs. 8.1.8 and 8.1.9 show that, in this interval, the highest point on the curve is $(-2, 69)$ and the lowest point is $(3, -56)$. ◤

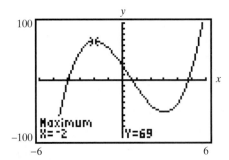

Figure 8.1.8   The highest point for $-4 \le x \le 4$ is $(-2, 69)$.

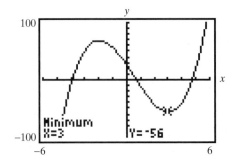

Figure 8.1.9   The lowest point for $-4 \le x \le 4$ is $(3, -56)$.

Again, it is important to distinguish between the high/low **points** on the **graph** $y = f(x)$ and the maximum/minimum **values** of the **function** $f(x)$. The maximum and minimum values of the function $f(x)$ are the maximum and minimum *heights* (y-coordinates) of points on the graph. In Example 3 we found the high point $(-2, 69)$ and the low point $(3, -56)$. This means that the maximum and minimum *values* attained by the function $f(x) = 2x^3 - 3x^2 - 36x + 25$ for $-4 \le x \le 4$ are

- $y_{\max} = f(-2) = 69$, and
- $y_{\min} = f(3) = -56$.

You can remember that high/low **points** are just that—*points* with xy-coordinates (and thus number pairs), while maximum/minimum **values** are just that—*y-values* (and thus numbers). Finally, if we had only been asked *where* in the interval these maximum and minimum values occur, the answer would have been this: The maximum value of $f(x)$ occurs at $x = -2$ and the minimum value occurs at $x = 3$.

Examples 1 through 3 illustrate the following systematic method for solving maximum-minimum problems.

The Graphical Maximum–Minimum Method

To find the maximum value of the function $f(x)$ for values of x in the interval $a \le x \le b$, we carry out the following steps.

- Construct the graph $y = f(x)$.
- Find the highest point (x_m, y_m) on the graph.
- Then $x = x_m$ gives the maximum value $y_m = f(x_m)$ of the function.

With a graphing calculator this is easily done using the **CALC maximum** facility. To find the minimum value of $f(x)$, proceed similarly, except using the **CALC minimum** facility to find the lowest point on the graph.

We consider next some simple applications of this method.

The Maximum Height of a Ball

If a ball is thrown straight upward at time $t = 0$ with initial velocity v_0 feet per second from an initial height y_0 feet above the ground, then its height y after t seconds is given by the known formula

$$y(t) = -16t^2 + v_0 t + y_0. \tag{1}$$

For instance, suppose a ball is thrown straight upward from the ground with initial velocity $v_0 = 100$ ft/sec. Then substitution of $y_0 = 0$ and $v_0 = 100$ into (1) gives

$$y(t) = -16t^2 + 100t$$

for the ball's height (in feet) after t seconds. Thus its height above the ground after $t = 5$ seconds is

$$y(5) = -16(5)^2 + 100(5) = -400 + 500 = 100 \text{ feet.}$$

Example 4

Suppose a baseball is thrown upward with velocity 45 mph in the air from the top of a coaching tower with height $y_0 = 40$ ft. We want to answer the following two questions.

(a)   How high in the air does the ball go before starting back downward?
(b)   How long is it in the air before it hits the ground at the bottom of the tower?

We give the initial velocity in miles per hour because velocity in feet per second has little intuitive meaning to most people. However, we must express all quantities in feet and seconds in order to use formula (1). For this purpose we use the handy conversion factor

$$60 \text{ mph} = 88 \text{ ft/sec,}$$

which (for whatever reason) is sometimes mentioned in driver's license exam study booklets. We then see that our baseball's initial velocity in ft/sec is

$$v_0 = 45 \text{ mph} \times \frac{88 \text{ ft/sec}}{60 \text{ mph}} = \frac{45 \times 88}{60} \frac{\text{ft}}{\text{sec}} = 66 \frac{\text{ft}}{\text{sec}}.$$

Then substitution of $v_0 = 66$ (ft/sec) and $y_0 = 40$ (ft) in (1) yields the ball's *height function*

$$y(t) = -16t^2 + 66t + 40. \qquad (2)$$

In principle, this function tells everything there is to know about the ball's ascent to its apex and subsequent fall back to the ground. In particular, it's the key to answering questions (a) and (b).

(a)   Figure 8.1.10 shows the result when we define **Y₁=−16X^2+66X+40** (with the calculator's **X** instead of t as the independent variable) and use the calculator's **CALC maximum** facility to locate the visible high point. The coordinates (2.0625, 108.0625) of the high point marked on the graph give the time $t = 2.0625$ sec that it takes the ball to reach its apex at a height of $y_{\max} = 108.0625$ feet (above the ground, not above the top of the tower where it was thrown).

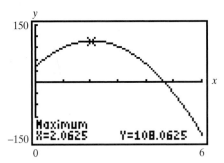

Figure 8.1.10   Graph of the baseball's height function.

(b)   Now we need only find when **Y₁=0**. The more familiar **CALC zero** calculator facility (Fig. 8.1.11)—or, alternatively, we could use the quadratic formula—shows that $y = 0$ (at the ground) when $x = 4.6613$. Thus the ball is in the air for a total of $t = 4.6613$ seconds (changing the independent variable back from the calculator's **X** to our t).

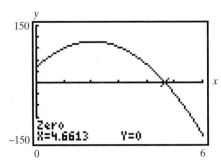

Figure 8.1.11   The baseball's impact with the ground.

In summary, the baseball of Example 4 takes about 2.06 seconds to ascend to its apex about 108.06 feet above the ground, and then takes about 4.66 − 2.06 = 2.60 seconds to fall back to the ground at the foot of the tower. ∎

The Minimum Population of a City

If a population model $P(t)$ is given, we can apply the graphical maximum-minimum method to determine the maximum or minimum population that occurs during a given time interval. In the following example a quadratic population model is given.

Example 5

A city has an initially declining population, given (in thousands) t years after January 1, 1999 by the quadratic model

$$P(t) = 100 - 2.4t + 0.2t^2. \tag{3}$$

We want to answer the following three questions.

(a) What is minimum population the city reaches before rebounding?
(b) When does the city regain its initial population?
(c) When will the city reach a population of 125 thousand?

(a) Figure 8.1.12 shows the result when we define **Y₁=100–2.4X+0.2X^2** (with the calculator's **X** instead of t as the independent variable, and **Y** instead of P as the dependent variable) and plot our city's population function in the window $0 \le t \le 20$, $75 \le P \le 125$. The plot confirms what we know about such a quadratic function—the population declines at first, reaches a minimum value, then rebounds and thereafter increases. We have used our calculator's **CALC minimum** facility to locate the visible low point.

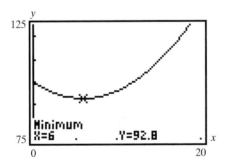

Figure 8.1.12   Graph of the population function $P(t) = 100 - 2.4t + 0.2t^2$ for $0 \le t \le 20$, $75 \le P \le 125$.

The coordinates $(6, 92.8)$ of the low point marked on the graph give the time $t_{min} = 6$ years that it takes the city to reach its minimum population of $P_{min} = 92.8$ thousand people. Starting on January 1, 1999, this minimum population would be attained on January 1, 2005.

(b) Here we need only solve the especially simple (why?) quadratic equation

$$100 - 2.4t + 0.2t^2 = 100$$

for $t = 12$. Thus the city regains its original population of 100 thousand people at the beginning of the year 2011.

(c) Finally, we need to solve the quadratic equation

$$100 - 2.4t + 0.2t^2 = 125$$

to find when the city's population reaches 125 thousand. In Fig. 8.1.13 we have plotted both sides of this equation in the window $0 \leq t \leq 30, 50 \leq P \leq 175$. The **CALC intersect** solution shown in the figure indicates that it takes $t = 18.6886$ years for the city to rebound to a population of 125 thousand. Now 18 years after January 1, 1999 is January 1, 2017. Since 0.6886×12 months ≈ 8.26 months, and September is the ninth month of the year, we see that the city's population reaches 125 thousand about one week into September of the year 2017.   ◣

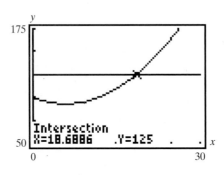

Figure 8.1.13   Finding when $100 - 2.4t + 0.2t^2 = 125.$

8.1
PROBLEMS

In Problems 1–14, find the maximum and minimum values of the given function $f(x)$ for x in the given range $a \leq x \leq b$.

1. $f(x) = 3x - 2, \quad -1 \leq x \leq 4$
2. $f(x) = 7 - 4x, \quad -3 \leq x \leq 5$
3. $f(x) = x^2 - 4x + 3, \quad -2 \leq x \leq 1$
4. $f(x) = x^2 - 4x + 3, \quad 2 \leq x \leq 5$
5. $f(x) = x^2 - 4x + 3, \quad -1 \leq x \leq 4$
6. $f(x) = 5 + 2x - x^2, \quad -2 \leq x \leq 1$
7. $f(x) = 5 + 2x - x^2, \quad 2 \leq x \leq 5$
8. $f(x) = 5 + 2x - x^2, \quad -3 \leq x \leq 4$
9. $f(x) = 2x^2 - 10x + 9, \quad 0 \leq x \leq 5$
10. $f(x) = 10 - 15x - 3x^2, \quad -10 \leq x \leq 5$
11. $f(x) = x^3 - 3x^2 - 9x + 5, \quad -2 \leq x \leq 4$
12. $f(x) = x^3 - 3x^2 - 9x + 5, \quad -4 \leq x \leq 6$
13. $f(x) = 70x - x^2 - 4x^3, \quad -4 \leq x \leq 4$
14. $f(x) = 70x - x^2 - 4x^3, \quad -5 \leq x \leq 5$

In Problems 15 and 16, a ball is thrown straight upward at time $t = 0$ from the top of a building y_0 feet above the ground (where $y = 0$). Recall that if the projectile's initial velocity is v_0 feet/sec, then (neglecting air resistance) its height y above the ground after t seconds is given by $y = -16t^2 + v_0 t + y_0$, as in Eq. (1) of this section. In each problem find

(a)   the maximum height reached by the ball, and
(b)   how long it remains in the air before hitting the ground.

15. $y_0 = 100$ feet and $v_0 = 50$ ft/sec
16. $y_0 = 125$ feet and $v_0 = 75$ ft/sec
17. A powerful crossbow fires a bolt straight upward from the ground with an initial velocity of 320 ft/sec. How high does it go, and how long is it in the air?

18. The same as Problem 17, except now it's a bullet fired straight upward from the ground, with a powerful rifle with a muzzle velocity of 640 ft/sec. Express its maximum height in miles.

In Problems 19 and 20, a projectile is fired at a 45° angle from the ground with the vertical and horizontal components of its velocity both being v_0 ft/sec. Its height y above the ground after it has traveled x feet horizontally is then given by $y = x - 16(x/v_0)^2$. In each problem find

(a) the maximum height reached by the projectile, and

(b) how far away it hits the ground.

19. The projectile is a ball thrown with $v_0 = 64$ ft/sec.

20. The projectile is a rifle bullet fired with $v_0 = 250$ ft/sec.

In Problems 21 and 22, the initially declining population (in thousands) of a city t years after January 1, 1999 is given by the specified quadratic population model. Find

(a) the minimum population reached by the city,

(b) when the city regains its initial population, and

(c) when the city reaches double its initial population.

21. $P(t) = 200 - 5.2t + 0.47t^2$

22. $P(t) = 350 - 11t + 1.16t^2$

8.2 APPLIED MAXIMA AND MINIMA I

As we have seen previously, solving an applied problem often requires defining a function to model a physical situation. The following example illustrates this process.

Example 1

A rectangular box with square base has volume $V = 125$. Express its total surface area A as a function of the edge length x of its base.

The first step is to draw a sketch and to label the relevant dimensions. Figure 8.2.1 shows a rectangular box with square base of edge length x and height y. We are given that the volume of the box—the product of its three dimensions—is

$$V = x^2y = 125. \tag{1}$$

Both the top and the bottom of the box have area x^2, and each of its four vertical sides has area xy, so the total surface area of the box is

$$A = 2x^2 + 4xy. \tag{2}$$

But this is a formula for A in terms of the *two* variables x and y rather than a function of the *single* variable x. To eliminate y and thereby obtain A in terms of x alone, we solve Eq. (1) for $y = 125/x^2$ and then substitute this result in (2) to obtain the formula

$$A = 2x^2 + 4x \cdot \frac{125}{x^2} = 2x^2 + \frac{500}{x}.$$

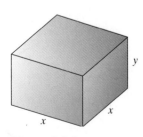

Figure 8.2.1 The box with square base (Example 1).

Thus the total surface area A of the box is given as a function of its edge length x by the function

$$A(x) = 2x^2 + \frac{500}{x}.$$

In Example 1 our goal was to express the dependent variable A as a function of the independent variable x. Initially, the geometric situation of Fig. 8.2.1 provided us instead with

- The *formula* in (1) expressing A in terms of both x and the additional variable y, and
- The *relation* in (2) between x and y, which we used to *eliminate* the extra variable y and thereby obtain A as a function of x alone.

We will see that this is a common pattern in many different applied problems, such as the one that follows.

Example 2

You have 40 yards of fence to enclose a rectangular animal pen. What are the dimensions of the pen of maximum possible area that you can build using this available fencing?

Figure 8.2.2 shows the animal pen and its dimensions x and y. If we can express the quantity to be maximized—in this case, the area—as a function of some independent variable, then we can graph the function, locate the high point on its graph, and thereby find the maximum value attained by the function.

We have already indicated in Fig. 8.2.2 the first step in any such geometric problem—to **draw** and label a figure. The quantity to be maximized—the area A of the rectangle in Fig. 8.2.2—is given by the **formula**

$$A = xy, \tag{3}$$

which expresses A in terms of the two variables x and y. But the four sides of the rectangle must add up to the available 40 yards of fence, so x and y must satisfy the **relation**

$$2x + 2y = 40. \tag{4}$$

We can now **eliminate** the extra variable y by solving this relation for

$$y = 20 - x. \tag{5}$$

Then substitution of y as given by (5) into (3) finally gives the **function**

$$A(x) = x(20 - x), \tag{6}$$

which expresses the area A of the animal pen in terms of its base x.

It remains only to **graph** this function and locate the high point on the graph. Figure 8.2.3 shows the graph in the window $0 \leq x \leq 20, 0 \leq y \leq 150$, together with the information provided by our calculator's **CALC maximum** facility. The calculator's dependent variable **Y** being our A, we see that the maximum value

$$A_{max} = A(10) = 100$$

is obtained with the value $x = 10$.

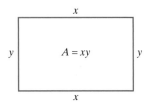

x

y $A = xy$ y

x

Figure 8.2.2   The animal pen of Example 2.

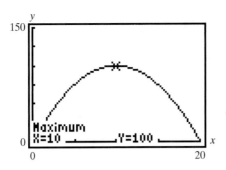

Figure 8.2.3 Graph of the area function $A(x) = x(20 - x)$ for $0 \leq x \leq 20$.

But we must not forget to **answer** the question that was originally asked: What are the dimensions of the pen of maximum possible area? With $x = 10$ yd we see that Eq. (5) gives $y = 10$ yd also. Thus the desired pen is a 10 yd $\times$ 10 yd *square*.   ◼

You should note the **keyword steps**—highlighted in the solution of Example 2—for the solution of applied maximum-minimum problems:

- **Draw**   and label a figure in order to find both a
- **Formula**   for the quantity in question and a
- **Relation**   between the geometric variables. Use this relation to
- **Eliminate** the extra variable to get a
- **Function**   giving the quantity to be maximized or minimized.
- **Graph**   this function and locate the high/low point to finally
- **Answer**   the original question.

Remember that here a *function* means a function of a *single* variable that we can graph in order to see visually the high or low point on the graph.

Example 3

You want to build an animal pen as in Example 2, except now an existing stone wall can be used as one side of the pen, with your 40 yards of fencing to be used on the other three sides. Now what are the maximum possible area of the pen *and* the optimal dimensions that yield this area?

Figure 8.2.4 provides the first step—to **draw** and label a figure. The area A to be maximized is given by the same **formula**

$$A = xy \tag{7}$$

as before. But now we must build only three sides using the available 40 yd of fence—the side of length x parallel to the wall, and the two sides of length y perpendicular to the wall. So now x and y must satisfy the **relation**

$$x + 2y = 40. \tag{8}$$

We can now **eliminate** the extra variable y by solving this relation for

$$y = \frac{1}{2}(40 - x). \tag{9}$$

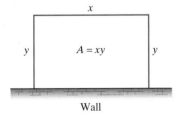

Figure 8.2.4 The animal pen and existing wall of Example 3.

Then substitution of y as given by (9) into (7) gives the **function**

$$A(x) = \frac{1}{2}x(40 - x), \tag{10}$$

which expresses the area A of our new animal pen in terms of its base x.

It remains only to **graph** this function and locate the high point on the graph. Figure 8.2.5 shows the graph in the window $0 \le x \le 40, 0 \le y \le 300$, together with the information provided by our calculator's **CALC maximum** facility.

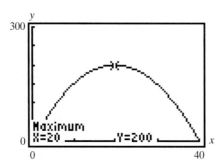

Figure 8.2.5   Graph of the area function $A(x) = \frac{1}{2}x(40 - x)$ for $0 \le x \le 40$.

The calculator's dependent variable **Y** being our A, we see that the maximum value

$$A_{\max} = A(20) = 200$$

is obtained with $x = 20$. We have *doubled* the area of our optimal pen by using the existing wall for one of its sides.

To complete our **answer** to the question that was originally asked, we substitute $x = 20$ yd into (9) and get $y = 10$ yd. Thus the desired pen is now a 20 yd $\times$ 10 yd rectangle. ◼

There's a reason why $0 \le x \le 40$ is the best x-interval to use when graphing $A(x)$ as in Fig. 8.2.5. It's because the length x is certainly not negative (so $0 \le x$), and we only have 40 yd of fencing available and hence x certainly cannot be greater than 40 (so $x \le 40$). Thus the interval $0 \le x \le 40$ describes the *physically possible* range of values of x for our problem. The other values of x—negative values and ones greater than 40—are *mathematically possible* in that they could be substituted into the formula $A(x) = \frac{1}{2}x(40 - x)$. However, they would yield (physically impossible) negative values for the area A, and this is a tip-off that they are physically impossible values of x. What this means is that it's the whole function

$$A(x) = \frac{1}{2}x(40 - x), \quad 0 \le x \le 40 \tag{11}$$

comprised of *both* its formula *and* its domain of definition that provides a mathematical model of the fence problem in Example 3.

Example 4

Finally, you plan also to paint your animal pen. The existing wall part will cost $1/yd to paint, but the other three sides will cost $5/yd to build *and* paint. You have $180 to spend. Now what are the maximum possible area of the pen and its dimensions?

Figure 8.2.6 shows the animal pen with its dimensions and the given cost figures labeled.

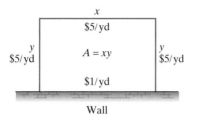

Figure 8.2.6   The fence with painted walls (Example 4).

The area A to be maximized is still given by the **formula**

$$A = xy. \tag{12}$$

But now the lengths (in yd) of the *four* sides of the pen—each multiplied by its cost in dollars/yd—must add up to the available $180. That is,

$$(x \text{ yd})(1 \text{ \$/yd}) + (y \text{ yd})(5 \text{ \$/yd}) + (x \text{ yd})(5 \text{ \$/yd}) + (y \text{ yd})(5 \text{ \$/yd}) = \$180,$$

so x and y must satisfy the **relation**

$$6x + 10y = 180. \tag{13}$$

We can now **eliminate** the extra variable y by solving this relation for

$$y = \frac{1}{10}(180 - 6x). \tag{14}$$

Then substitution of (14) into (12) gives the **function**

$$A(x) = \frac{1}{10}x(180 - 6x), \tag{15}$$

which now expresses the area A of our animal pen in terms of its base x.

If you look at Eq. (14), you should see that x cannot be larger than 30, or else y would be negative. We therefore plot the area function in (15) on the interval $0 \le x \le 30$. Figure 8.2.7 shows the result when we apply calculator's **CALC maximum** facility.

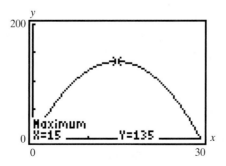

Figure 8.2.7   Graph of the area function $A(x) = \frac{1}{10}x(180 - 6x)$ for $0 \le x \le 30$.

The calculator's dependent variable **Y** being our A, we see that the maximum value

$$A_{\max} = A(15) = 135$$

is obtained with $x = 15$.

To complete our **answer** to the question that was originally asked, we substitute $x = 15$ yd into (14) and get $y = 9$ yd. Thus the desired pen is a 15 yd $\times$ 9 yd rectangle.   ◨

Example 5

Let's take another look at the popcorn tray constructed in Example 4 of Section 5.1. We want to make a tray out of a sheet of cardboard of length $p = 30$ cm and width $q = 20$ cm. The tray will be constructed by cutting equal squares out of the corners of the cardboard sheet, and then folding up the remaining flaps to form a box (Fig. 8.2.8). Thus an x-by-x square is first cut from each corner of the original p-by-q cardboard rectangle. Then the four flaps are folded up to form the vertical sides of the tray.

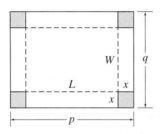

Figure 8.2.8   The popcorn tray construction.

In Section 5.1 we asked how this should be done in order that the resulting tray would have a volume of exactly 500 cm³. Now we ask a different question: What are the dimensions of the tray of *maximal volume* that can be constructed in this way?

Because the tray on the right in Fig. 8.2.8 has dimensions $L = p - 2x = 30 - 2x$ and $W = q - 2x = 20 - 2x$ (as well as height x), its volume is given as a function of x by

$$V(x) = x(30 - 2x)(20 - 2x). \tag{16}$$

As we noted when we discussed this previously, we can make a tray with any corner notch edge length x in the interval $0 \le x \le 10$ (10 being half the width of our cardboard sheet). So in order to find the maximum possible volume of such a tray, we need only find the maximum value of $V(x)$ for $0 \le x \le 10$. And thus we need only find the highest point on the graph of $V(x)$ on this interval.

Figure 8.2.9 shows the result of graphing $V(x)$ and using the calculator's **CALC maximum** facility to locate the visible high point (3.9237, 1056.3059). Thus a corner notch of size $x = 3.9237$ cm yields a tray with the maximum possible volume, $V_{\max} = 1056.3059$ cm³. Its length and width are

$$L = 30 - 2(3.9237) = 22.1526 \text{ cm,}$$
$$W = 20 - 2(3.9237) = 12.1526 \text{ cm.}$$

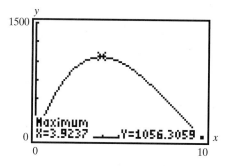

Figure 8.2.9 The graph of the volume function $V(x) = x(30 - 2x)(20 - 2x)$ for $0 \le x \le 10$.

We therefore see that our maximum-volume tray (with its dimensions rounded off accurate to 2 decimal places) measures approximately 22.15 cm $\times$ 12.15 cm $\times$ 3.92 cm. ◼

8.2 PROBLEMS

1. Express the area $A = x^2$ of a square as a function of its perimeter $P = 4x$.

2. If a rectangle has area $A = 100$, express its perimeter as a function of its base x.

3. Express the area $A = \pi r^2$ of a circle as a function of its circumference $C = 2\pi r$.

4. Express the volume $V = (4/3)\pi r^3$ of a sphere as a function of its surface area $S = 4\pi r^2$.

5. If the sum of two numbers is 100, what is the greatest possible value of their product? *Hint:* If x denotes one of the numbers, then the other is $100 - x$ (why?), so $y = x(100 - x)$ is their product.

6. What is the greatest possible value of the sum of the *squares* of the two numbers in Problem 5?

7. You have 160 feet of fencing available to build a rectangular pen for your dog. What is the largest possible area of the pen you can build? What will be the shape of this optimal pen?

8. Now you have the same 160 feet of fencing as in Problem 7, but you can use an existing long brick wall at the back of your yard as one side of your dog pen. Hence you can use all the available fencing for just three sides of the pen. Now what is the largest possible area of the pen, and what will be the shape of the optimal pen?

9. Now you have \$160 to spend on the dog pen of Problem 8. It will cost you \$3/ft to paint the brick wall side of the pen, and \$5/ft to build each of the other three sides. What are the dimensions of the pen of maximal area that you can build?

10. The same as Problem 9, except that you have \$240 to spend on your dog pen. It will cost you \$2/ft to paint the wall side of the pen, and \$6/ft to build each of the other three sides.

11. The same as Problem 9, except that you have \$180 to spend on your dog pen. It will cost you \$4/ft to paint the wall side of the pen, and \$5/ft to build each of the other three sides.

12. You have 160 feet of fencing. According to the answer to Problem 7, the rectangle of maximal area that you can enclose with this fencing is a square. But now you want to build two square dog pens—you will use x feet of the fencing to make one square pen, and the remaining $160 - x$ feet of fencing to make another square pen. What should x be in order to minimize the sum of the areas of these two pens? What will be the dimensions of the resulting square pens?

13. The same as Problem 12, except that the first pen with perimeter x is a rectangle whose length is twice its width, and the second pen with perimeter $160 - x$ is still a square.

14. The same as Problem 12, except that the first pen with perimeter x is now a circle of radius r, but the second pen with perimeter $160 - x$ is still a square.

In Problems 15–18, the dimensions of a square piece of cardboard are given. You plan to make a tray by cutting equal squares out of the four corners and turning up the remaining flaps. You are to find both

(a) the greatest possible volume V of the resulting box, and its dimensions; and

(b) the possible dimensions of such a box with the given volume V_0.

15. 50″ by 50″; $V_0 = 6000$ cubic inches

16. 45″ by 45″; $V_0 = 4000$ cubic inches

17. 40″ by 40″; $V_0 = 3000$ cubic inches

18. 35″ by 35″; $V_0 = 2000$ cubic inches

In Problems 19–22, you have the given amount A to spend on a fancy rectangular animal pen to be built along an existing long brick wall. The cost per foot to paint the wall side of the pen, and the cost per foot to build each of the other three sides, are also given. Find the dimensions of the pen of maximal area that you can build.

19. $A = \$700$; \$2/ft for the wall side of the pen, \$5/ft for each of the other three sides

20. $A = \$160$; \$3/ft for the wall side of the pen, \$5/ft for each of the other three sides

21. $A = \$240$; \$2/ft for the wall side of the pen, \$6/ft for each of the other three sides

22. $A = \$180$; \$4/ft for the wall side of the pen, \$5/ft for each of the other three sides

8.3 APPLIED MAXIMA AND MINIMA II

This section consists largely of examples that illustrate and develop further the optimization methods introduced in Sections 8.1 and 8.2. Recall the seven *keyword steps* for the solution of a typical applied optimization problem that were emphasized in Section 8.2:

- **Draw**   and label a figure in order to find both a
- **Formula**   for the quantity in question and a
- **Relation** between the geometric variables. Use this relation to
- **Eliminate** the extra variable to get a
- **Function** giving the quantity to be maximized or minimized.
- **Graph**   this function and locate the high/low point to finally
- **Answer**   the original question.

Rectangular Boxes

Examples 1 through 3 should be read and compared carefully. They describe similar but different boxes. We are concerned with the total surface area of the boxes in Problems 1 and 2, but with the total cost of the box in Example 3.

Example 1

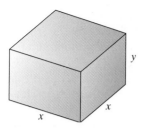

Figure 8.3.1   The square-based box of Example 1.

Suppose you want to make a square-based rectangular cardboard box with a volume of 1000 cubic inches. What dimensions will minimize the total surface area of this box so that the least possible amount of cardboard material will be required?

Our first step is to **draw** and label a figure (Fig. 8.3.1). Because the box is to be square based, both its length and its width are labeled with the same letter x; its height is labeled y. The box then has a top and a bottom each having area x^2, as well as four vertical sides (its front and back and its two ends) each having area xy. Adding up the areas of these six faces of the box, we find that its total surface area—the quantity to be minimized—is given by the **formula**

$$A = 2x^2 + 4xy. \tag{1}$$

Because the volume $V = x^2 y$ of the box is the product of its base area x^2 and its height y, the given volume of 1000 in^3 provides the **relation**

$$x^2 y = 1000 \tag{2}$$

between x and y. To **eliminate** the extra variable y, we need only solve (2) for the height

$$y = \frac{1000}{x^2}. \tag{3}$$

Substitution of (3) for y in (1) then yields the area **function** defined by

$$A(x) = 2x^2 + 4x \cdot \frac{1000}{x^2} = 2x^2 + \frac{4000}{x}. \tag{4}$$

It remains only to **graph** $A(x)$ so as to locate the low point on the graph. As indicated in Fig. 8.3.2, our calculator's **CALC minimum** facility then yields the low point $(10, 600)$ on the graph.

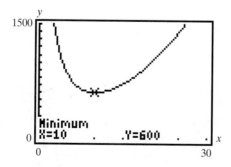

Figure 8.3.2   Graph of the area function $A(x) = 2x^2 + \frac{4000}{x}$ of Example 1.

Since the calculator's dependent variable **Y** is our A, this means that a box with minimal total surface area $A_{min} = 600$ results if its square base edge length is $x = 10$ in. Then (3) shows that the height of the box is then $y = 1000/10^2 = 10$ (also). Thus the **answer** to the question posed is this: The square-based box with volume 1000 in^3 and minimum possible total surface area is a $10'' \times 10'' \times 10''$ *cube*.

Example 2

Suppose a square-based rectangular box is to be constructed just as in Example 1, except that it now is open-topped—it has a bottom and 4 sides but *no* top—and its volume is to be 500 in³ (instead of 1000 in³). Now what is the minimum possible total surface area of the box?

The box still looks as drawn in Fig 8.3.1. But because it has only a bottom of area x^2 plus four vertical sides each having area xy, its total surface area—the quantity to be minimized—is now given by the **formula**

$$A = x^2 + 4xy \tag{5}$$

instead of (1). Because the volume of the box is 500 in³, x and y are now connected by the **relation**

$$x^2y = 500 \tag{6}$$

instead of (2). To **eliminate** the extra variable y, we solve (6) for

$$y = \frac{500}{x^2} \tag{7}$$

and substitute for y in (5). This gives the area **function**

$$A(x) = x^2 + 4x \cdot \frac{500}{x^2} = x^2 + \frac{2000}{x}. \tag{8}$$

Figure 8.3.3 shows the **graph** of this new area function $A(x)$. As indicated, the **CALC minimum** calculator facility yields the low point $(10, 300)$ on the graph.

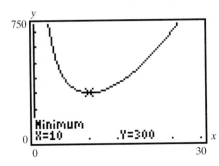

Figure 8.3.3 Graph of the area function $A(x) = x^2 + \frac{2000}{x}$ of Example 2.

Since the calculator's dependent variable **Y** is our A, this means that a box with minimal total surface area $A_{\min} = 300$ results if its square base edge length is $x = 10$ in. Then (7) shows that the height of the box is then $y = 500/10^2 = 5$. Thus the **answer** to the question posed is this: The square-based open-topped box with volume 500 in³ and minimum possible total surface area has dimensions $10'' \times 10'' \times 5''$. Notice that its height is *half* its base edge length, so our box is now half a cube rather than the whole cube of Example 1. ◼

Example 3

Now suppose our square-based box is again closed as in Example 1, but now its top and bottom cost 3 cents/in² while the four vertical sides cost 5 cents/in². If its volume is 600 in³, what dimensions will minimize its total cost?

Now the dependent variable to be minimized is the *cost C* of the material required to make the top, bottom, and four sides of the box. If we add up the areas of these six faces—but multiplying each by its own cost in cents per square inch—then we get the cost formula

$$C = 2(x^2 \text{ in}^2)\left(3\frac{\text{cents}}{\text{in}^2}\right) + 4(xy \text{ in}^2)\left(5\frac{\text{cents}}{\text{in}^2}\right),$$

looking at Fig. 8.3.1 to recall that the top and bottom each have area x^2, while each of the four vertical sides has area xy. Thus the total cost of the box is

$$C = 6x^2 + 20xy \tag{9}$$

(cents). Because the volume of the box is 600 in³, its dimensions x and y are connected by the **relation**

$$x^2 y = 600. \tag{10}$$

To **eliminate** the extra variable y, we solve (10) for

$$y = \frac{600}{x^2} \tag{11}$$

and substitute for y in (9). This gives the cost **function**

$$C(x) = 6x^2 + 20x \cdot \frac{600}{x^2} = 6x^2 + \frac{12{,}000}{x}, \tag{12}$$

which tells how much (in cents) the box will cost if its base edge length is x inches.

Figure 8.3.4 shows the **graph** of $C(x)$. As indicated, the **CALC minimum** calculator facility yields the low point $(10, 1800)$ on the graph.

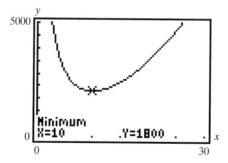

Figure 8.3.4   Graph of the cost function $C(x) = 6x^2 + \frac{12{,}000}{x}$ of Example 3.

Since the calculator's dependent variable **Y** is our C, this means that a box with minimal total cost $C_{\min} = 1800$ (cents) results if its square base edge length is $x = 10$ in. Then (11) shows that the height of the box is then $y = 600/10^2 = 6$. Thus, with the given cost figures, the box of minimal cost and volume 600 cubic inches has dimensions 10″ × 10″ × 6″. (Since it costs $18, it's evidently a jewel box rather than a peanut box.) ◼

Cylindrical Cans

Now we turn our attention from square-based rectangular boxes to cylindrical cans. First, let's review the pertinent area and volume formulas for a circular cylinder of radius r and height h (Fig. 8.3.5). Its top and bottom (base) are circles of radius r so each has area

$$A_{\text{base}} = A_{\text{top}} = \pi r^2. \tag{13}$$

The volume V of the cylinder is obtained upon multiplying its base area by its height, so

$$V = A_{\text{base}} \cdot h = \pi r^2 h. \tag{14}$$

The lateral (side) surface area of the cylinder is obtained upon multiplying the circumference $C = 2\pi r$ of its base by its height h, so

$$A_{\text{side}} = C \cdot h = 2\pi rh. \tag{15}$$

Example 4

You want to make a cylindrical can with a volume of 250π cubic centimeters. What dimensions r and h will minimize the total surface area of this can?

Your can is shown in Fig 8.3.5. Its total surface area A—the quantity to be minimized—is the sum of the areas of its top and bottom and of its curved lateral surface. Thus A is given by the **formula**

$$A = A_{\text{base}} + A_{\text{top}} + A_{\text{side}} = 2\pi r^2 + 2\pi rh. \tag{16}$$

Because the volume $V = \pi r^2 h$ of the can is 250π cm^3, its radius and height r and h are now connected by the **relation**

$$r^2 h = 250, \tag{17}$$

which is obtained from $250\pi = \pi r^2 h$ upon dividing by π. To **eliminate** the extra variable h, we solve (17) for

$$h = \frac{250}{r^2} \tag{18}$$

and substitute for h in (16). This gives the area **function**

$$A(r) = 2\pi r^2 + 2\pi r \cdot \frac{250}{r^2} = 2\pi r^2 + \frac{500\pi}{r}. \tag{19}$$

Note that the independent variable in (19) is r. So in order to **graph** the function $A(r)$ with a calculator, we must define **Y1=2πX^2+500π/X** and remember the following correspondence:

Calculator variable	Our variable
X	r
Y	A

Figure 8.3.6 shows the resulting graph with the window defined by $0 \leq r \leq 15, 0 \leq A \leq 1250$. As indicated, our calculator's **CALC minimum** facility yields the low point $(5, 471.2389)$ on the graph.

Figure 8.3.5   The cylindrical can of Example 4.

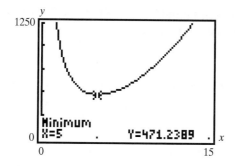

Figure 8.3.6   Graph of the area function $A(r) = 2\pi r^2 + \frac{500\pi}{r}$ of Example 4 for $0 \le r \le 15$.

Since the calculator's independent variable **X** is our r, and its dependent variable **Y** is our A, this means that a can with minimal total surface area $A_{\min} \approx 471.24$ cm^2 results if its radius is $r = 5$ cm. Then (18) shows that the height of the can is

$$h = \frac{250}{5^2} = 10 \text{ cm.}$$

Its diameter (twice its radius) is also 10 cm, so this **answer** says that *the optimal can has equal diameter and height*—rather like the cube of Example 1 having equal height and base edge length. Can you see that this implies that both the cube and the can, looked at from the side, would look like a vertical square with edge length 10 cm?   ◼

Example 5

This is the same as Example 4, except now you want to make an open-topped cylindrical pot—that is, it has no top—with a volume of 125π cubic centimeters. What dimensions r and h will minimize the total surface area of this pot?

Figure 8.3.5, as well as Eqs. (13)–(15) giving its base area, volume, and side surface area, will serve also for this open-topped pot. Its total area A—the quantity to be minimized—is the sum of the area $A_{\text{base}} = \pi r^2$ of its bottom and the area $A_{\text{side}} = 2\pi rh$ of its curved lateral surface. Thus A is given by the **formula**

$$A = A_{\text{base}} + A_{\text{side}} = \pi r^2 + 2\pi rh. \tag{20}$$

Because the volume $V = \pi r^2 h$ of the pot is 125π cm^3, its radius and height r and h are (equating and then dividing by π) connected by the **relation**

$$r^2 h = 125. \tag{21}$$

To **eliminate** the extra variable h, we solve (21) for

$$h = \frac{125}{r^2} \tag{22}$$

and substitute for h in (20). This gives our pot's area **function**

$$A(r) = \pi r^2 + 2\pi r \cdot \frac{125}{r^2} = \pi r^2 + \frac{250\pi}{r}. \tag{23}$$

Remembering the correspondence between our (r, A) variables and the calculator's $(\textbf{X}, \textbf{Y})$ variables, it remains only to graph the calculator function defined by $\textbf{Y1} = \pi \textbf{X}^{\wedge}\textbf{2} + \textbf{250}\pi/\textbf{X}$ and locate the low point on the graph (since we're looking for a minimum value).

Figure 8.3.7 shows the resulting graph with the window defined by $0 \le r \le 15, 0 \le A \le 600$. As indicated, our calculator's **CALC minimum** facility yields the low point $(5, 235.6194)$ on the graph.

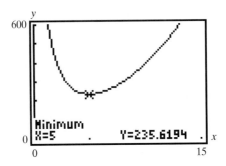

Figure 8.3.7   Graph of the area function $A(r) = \pi r^2 + \frac{250\pi}{r}$ of Example 5 for $0 \le r \le 15$.

Since the calculator's independent variable $\textbf{X}$ is our r, and its dependent variable $\textbf{Y}$ is our A, this means that an open-topped pot with minimal total surface area $A_{\min} \approx 235.62$ cm^2 results if its radius is $r = 5$ cm. Then (22) shows that the height of the pot is then $h = 125/25 = 5$ cm also. It might be observed that this **answer** says that *the height of the optimal pot is half its diameter* (rather like the box of Example 2 whose height is half its base edge length). ∎

If you compare Eqs. (19) and (23), you should notice that the surface area of the open-topped Example 5 pot is exactly half the surface area of the closed-top Example 4 can of the same radius r. Can you explain why there was therefore no need to graph the area function defined in (23)? That is, why does the fact that the can area function in (19) attains its minimum value when $r = 5$ imply that the same is true of the pot area function in (23)?

We end this section with a example illustrating the use of optimization methods to solve an actual manufacturing **design problem.**

Example 6

You want to make a soft drink can with a volume of 32π cm^3 (just a bit more than a tenth of a liter). In order that the top of the can will not be ripped off when it's opened, its top must be three times as thick as its curved side and bottom. What dimensions r and h will minimize the total *amount of material* required to make this can?

Figure 8.3.5, as well as the previous equations giving the base area $A_{\text{base}} = \pi r^2$, side surface area $A_{\text{side}} = 2\pi rh$, and volume $V = \pi r^2 h$ of a circular cylinder of radius r and height h, will serve here again. We can measure the amount of material needed by the area of the can's total surface if we count the area of the top three times because the top is three times as thick as the rest of the surface—it's just as though we need three tops glued together. Understanding this, the total area A is given by the **formula**

$$A = A_{\text{base}} + 3A_{\text{top}} + A_{\text{side}}$$
$$= \pi r^2 + 3\pi r^2 + 2\pi rh = 4\pi r^2 + 2\pi rh. \tag{24}$$

Because the volume $V = \pi r^2 h$ of the can is 32π cm^3, its radius and height r and h are (equating and then dividing by π) connected by the **relation**

$$r^2 h = 32. \tag{25}$$

To **eliminate** the extra variable h, we solve (25) for

$$h = \frac{32}{r^2} \tag{26}$$

and substitute for h in (24). This gives the can's total area **function**

$$A(r) = 4\pi r^2 + 2\pi r \cdot \frac{32}{r^2} = 4\pi r^2 + \frac{64\pi}{r}. \tag{27}$$

Remembering the correspondence between our (r, A) variables and the calculator's $(\mathbf{X}, \mathbf{Y})$ variables, it remains only to graph the calculator function defined by $\mathbf{Y1=4\pi X^2+64\pi/X}$ and locate the low point on the graph (since we're looking for a minimum value).

Figure 8.3.8 shows the resulting graph in the window defined by $0 \le r \le 5, 0 \le A \le 300$. As indicated, our calculator's **2nd CALC minimum** facility yields the low point $(2, 150.7964)$ on the graph.

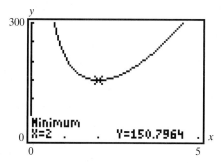

Figure 8.3.8   Graph of the area function $A(r) = 4\pi r^2 + \frac{64\pi}{r}$ of Example 6 for $0 \le r \le 5$.

Since the calculator's independent variable $\mathbf{X}$ is our r, and its dependent variable $\mathbf{Y}$ is our A, this means that our can has minimal total surface area $A_{min} \approx 150.80$ cm^2 (including the top of triple thickness) if its radius is $r = 2$ cm, so its diameter is 4 cm. Then (26) shows that the height of the box is then $h = 32/(2)^2 = 8$ cm. This **answer** says that *the height of the optimal soft drink can is exactly* **twice** *its diameter.*   ◼

You might check the flip-top soft drink cans in a grocery store to verify that they are shaped like the ones of Example 6—with heights (at least very close to) *twice* their widths. Example 6 explains *why* this is so. The very first soft drink cans introduced on the market did not have thickened tops. Customers naturally reacted adversely to the jagged edge left when the top was inadvertently ripped off upon opening a can, so soft drink companies tripled the thickness of the tops of their cans. Example 6 implies that such a can requires the least material—and therefore is cheapest to make—if its height is twice its diameter. Can you find any other cans in the grocery store with this same shape ratio? (Don't bother to look at the tuna fish cans!)

8.3

PROBLEMS

The optimization problems of this section involve volumes of rectangular boxes and cylinders. Problems 1–16 provide plenty of opportunity to review volume concepts before proceeding to the maximum-minimum problems in Problems 17–32.

In Problems 1–4, a given cube has the given volume V_0. Find the edge length x of a cube whose volume V is the indicated percentage larger or smaller than V_0.

1. $V_0 = 64$ in³;   75% larger
2. $V_0 = 125$ in³;   55% larger
3. $V_0 = 64$ cm³;   25% smaller
4. $V_0 = 125$ cm³;   35% smaller

In Problems 5–8, the dimensions of a rectangular iron block are given. This block is to be plated with brass in such a way that each of the block's three dimensions is increased by the same amount x. Determine x so that the volume of the resulting brass-plated block is the given percentage larger than the volume of the original iron block.

5. $2'' \times 3'' \times 5''$;   60% larger
6. $2'' \times 5'' \times 7''$;   55% larger
7. $3'' \times 5'' \times 5''$;   65% larger
8. $3'' \times 4'' \times 5''$;   85% larger

In Problems 9–12, the radius r and height h of a solid cylinder are given. Each is to be increased by the same percentage. What are the dimensions of the new cylinder if its volume is the indicated percentage larger than the volume of the original cylinder?

9. $r = h = 5$ cm;   60% larger
10. $r = h = 4$ cm;   55% larger
11. $r = h = 6$ cm;   65% larger
12. $r = h = 7$ cm;   45% larger

In Problems 13–16, the radius r and height h of a solid iron cylinder are given. It is to be plated with brass so that r is increased by the amount x, while h is increased by the amount $2x$. What are the dimensions of the brass-plated cylinder if its volume is the indicated percentage larger than the volume of the unplated cylinder?

13. $r = 3$ in and height $h = 5$ in;   60% larger
14. $r = 5$ in and height $h = 4$ in;   55% larger
15. $r = 4$ in and height $h = 6$ in;   65% larger
16. $r = 5$ in and height $h = 7$ in;   85% larger

In Problems 17–20, you want to make a square-based closed-topped rectangular box with the given volume V. The cost per square inch of its top and bottom, and also the cost of its four vertical sides, are given. Find what dimensions will minimize the total cost of this box.

17. $V = 288$ in³;   0.4 cents/in² for the top and bottom, 0.3 cents/in² for the four sides
18. $V = 48$ in³;   0.3 cents/in² for the top and bottom, 0.4 cents/in² for the four sides
19. $V = 50$ in³;   0.2 cents/in² for the top and bottom, 0.5 cents/in² for the four sides

20. $V = 75$ in³;   0.3 cents/in² for the top and bottom, 0.5 cents/in² for the four sides

In Problems 21–24, you want to make a closed-topped cylindrical can with the given volume *V*. The cost per square inch of its top and bottom, and also the cost of its vertical curved side surface, are given. Find what dimensions will minimize the total cost of this can.

21. $V = 200\pi$ in³;   0.4 cents/in² for the top and bottom, 0.5 cents/in² for the curved side

22. $V = 100\pi$ in³;   0.2 cents/in² for the top and bottom, 0.5 cents/in² for the curved side

23. $V = 150\pi$ in³;   0.3 cents/in² for the top and bottom, 0.5 cents/in² for the curved side

24. $V = 96\pi$ in³;   0.3 cents/in² for the top and bottom, 0.4 cents/in² for the curved side

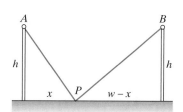

Figure 8.3.9   The rope and flagpoles of Problems 25–28.

Figure 8.3.9 shows two flagpoles each of height *h* standing a distance *w* apart on level ground (with *h* and *w* given in Problems 25–28). It also shows a rope of length *L* that is stretched from the top *A* of the first pole to a point *P* on the ground *x* feet from the bottom of the first pole, and then on to the top *B* of the second pole. In Problems 25–28,

(a) First write the Pythagorean formula for each of the two right triangles in the figure, and thereby express *L* as a function of *x*.

(b) Determine the minimum possible length *L* of the rope.

(c) For this part (only), the length *L* of the rope is given, and you are to find the possible value(s) of *x*.

25. $h = 50$ feet and $w = 80$ feet for all three parts; $L = 135$ feet for part (c)
26. $h = 45$ feet and $w = 70$ feet for all three parts; $L = 120$ feet for part (c)
27. $h = 65$ feet and $w = 90$ feet for all three parts; $L = 170$ feet for part (c)
28. $h = 40$ feet and $w = 60$ feet for all three parts; $L = 105$ feet for part (c)

Figure 8.3.10 shows a ladder of length *L* leaning across a fence of given height *q* feet. The ladder touches a high wall that is *p* feet behind the fence. In Problems 29–32,

(a) First write the Pythagorean theorem for the large right triangle in the figure, and then solve for *L* in terms of the indicated unknown lengths *x* and *y*.

(b) Now write the equality of base/height ratios for the two smaller right triangles in the figure.

(c) Then eliminate *y* in order to express *L* as a function $L(x)$ of the unknown distance *x* between the bottom of the fence and the foot of the ladder.

(d) Finally, determine the numerical value of *x* (2-decimal place accuracy) that yields the minimal value of $L(x)$. What is this minimal possible length of the ladder?

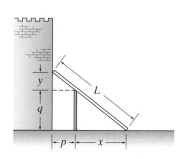

Figure 8.3.10   The leaning ladder of Problems 29–32.

29. $p = 3$ feet, $q = 5$ feet
30. $p = 4$ feet, $q = 6$ feet
31. $p = 5$ feet, $q = 9$ feet
32. $p = 7$ feet, $q = 12$ feet

C H A P T E R   8   R E V I E W

In this chapter, you learned about finding maximum and minimum values for functions. After completing the chapter, you should be able to

- Determine the maximum or minimum value of a function on a given interval.
- Determine where, on a given interval, the maximum or minimum value of a function occurs.
- Use function models and optimization techniques to solve applied maxima and minima problems.

REVIEW PROBLEMS

In Problems 1–4, find **(a)** the maximum and minimum values of the given function $f(x)$ for x in the given interval, and **(b)** the values of x at which those maximum and minimum values occur.

1. $f(x) = -3x^2 + 2x + 3, \quad -1 \leq x \leq 3$
2. $f(x) = 0.5x^2 - 6x + 7, \quad 1 \leq x \leq 8$
3. $f(x) = 2x^3 - 8x^2 + 5x + 2, \quad -2 \leq x \leq 3$
4. $f(x) = 2x^3 - 8x^2 + 5x + 2, \quad 0 \leq x \leq 6$
5. The annual tobacco production (in millions of pounds) in the United States can be approximated by the quadratic function $f(x) = -15.7x^2 + 138.1x + 1387.8$, where x represents years after 1988. Find the maximum annual tobacco production predicted by this model.

6. A ball is thrown straight up upward at time $t = 0$ from an initial height of 15 feet and with an initial velocity of 40 feet per second. How high does the ball go, and how long does it take to reach this maximum height?

7. The sum of two numbers is 24. What is the smallest possible value for the sum of their cubes?

8. Shawna wants to construct rectangular wooden trays to hold the spiced almonds she plans to give as holiday gifts. Each tray is to be twice as long as it is wide, and it must hold 36 cubic inches of almonds. What dimensions for the tray will minimize the amount of wood required?

A C T I V I T Y

Minimizing Inventory Cost

For a retail business selling goods (rather than services), proper inventory control is an important issue. If a business sells a certain number of items each year, it can purchase all of the needed items at once, and store them all year, or it can purchase smaller amounts at various times throughout the year. Either way, it incurs costs not directly related to the cost of the goods themselves. These costs fall into two categories: first, the costs relating to *obtaining* the inventory, and second, the costs relating to *maintaining* the inventory.

The costs of *obtaining* the inventory include any charges to set up the manufacturing process or to place an order. In this activity, we will refer to these costs as **ordering cost.**

The costs of *maintaining* the inventory include such things as storage charges, insurance premiums, or loss of interest on money tied up in the inventory. In this activity, we will refer to these costs as **storage cost.**

The total inventory cost is the sum of these two types of cost. That is,

total inventory cost = ordering cost + storage cost.

Consider the following example. If the owner of a craft store knows that she will sell (approximately) 1000 cans of forest green stenciling paint a year, she would probably order the paint in several different batches so that she wouldn't have to store so many cans. But how often should she order, and how many cans should she order each time?

Since the owner would like to minimize her inventory cost, finding the optimal order size involves constructing a function model for the inventory cost and then determining the minimum value of the function.

Let's examine the situation a bit more closely. In order to find the total inventory cost, we need both the ordering cost and the storage cost. If the store owner orders x cans of paint y times per year, then the ordering cost is just the cost per order times the number of orders (y).

But what about the storage cost? We will assume that the paint is sold at a steady rate, and that the last can of one shipment is sold just as the next shipment arrives. So, for each order, the quantity in storage declines steadily from x to 0. *On average,* then, there are $x/2$ cans of paint being stored on any given day. Therefore, the number of cans being stored for a year is $x/2$—despite the fact that no particular can is stored all year. The storage cost is cost to store one can times the number of cans stored ($x/2$).

Finally, we need to express the total inventory cost as a function of a single variable. Recall our pattern of using a relation between the variables to accomplish this. In this case, we know that $x \cdot y = 1000$. (Why?) We can easily solve this equation for either x or y. If we solve for x, the number of cans of paint in each order, we have $y = 1000/x$. Thus,

$$
\begin{aligned}
\text{total inventory cost} &= \text{ordering cost} + \text{storage cost} \\
&= (\text{cost per order}) \cdot y + (\text{cost to store one can}) \cdot \frac{x}{2} \\
&= (\text{cost per order}) \cdot \frac{1000}{x} + (\text{cost to store one can}) \cdot \frac{x}{2}.
\end{aligned}
$$

This is the function we need to minimize once we are told the particular dollar amounts for both the cost per order and the cost to store one can.

The situation is the same, regardless of what you are ordering, as long as the goods are used at a steady rate and can be stored essentially indefinitely. Suppose that you are the owner of a small restaurant, Tropicalle, which features Polynesian cuisine. Tropicalle's signature dessert, Hula Pie, is a chocolate macadamia nut ice cream pie with a coconut crust, which is manufactured exclusively for Tropicalle by a dairy on Maui. The pie can be frozen for up to a year, with a yearly storage cost of $12. Since the dairy makes this pie only for Tropicalle, it charges $100 per order to set up the production line.

1. If Tropicalle uses 600 pies a year, what is the optimal order size for the Hula Pie? What is the total inventory cost in this case?

2. How many pies should you order each time if the dairy raises its ordering charge to $225 per order? What is the total inventory cost?

3. You have heard that the electric cooperative that provides Tropicalle with electricity is being sold to a for-profit utility company. It is predicted that electric bills will skyrocket, and you estimate that the yearly storage cost for the Hula Pie will quadruple. Assuming both the increased ordering charge and the increased storage cost, how many pies should you order each time, and what is the total inventory cost?

4. If each pie yields 10 slices, and you sell each slice for $3.00, do you need to raise prices to cover the total inventory cost?

CHAPTER 1

Section 1.1

1. independent variable x, dependent variable y
3. independent variable h, dependent variable v
5. independent variable r, dependent variable C
7. yes, does define a function
9. no, does not define a function
11. yes, does define a function
13. no, does not define a function
15. $f(-1) = 1, f(0.5) = 4, f(\sqrt{2}) = 2\sqrt{2} + 3,$
    $f(a^2) = 2a^2 + 3, f(2 - a) = 7 - 2a$
17. $f(-1) = -1, f(0.5) = 0.5, f(\sqrt{2}) = 1/(2\sqrt{2} + 1),$
    $f(a^2) = 1/(2a^2 + 1), f(2 - a) = 1/(5 - 2a)$
19. $a = 3$
21. $a = 33$
23. all real numbers x
25. all real numbers $x \geq 3$
27. all real numbers x except $x = 1$
29. all real numbers t except $t = -2$ or $t = 2$
31. $\{1000, 1010, 1020, 1030, \ldots\}$
33. all real numbers
35. all real numbers $f(x) \geq 8$
37. If x is the base, then the height h is $\frac{100 - 2x}{2} = 50 - x$ and the area is $A(x) = x(50 - x)$. Since both the base and the height must be positive numbers, $0 < x < 50$.
39. Both the base and the height are 50, so the rectangle is actually a square.
41. $P = 4\sqrt{A}$
43. $A = 6\sqrt[3]{V^2}$
45. $\mathrm{roof}(x) = -\mathrm{int}(-x)$ for all x

Section 1.2

1. $f(x) = 2x + 3$
3. $f(x) = -7x + 5$
5. $y = 5x + 2$
7. $y = (26/3)x + 24$
9. $y = (3/2)x$
11. $y = -5$
13. $y = (1/2)x - 7/2$
15. Yes, the three points do lie on a straight line.
17. No, the three points do not lie on a straight line.
18. No, the three points do not lie on a straight line.

In Problems 19–25, you are supposed to sketch the desired graph without using your calculator. Then use your graphing calculator to check your answer.

27. $L = 0.00213C + 124.899$
29. $P = -5x + 4100$
31. $f(x) = \begin{cases} 2x + 6 & \text{if } -3 \leq x < -2, \\ 2 & \text{if } -2 \leq x < 2, \\ (-2/3)x + (10/3) & \text{if } 2 \leq x \leq 5. \end{cases}$

33.

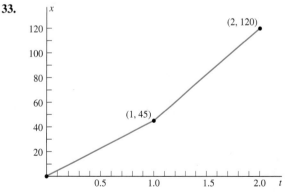

$x(t) = \begin{cases} 45t & \text{if } 0 < t \leq 1, \\ 75t - 30 & \text{if } 1 < t \leq 2. \end{cases}$

35.

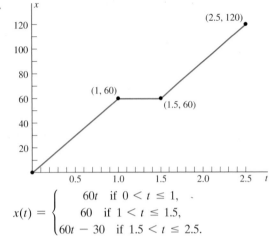

$$x(t) = \begin{cases} 60t & \text{if } 0 < t \le 1, \\ 60 & \text{if } 1 < t \le 1.5, \\ 60t - 30 & \text{if } 1.5 < t \le 2.5. \end{cases}$$

37. **(a)** $C = 0.03p + 0.68$

(b) $2.18

(c) The slope 0.03 is the marginal cost of each additional page printed, while the intercept 0.68 is the fixed cost (even if the pamphlet had no pages).

39. The graph illustrates the fact that an 8-oz letter costs $8.00 to send; a 12-oz letter costs $11.20 to send; and a 16-oz letter costs $14.40 to send.

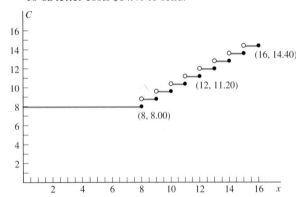

Section 1.3

1. B is a function of A; B is a linear function of A (the constant rate of change is 2).

3. B is not a function of A (the input 5 has two different outputs).

5. $P(t) = 42 + 5t$

7. $P(t) = 324.175 + 15.383t$

9. $P_0 = 123$ thousand people, $m = 6$ thousand people per year

11. $P_0 = 487.139$ thousand people, $m = 20.558$ thousand people per year

13. $P(t) = 375 + 12(t - 1987) = 12t - 23469$

15. $P(t) = 227.625 + 17.234(t - 1991) = 17.234t - 34085.269$

17. $m = 1.4$

(a) $P(t) = 23 + 1.4t$, where t is years after Jan. 1, 1985

(b) $P(t) = 23 + 1.4(t - 1985)$

19. $m = 4.7333$ (rounded to 4 decimal places)

(a) $P(t) = 137 + 4.7333t$, where t is years after Jan. 1, 1978

(b) $P(t) = 137 + 4.7333(t - 1978)$

21. 8 years, 146 days

23. 20 years, 183 days

25. **(a)** 61,000 people   **(b)** February 2014

27. **(a)** 61,705 people   **(b)** March 2012

29. February 2001

31. **(a)** $114.00

(b) $220.00

(c) $4920.00

(d) $$T(I) = \begin{cases} 0.02I & \text{if } 0 < I \le 1000, \\ 20 + 0.04(I - 1000) & \text{if } 1000 < I \le 6000, \\ 220 + 0.05(I - 6000) & \text{if } I > 6000. \end{cases}$$

33. **(a)** $70.50

(b) $188.75

(c) $5492.50

(d) $$T(I) = \begin{cases} 0.02I & \text{if } 0 < I \le 3000, \\ 60 + 0.03(I - 3000) & \text{if } 3000 < I \le 5000, \\ 120 + 0.05(I - 5000) & \text{if } 5000 < I \le 17{,}000, \\ 720 + 0.0575(I - 17{,}000) & \text{if } I > 17{,}000. \end{cases}$$

Section 1.4

1. **(a)** $P(t) = 6t + 200$, SSE $= 100$

(b) $P(t) = 5t + 220$, SSE $= 400$

3. **(a)** $P(t) = 14t - 27{,}145$, SSE $= 900$

(b) $P(t) = 11t - 21{,}175$, SSE $= 3600$

5. **(a)** $P(t) = 4t + 240$, average error ≈ 14.14

(b) $P(t) = 300$, average error ≈ 42.43

7. **(a)** $P(t) = 15t - 28{,}800$, average error ≈ 35.36

(b) $P(t) = 15t - 28{,}750$, average error ≈ 35.36

9. $P(t) = 3.6t + 246$, average error ≈ 13.42

11. $P(t) = 15t - 28{,}775$, average error $= 25$

13. **(a)** $P(t) = 18.57t - 35{,}865$

(b) $P(2000) = 1275 \Rightarrow$ year 2000 population prediction is 1,275,000 people

(c)

Actual Population	Predicted Population	Error
334	346.5	−12.5
573	532.2	40.8
697	717.9	−20.9
876	903.6	−27.6
1111	1089.3	21.7

15. **(a)** $P(t) = 4.47t - 8672.1$

(b) $P(2000) = 267.9 \Rightarrow$ year 2000 population prediction is 267,900 people

(c)

Actual Population	Predicted Population	Error
47	44.4	2.6
84	89.1	-5.1
140	133.8	6.2
171	178.5	-7.5
227	223.2	3.8

17. **(a)** $S(t) = 81.7t - 162{,}289.46$

(b) $S(1995) = 702.04$ million, somewhat less than the actual sales of 722.9 million

(c) $S(2002) = 1273.94$ million

(d) We should expect the 1995 prediction to be closer to actual sales, since 1995 lies between two data points.

19. **(a)** $P(Y) = 91.56Y + 6404.66$

(b) This model underestimates the pay in years 2, 4, 16, and 20.

21. **(a)** $W(h) = 7.33h - 348.33$

(b) $W(72) = 179.43$ pounds

(c) No, a professional baseball player is not a typical American male.

Chapter 1 Review

1. **(a)** Yes, each x-value has only one y-value.

(b) No, the average rate of change is not constant.

2. **(a)** Yes, each x-value has only one y-value.

(b) Yes, the average rate of change is -0.75.

3. **(a)** Yes, each x-value has only one y-value.

(b) No, the average rate of change is not constant.

4. **(a)** Yes, each x-value has only one y-value.

(b) Yes, the average rate of change appears to be 3/2.

5. **(a)** No, there are x-values ($x = 1$ for example) which have more than one y-value.

(b) Not applicable

6. **(a)** Yes, each x-value has only one y-value.

(b) No, the function is quadratic.

7. **(a)** Yes, each x-value has only one y-value.

(b) Yes, the average rate of change is $-3/4$.

8. domain $= \{300, 320, 430, 530, 550, 680, 710, 750\}$
range $= \{5, 9, 20, 26, 29, 33, 43\}$

9. domain $= [0, 2]$; range $= [0, 1]$

10. domain $= \mathbb{R}$; range $= [-3, \infty)$

11. $P(t) = 12{,}452.17(x - 1981) + 227{,}352$

12. **(a)** $W(h) = 100 + 5(h - 60), h \geq 60$

(b) $W(66) = 130$ pounds

13. 13.35 hours

14. **(a)** $p(x) = -1.25x + 85$

(b) 24 sprinklers

(c) \$47.50

(d) The y-intercept represents the price at which demand is zero. If Pomelia prices the sprinklers at \$85, she will sell no sprinklers. The x-intercept represents the demand when the price is zero. If the sprinklers were free, Pomelia could give away 68 per month.

15. **(a)** $P(t) = 2.44t - 5.46$

(b) $P(53.18) = 124.30 \Rightarrow$ the price should be \$124.30

(c) For each additional minute in total grinding and polishing time, the price increases by \$2.44.

CHAPTER 2

Section 2.1

1. $a = 2$

3. $a = -4$

5. $b = 2, c = 3$

7. $b = -3, c = 7$

9. Figure 2.1.25

11. Figure 2.1.22

13. Figure 2.1.26

15. Figure 2.1.32

17. Figure 2.1.33

19. Figure 2.1.29

21. quadratic

23. linear

25. cubic

27. 3 real solutions: $x_1 \approx -2, x_2 \approx 0, x_3 \approx 2$

29. 2 real solutions: $x_1 \approx -1, x_2 \approx 3$

31. For different values of c we have parallel straight lines. Larger values of c give higher lines.

33. For negative values of c we have downward-opening parabolas. For positive values of c we have upward-opening parabolas. Numerically smaller values of c give broader parabolas. When $c = 0$ we have the straight line $y = -3x$.

35. For c negative the cubic curve $y = x^3 + cx$ has 3 real roots, one of them zero. As c starts at -5 and increases, the positive and negative roots get closer to zero. When c is zero or positive there is only one root, and the curve gets steeper as c increases.

37. If $c = -4$ there is only one solution, while there are 3 different solutions if $c = -3$. By trying different values of c between -4 and -3, one can attempt to find a value of c so that the graph has only two x-intercepts. This happens at about $c = -3.0792$.

Section 2.2

1. $x = -3, 5$
3. $x = 1/2, 2$
5. $x = -25/4, 17/5$
7. 12 years, 132 days
9. 8 years, 143 days
11. February 2006
13. 20 seconds
15. It passes the top of the building on the way down after 6.25 sec in the air, and hits the ground after 7.13 sec.
17. (a) after 5.48 sec   (b) after 4.13 sec
19. 4.33 sec
21. 3.3122 ft $\approx$ 3 ft 3 3/4 in
23. 3.0878 ft $\approx$ 3 ft 1 in

Section 2.3

1. Average error $= 1$
3. Average error $= 2.12$
5. Average error $= 5.92$
7. Average error $= 4.10$
9. $q(x) = -4 + 0.3333x + 1.6667x^2$; average error $= 0$
11. $q(x) = 5.1202 - 4.7976x + 1.3385x^2$; average error $= 0.9170$
13. $q(x) = -10.2857 + 6.3000x + 2.9857x^2$; average error $= 3.0237$
15. $q(x) = 12.5000 - 11.4643x + 3.0357x^2$; average error $= 2.8242$
17. (a) $P(t) = 21.3714 - 1.9143t + 0.2129t^2$
    (b)

Year	Actual Population (thousands)	Predicted Population (thousands)	Error (thousands)
1950	17	21.3714	-4.3714
1960	34	23.5143	10.4857
1970	63	68.2286	-5.2286
1980	152	155.5143	-3.5143
1990	288	285.3714	2.6286

(c) $P(50) = 457.8$ (thousand)

19. (a) $P(t) = 10.5429 + 1.8014t + 0.1107t^2$
    (b)

Year	Actual Population (thousands)	Predicted Population (thousands)	Error (thousands)
1950	8	10.5429	-2.5429
1960	45	39.6286	5.3714
1970	90	90.8571	-0.8571
1980	160	164.2286	-4.2286
1990	262	259.7429	2.2571

(c) $P(50) = 377.4$ (thousand)

21. (a) $P(t) = 1387.83 + 138.121t - 15.6964t^2$ (with $t = 0$ on Jan. 1, 1988); average error $= 38.79$;
    (b) $P = 1400$ when $t = 0.09$ and when $t = 8.71$, the latter being in 1997.

23. (a) $P(t) = 770.7271 + 45.4310t + 2.5321t^2$ (with $t = 0$ on Jan. 1, 1985).
    (b) $P(t) = 650$ when $t = -3.24$—that is, 3.24 years before 1985, so toward the end of 1981.
    $P(t) = 900$ when $t = 2.50$—that is, in the middle of the year 1987.
    (c) We should have less confidence in the 1981 date, because it is outside the range of the given data, while 1988 is within it.

Chapter 2 Review

1. Yes, y is a quadratic function of x.
2. No, y is a not a quadratic function of x.
3. No, y is not a quadratic function of x.
4. Yes, y is a quadratic function of x.
5. No, y is not a quadratic function of x.
6. Yes, y is a quadratic function of x.
7. Yes, y is a quadratic function of x.
8. Based strictly on the table, the domain is $\{0, 0.2, 0.4, 0.6, 0.8, 1.0\}$ and the range is $\{0, 5.76, 10.24, 13.44, 15.36, 16\}$. However, since the situation involves the height of a ball for times between 0 and 1 second, we can reasonably conclude that the domain is $[0, 1]$ and the range is $[0, 16]$.
9. domain $[-3, 1]$; range $[-2.5, 2]$
10. domain $\mathbb{R}$; range $(-\infty, 4]$
11. (a) $R(x) = x(-1.25x + 85) = -1.25x^2 + 85x$
    (b) The revenue is \$1200 when 20 sprinklers are sold.

12. (a) $P(t) = 72.5143 + 0.2771t + 0.0786t^2$ where t is years after Jan. 1, 1950

(b) $P(t) = 250$ when $t = 45.79$—that is, toward the end of 1995.

13. (a) $P(t) = 11.7649 - 0.3560t + 0.0048t^2$ where t is years after Jan. 1, 1930

(b) 10.4 percent of the population

CHAPTER 3

Section 3.1

1. (a) 10   **(b)** 24.5   **(c)** 1.75   **(d)** 4.875
   (e) 0.405   **(f)** 1.7625   **(g)** 1.8315   **(h)** 2.444865

3. First, note that 15% = 10% + 5%. You get 10% of A when you move the decimal point one unit to the left. Then you get 5% of A when you divide the result by 2. Thus addition of these two results gives the tip of 15% of A.

5. $20,800.00

7. Increase its edge by 10%.

9. Decrease its edge by 10.56%.

11. Increase its radius by 14.02%.

15. After 7 years you have only $974.36, and after 8 years you have $1071.79. So after 8 years you will have at least $1000.

17. After 9 years you have $999.50, and after 10 years you have $1079.46. So after 9 years you are closest to $1000.

19. If we note that 6 times 12 and 8 times 9 are both equal to 72, we might guess the "Rule of 72," which says to divide the interest rate (in percentage points) into 72 in order to find out how many years it will take to double your money.

21. Starting with $1013, you'd have $1999.48 after 6 years. Starting with $1014, you'd have $2001.46. So the answer is $1013.

23. You've got to do this one yourself.

25. (a) Under the flat tax proposal, the family would pay $27,880 as income tax, which is 13.94% of their taxable income.

(b) Under the tax rate as quoted, the family would pay $56,495, which is 28.25% of their taxable income.

27. A negative initial guess leads to the negative square root of the number.

29. Calculate $A^{\wedge}(1/q)$ with your calculator to check qth root results.

Section 3.2

1. 7.27 years $\approx$ 7 years 14 weeks

3. 9.01 years $\approx$ 9 years 1 week

5. 22.52 years $\approx$ 22 years 27 weeks

7. 11.90 years $\approx$ 11 years 47 weeks

9. 11.53 years $\approx$ 11 years 28 weeks

11. 7.273 years $\approx$ 7 years 100 days

13. 9.006 years $\approx$ 9 years 2 days

15. 22.517 years $\approx$ 22 years 189 days

17. 31.62

19. 3.47

21. 1.4142

23. 4.6416

25. 1.9953

27. $963.86

29. $r = 0.1161 = 11.61\%$

Section 3.3

1. $P(t) = 75 \cdot 2^t$

3. $P(t) = 100 \cdot 2^{t/2.5} \approx 100 \cdot (1.3195)^t$

5. $P(t) = 100 \cdot (175/100)^t = 100 \cdot (1.75)^t$

7. $P(t) = 400 \cdot (155/400)^t = 400 \cdot (0.3875)^t$

In Problems 9–15 we give the population model $P(t)$ (where t denotes the number of years after the initial date given), the annual percentage increase r, and the expected 1990 and 2000 populations.

9. $P(t) = 112 \cdot (175/112)^{t/20}$; $r = 2.26\%$; 219 thousand in 1990; 273 thousand in 2000

11. $P(t) = 3.94 \cdot (5.46/3.94)^{t/20}$; $r = 1.64\%$; 6.43 million in 1990; 7.57 million in 2000

13. $P(t) = 375 \cdot (491/375)^{t/10}$; $r = 2.73\%$; 643 million in 1990; 842 million in 2000

15. $P(t) = 1.002 \cdot (1.176/1.002)^{t/20}$; $r = 0.80\%$; 1.224 billion in 1990; 1.326 billion in 2000

In Problems 17–19 we give the population model $P(t)$ (where t denotes the number of years after 1985), the annual percentage increase r, and the expected 2010 and 2020 populations in millions.

17. $P(t) = 14.9 \cdot (25.4/14.9)^{t/15}$; $r = 3.62\%$; 36.2 million in 2010; 51.7 million in 2020

19. $P(t) = 9.64 \cdot (10.71/9.64)^{t/15}$; $r = 0.70\%$; 11.49 million in 2010; 12.32 million in 2020

21. 2.377 hrs $\approx$ 2 hr 23 min

23. 93 rabbits (rounded off) after 1 year

25. (a) $P(t) = 49 \cdot (6)^t$

(b) 971 bacteria at 1:40 P.M. **(c)** 20 thousand bacteria at 3:21 P.M.

27. (a) $A(t) = 10 \cdot (3)^{t/7.5}$

(b) 20.8 pu after 5 years **(c)** 15.719 years $\approx$ 15 years 262 days

29. (a) $N(t) = 29(1 + r)^t$ in thousands of transistors

(b) $r = (3100/29)^{1/14} - 1 \approx 0.39613 = 39.613\%$ annual growth rate

(c) 2.077 years $\approx$ 25 months to double the number of transistors

(d) Our model predicts 44,747 thousand or about 45 million transistors in the year 2001.

31. Starting with $N_0 = 1$ original human language family, the model $N(t) = (1.5)^{t/6000}$ predicts that one original Indian language family would grow to 150 Indian language families after about 74 thousand years.

Section 3.4

1. $y = 10 \cdot 2^x$

3. $y = 80 \cdot (\frac{1}{2})^x = 80 \cdot 2^{-x}$

5. $y = 3 \cdot 3^{x/2} = 3 \cdot (\sqrt{3})^x$

7. $y = 160 \cdot 2^{-x/4} = 160 \cdot (2^{-1/4})^x$

In Problems 9–15, part (a) answers vary depending on the two points chosen. Part (b) answers given here vary slightly depending on the number of decimal places in your calculator's mode setting. Hence your answers may differ a bit in the third decimal place.

9. $y = 4.843 \times 1.464^x$; average error $= 0.390$

11. $y = 15.263 \times 1.396^x$; average error $= 1.601$

13. $y = 40.818 \times 0.645^x$; average error $= 0.474$

15. $y = 111.438 \times 0.496^x$; average error $= 1.112$

17. $P(t) = 453.852 \times 1.0224^t$; 2.24% annual growth; ave. error $= 8.391$, $P_{2000} \approx 1374$ thous

19. $P(t) = 491.768 \times 1.0159^t$; 1.59% annual growth; ave. error $= 13.124$, $P_{2000} \approx 1081$ thous

21. $P(t) = 633.258 \times 0.9830^t$; 1.70% annual decline; ave. error $= 13.145$, $P_{2000} \approx 269$ thous

23. With time measured in minutes and with $t = 0$ at 5 P.M., we find the best fit $u(t) = 176.28 \times 0.9822^t$ with an average error of only 1.25 degrees. Finally we solve the equation $u(t) = 35$ (graphically) for $t = 89.89$ (min), about one and a half hours. Thus the cake has cooled to 35 degrees at about 6:30 P.M.

25. With the intensity I measured in percentage points, we find the best fit $I(x) = 101.265 \times 0.8982^x$ with an average error of about 0.78. Finally we solve the equation $I(x) = 1$ (graphically) for $x = 43.02$ (feet). Thus, when you dive to a depth of 43 feet, the light is only 1% as bright as at the surface.

27. With time measured in years after 1875, the best fit is $W(t) = 2677.31 \cdot 1.0473^t$. If we solve $W(t) = 1,000,000$, we get $t = 128.25$. So we would expect the prize money to grow to $1,000,000 in 2003.

Chapter 3 Review

1. y is a quadratic function of x; $y = \frac{1}{2}x^2$.

2. y is an exponential function of x; $y = 8 \cdot (\frac{1}{2})^x$.

3. y is a linear function of x; $y = -3x + 17$.

4. y appears to be a linear function of x.

5. y appears to be an exponential function of x.

6. y is a quadratic function of x.

7. y is an exponential function of x.

8. The best fitting exponential function is $y = 0.08 \cdot 1.041^x$, where x is years after 1938. Since 2023 is 85 years after 1938, $0.08 \cdot 1.041^{85} \approx 2.43$. The little girl's daughter should get $2.43.

9. About 645.57 days $= 1$ year and 281 days

10. We need to determine when $(1.06)^t = 2(1.03)^t$. This occurs when $t = 24.14$ years, thus early in the year 2023.

11. An exponential model for the professor's salary is $S(t) = 25,600 \cdot (\frac{49,585}{25,600})^{t/10}$, where t is years after 1989. $\sqrt[10]{\frac{49,585}{26,500}} \approx 1.0647$, so the professor's average annual salary increase was approximately 6.47%.

12. $R(t) = 32.787 \cdot 1.068^t$, where t is years after 1957. $R(t) = 700$ when $t = 46.53$, so the revenue will grow to 700 million dollars in 2003.

CHAPTER 4
Section 4.1

1. (a) $1040.60   **(b)** $1040.74   **(c)** $1040.79
(d) $1040.81   **(e)** $1040.81

3. (a) $4930.86   **(b)** $4941.03   **(c)** $4944.98
(d) $4945.99   **(e)** $4946.16

5. (a) $13,557.59   **(b)** $13,580.10   **(c)** $13,588.80
(d) $13,591.04   **(e)** $13,591.41

7. (a) 4.188 years $\approx$ 4 years 10 weeks
(b) 3.851 years $\approx$ 3 years 44 weeks
(c) The rule of 72 says the money should double in 4 years; since there are 52 weeks in a year, the time for the continuous compounding is closer.

9. (a) 11.896 years $\approx$ 11 years 47 weeks
(b) 11.552 years $\approx$ 11 years 29 weeks
(c) The 11 years 47 weeks is closer to the 12 years given by rule of 72.

11. 3.56%

13. 3.05%

15. The effective annual yield at 4.65% compounded continuously is 4.76%. The better investment is the one earning 5% compounded quarterly, with an effective annual yield of 5.09%.

17. 2.3026

19. 0.6931

21. 32.106 years

23. There will be 3320 bacteria after 6 hours. It will take 8.05 hours for the colony to grow from 1000 to 5000 bacteria.

25. The following table gives the 5-place values of the expression $E(n) = (1 - 1/k)^k$ with $k = 10^n$ for $n = 1, 2, 3, 4, 5, 6$. The 6-place value of $e^{-1} = 1/e$ is 0.367879.

n	1	2	3
$E(n)$	0.34868	0.36603	0.36770

n	4	5	6
$E(n)$	0.36786	0.36788	0.36788

Section 4.2

1. (a) 2^5 (b) 2^6 (c) 2^8

3. (a) e^{2x+3} (b) e^{3x+1} (c) e^{5x+3}

5. (a) $\ln 2 + \ln 3$ (b) $3 \ln 2$

(c) $2 \ln 2 + \ln 3 - 2 \ln 5$

7. $2^{(3^4)} = 2^{81} > 2^{12} = (2^3)^4$

9. (a) $\ln 25 \approx 3.2189$ (b) $\ln 1000 \approx 6.9078$

11. $g(x) = \frac{x}{7}$

13. $g(x) = x^2 - 1$

15. $x = (\ln 100)/(\ln 2) \approx 6.6439$

17. $x = -(\ln 17)/(\ln 5) \approx -1.7604$

19. $x = \frac{1}{3}e^5 \approx 49.4711$

21. $x = \frac{1}{3}(5 + \ln \frac{1}{7}) \approx 1.0180$

23. $x = \frac{1}{3}\ln(\frac{1}{2}e^5 - 2) \approx 1.4265$

25. $10(\ln 2)/(\ln 6) \approx 3.8685$ hours

27. $\dfrac{25000}{1.06^{18}} \approx \$8758.60$

29. 41.4% still in use in the year 2000

31. (a) $A(t) = 15\left(\dfrac{2}{3}\right)^{\frac{t}{5}}$ (b) 7.84 su

(c) $5 \ln(1/15)/\ln(2/3) \approx 33.39 \approx 34$ months

33. $6000 \ln(3300)/\ln(1.5) \approx 120$ thousand years ago

35. $100 \ln(150)/\ln(2) \approx 723$ days is a bit less than 2 years. Hence, if the 1998 rate had continued, the world's population would have been internet-saturated sometime in the year 1999. This has not yet occurred, so the rate of growth of internet usage must have declined.

Section 4.3

1. $y = 5 \cdot 3^x = 5 \cdot e^{(\ln 3)x} \approx 5 \cdot e^{1.0986x}$

3. $y = 100 \cdot 5^{-x} = 100 \cdot e^{-(\ln 5)x} \approx 100 \cdot e^{-1.6094x}$

In Problems 5–7, the answers vary slightly depending on the number of decimal places in your calculator's mode setting. Hence your answers may differ a bit in the third decimal place.

5. $y = 15.263 \times 1.396^x \approx 15.263 \times e^{0.334x}$

7. $y = 111.438 \times 0.496^x \approx 111.438 \times e^{-0.701x}$

9. $P(t) = 453.852 \times 1.0224^t \approx 453.852 \times e^{0.0222t}$, $P_{2000} \approx 1374$ thous

11. $P(t) = 491.768 \times 1.0159^t \approx 491.768 \times e^{0.0158t}$, $P_{2000} \approx 1084$ thous

13. $P(t) = 633.258 \times 0.9830^t \approx 633.258 \times e^{-0.0171t}$, $P_{2000} \approx 269$ thous

15. $y = 4.961 + 9.988 \ln x$, average error $= 0.0765$

17. $y = 30.936 - 6.974 \ln x$, average error $= 0.213$

19. $y = 4.024 + 1.996 \ln x$, average error $= 0.00847$

21. (a) $A(t) = 9.9923 \times e^{0.1571t}$

(b) $A = 100$ when $t = 14.66$. If we assume $t = 0$ on Jan. 1, 1990, then it will be dangerous to stay in the valley at the end of July, 2004.

23. We want to fit the data

t	0	15	30	45	60
u	300	283	268	254	240

where t is time in minutes past 11 A.M. and u is 350 minus the observed temperature T. The best fit is $u(t) = 299.621e^{-0.00370t}$, so the estimated temperature is given by $T(t) = 350 - 299.621e^{-0.00370t}$. We solve for $t = 187.0$ when $T = 200$. Hence the roast is ready to serve at 2:07 P.M.

25. (a) $C(W) = 43.60 - 19.99 \ln W$

(b) $-32.5°$

27. The best fit is $p(V) = 47.964 V^{-1.397}$. This gives $p(3) = 10.3$ atmospheres and $p(6) = 3.9$ atmospheres.

Chapter 4 Review

1. logarithmic

2. linear

3. exponential

4. logarithmic

5. exponential

6. neither

7. exponential

8. In 1920 the west longitude of the center of the U.S. population was (according to the given model) 86.6°. It was 84° in 73.3 years after 1800, so (letting $t = 0$ on Jan. 1, 1800) this occurred in April 1873.

9. The radiation level after t days is given by $A(t) = 10e^{-rt}$ with continuous rate of decay $r = 0.003567$.

10. The state's Medicaid expenditures t years after 1/1/2000 are given by $A(t) = 1.3e^{0.05827t}$. This model predicts state Medicaid expenditures of $1.74 billion in 2005.

11. To the nearest hundred dollars, the Explorer is worth about $16,400 in 2002. It is worth half of its original value after about 7.3 years, so (letting $t = 0$ on Jan. 1, 1997) this occurred in April 2004, that is, in 2004.

12. **(a)** $R(t) = 1052.63 + 106.91t - 2.90t^2$ with average error 12.40.

   (b) $R(t) = 872.73 + 401.96 \ln t$ with average error 12.51.

   (c) $R(t) = 997.15t^{0.26}$ with average error 12.24.

   (d) Since it has the smallest average error, the power model fits the data a bit better than the other two.

CHAPTER 5
Section 5.1

1. $x = -2, 1, 3$

3. $x = -3, -1, 2, 4$

5. $x = -5/2, 2/3, 3$

7. $x = -5/2, -1, 2, 7/2$

9. $x = -13/4, -3/2, 12/5$

11. $x = -13/3, -3/4, 3/5, 7/2$

13. 2.4941 in $\times$ 4.4941 in $\times$ 7.4941 in

15. The length of the cut-out square is either 2.94 inches or 13.30 inches. In the first case, the dimensions of the tray are 39.12″ $\times$ 39.12″ $\times$ 2.94″. In the second case, the dimensions of the tray are 18.40″ $\times$ 18.40″ $\times$ 13.30″.

17. $x^4 + 8x^3 - 237x^2 + 288x + 576 = 0$
$x = 2.47$ ft = 2 ft 5.6 in or $x = 10.89$ ft = 10 ft 10.7 in

19. $x = 14$ ft 10 in or $x = 31$ ft 1 in

21. $x^3 - 3x^2 + 1 = 0; x = 0.653$ ft = 7.836 in

23. $3x^3 - 9x^2 + 8 = 0; x = 1.226$ ft = 1 ft 2.712 in

Section 5.2

1. $x = 2, y = 3$

3. $x = 16/3, y = -5/6$

4. $x = -8, y = 22/3$

5. $x = -1/5, y = 4/5$

7. $x = -1, y = -7$

9. $x = 2604, y = 1501$

11. 54 nickels and 23 dimes

13. 15 dimes and 34 quarters

15. 15 hamburgers and 9 cheeseburgers

17. 480 bottles of wine and 216 bottles of liquor

19. 10 gal of 6% solution and 20 gal of 12% solution

21. 36 grams of pure gold and 84 grams of 14-karat gold

23. 30 lb of 75% brass and 120 lb of 90% brass

25. 2.1 gal of 25% blue paint and 0.9 gal of 65% blue paint

Section 5.3

1. 93

3. 27

5. $x = 3, y = 1, z = 2$

7. $x = 4, y = 2, z = 5$

9. $x = 10, y = -5, z = -10$

11. $x = 39, y = 27, z = 44$

13. $x = 57, y = -29, z = 34$

15. $w = -22, x = -5, y = 15, z = -18$

17. 19 half-ounce coins, 24 quarter-ounce coins, 15 tenth-ounce coins

19. 24 gal of reddish paint, 15 gal of bluish paint, 12 gal of greenish paint

21. 22 adults, 12 children, 11 senior citizens

23. $14 for a Happy, $23 for a Hippity, $39 for a Hoot

25. $1.59 per hamburger, $1.89 per cheeseburger, $2.39 per roast beef, $2.19 per chicken sandwich

Section 5.4

1. $P(t) = 2284.03 - 2.3789t + 0.00062t^2$, $P(2000) = 6.228$ (billion)

3. Verification of answer given in the text.

5. $P(t) = -99.929 + 0.0802t$

7. $P(t) = -1860.599 + 0.9615t$

9. $P(t) = 31,160.877 - 31.5134t + 0.00798t^2$

11. $P(t) = -50,680.25 + 50.13665t - 0.012375t^2$

13. $P(t) = -25,282.194 + 23.496t - 0.00536t^2$

15. $P(t) = -1,606,177.985 + 2418.822t - 1.214t^2 + 0.000203t^3$

17. $P(t) = 367,520.017 - 545.89497t + 0.26975t^2 - 0.000044333t^3$

19. $P(t) = 327,409 - 507.5751t + 0.262115t^2 - 4.50833 \times 10^{-5}t^3$; average error = 1.091

21. $P(t) = -452,405 + 706.935t - 0.368403t^2 + 6.40313 \times 10^{-5}t^3$; average error = 0.249

23. $P(t) = 319{,}035 - 476.262t + 0.235858t^2$
$- 3.87083 \times 10^{-5}t^3$; average error $= 3.054$

25. $P(t) = -3.120373 \times 10^7 + 64{,}372.1t - 49.7948t^2$
$+ 0.017118t^3 - 2.20651 \times 10^{-6}t^4$;
average error $= 0.784$

27. $P(t) = -1.74629 \times 10^7 + 35{,}885.8t - 27.6472t^2$
$+ 0.00946411t^3 - 1.21455 \times 10^{-6}t^4$;
average error $= 0.528$

29. center $(1, -2)$ and radius 5

31. center $(-5, -10)$ and radius 17

33. center $(1, 2, 3)$ and radius 13

Chapter 5 Review

1. $f(x)$ is exponential (E-II).

2. $f(x)$ is a quartic polynomial (D-I).

3. $f(x)$ is linear (A-I).

4. $f(x)$ is logarithmic (F-III).

5. $f(x)$ is a quadratic polynomial (B-I).

6. $f(x)$ is a cubic polynomial (C-I).

7. $x = -12/5, 5/3, 4$

8. $x = -25/8, -5/4, 5/6, 10/3$

9. (a) We find that $F(100) = 12.7773$, so about 12.78% of the U.S. population in 2000 will be foreign-born.

(b) We find that $F(t) = 10$ when $t \approx 36.33$ and when $t \approx 94.95$. Looking at Fig. 5.0.1, we see that this means more than 10% of the population is foreign-born during the years 1936–1994.

10. A hot dog costs $1.50, a bag of chips $0.50, and a soft drink $1.00. Hence the student was charged $4.50.

11. (a) The interpolating quartic polynomial (with t denoting years past 1990) is $P(t) = 0.2 + 5.675t - 0.104167t^2 - 0.425t^3 + 0.0541667t^4$.

(b) This gives $P(9) = 88.4\%$, which is an extremely high percentage of all music sold, so the quartic model does not seem a good one to predict rap music sales.

12. (a) $E_3(x) = 7296.79 - 380.943x - 27.9586x^2 + 4.74553x^3$

(b) $E_4(x) = 7262.41 - 237.656x - 108.358x^2 + 19.0742x^3 - 0.796037x^4$

(c) Taking $t = 12$ for 1998, we calculate $E_3(12) \approx 6900$ and $E_4(12) \approx 5261$. The latter fits in much better with the given data, so the quartic model seems more reliable for short-term prediction. However, the cubic model predicts greater future pollution, so you might use it to argue for stronger pollution control laws. Unfortunately, this kind of deliberate obfuscation is not uncommon in the political use (or misuse) of mathematics.

CHAPTER 6

Section 6.1

1. (a) $\pi/6$ **(b)** $5\pi/6$ **(c)** $7\pi/6$

3. (a) $3\pi/4$ **(b)** $5\pi/4$ **(c)** $7\pi/4$

5. (a) $18°$ **(b)** $20°$ **(c)** $36°$

7. (a) $54°$ **(b)** $80°$ **(c)** $252°$

9. (a) $1/2$ **(b)** $-1/2$ **(c)** $-1/2$

11. (a) $-1/2$ **(b)** $-1/2$ **(c)** $1/2$

13. Fig. 6.1.24

15. Fig. 6.1.22

17. Fig. 6.1.29

19. Fig. 6.1.25

21. $f(g(x)) = -4x^2 - 12x - 8, g(f(x)) = 5 - 2x^2$

23. $f(g(x)) = \sqrt{x^4 + 6x^2 + 6}, g(f(x)) = x^2$

25. $f(g(x)) = x, g(f(x)) = x$

27. $f(g(x)) = \sin(x^3), g(f(x)) = \sin^3 x$

29. $f(g(x)) = 2^{(x^2)}, g(f(x)) = 2^{(2x)}$

31. $x = 0.4502$

33. $x = 1.4277$

35. $x = -4.0886, x = -1.8362, x = 1.3733, x = 5.6522,$
$x = 6.6160$

37. $x = -5.9245, x = -3.2472, x = 0, x = 3.0485,$
$x = 6.7574, x = 8.5939$

Section 6.2

In Problems 1–3 you can check your sketch by graphing $y(x)$ in the window $-P < x < 2P, A - 2B < y < A + 2B$.

1. $y(x) = 5 + 2 \sin 2\pi x$

3. $y(x) = 4 + 3 \sin(\pi(x - 1))$

5. $A = 7, B = 3, P = 2\pi, D = 0$

7. $A = 5, B = 3, P = 2\pi, D = 2$

9. $A = 5, B = 10, P = \pi/2, D = 1/2$

11. (a) $A = 54, B = 18$ **(b)** $k = \pi/6$ if t is in months

It probably is more instructive to solve Problems 13–17 by inspection of the data to determine the function's average, period, and amplitude than to use the calculator's sine regression facility.

13. $y = 3 \sin x + 4, A = 4, B = 3, P = 2\pi, D = 0$

15. $y = 4 \sin(\pi x/2) + 3, A = 3, B = 4, P = 4, D = 0$

17. $y = 12 \sin(\pi x/6) + 5, A = 5, B = 12, P = 12, D = 0$

In Problems 19–25 we enter 24 months worth of data (as in Example 5).

19. $f(t) = 22.05 \sin(0.52t - 1.73) + 51.38$

21. $f(t) = 15.95 \sin(0.52t - 1.59) + 67.90$

23. $f(t) = 0.58 \sin(0.52t - 1.18) + 12.14$

25. $f(t) = 2.77 \sin(0.52t - 1.16) + 12.20$

27. The constant terms in the formulas of Problems 23–26 are all a bit more than 12, the annual average length of days at any latitude. However, we see that the coefficient of the sine term increases significantly as the latitude increases. This means that there is more *seasonal variation* in the length of days at higher latitudes. The following table exhibits this fact dramatically. (Do you see where we got these figures from the answers to Problems 23–26?)

Latitude	Shortest day (hrs)	Longest day (hrs)
10°	11.56	12.72
20°	10.93	13.33
40°	9.43	14.97
60°	6.27	18.35

At a location on the equator (0° latitude) the length of a day should be 12 hours year round. But at 60° latitude (near Anchorage, Alaska, or St. Petersburg, Russia, for instance) we have winter days only six and a half hours long—sunrise at 8:45 A.M. and sundown at 3:15 P.M.—and summer days eighteen and a half hours long—sunrise at 2:45 A.M. and sundown at 9:15 P.M.

Chapter 6 Review

1. Trigonometric
2. Quadratic
3. Trigonometric
4. Neither
5. Quadratic
6. Trigonometric
7. $\sin(4\pi/3) = -\sqrt{3}/2$ and $\cos(5\pi/6) = -\sqrt{3}/2$
8. $x = \pm\pi/3$ are two values; another is $x = 5\pi/3$.
9. $x \approx \pm 0.6449$
10. $f(t) = 23.49 \sin(0.52t - 1.63) + 44.66$

CHAPTER 7
Section 7.1

1. Value of $f(x)$ is 150 when $x \approx 17.9176$.
3. Value of $f(x)$ is 3 when $x \approx 0.2027$.

In Problems 5–9, the rate constant b was found symbolically.

5. $P(t) = \dfrac{12,500}{50 + 200e^{-0.1792t}}$

7. $P(t) = \dfrac{7}{1 + 6e^{-2.7081t}}$

9. $P(t) = \dfrac{30,000}{300 - 200e^{-0.02877t}}$

In Problems 11–15, the value of t was found graphically.

11. $t = 7.7360$
13. $t = 0.6616$
15. $t = 24.0927$

In Problems 17–23, the rate constant b was found symbolically, and the value of t was found graphically.

17. $P(t) = \dfrac{25,000}{50 + 450e^{-0.1352t}}$, with t measured in months; $P = 350$ when $t = 22.52$, in May 2002.

In Problems 19–21 the population P(t) is measured in thousands.

19. $P(t) = \dfrac{6000}{25 + 215e^{-0.09039t}}$, where $P(t)$ is measured in thousands; $P = 120$ when $t = 23.81$, in June 2002.

21. $P(t) = \dfrac{0.04}{0.002 + 19.998e^{-1.56645t}}$, where $P(t)$ is measured in thousands; $P = 10$ after $t = 5.88$ weeks.

In Problem 23 the population P(t) is given in percentage points.

23. $P(t) = \dfrac{500}{5 + 95e^{-0.3025t}}$, where $P(t)$ is given in percentage points; $P = 35$ after $t = 7.69$ weeks.

Section 7.2

1. $f(x) = \dfrac{6.335}{1 + 6.100e^{-0.782x}}$, ave. error = 0.0008

3. $f(x) = \dfrac{15.850}{1 + 1.819e^{-0.870x}}$, ave. error = 0.013

5. $f(x) = \dfrac{36.633}{1 + 5.111e^{-0.361x}}$, ave. error = 0.064

7. **(a)** $P(t) = \dfrac{673.865}{1 + 1.075e^{-0.024t}}$, where t is years after Jan. 1, 1960

   (b) $P \approx 549.7$ thousand in 2025.

   (c) $P = 90\%$ of limiting population of 673.865 thousand in the year 2054.

9. **(a)** $P(t) = \dfrac{255.598}{1 + 13.950e^{-0.161t}}$, where t is years after Jan. 1, 1960

   (b) $P \approx 255.5$ thousand in 2025.

   (c) $P = 90\%$ of limiting population of 255.598 thousand in the year 1990.

11. **(a)** $P(t) = \dfrac{324.348}{1 + 6.955e^{-0.091t}}$, where t is years after Jan. 1, 1960

   (b) $P \approx 318.4$ thousand in 2025.

   (c) $P = 90\%$ of limiting population of 324.348 thousand in the year 2005.

13. $P(t) = \dfrac{64.137}{1 + 4.333e^{-0.318t}}$, where P is given in percentage points. The limiting percentage is about 64%, so it is possible for this candidate to win. He has 50% approval after 8.575 weeks of campaigning, so any time after that he has a majority.

15. $P(t) = \dfrac{110.937}{1 + 2.705e^{-0.128t}}$; the limiting population is about 111 fish. It takes about 18.6 months to reach 80% of this number.

17. $P(t) = \dfrac{35.645}{1 + 8.106e^{-0.704t}}$; about 35.65% of the population will eventually suffer this disease. It will take about 7 weeks 1 day for 95% of this limiting percentage to contract it.

19. **(a)** $P(t) = \dfrac{865.082}{1 + 10.220e^{-0.016t}}$ (with $t = 0$ on Jan. 1, 1900).

(b) Limiting population about 865 million

(c) $P = 400$ million in the year 2035.

21. $P(t) = \dfrac{2751.239}{1 + 4.005e^{-0.026t}}$ (with $t = 0$ on Jan. 1, 1950). This model predicts a limiting population of about 2.75 billion for China, and that it will hit 2 billion early in the year 2041.

23. **(a)** $P(t) = \dfrac{13.323}{1 + 2.264e^{-0.026t}}$ (with $t = 0$ on Jan. 1, 1975).

(b) This model predicts a limiting world population of only about 13.3 billion, as compared with 26 billion in Problem 22. Evidently, world population growth slowed during the last quarter of the 20th century.

(c) It predicts that the world population will not hit 10 billion until the year 2048.

Section 7.3

1. If we first store $50 \to$ **P**, $0.005 \to$ **K**, $200 \to$ **M** then the iteration **P** + **K*P*(M − P)** $\to$ **P** gives increasing values of P that rapidly level off at $P = 200$.

3. P increases and eventually levels off at $P = 500$.

5. P oscillates above and below 300 as it eventually levels off at $P = 300$.

7. P eventually bounces back and forth between $P = 149.25$ and $P = 232.57$.

9. P immediately starts bouncing back and forth between $P = 300$ and $P = 600$.

11. Verification of results in text.

13. Answers vary, depending on choice of r. As r gets closer to 2, fewer iterations are necessary to get close to the limiting value.

Problems 15–19 are verifications of results in text.

Chapter 7 Review

1. $f(x)$ is a logistic function with formula of type C.

2. $f(x)$ is a polynomial function with formula of type A.

3. $f(x)$ is an exponential function with formula of type D.

4. $f(x)$ is a logarithmic function with formula of type B.

5. **(a)** $f(10) \approx 16$ **(b)** $f(0.2291) \approx 10$

6. The number of fish in the lake after t months is given by $P(t) = 80{,}000/(100 + 700e^{-0.11819t})$. There are 600 fish after about 25.76 months, during August 2002.

7. **(a)** $P(t) = 70.179/(1 + 94.687e^{-0.362t})$

(b) At age 30 weeks, Ripley will weigh just over 70 pounds.

(c) Her limiting weight is about 70 pounds 3 ounces, so she will be a bit lighter than the average female.

8. Using Eq. (6) in Section 7.3, the discrete logistic solution with limiting population $M = 180$ and growth rate parameter $k = 0.0062$ is described by the iterative model $P_{n+1} = P_n + 0.0062 P_n(180 - P_n)$. Starting with $P_0 = 60$, the population P_n approaches the limiting population of 180 rapidly, but briefly oscillates up and down about it:

n	0	1	2	3	4
P_n	60	104.640	153.531	178.727	180.138

n	5	6	7	8
P_n	179.984	180.002	180.000	180.000

CHAPTER 8
Section 8.1

1. Minimum value $f(-1) = -5$ and maximum value $f(4) = 10$

3. Minimum value $f(1) = 0$ and maximum value $f(-2) = 15$

5. Minimum value $f(2) = -1$ and maximum value $f(-1) = 8$

7. Minimum value $f(5) = -10$ and maximum value $f(2) = 5$

9. Minimum value $f(2.5) = -3.5$ and maximum value $f(0) = f(5) = 9$

11. Minimum value $f(3) = -22$ and maximum value $f(-1) = 10$

13. Minimum value $f(-5/2) = -118.75$ and maximum value $f(7/3) = 107.074$

15. **(a)** The ball reaches a maximum height of 139.0625 feet in 1.5625 seconds.

   (b) It hits the ground after 4.5106 seconds.

17. The bolt reaches a maximum height of 1600 ft in 10 seconds, and it hits the ground after 20 seconds.

19. The ball reaches a maximum height of 64 feet and hits the ground 256 feet away.

21. **(a)** The city reaches its minimum population of about 185,600 during July 2004.

   (b) It regains a population of 200 thousand during January 2010.

   (c) It should reach a population of 400 thousand during November 2025.

Section 8.2

1. $A(P) = P^2/16$

3. $r = C/(2\pi)$ so $A(C) = \pi(C/2\pi)^2 = C^2/4\pi$

4. $r = \sqrt{\dfrac{S}{4\pi}}$ so $V(S) = \dfrac{4}{3}\pi\left(\sqrt{\dfrac{S}{4\pi}}\right)^3 = \dfrac{1}{6}\sqrt{\dfrac{S^3}{\pi}}$

5. 2500

7. It will be a 40′ by 40′ square with area 1600 square feet.

9. 10 ft by 8 ft

11. 10 ft by 9 ft

12. Both squares will be 20 ft by 20 ft.

13. The rectangle is about 28′ 2.8″ by 14′ 1.4″ and the square has edge length about 18′ 9″.

15. **(a)** $V_{max} = 9259.26$ cubic in, $33.3333″ \times 33.3333″ \times 8.33333″$

   (b) $43.7228″ \times 43.7228″ \times 3.1386″$ or $20″ \times 20″ \times 15″$

17. **(a)** $V_{max} = 4740.74$ cubic in, $26.6667″ \times 26.6667″ \times 6.6667″$

   (b) $35.1414″ \times 35.1414″ \times 2.4293″$ or $15.7200″ \times 15.7200″ \times 12.1400″$

19. 50 ft by 35 ft

21. 15 ft by 10 ft

Section 8.3

1. edge length $= 4.8203$ in

3. edge length $= 3.6342$ in

5. $x = 0.4970$ in

7. $x = 0.7469$ in

9. $r = h = 5.8480$ cm

11. $r = h = 7.0900$ cm

13. $r = 3.4773$ in, $h = 5.9546$ in

15. $r = 4.6550$ in, $h = 7.3100$ in

17. $6″ \times 6″ \times 8″$

19. $5″ \times 5″ \times 2″$

21. $r = 5″, h = 8″$

23. $r = 5″, h = 6″$

25. **(b)** $L = 128.062$ ft

   (c) $x = 13.4824$ ft or $x = 66.5176$ ft

27. **(b)** $L = 158.114$ ft

   (c) $x = 8.1939$ ft or $x = 81.8061$ ft

29. **(d)** $L_{min} = 11.1941$ ft with $x = 4.2172$ ft

31. **(d)** $L_{min} = 19.5243$ ft with $x = 7.3986$ ft

Chapter 8 Review

1. Maximum value $f(1/3) = 10/3$, minimum value $f(3) = -18$

2. Maximum value $f(1) = 1.5$, minimum value $f(6) = -11$

3. Maximum value $f(0.3615) \approx 2.8565$, minimum value $f(-2) = -56$

4. Maximum value $f(6) = 176$, minimum value $f(2.3052) \approx -4.4862$

5. Maximum production 1691.5 million pounds when $x \approx 4.398$. For $x =$ years after Jan. 1, 1988, this occurs in 1992.

6. It takes the ball 1.25 seconds to reach its maximum height of 40 feet.

7. Minimum sum 3456 when each number is 12.

8. The tray should be $3″ \times 6″ \times 2″$.

INDEX

PHOTO CREDITS

Sections
10.6, 12.1, 12.2, 12.3, 12.5

Taken from:

Thinking Mathematically
by Robert Blitzer

Writing in Mathematics

37. Explain the following analogy:

In terms of formulas used to compute volume, a pyramid is to a rectangular solid just as a cone is to a cylinder.

38. Explain why a cylinder is not a polyhedron.

Critical Thinking Exercises

39. What happens to the volume of a sphere if its radius is doubled?

40. A scale model of a car is constructed so that its length, width, and height are each $\frac{1}{10}$ the length, width, and height of the actual car. By how many times does the volume of the car exceed its scale model?

In Exercises 41–42, find the volume of the shaded region. If necessary, round to the nearest whole number.

41.

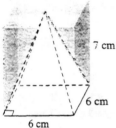

7 cm

6 cm

6 cm

42.

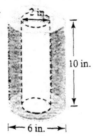

2 in.

10 in.

6 in.

43. Find the surface area of the figure shown.

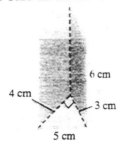

6 cm

4 cm

3 cm

5 cm

Group Exercise

44. People who love cars should be members of this group. The group will prepare a presentation to the class on how the power of a car engine is measured. One person, who has worked on car engines, should explain the details of how they work, including cylinders, pistons, fuel, and so on in the discussion. In explaining how the power of the engine is measured, be sure to discuss horsepower, cubic centimeters, and liters. Give examples of the measures of engines for various makes of cars, including more powerful upgrade options that are available.

SECTION 10.6 Right Triangle Trigonometry

Objectives

1. Use the lengths of the sides of a right triangle to find trigonometric ratios.

2. Use trigonometric ratios to find missing parts of right triangles.

3. Use trigonometric ratios to solve applied problems.

Ang Rita Sherpa climbed Mount Everest eight times, all without the use of bottled oxygen.

Mountain climbers have forever been fascinated by reaching the top of Mount Everest, sometimes with tragic results. The mountain, on Asia's Tibet-Nepal border, is Earth's highest, peaking at an incredible 29,029 feet. The heights of mountains can be found using **trigonometry**. The word *trigonometry* means *measurement of triangles*. Trigonometry is used in navigation, building, and engineering. For centuries, Muslims have used trigonometry and the stars to navigate across the Arabian desert to Mecca, the birthplace of the prophet Muhammad, the founder of Islam. The ancient Greeks used trigonometry to record the locations of thousands of stars and worked out the motion of the Moon relative to the Earth. Today, trigonometry is used to study the structure of DNA, the master molecule that determines how we grow from a single cell to a complex, fully developed adult.

Ratios in Right Triangles

The right triangle forms the basis of trigonometry. If either acute angle of a right triangle stays the same size, the shape of the triangle does not change even if it is made larger or smaller. Because of properties of similar triangles, this means that the ratios of certain lengths stay the same regardless of the right triangle's size. These ratios have special names and are defined in terms of the **side opposite** an acute angle, the **side adjacent** to the acute angle, and the **hypotenuse**. In Figure 10.51, the length of the hypotenuse, the side opposite the 90° angle, is represented by c. The length of the side opposite angle A is represented by a. The length of the side adjacent to angle A is represented by b.

The three fundamental trigonometric ratios, **sine** (abbreviated sin), **cosine** (abbreviated cos), and **tangent** (abbreviated tan) are defined as ratios of the lengths of the sides of a right triangle. In the box that follows, when a side of a triangle is mentioned, we are referring to the *length* of that side.

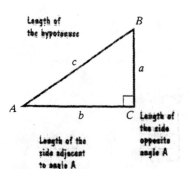

Figure 10.51 Naming a right triangle's sides from the point of view of an acute angle

1 Use the lengths of the sides of a right triangle to find trigonometric ratios.

Trigonometric Ratios

Let A represent an acute angle of a right triangle, with right angle C, shown in Figure 10.51. For A, the trigonometric ratios are defined as follows:

$$\sin A (\text{sine of } A) = \frac{\text{side opposite angle } A}{\text{hypotenuse}} = \frac{a}{c}$$

$$\cos A (\text{cosine of } A) = \frac{\text{side adjacent to angle } A}{\text{hypotenuse}} = \frac{b}{c}$$

$$\tan A (\text{tangent of } A) = \frac{\text{side opposite angle } A}{\text{side adjacent to angle } A} = \frac{a}{b}$$

Study Tip

The word

SOHCAHTOA (pronounced: so-cah-tow-ah)

is a way to remember the definitions of the three trigonometric ratios.

S	O H	C	A H	T	O A
↑	opp / hyp	↑	adj / hyp	↑	opp / adj
Sine		Cosine		Tangent	

"Some Old Hog Came Around Here and Took Our Apples."

EXAMPLE 1 Becoming Familiar with the Trigonometric Ratios

Find the sine, cosine, and tangent of A in Figure 10.52.

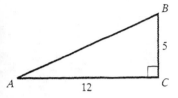

Figure 10.52

Solution We begin by finding the measure of hypotenuse c using the Pythagorean theorem.

$$c^2 = a^2 + b^2 = 5^2 + 12^2 = 25 + 144 = 169$$

$$c = \sqrt{169} = 13$$

Now, we apply the definitions of the trigonometric ratios.

$$\sin A = \frac{\text{side opposite angle } A}{\text{hypotenuse}} = \frac{5}{13}$$

$$\cos A = \frac{\text{side adjacent to angle } A}{\text{hypotenuse}} = \frac{12}{13}$$

$$\tan A = \frac{\text{side opposite angle } A}{\text{side adjacent to angle } A} = \frac{5}{12}$$

2 Use trigonometric ratios to find missing parts of right triangles.

A scientific or graphing calculator in the degree mode will give you decimal approximations for the trigonometric ratios of any angle. For example, to find an approximation for tan 37°, the tangent of 37°, a keystroke sequence similar to one of the following can be used:

Most scientific calculators: 37 | Tan |

Most graphing calculators: | Tan | 37 | ENTER |

The tangent of 37°, rounded to four decimal places, is 0.7536.

If you do not have your calculator with you, a table of trigonometric ratios appears on page 496. Table 10.4 is quite easy to use. To find tan 37°, simply locate 37° and then select the third decimal to the right under the tangent column.

If we are given the length of one side and the measure of an acute angle of a right triangle, we can use trigonometry to solve for the measures of the other parts. Example 2 illustrates how this is done.

EXAMPLE 2 Finding Missing Parts of a Right Triangle

Find $m\angle B$ and the lengths a and c for the right triangle in Figure 10.53.

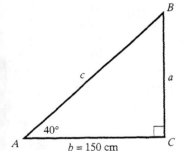

Figure 10.53

Solution We begin by finding the measure of angle B. We do not need to know trigonometric ratios to do so. Because angle B is the complement of angle A, which measures 40°, its measure is found by subtracting 40° from 90°.

$$m\angle B = 90° - 40° = 50°$$

Now, we need to find a. Let us identify a trigonometric ratio that will make it possible to do so. Our goal is to use a ratio in which two of the quantities are

Table 10.4 Trigonometric Ratios

Angle (degrees)	sine	cosine	tangent	Angle (degrees)	sine	cosine	tangent
0	0.0000	1.0000	0.0000	46	0.7193	0.6947	1.0355
1	0.0175	0.9998	0.0175	47	0.7314	0.6820	1.0724
2	0.0349	0.9994	0.0349	48	0.7431	0.6691	1.1106
3	0.0523	0.9986	0.0524.	49	0.7547	0.6561	1.1504
4	0.0698	0.9976	0.0699	50	0.7660	0.6428	1.1918
5	0.0872	0.9962	0.0875	51	0.7771	0.6293	1.2349
6	0.1045	0.9945	0.1051	52	0.7880	0.6157	1.2799
7	0.1219	0.9925	0.1228	53	0.7986	0.6018	1.3270
8	0.1392	0.9903	0.1405	54	0.8090	0.5878	1.3764
9	0.1564	0.9877	0.1584	55	0.8192	0.5736	1.4281
10	0.1736	0.9848	0.1763	56	0.8290	0.5592	1.4826
11	0.1908	0.9816	0.1944	57	0.8387	0.5446	1.5399
12	0.2079	0.9781	0.2126	58	0.8480	0.5299	1.6003
13	0.2250	0.9744	0.2309	59	0.8572	0.5150	1.6643
14	0.2419	0.9703	0.2493	60	0.8660	0.5000	1.7321
15	0.2588	0.9659	0.2679	61	0.8746	0.4848	1.8040
16	0.2756	0.9613	0.2867	62	0.8829	0.4695	1.8807
17	0.2924	0.9563	0.3057	63	0.8910	0.4540	1.9626
18	0.3090	0.9511	0.3249	64	0.8988	0.4384	2.0503
19	0.3256	0.9455	0.3443	65	0.9063	0.4226	2.1445
20	0.3420	0.9397	0.3640	66	0.9135	0.4067	2.2460
21	0.3584	0.9336	0.3839	67	0.9205	0.3907	2.3559
22	0.3746	0.9272	0.4040	68	0.9272	0.3746	2.4751
23	0.3907	0.9205	0.4245	69	0.9336	0.3584	2.6051
24	0.4067	0.9135	0.4452	70	0.9397	0.3420	2.7475
25	0.4226	0.9063	0.4663	71	0.9455	0.3256	2.9042
26	0.4384	0.8988	0.4877	72	0.9511	0.3090	3.0777
27	0.4540	0.8910	0.5095	73	0.9563	0.2924	3.2709
28	0.4695	0.8829	0.5317	74	0.9613	0.2756	3.4874
29	0.4848	0.8746	0.5543	75	0.9659	0.2588	3.7321
30	0.5000	0.8660	0.5774	76	0.9703	0.2419	4.0108
31	0.5150	0.8572	0.6009	77	0.9744	0.2250	4.3315
32	0.5299	0.8480	0.6249	78	0.9781	0.2079	4.7046
33	0.5446	0.8387	0.6494	79	0.9816	0.1908	5.1446
34	0.5592	0.8290	0.6745	80	0.9848	0.1736	5.6713
35	0.5736	0.8192	0.7002	81	0.9877	0.1564	6.3138
36	0.5878	0.8090	0.7265	82	0.9903	0.1392	7.1154
37	0.6018	0.7986	0.7536	83	0.9925	0.1219	8.1443
38	0.6157	0.7880	0.7813	84	0.9945	0.1045	9.5144
39	0.6293	0.7771	0.8098	85	0.9962	0.0872	11.4300
40	0.6428	0.7660	0.8391	86	0.9976	0.0698	14.3007
41	0.6561	0.7547	0.8693	87	0.9986	0.0523	19.0812
42	0.6691	0.7431	0.9004	88	0.9994	0.0349	28.6364
43	0.6820	0.7314	0.9325	89	0.9998	0.0175	57.2900
44	0.6947	0.7193	0.9657	90	1.0000	0.0000	undefined
45	0.7071	0.7071	1.0000				

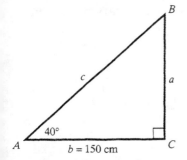

Figure 10.53 Shown again so you do not have to turn back a page.

known and the unknown third quantity is a. This will enable us to solve for a. We know the length of b, namely 150 centimeters. Thus, either the numerator or the denominator of the ratio we select must involve b. Let us consider the three trigonometric ratios.

$$\sin A = \frac{\text{side opposite } A}{\text{hypotenuse}} = \frac{a}{c}$$

$$\cos A = \frac{\text{side adjacent to } A}{\text{hypotenuse}} = \frac{b}{c}$$

$$\tan A = \frac{\text{side opposite } A}{\text{side adjacent to } A} = \frac{a}{b}$$

The third ratio in the list, the tangent of angle A, is the only trigonometric ratio that involves both the given length, b ($b = 150$ cm), and the length we need to find, a. As the measure of angle A is given to be 40°, we can solve for a as follows:

$$\tan A = \frac{\text{side opposite } A}{\text{side adjacent to } A}$$

$$\tan 40° = \frac{a}{150}$$

Now, use your calculator or Table 10.4 to find $\tan 40°$.

$$0.8391 = \frac{a}{150}$$

We solve for a by multiplying both sides by 150.

$$a = 150(0.8391) \approx 126 \text{ cm}$$

Thus, the measure of one leg is approximately 126 centimeters.

There are a number of different ways to find c. One method is to use the Pythagorean theorem.

$$c^2 = a^2 + b^2 = 126^2 + 150^2 = 38{,}376$$
$$c = \sqrt{38{,}376} \approx 196$$

We can also use a trigonometric ratio to find c. Because c is the hypotenuse and we know the length of the side adjacent to angle A, 150 centimeters, we use the cosine ratio.

$$\cos A = \frac{\text{side adjacent to } A}{\text{hypotenuse}}$$

$$\cos 40° = \frac{150}{c}$$

$$0.766 = \frac{150}{c} \qquad \text{Use a calculator or Table 10.4.}$$

$$0.766c = 150 \qquad \text{Multiply both sides by } c.$$

$$c = \frac{150}{0.766} \approx 196 \qquad \text{Divide both sides by 0.766.}$$

Using either the Pythagorean theorem or a ratio, we see that the hypotenuse measures approximately 196 centimeters.

In summary, $m\angle B = 50°$, $a \approx 126$ centimeters, and $c \approx 196$ centimeters.

3 Use trigonometric ratios to solve applied problems.

Applications of the Trigonometric Ratios

Example 3 illustrates the use of trigonometry in surveying.

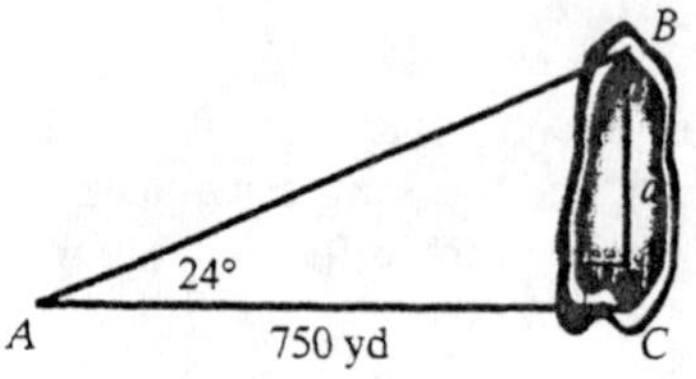

EXAMPLE 3 Problem Solving Using a Trigonometric Ratio

The irregular blue shape in Figure 10.54 represents a lake. The distance across the lake, a, is unknown. To find this distance, a surveyor took the measurements shown in the figure. What is the distance across the lake?

Solution We need to identify a trigonometric ratio that will make it possible to find a. In terms of the 24° angle, we are looking for the side opposite the angle. The surveyor measured the side adjacent to the angle as 750 yards. Since we have a known angle, an unknown opposite side, and a known adjacent side, we will select the tangent ratio.

$$\tan A = \frac{\text{side opposite angle } A}{\text{side adjacent to angle } A}$$

$$\tan 24° = \frac{a}{750}$$

$$0.4452 = \frac{a}{750} \qquad \text{Use a calculator or Table 10.4.}$$

$$a = 750(0.4452) \qquad \text{Multiply both sides by 750.}$$

$$a \approx 334$$

The distance across the lake is approximately 334 yards.

Figure 10.54

Many applications of right triangles involve the angle made with an imaginary horizontal line. As shown in Figure 10.55, an angle formed by a horizontal line and the line of sight to an object that is above the horizontal line is called the **angle of elevation**. The angle formed by a horizontal line and the line of sight to

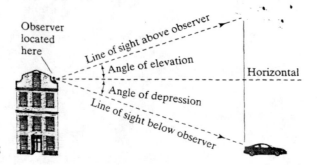

Figure 10.55

an object that is below the horizontal line is called the **angle of depression**. Transits and sextants are instruments used to measure such angles.

EXAMPLE 4   Problem Solving Using an Angle of Elevation

Sighting the top of a building, a surveyor measured the angle of elevation to be 22°. The transit is 5 feet above the ground and 300 feet from the building. Find the building's height.

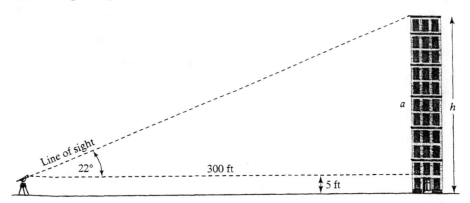

Figure 10.56

Solution   The situation is illustrated in Figure 10.56. If a is the height of the portion of the building that lies above the transit,

$$\tan 22° = \frac{a}{300} \quad \text{and} \quad a = 300 \tan 22° \approx 300(0.404) \approx 121.$$

The height of the part of the building above the transit is 121 feet. Thus, the height of the building is determined by adding the transit's height, 5 feet, to 121 feet.

$$h = 5 + 121 = 126$$

The building's height is 126 feet.

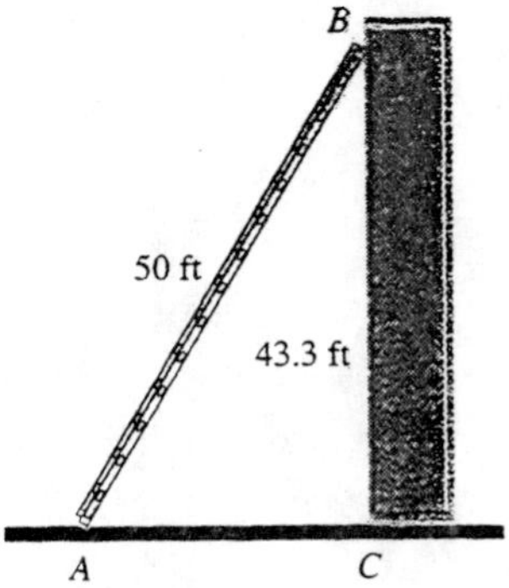

If the measures of two sides of a right triangle are known, the measures of the two acute angles can be found using Table 10.4 or a calculator. For example, Figure 10.57 shows a 50-foot ladder reaching 43.3 feet on a vertical wall. To find the measure of $\angle A$, the angle that the ladder makes with the ground, we can use the sine ratio.

$$\sin A = \frac{\text{side opposite angle } A}{\text{hypotenuse}} = \frac{43.3}{50}$$

To find the measure of $\angle A$ using Table 10.4, perform the division on the right, $43.3 \div 50$:

$$\sin A = 0.866$$

Figure 10.57

Now, look down the sine column in Table 10.4 until you find the displayed decimal that is the closest to 0.866. In this instance, 0.866 occurs in the sine column to the right of 60°, so the measure of angle A is 60°.

Finding the measure of angle A with either a scientific or graphing calculator requires the use of the *inverse sine key*, usually labeled $\boxed{\sin^{-1}}$. Given that

$$\sin A = \frac{43.3}{50},$$

here are the keystroke sequences used on most calculators:

Most scientific calculators:

$$43.3 \boxed{\div} 50 \boxed{=} \boxed{\text{2nd Function}} \boxed{\sin/\sin^{-1}}$$

Most graphing calculators:

$$\boxed{\text{2nd}} \boxed{\sin/\sin^{-1}} \boxed{(} 43.3 \boxed{\div} 50 \boxed{)} \boxed{\text{ENTER}}$$

The display should show approximately 59.99°, which can be rounded to 60°.

EXAMPLE 5   Determining the Angle of Elevation

A building that is 21 meters tall casts a shadow 25 meters long. Find the angle of elevation of the sun.

Solution   The situation is illustrated in Figure 10.58. We are asked to find $m\angle A$. We begin with the tangent ratio.

$$\tan A = \frac{21}{25} = 0.84$$

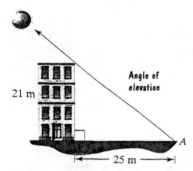

Angle of elevation

21 m

25 m

A

Figure 10.58

Using Table 10.4, the value in the tangent column that comes closest to 0.84 is 0.8391, which appears to the right of 40°. So, the angle of elevation is 40°. Using a calculator, it is necessary to use the inverse tangent key.

Since $\tan A = 0.84$, then $A = \tan^{-1} 0.84$.

Scientific Calculator: $.84 \boxed{\text{2nd Function}} \boxed{\tan/\tan^{-1}}$

Graphing Calculator: $\boxed{\text{2nd}} \boxed{\tan/\tan^{-1}} .84 \boxed{\text{ENTER}}$

The display should show approximately 40°.

Using Table 10.4 or a calculator, the angle of elevation of the sun is approximately 40°.

Exercise Set 10.6

✓ Practice Exercises

In Exercises 1–8, use the given right triangles to find sin *A,* cos *A, and* tan *A.*

1.

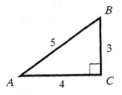

2.

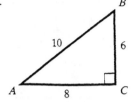

3.

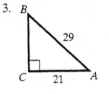

4.

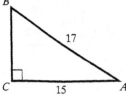

5.

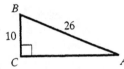

6.

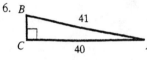

7.

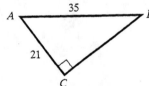

8.

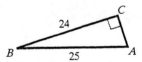

In Exercises 9–18, find the measure of the side of the right triangle whose length is designated by a lowercase letter. Round answers to the nearest whole number.

9.

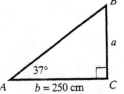

10.

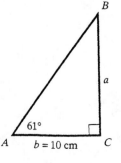

11.

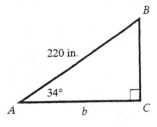

12.

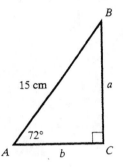

13.

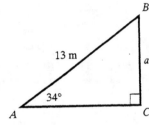

14.

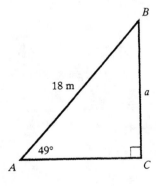

15.

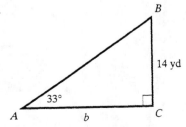

16.

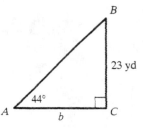

17.

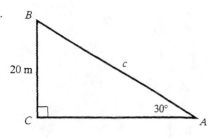

18.

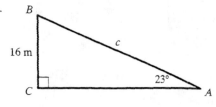

In Exercises 19–22, find the measures of the parts of the right triangle that are not given. Round all answers to the nearest whole number.

19.

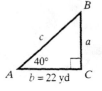

20.

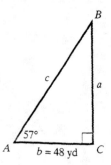

21.

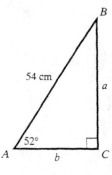

22.

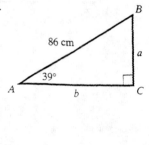

In Exercises 23–26, use Table 10.4 or the inverse trigonometric keys on a calculator to find the measure of angle A, rounded to the nearest whole degree.

23.

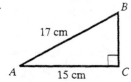

24.

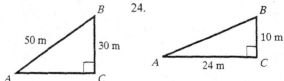

25.

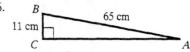

26.

 Application Exercises

27. To find the distance across a lake, a surveyor took the measurements in the figure shown. Use these measurements to determine how far it is across the lake. Round to the nearest yard.

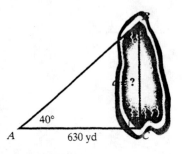

28. At a certain time of day, the angle of elevation of the sun is 40°. To the nearest foot, find the height of a tree whose shadow is 35 feet long.

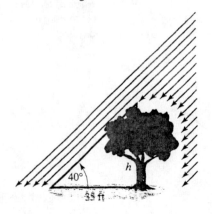

29. A plane rises from a take-off and flies at an angle of 10° with the horizontal runway. When it has gained 500 feet, find the distance, to the nearest foot, the plane has flown.

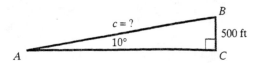

30. A road is inclined at an angle of 5°. After driving 5000 feet along this road, find the driver's increase in altitude. Round to the nearest foot.

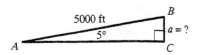

31. Sighting the top of a hill, a surveyor measured the angle of elevation to be 16°. The transit is 5 feet above the ground and 282 feet from the hill. Find the height of the hill, rounded to the nearest foot.

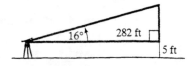

32. If a 40-foot ladder leaning against a vertical wall makes a 75° angle with the horizontal ground, how far up the wall does the ladder reach? Round the answer to the nearest foot.

33. A building that is 65 feet tall casts a shadow 55 feet long. Find the angle of elevation of the sun, rounded to the nearest degree.

34. A person 5.8 feet tall casts a shadow 8.1 feet long. Find the angle of elevation of the sun, rounded to the nearest degree.

35. At a point 70 feet on level ground from the base of a tree, the angle of elevation to the top of the tree is measured to be 65°. Find the height of the tree, rounded to the nearest foot.

36. Radar shows that the distance to an approaching airplane is 7.4 miles. If the angle of elevation to the plane is 24°, find the altitude at which the plane is flying. Round the answer to the nearest mile.

37. From the top of a 200-foot lighthouse, the angle of depression of a ship is 26°. Find the distance of the ship from the foot of the lighthouse, rounded to the nearest foot.

38. At a certain time of the day, the angle of elevation of the sun is 38°. Find the length of the shadow cast by a 90-foot building, rounded to the nearest foot.

Writing in Mathematics

39. If you are given the lengths of the sides of a right triangle, describe how to find the sine of either acute angle.

40. Describe one similarity and one difference between the sine ratio and the cosine ratio in terms of the sides of a right triangle.

41. If one of the acute angles of a right triangle is 37°, explain why the sine ratio does not increase as the size of the triangle increases.

42. If the measure of one of the acute angles and the hypotenuse of a right triangle are known, describe how to find the measure of the remaining parts of the triangle.

43. Describe what is meant by an angle of elevation and an angle of depression.

44. Give an example of an applied problem that can be solved using one or more trigonometric ratios. Be as specific as possible.

45. Use Table 10.4 or a calculator to find each of the following: sin 32° and cos 58°; sin 17° and cos 73°; sin 50° and cos 40°; sin 88° and cos 2°. Describe what you observe. Based on your observations, what do you think the *co* in *cosine* stands for?

Critical Thinking Exercises

46. Explain why the sine or cosine of an acute angle cannot be greater than or equal to 1.

47. Describe what happens to the tangent of an angle as the measure of the angle gets close to 90°. What happens at 90°?

48. From the top of a 250-foot lighthouse, a plane is sighted overhead and a ship is observed directly below the plane. The angle of elevation of the plane is 22° and the angle of depression of the ship is 35°. Find a. the distance of the ship from the lighthouse; b. the plane's height above the water. Round to the nearest foot.

SECTION 12.1   Sampling, Frequency Distributions, and Graphs

Objectives

1. Describe the population whose properties are to be analyzed.
2. Select an appropriate sampling technique.
3. Organize and present data.
4. Identify deceptions in visual displays of data.

"M*A*S*H" took place in the early 1950s, during the Korean War. By the final episode, the show had lasted four times as long as the Korean War.

At the end of the twentieth century, there were 94 million households in the United States with television sets. The television program viewed by the greatest percentage of such households in that century was the final episode of "M*A*S*H." Over 50 million American households watched this program.

Numerical information, such as the information about the top three TV shows of the twentieth century shown in Table 12.1, is called **data**. The word **statistics** is often used when referring to data. However, statistics has a second meaning: Statistics is also a method for collecting, organizing, analyzing, and interpreting data, as well as drawing conclusions based on the data. This methodology divides statistics into two main areas. **Descriptive statistics** is concerned with collecting, organizing, summarizing, and presenting data. **Inferential statistics** has to do with making generalizations about and drawing conclusions from the data collected.

Table 12.1   TV Programs with the Greatest U.S. Audience Viewing Percentage of the Twentieth Century

Program	Households total	Viewing percentage
1. "M*A*S*H" Feb. 28, 1983	50,150,000	60.2%
2. "Dallas" Nov. 21, 1980	41,470,000	53.3%
3. "Roots" Part 8 Jan. 30, 1977	36,380,000	51.1%

Source: Nielsen Media Research

1 Describe the population whose properties are to be analyzed.

Populations and Samples

Consider the set of all American TV households. Such a set is called the *population*. In general, a **population** is the set containing all the people or objects whose properties are to be described and analyzed by the data collector.

The population of American TV households is huge. At the time of the "M*A*S*H" conclusion, there were nearly 84 million such households. Did over 50 million American TV households really watch the final episode of "M*A*S*H"? A friendly phone call to each household ("So, how are you? What's new? Watch any good television last night? If so, what?") is, of course, absurd. A **sample**, which is a subset or subgroup of the population, is needed. In this case, it would be appropriate to have a sample of a few thousand TV households to draw conclusions about the population of all TV housholds.

EXAMPLE 1 Populations and Samples

A group of hotel owners in a large city decide to conduct a survey among citizens of the city to discover their opinions about casino gambling.

a. Describe the population.
b. One of the hotel owners suggests obtaining a sample by surveying all the people at six of the largest nightclubs in the city on a Saturday night. Each person will be asked to express his or her opinion on casino gambling. Does this seem like a good idea?

Solution

a. The population is the set containing all the citizens of the city.
b. Questioning people at six of the city's largest nightclubs is a terrible idea. The nightclub subset is probably more likely to have a more positive attitude toward casino gambling than the population of all the city's citizens.

Random Sampling

There is a way to use a small sample to make generalizations about a large population: Guarantee that every member of the population has an equal chance to be selected for the sample. Surveying people at six of the city's largest nightclubs does not provide this guarantee. Unless it can be established that all citizens of the city frequent these clubs, which seems unlikely, this sampling scheme does not permit each citizen an equal chance of selection.

Random Samples

A **random sample** is a sample obtained in such a way that every element in the population has an equal chance of being selected for the sample.

Suppose you are elated with the quality of one of your courses. Although it's an auditorium section with 120 students, you feel that the professor is lecturing right to you. During a wonderful lecture, you look around the auditorium to see if any of the other students are sharing your enthusiasm. Based on body language, it's hard to tell. You really want to know the opinion of the population of 120 students taking this course. You fantasize about asking students to grade the course on an A to F scale, anticipating a unanimous A. You cannot survey everyone. Eureka! Suddenly you have an idea on how to take a sample. Put cards numbered from 1 to 120, one number per card, in a box. Because the course has assigned seating by number, each numbered card corresponds to a student in the

class. Reach in and randomly select six cards. Each card, and therefore each student, has an equal chance of being selected. Then use the opinions of the course from the six randomly selected students to generalize about the course opinion for the entire 120-student population.

Your idea is precisely how random samples are obtained. In random sampling, each element in the population must be identified and assigned a number. The numbers are generally assigned in order. The way to sample from the larger numbered population is to generate random numbers using a computer or calculator. Each numbered element from the population that corresponds to a random number is selected for the sample.

Call-in polls on radio and television are not reliable because those polled do not represent the larger population. A person who calls in is likely to have feelings about an issue that are consistent with the politics of the show's host. For a poll to be accurate, the sample must be chosen randomly from the larger population. The A.C. Nielsen Company uses a random sample of about 5000 TV households to measure the percent of all 94 million households tuned in to every television program.

2 Select an appropriate sampling technique.

LAFF-A-DAY

"We've polled the entire populace, Your Majesty, and we've come up with exactly the results you ordered!"

© 1993 King Features Syndicate Inc. World rights reserved. Reprinted with special permission of King Features Syndicate.

EXAMPLE 2   Selecting an Appropriate Sampling Technique

We return to the hotel owners in the large city who are interested in how the city's citizens feel about casino gambling. Which of the following would be the most appropriate way to select a random sample?

a. Randomly survey people who live in the oceanfront condominiums in the city.

b. Survey the first 200 people whose names appear in the city's telephone directory.

c. Randomly select neighborhoods of the city and then randomly survey people within the selected neighborhoods.

Solution   Keep in mind that the population is the set containing all the city's citizens. A random sample must give each citizen an equal chance of being selected.

a. Randomly selecting people who live in the city's oceanfront condominiums is not a good idea. Many hotels lie along the oceanfront, and the oceanfront property owners might object to the traffic and noise as a result of casino gambling. Furthermore, this sample does not give each citizen of the city an equal chance of being selected.

b. If the hotel owners survey the first 200 names in the city's telephone directory, all citizens do not have an equal chance of selection. For example, individuals whose last name begins with a letter toward the end of the alphabet have no chance of being selected.

c. Randomly selecting neighborhoods of the city and then randomly surveying people within the selected neighborhood is an appropriate technique. Using this method, each citizen has an equal chance of being selected. In summary, given the three options, the sampling technique in part (c) is the most appropriate.

3 Organize and present data.

Frequency Distributions

After data have been collected from a sample of the population, the next task facing the statistician is to present the data in a condensed and manageable form. In this way, the data can be more easily interpreted.

Suppose, for example, that researchers are interested in determining the age at which adolescent males show the greatest rate of physical growth. A random sample of 35 10-year-old boys is measured for height and then remeasured each year until they reach 18. The age of maximum yearly growth for each subject is as follows:

12, 14, 13, 14, 16, 14, 14, 17, 13, 10, 13, 18, 12, 15, 14, 15, 15, 14, 14, 13, 15,
16, 15, 12, 13, 16, 11, 15, 12, 13, 12, 11, 13, 14, 14

A piece of data is called a **data item**. This list of data has 35 data items. Some of the data items are identical. Two of the data items are 11 and 11. Thus, we can say that the **data value** 11 occurs twice. Similarly, because 5 of the data items are 12, 12, 12, 12, and 12, the data value 12 occurs five times.

Collected data can be presented using a **frequency distribution**. Such a distribution consists of two columns. The data values are listed in one column. Numerical data are generally listed from smallest to largest. The adjacent column is labeled **frequency** and indicates the number of times each value occurs.

EXAMPLE 3 · Constructing a Frequency Distribution

Construct a frequency distribution for the data of the age of maximum yearly growth for 35 boys:

12, 14, 13, 14, 16, 14, 14, 17, 13, 10, 13, 18, 12, 15, 14, 15, 15, 14, 14, 13, 15,
16, 15, 12, 13, 16, 11, 15, 12, 13, 12, 11, 13, 14, 14

Solution It is difficult to determine trends in the data above in its current format. Perhaps we can make sense of the data by organizing it into a frequency distribution. Let us create two columns. One lists all possible data values, from smallest (10) to largest (18). The other column indicates the number of times the value occurs in the sample. The frequency distribution is shown in Table 12.2.

The frequency distribution indicates that one subject had maximum growth at age 10, two at age 11, five at age 12, seven at age 13, and so on. The maximum growth for most of the subjects occurred between the ages of 12 and 15. Nine boys experienced maximum growth at age 14, more than at any other age within the sample. The sum of the frequencies, 35, is equal to the original number of data items.

Table 12.2 A Frequency Distribution for a Boy's Age at Maximum Yearly Growth

Age of Maximum Growth	Number of Boys (Frequency)
10	1
11	2
12	5
13	7
14	9
15	6
16	3
17	1
18	1
	35

35 is the sum of the frequencies.

The frequency distribution shows 10 occurs once, 11 twice, 12 five times, 13 seven times, and so on.

A frequency distribution that lists all possible data items can be quite cumbersome when there are many such items. For example, consider the following data items. These are statistics test scores made by a group of 40 students.

82	47	75	64	57	82	63	93
76	68	84	54	88	77	79	80
94	92	94	80	94	66	81	67
75	73	66	87	76	45	43	56
57	74	50	78	71	84	59	76

It's difficult to determine how well the group did when the grades are displayed like this. Because there are so many data items, one way to organize this data so the results are more meaningful is to arrange the grades into groups, or **classes**, based on something that interests us. Many grading systems assign an A to grades in the 90–100 class, B to grades in the 80–89 class, C to grades in the 70–79 class, and so on. These classes provide one way to organize the data.

Looking at the 40 statistics test scores, we see that they range from a low of 43 to a high of 94. We can use classes that run from 40 through 49, 50 through 59, 60 through 69, and so on up to 90 through 99, to organize the scores. In Example 4, we go through the data and tally each item into the appropriate class. This method for organizing data is called a **grouped frequency distribution**.

EXAMPLE 4   Constructing a Grouped Frequency Distribution

Use the classes 40–49, 50–59, 60–69, 70–79, 80–89, and 90–99 to construct a grouped frequency distribution for the 40 test scores listed on page 595.

Solution   We use the 40 given scores and tally the number of scores in each interval.

Test Scores (Class)	Tally	Number of Students (Frequency)
40–49	|||	3
50–59	|||||		6
60–69	|||||		6
70–79	||||| |||||		11
80–89	||||| ||||	9
90–99	|||||	5

Table 12.3   A Grouped Frequency Distribution Organizing 40 Test Scores

Class	Frequency
40–49	3
50–59	6
60–69	6
70–79	11
80–89	9
90–99	5
	40

40, the sum of the frequencies, is the number of data items.

Omitting the tally column results in the grouped frequency distribution in Table 12.3. The distribution shows that the greatest frequency of students scored in the 70–79 class. The number of students decreases in classes that contain successively lower and higher scores. The sum of the frequencies, 40, is equal to the original number of data items.

We can use other classes to organize the 40 statistics test scores. Most grading systems assign a grade of F to numerical grades below 60. Thus, the classes 40–59, 60–69, 70–79, 80–89, and 90–99 can be used. The last class can also be selected as 90–100. It is not uncommon to see a grouped frequency distribution in which the first and last class are wider or narrower than the rest.

Histograms and Frequency Polygons

Take a second look at the frequency distribution for the age of a boy's maximum yearly growth, shown in Table 12.2, repeated on page 597. A bar graph with bars that touch can be used to visually display the data. Such a graph is called a **histogram**. Figure 12.1 illustrates a histogram that was constructed using the frequency distribution in Table 12.2. A series of rectangles whose lengths represent the frequencies are placed next to each other. For example, the length of the bar for the data value 10, shown at the far left of Figure 12.1, is 1. This corresponds to

Table 12.2 A Boy's Age at Maximum Yearly Growth

Age of Maximum Growth (Data Value)	Number of Boys (Frequency)
10	1
11	2
12	5
13	7
14	9
15	6
16	3
17	1
18	1
	35

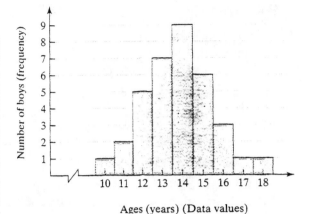

Figure 12.1 A histogram for a boy's age at maximum yearly growth

the frequency for 10 given in Table 12.2. The higher the bar, the more frequent the score. The break along the horizontal axis, symbolized by ⌐/⌐, eliminates listing the ages 1 to 9.

A line graph called a **frequency polygon** can also be used to visually convey the information shown in Figure 12.1. The axes are labeled just like those in a histogram. Thus, the horizontal axis shows data values and the vertical axis shows frequencies. Once a histogram has been constructed, it's fairly easy to draw a frequency polygon. Figure 12.2 shows a histogram with a dot at the top of each rectangle at its midpoint. Connect each of these midpoints with a straight line. To complete the frequency polygon at both ends, the lines should be drawn down to touch the horizontal axis. The completed frequency polygon is shown in Figure 12.3.

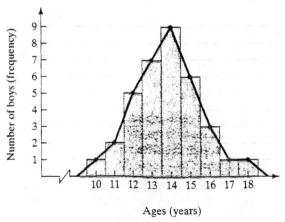

Figure 12.2 A histogram for a boy's age at maximum yearly growth with a superimposed frequency polygon

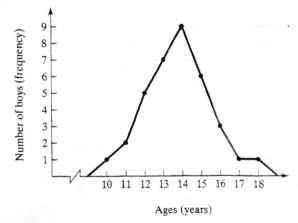

Figure 12.3 A frequency polygon for a boy's age at maximum yearly growth

Stem-and-Leaf Plots

A unique way for displaying data uses a tool called a **stem-and-leaf plot**. Example 5 illustrates how we sort the data, revealing the same visual impression created by a histogram.

EXAMPLE 5   Constructing a Stem-and-Leaf Plot

Use the data showing statistics test scores for 40 students to construct a stem-and-leaf plot.

82	47	75	64	57	82	63	93
76	68	84	54	88	77	79	80
94	92	94	80	94	66	81	67
75	73	66	87	76	45	43	56
57	74	50	78	71	84	59	76

Solution   The plot is constructed by separating each number into two parts. The first part is the *stem*. The **stem** consists of the tens' digit. For example, the stem for the score of 82 is 8. The second part is the *leaf*. The **leaf** consists of the units' digit for a given value. For the score of 82, the leaf is 2. The possible stems for the 40 scores are 4, 5, 6, 7, 8, and 9, entered in the left column of the plot.

Begin by entering each data item in the first row.

Entering 8 2:

Stems	Leaves
4	
5	
6	
7	
8	2
9	

Adding 4 7:

Stems	Leaves
4	7
5	
6	
7	
8	2
9	

Adding 7 5:

Stems	Leaves
4	7
5	
6	
7	5
8	2
9	

Adding 6 4:

Stems	Leaves
4	7
5	
6	4
7	5
8	2
9	

Adding 5 7:

Stems	Leaves
4	7
5	7
6	4
7	5
8	2
9	

Adding 8 2:

Stems	Leaves
4	7
5	7
6	4
7	5
8	2 2
9	

Adding 6 3:

Stems	Leaves
4	7
5	7
6	4 3
7	5
8	2 2
9	

Adding 9 3:

Stems	Leaves
4	7
5	7
6	4 3
7	5
8	2 2
9	3

Figure 12.4 shows the stem-and-leaf plot, constructed by entering the data items from the first row of the given data, from left to right, then the items from the second row, and so on through the fifth row. If you turn the page so that the left margin is on the bottom and facing you, the visual impression created by the enclosed leaves is the same as that created by a histogram. The enclosed leaves extend farthest to the right when the stem is 7. This shows that the greatest frequency of students scored in the 70s.

Stems	Leaves
4	7 5 3
5	7 4 6 7 0 9
6	4 3 8 6 7 6
7	5 6 7 9 5 3 6 4 8 1 6
8	2 2 4 8 0 0 1 7 4
9	3 4 2 4 4

Figure 12.4 A steam-and-leaf plot displaying 40 test scores

4 Identify deceptions in visual displays of data.

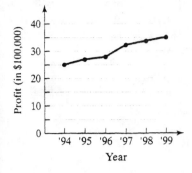

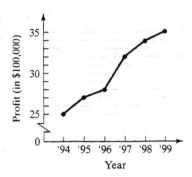

Figure 12.5 The graph on the bottom uses a scale that might exaggerate the increasing profits.

Deceptions in Visual Displays of Data

Benjamin Disraeli, Queen Victoria's prime minister, stated that there are "lies, damned lies, and statistics." The problem is not that statistics lie, but rather that liars use statistics. Graphs can be used to distort the underlying data, making it difficult for the viewer to learn the truth. One potential source of misunderstanding is an exaggerated scale on the vertical axis, illustrated in Figure 12.5. The two graphs convey the same data items, although the scale on the bottom makes the company's profits look as if they are increasing more dramatically over time.

The bottom graph in Figure 12.5 *is* more effective in terms of reading differences between years. The graph does tell the truth, although the deceptive scale can lead to an incorrect interpretation of how quickly profits are increasing over time.

The graph in Figure 12.6 creates the impression that Congress has set forth unreasonable fuel economy standards for automobiles. The line representing 18 miles per gallon for 1978 is 0.6 inch long, so the line representing 27.5 miles per gallon for 1985 should be about 0.92 inch long.

$$\frac{inches}{miles\ per\ gallon} : \frac{0.6}{18} = \frac{x}{27.5}$$

$$18x = 0.6(27.5)$$

$$x = \frac{0.6(27.5)}{18} \approx 0.92$$

Rather than 0.92 inch, the line is 5.3 inches long. Because this line represents 27.5 miles per gallon, its length compared to that of the short line for 1978 creates the impression that fuel standards for 1985 are unreasonable.

Do you notice anything else that is unusual about the graph in Figure 12.6? The dates on the left are all the same size. The numbers on the right are different sizes. The largest number in the figure is $27\frac{1}{2}$, which also exaggerates the severity of the 1985 mileage standard. Figure 12.7 shows how the data can be presented in a nondeceptive manner.

This line, representing 18 miles per gallon in 1978, is 0.6 inches long.

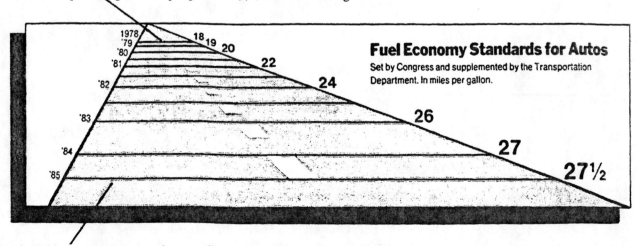

This line, representing 27.5 miles per gallon in 1985, is 5.3 inches long.

Figure 12.6 *Source*: *New York Times*, August 9, 1978, p. D-2. Reprinted by permission.

Required fuel economy standards: new cars built from 1978 to 1985

Figure 12.7 Required fuel economy standards: new cars built from 1978 to 1985

The graph in Figure 12.8 varies both the length and width of each dollar bill as the purchasing power of the bill diminishes. The 1958 dollar was worth $1.00. By contrast, the 1978 dollar is worth 44¢. Thus, the 1978 dollar should be drawn to be slightly less than half the size of the 1958 dollar. If the area of the dollar were drawn to reflect its purchasing power, the 1978 dollar would be approximately twice as large as the one shown in the visual display.

Figure 12.8 *Source: Washington Post*, October 25, 1978, p. 1.

Figure 12.9 Day Mines, Inc., *1974 Annual Report*, p. 1.

Figure 12.9 is another example of a graph that uses deception in its visual display. The company hopes that the viewer will not notice the loss in 1970. This loss is disguised because the graph does not provide a scale on the vertical axis. The bars begin at the bottom at approximately negative $4,200,000.

Examples of graphs that contain visual frauds are endless. We need to become aware of ways that visual displays can be deceptive. With this knowledge we can avoid interpreting potentially deceptive graphs incorrectly.

Exercise Set 12.1

 Practice and Application Exercises

Exercises 1–6 present numerical information. Describe the population whose properties are analyzed by the data.

1. In 1997, 42.7% of college professors in the United States were women. (*Source:* U.S. Bureau of Labor Statistics)

2. In 1999, using interviews with 1172 U.S. children ages 6 to 14, researchers concluded that 62% of U.S. children would not like to be president of the country. (*Source: Time,* July 5, 1999)

3. In 1997, there were 634 violent crimes in the United States per 100,000 residents. (*Source:* F.B.I.)

4. In 1999, 66% of world on-line households were in North America. (*Source:* Jupiter Comunications)

5. In 1997, 88% of high school students in Connecticut took the SAT. (*Source: New York Times*)

6. Approximately 54% of New York City's workers get to work by public transportation. (*Source:* American Public Transit Association)

7. The government of a large city needs to determine if the city's residents will support the construction of a new jail. The government decides to conduct a survey of a sample of the city's residents. Which one of the following procedures would be most appropriate for obtaining a sample of the city's residents?
   a. Survey a random sample of the employees and inmates at the old jail.
   b. Survey every fifth person who walks into City Hall on a given day.
   c. Survey a random sample of persons within each geographic region of the city.
   d. Survey the first 200 people listed in the city's telephone directory.

8. The city council of a large city needs to know if its residents will support the building of three new schools. The council decides to conduct a survey of a sample of the city's residents. Which procedure would be most appropriate for obtaining a sample of the city's residents?
   a. Survey a random sample of teachers who live in the city.
   b. Survey 100 individuals who are randomly selected from a list of all people living in the state in which the city in question is located.
   c. Survey a random sample of persons within each neighborhood of the city.
   d. Survey every tenth person who enters City Hall on a randomly selected day.

9. A random sample of 30 college students is selected. Each student is asked how much time he or she spent on homework during the previous week. The following times (in hours) are obtained:

16, 24, 18, 21, 18, 16, 18, 17, 15, 21, 19, 17, 17, 16, 19, 18,

15, 15, 20, 17, 15, 17, 24, 19, 16, 20, 16, 19, 18, 17

Construct a frequency distribution for the data.

10. A random sample of 30 male college students is selected. Each student is asked his height (to the nearest inch). The heights are as follows:

· 72, 70, 68, 72, 71, 71, 71, 69, 73, 71, 73, 75, 66, 67, 75·

74, 73, 71, 72, 67, 72, 68, 67, 71, 73, 71, 72, 70, 73, 70

Construct a frequency distribution for the data.

11. The ages of 40 runners who participated in a 10-kilometer run are as follows:

17, 54, 22, 25, 30, 37, 37, 18, 19, 16, 25, 46, 48, 61, 53,

32, 28, 20, 10, 13, 49, 39, 26, 28, 22, 22, 14, 19, 48, 69,

51, 47, 23, 28, 32, 38, 45, 51, 24, 27

Construct a grouped frequency distribution for the data. Use the classes 10–19, 20–29, 30–39, 40–49, 50–59, and 60–69.

12. The IQ scores of 70 students enrolled in a liberal arts course at a college are as follows:

102, 100, 103, 86, 120, 117, 111, 101, 93, 97, 99, 95, 95, 104,
104, 105, 106, 109, 109, 89, 94, 95, 99, 99, 103, 104, 105, 109,
110, 114, 124, 123, 118, 117, 116, 110, 114, 114, 96, 99, 103,
103, 104, 107, 107, 110, 111, 112, 113, 117, 115, 116, 100,
104, 102, 94, 93, 93, 96, 96, 111, 116, 107, 109, 105, 106, 97,
106, 107, 108

Construct a grouped frequency distribution for the data. Use the classes 85–89, 90–94, 95–99, 100–104, 105–109, 110–114, 115–119, and 120–124.

In Exercises 13–14, construct a histogram and a frequency polygon for the given data.

13.

Size of U.S. Family	Number of Families (in millions) (Frequency)
2	30
3	16
4	15
5	6
6	2

Source: U.S. Bureau of the Census

14.

Lifestyle	Number of Americans per 100 Adults
1 Very active	43
2 Somewhat active	44
3 Not very active	10
4 Not at all active	3

Source: Penn, Schoen, and Berland

15. Construct a histogram and a frequency polygon for the data in Exercise 9.

16. Construct a histogram and a frequency polygon for the data in Exercise 10.

17. The histogram shows the distribution of starting salaries (rounded to the nearest thousand) for college graduates based on a random sample of recent graduates.

Starting Salaries of Recent College Graduates

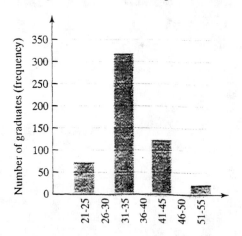

Salary in thousands of dollars

Which one of the following is true according to the graph?

a. The graph is based on a sample of approximately 500 recent college graduates.

b. More college graduates had starting salaries in the $41,000–$45,000 range than in the $26,000–$30,000 range.

c. If the sample is truly representative, then for a group of 400 college graduates, we can expect about 28 of them to have starting salaries in the $21,000–$25,000 range.

d. The percent of starting salaries falling above those shown by any rectangular bar is equal to the percent of starting salaries falling below that bar.

18. The frequency polygon at the top of the next column shows a distribution of IQ scores. Which one of the following is true based upon the graph?

a. The graph is based on a sample of approximately 50 people.

b. More people had an IQ score of 100 than any other IQ score, and as the deviation from 100 increases or decreases, the scores fall off in a symmetrical manner.

c. More people had an IQ score of 110 than a score of 90.

d. The percent of scores above any IQ score is equal to the percent of scores below that score.

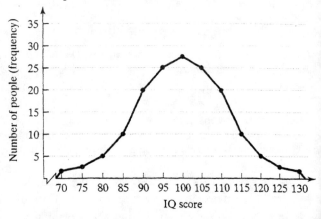

19. A random sample of 40 college professors is selected from all professors at a university. The following list gives their ages.

63, 48, 42, 42, 38, 59, 41, 44, 45, 28, 54, 62, 51, 44, 63,
66, 59, 46, 51, 28, 37, 66, 42, 40, 30, 31, 48, 32, 29, 42,
63, 37, 36, 47, 25, 34, 49, 30, 35, 50

Construct a stem-and-leaf display for the data. What does the shape of the display reveal about the ages of the professors?

20. Construct a stem-and-leaf display for the data given in Exercise 11.

21. In "Ages of Oscar-Winning Best Actors and Actresses" (*Mathematics Teacher* magazine) by Richard Brown and Gretchen Davis, the stem-and-leaf plots shown compare the ages of actors and actresses for 30 winners of the Oscar at the time they won the award. Use the plot to write the ages of the 30 actors and of the 30 actresses. What differences do you observe between the two sets of data? What explanations can you offer for these differences?

Actors	Stems	Actresses
	2	146667
98753221	3	00113344455778
88767543322100	4	11129
6651	5	
210	6	011
6	7	4
	8	0

22. The stem-and-leaf plot shown on page 603 displays the heights of 218 volcanoes. The unit is 100 feet, so the entry 18|5 represents a volcano whose height is 185(100) = 18,500 feet

a. What is the height of the tallest volcano?

b. What is the height of the least tall of the volcanoes?

c. What is the greatest height shared by at least two of the volcanoes?

d. Describe a trend shown by the stem-and-leaf display.

0	98766562
1	97719630
2	69987766544422211009850
3	876655412099551426
4	99988443319294333361107
5	97666666554422210097731
6	898665441077761065
7	98855431100652108073
8	653322122937
9	377655421000493
10	0984433165212
11	4963201631
12	45421164
13	47830
14	00
15	676
16	52
17	92
18	5
19	39730

23. The graph shown indicates a decline in commission payments to travel agents in 1978. Or does it? Describe what is misleading about the four "declines" in this visual display.

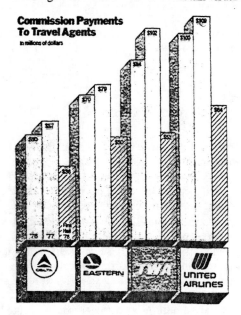

Commission Payments To Travel Agents
In millions of dollars

Source: *New York Times*, August 8, 1978, p. D-1.
Reprinted by permission.

24. Describe the error in the visual display shown. What is misleading about this error? (*Note:* The abbreviation bbl. stands for *barrel.*)

IN THE BARREL...
Price per bbl. of light crude, leaving Saudi Arabia on Jan. 1

April 1 $14.55

$13.34

$12.70

$12.09

$11.51

$10.48

$10.95

$2.41

Source: *Time*, April 9, 1979, p. 57; © 1979 Time Inc.
Reprinted by permission.

 Writing in Mathematics

25. What is a population? What is a sample?

26. Describe what is meant by a random sample.

27. Suppose you are interested in whether or not the students at your college would favor a grading system in which students may receive final grades of A+, A, A−, B+, B, B−, C+, C, C−, and so on. Describe how you might obtain a random sample of 100 students from the entire student population.

28. For Exercise 27, would questioning every fifth student as he or she is leaving the campus library until 100 students are interviewed be a good way to obtain a random sample? Explain your answer.

29. What is a frequency distribution?

30. What is a histogram?

31. What is a frequency polygon?

32. Describe how to construct a frequency polygon from a histogram.

33. Describe how to construct a stem-and-leaf plot from a set of data.

34. Describe two ways that graphs can be used to distort data.

35. Did Sir Francis Bacon write some or all of the plays attributed to William Shakespeare? In an attempt to determine whether this is true, scholars sampled words from Shakespeare's plays and Bacon's writings, counting the number of letters per word. The results are presented in the histograms shown on page 604.

Shakespeare's plays

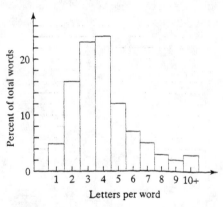

Bacon's writings

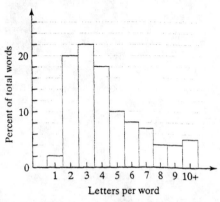

a. Describe what these histograms show about each author's use of words that are less than five letters long.
b. Describe what these histograms show about each author's use of words that are more than five letters long.
c. Do these histograms suggest that Bacon wrote some of Shakespeare's plays? Explain your answer.

 Critical Thinking Exercises

For each frequency polygon shown in Exercises 36–37, describe a situation that might result in a distribution of scores that takes on this shape.

36.

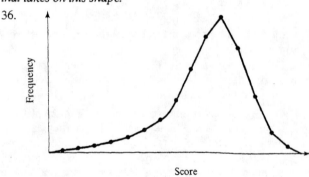

37.

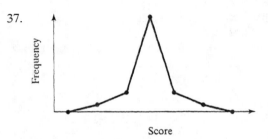

 Technology Exercises

38. Using a spreadsheet, enter the following exam scores into a spreadsheet column: 4 A's, 7 B's, 3 C's, 4 D's, and 1 F.

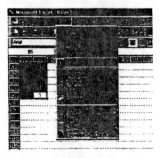

After entering the data, use the computer's mouse to highlight the cells containing the data. Then activate the Chart Option of the spreadsheet by clicking on the Insert pull-down menu and selecting Chart. (See image.) Select the Column chart option and click the "Next" button. Work your way through the options, including the labels and cosmetic effects. Once you have decided on all of the options (don't worry, you can go back and change them), click the "Finish" button.

39. Use a spreadsheet to create a histogram for the following distribution of grades: 14 A's, 34 B's, 65 C's, 28 D's, and 10 F's.

 Group Exercises

40. The classic book on distortion using statistics is *How to Lie with Statistics* by Darrell Huff. This activity is designed for five people. Each person should select two chapters from Huff's book and then present to the class the common methods of statistical manipulation and distortion that Huff discusses.

41. Each group member should find one example of a graph that presents data with integrity and one example of a graph that is misleading. Use newspapers, magazines, the Internet, books, and so forth. Once graphs have been collected, each member should share his or her graphs with the entire group. Be sure to explain why one graph depicts quantitative data in a forthright manner and how the other graph deliberately misleads the viewer.

SECTION 12.2 *Measures of Central Tendency*

Objectives

1. Determine the mean for a data set.
2. Determine the median for a data set.
3. Determine the mode for a data set.
4. Determine the midrange for a data set.

RELEASE WEEK OF NOVEMBER 29, 1976
Release Monday

© Field Enterprise Inc., 1976. Reprinted with special permission of King Features Syndicate.

Median Age of U.S. Whites, Blacks, and Hispanics

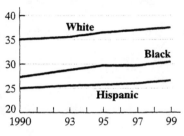

Figure 12.10 *Source*: U.S. Census Bureau

1 Determine the mean for a data set.

Table 12.4 Mean Major League Baseball Salaries

Year	Mean Salary
1990	$597,537
1991	$851,492
1992	$1,028,667
1993	$1,076,089
1994	$1,168,263
1995	$1,110,766
1996	$1,119,981
1997	$1,336,609

Source: Major League Baseball Players Association

Singers Ricky Martin and Jennifer Lopez, television journalist Soledad O'Brien, boxer Oscar De La Hoya, Internet entrepreneur Carlos Cardona, actor John Leguizamo, and political organizer Luigi Crespo are members of a generation of young Hispanics that is changing the way America looks, feels, thinks, eats, dances, and votes. There are 31 million Hispanics in the United States, pumping $300 billion a year into the economy. By 2050, the Hispanic population is expected to reach 96 million—an increase of more than 200 percent. And Hispanics are younger than the rest of the nation: A third are under 18. The graph in Figure 12.10 shows the *median* age of whites, African-Americans, and Americans of Hispanic origin.

The *what* age? Perhaps you have seen the word *median* in the presentation of numerical information. The median age for U.S. Latinos in 1999 was 27: The number of Latinos who are older than 27 is the same as the number who are younger than 27. The single number 27 represents what is "average" or "typical" of the age of Latino-Americans. In statistics, such a value is known as a **measure of central tendency** because it is generally located toward the center of a distribution. Four such measures are discussed in this section: the mean, the median, the mode, and the midrange. Each measure of central tendency is calculated in a different way. Thus, it is better to use a specific term (mean, median, mode, or midrange) than to use the generic descriptive term "average."

The Mean

By far the most commonly used measure of central tendency is the *mean*. The **mean** is obtained by adding all the data items and then dividing the sum by the number of items. For example, Table 12.4 shows the mean U.S. major league baseball salaries. The mean salary for 1997, $1,336,609, was determined by adding up the baseball salaries of all major league players and then dividing the sum by the number of major league players.

EXAMPLE 1 Calculating the Mean

Table 12.5 on page 606 shows the all-time top point scorers in a National Football League season. Find the mean points scored per season for the top 11 scorers.

Paul Hornung of the Green Bay Packers

Table 12.5 Top Point Scorers in an NFL Season (through 1998)

Player	Team	Year	Points
Paul Hornung	Green Bay Packers	1960	176
Mark Moseley	Washington Redskins	1983	161
Gino Cappelletti	Boston Patriots	1964	155
Emitt Smith	Dallas Cowboys	1995	150
Chip Lohmiller	Washington Redskins	1991	149
Gino Cappelletti	Boston Patriots	1961	147
Paul Hornung	Green Bay Packers	1961	146
Jim Turner	New York Jets	1968	145
John Kasay	Carolina Panthers	1996	145
John Riggins	Washington Redskins	1983	144
Kevin Butler	Chicago Bears	1985	144

Source: National Football League

Solution   We find the mean by adding the points scored and dividing this sum by 11, the number of data items.

$$\text{Mean} = \frac{176 + 161 + 155 + 150 + 149 + 147 + 146 + 145 + 145 + 144 + 144}{11}$$

$$= \frac{1662}{11} \approx 151.09$$

The mean points scored per season for the top 11 scorers is approximately 151.

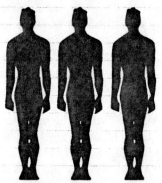

The Mean American Guy According to researchers, "Robert" is 31, 5 feet 10 inches, 172 pounds, watches TV 2567 hours yearly, commutes to work, works 6.1 hours daily, and sleeps 7.7 hours.

One and only one mean can be calculated for any group of numerical data. The mean may or may not be one of the actual data items. In Example 1, the mean was approximately 151. However, none of the 11 players scored 151 points in a season.

The Greek letter sigma, Σ, is called a **symbol of summation**. It is used to indicate the sum of the data items. The notation Σx, read "the sum of x," means to add all the data items. We can use this symbol to give a formula for calculating the mean.

The Mean

The **mean** is the sum of the data items divided by the number of items.

$$\text{Mean} = \frac{\Sigma x}{n},$$

where Σx represents the sum of all the data items and n represents the number of items.

Take another look at the points for the top point scorers in an NFL season (Table 12.5). Some of the data items are identical. Two of the data items are 145 and 145. Thus, the data value 145 occurs twice. Similarly, because two of the data items are 144 and 144, the data value 144 also occurs twice. Table 12.6 shows a frequency distribution for the season points of the top NFL scorers.

Table 12.6 A Frequency Distribution for Points by Top Point Scorers in an NFL Season

Points x	Number of Players with These Points Frequency: f
144	2
145	2
146	1
147	1
149	1
150	1
155	1
161	1
176	1
	11

Total frequency

In Example 1, in computing the mean, we added 145 twice and 144 twice. Another option is to multiply 145 by 2 and 144 by 2. Indeed, if you multiply each value of x in Table 12.6 by its frequency (xf) and then add these products (Σxf), you will get 1662. This is the sum from Example 1 that we obtained by adding all the data items. When many data values occur more than once and a frequency distribution is used to organize the data, we can use the following formula for calculating the mean.

Calculating the Mean for a Frequency Distribution

$$\text{Mean} = \frac{\Sigma xf}{n}$$

in which

x refers to each data value.

f refers to the frequency of that data value.

Σxf refers to the sum of all the products obtained by multiplying each data value by its frequency.

n refers to the *total frequency* of the distribution.

EXAMPLE 2 Calculating the Mean for a Frequency Distribution

Table 12.7 shows the age of maximum growth for a group of 35 boys. Find the mean age of maximum growth.

Solution We use the formula

$$\text{Mean} = \frac{\Sigma xf}{n}.$$

First, we must find xf, obtained by multiplying each data value, x, by its frequency, f. Then, we need to find the sum of these products: Σxf. We can use the frequency distribution to organize these computations. Add a third column in which each data value is multiplied by its frequency. This column, shown below, is headed xf. Then, find the sum of the values (Σxf) in this column.

Table 12.7 A Boy's Age at Maximum Yearly Growth

Age of Maximum Growth x	Number of Boys Frequency: f
10	1
11	2
12	5
13	7
14	9
15	6
16	3
17	1
18	1
	35

x	f	xf
10	1	$10 \cdot 1 = 10$
11	2	$11 \cdot 2 = 22$
12	5	$12 \cdot 5 = 60$
13	7	$13 \cdot 7 = 91$
14	9	$14 \cdot 9 = 126$
15	6	$15 \cdot 6 = 90$
16	3	$16 \cdot 3 = 48$
17	1	$17 \cdot 1 = 17$
18	1	$18 \cdot 1 = 18$
	35	$\Sigma xf = 482$

Σxf is the sum of the values in the third column:
10 + 22 + 60 + 91 + 126 + 90 + 48 + 17 + 18 = 482

This value is n, the total frequency of the distibution.

Mean Weekly Hours and Minutes of Viewing per U.S. TV Household

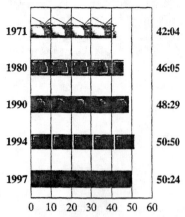

1971   42:04

1980   46:05

1990   48:29

1994   50:50

1997   50:24

0 10 20 30 40 50 60

Figure 12.11 *Source*: Nielsen Media Research

Colombian-born actor John Leguizamo is a member of a generation of young Hispanics shaping American pop culture.

2 Determine the median for a data set.

Now, substitute these values into the formula for the mean. Remember that n is the *total frequency* of the distribution, or 35.

$$\text{Mean} = \frac{\Sigma xf}{n} = \frac{482}{35} \approx 13.77$$

The mean age of maximum growth is approximately 13.77 or, rounded to the nearest whole year, 14 years of age.

We saw that in 1997, the mean salary for major league baseball players was $1,336,609. This is the mean for the *entire population* of 1997 major league baseball players. By contrast, the graph in Figure 12.11 indicates that in 1997, the mean weekly TV viewing time per TV household in the United States was 50 hours, 24 minutes. This mean was obtained *using a random sample* of the population. Unlike the population of major league baseball players, the population of 94 million TV households is too large to obtain a data item from every member. By calculating the mean for a random sample, statisticians can gain a reasonable estimate for the mean in the entire population.

The Median

We have seen that the median age for U.S. Latinos in 1999 was 27. To find this value, researchers begin with a random sample of all U.S. Latinos. The data items— that is, the ages for sampled Latinos—are arranged in order, from youngest to oldest. The **median** age is the data item in the middle of this set of ranked data.

The Median

To find the **median** of a group of data items,
1. Arrange the data items in order, from smallest to largest.
2. If the number of data items is odd, the median is the data item in the middle of the list.
3. If the number of data items is even, the median is the mean of the two middle data items.

EXAMPLE 3   Finding the Median

Find the median for each of the following groups of data.

a. 84, 90, 98, 95, 88
b. 68, 74, 7, 13, 15, 25, 28, 59, 34, 47

Solution

a. Arrange the data items in order, from smallest to largest. The number of data items in the list, five, is odd. Thus, the median is the middle number.

84, 88, 90, 95, 98

Middle data item

The median is 90. Notice that two data items lie above 90 and two data items lie below 90.

b. Arrange the data items in order, from smallest to largest. The number of data items in the list, ten, is even. Thus, the median is the mean of the two middle data items.

$$7, 13, 15, 25, 28, 34, 47, 59, 68, 74$$

Middle data items
are 28 and 34.

$$\text{Median} = \frac{28 + 34}{2} = \frac{62}{2} = 31$$

The median is 31. Five data items lie above 31 and five data items lie below 31.

If a relatively long list of data items is arranged in order, it may be difficult to identify the item or items in the middle. In cases like this, the median can be found by determining its position in the list of items.

Position of the Median

If n data items are arranged in order, from smallest to largest, the median is the value in the

$$\frac{n + 1}{2}$$

position.

EXAMPLE 4   Finding the Median Using the Position Formula

Listed below are the points scored per season by the 11 top point scorers in the NFL. Find the median points scored per season for the top 11 scorers.

$$144, 144, 145, 145, 146, 147, 149, 150, 155, 161, 176$$

Solution   The data items are arranged from smallest to largest.

There are 11 data items, so $n = 11$. The median is the value in the

$$\frac{n + 1}{2} \text{ position} = \frac{11 + 1}{2} \text{ position} = \frac{12}{2} \text{ position} = \text{sixth position.}$$

We find the median by selecting the data item in the sixth position:

Position Position
   3   4

$$144, \ 144, \ 145, \ 145, \ 146, \ 147, \ 149, \ 150, \ 155, \ 161, \ 176$$

Position Position   Position Position
  1   2   5   6

The median is 147. Notice that five data items lie above 147 and five data items lie below it. The median points scored per season for the top 11 scorers is 147.

Study Tip

The formula

$$\frac{n + 1}{2}$$

gives the *position* of the median, and not the actual value of the median. When finding the median, be sure to first arrange the data items in order from smallest to largest.

EXAMPLE 5 Finding the Median Using the Position Formula

Find the median for the following group of data items:

$$109, 123, 192, 170, 99, 108, 168, 146, 126, 129.$$

Solution Arrange the data items in order, from smallest to largest:

$$99, 108, 109, 123, 126, 129, 146, 168, 170, 192$$

There are ten data items, so $n = 10$. The median is the value in the

$$\frac{n + 1}{2} \text{ position} = \frac{10 + 1}{2} \text{ position} = \frac{11}{2} \text{ position} = 5.5 \text{ position}.$$

This means that the median is the mean of the data items in positions 5 and 6:

$$99, 108, 109, 123, 126, 129, 146, 168, 170, 192$$

	Position 5	Position 6	

$$\text{Median} = \frac{126 + 129}{2} = \frac{255}{2} = 127.5$$

The median is 127.5.

Table 12.2 A Boy's Age at Maximum Yearly Growth

Age of Maximum Growth x	Number of Boys Frequency: f
10	1
11	2
12	5
13	7
14	9
15	6
16	3
17	1
18	1
	35

When individual data items are listed from smallest to largest, you can find the median by identifying the item or items in the middle or by using the $\frac{n + 1}{2}$ formula for its position. However, the formula for the position of the median is useful when data items are organized in a frequency distribution.

EXAMPLE 6 Finding the Median for a Frequency Distribution

Table 12.2, showing the age of maximum growth for a group of 35 boys, is repeated in the margin. Find the median age of maximum growth.

Solution There are 35 data items, so $n = 35$. The median is the value in the

$$\frac{n + 1}{2} \text{ position} = \frac{35 + 1}{2} \text{ position} = \frac{36}{2} \text{ position} = 18\text{th position}.$$

We find the median by selecting the data item in eighteenth position. Table 12.2 indicates that the data items begin with

$$10, 11, 11, 12, 12, 12, 12, 12, \ldots$$

and so on. We can write them all out and then select the median, the eighteenth data item. A more efficient way to proceed is to count down the frequency column in the distribution until we reach the eighteenth data item:

x	f	
		We count down the frequency column.
10	1	1
11	2	2, 3
12	5	4, 5, 6, 7, 8
13	7	9, 10, 11, 12, 13, 14, 15
14	9	16, 17, 18
15	6	
16	3	
17	1	
18	1	
	35	

The eighteenth data item is 14. The median age of maximum growth is 14.

Table 12.8 Median Weekly Earnings

For Workers 15 and Older			
Male	**1990**	**1993**	**1997**
Blacks	$303	$311	$348
Whites	$499	$469	$502
Female	**1990**	**1993**	**1997**
Blacks	$196	$203	$250
Whites	$243	$240	$265

Source: Bureau of Labor Statistics

Table 12.8 shows the median weekly earnings for U.S. workers 15 and older. The table indicates that in 1997, the median weekly earning for black men was $348. By definition, in 1997 the number of black men in the United States who earned less than $348 per week is the same as the number who earned more. Notice how these numbers tell a story. For all four groups, the median weekly earnings in 1997 is greater than in 1990. However, there are gaps between blacks and whites, as well as between women and men.

Statisticians generally use the median, rather than the mean, when reporting income. Why? Our next example will help to answer this question.

EXAMPLE 7   Comparing the Median and the Mean

Five employees in the assembly section of a television manufacturing company earn salaries of $19,700, $20,400, $21,500, $22,600, and $23,000 annually. The section manager has an annual salary of $95,000.

a. Find the median annual salary for the six people.

b. Find the mean annual salary for the six people.

Solution

> **"**People generally think of the numbers and less of what is to me the interesting part: using the numbers to make decisions about everything under the sun.**"**
>
> HAL STERN
> mathematician

a. To compute the median, first arrange the salaries in order.

$$\$19,700, \$20,400, \$21,500, \$22,600, \$23,000, \$95,000$$

Because the list contains an even number of data items, six, the median is the mean of the two middle items.

$$\text{Median} = \frac{\$21,500 + \$22,600}{2} = \frac{\$44,100}{2} = \$22,050$$

The median annual salary is $22,050.

612 • Statistics • Chapter 12

The SAT

Should the SAT, a test that has been taken by many college-bound seniors since 1941, be used to determine the state of American education? With a test that changes from year to year, recent adjustments in the scoring system, the use of calculators beginning in 1994, and huge variations from state to state in terms of the percent of students taking the test, there is no easy answer to this question. Mean SAT scores for 1997 and 1998 are shown below.

	1997	1998
Verbal Scores	505	505
Male	507	509
Female	503	502
Math Scores	511	512
Male	530	531
Female	494	496

Source: The College Board

3 Determine the mode for a data set.

b. We find the mean annual salary by adding the six annual salaries and dividing by 6.

$$\text{Mean} = \frac{\$19,700 + \$20,400 + \$21,500 + \$22,600 + \$23,000 + \$95,000}{6}$$

$$= \frac{\$202,200}{6} = \$33,700$$

The mean annual salary is $33,700.

In Example 7, the median annual salary is $22,050 and the mean annual salary is $33,700. Why such a big difference between these two measures of central tendency? The relatively high annual salary of the section manager, $95,000, pulls the mean salary to a value considerably higher than the median salary. When one or more data items are much greater than the other items, these extreme values can greatly influence the mean. In cases like this, the median is often more representative of the data.

This is why the median, rather than the mean, is used to summarize the weekly earnings for black men, white men, black women, and white women in Table 12.8 on page 611. Because no one can earn less than $0 per week, the distribution of weekly income must come to an end at $0 for each of these four groups. By contrast, there is no upper limit on weekly earnings on the high side. In the United States, the wealthiest 5% of the population earn about 21% of the total income. The relatively few people with very high weekly incomes tend to pull the mean income to a value considerably greater than the median income. Reporting mean incomes in Table 12.8 would inflate the numbers shown, making them nonrepresentative of the millions of workers in each of the four groups.

The Mode

Table 12.9 shows the ten longest running national network television series of the twentieth century. Using the number of seasons for the top ten shows, we construct a frequency distribution:

Table 12.9 Ten Longest-Running National Network TV Series of the Twentieth Century

Program	Number of Seasons the Show Ran
"Walt Disney"	33
"60 Minutes"	33
"The Ed Sullivan Show"	24
"Gunsmoke"	20
"The Red Skelton Show"	20
"Meet the Press"	18
"What's My Line?"	18
"I've Got a Secret"	17
"Lassie"	17
"The Lawrence Welk Show"	17

Source: Nielsen Media Research

A Frequency Distribution for the Number of Seasons for the Longest-Running TV Series

Number of Seasons the Show Ran x	Number of Shows Frequency
17	3
18	2
20	2
24	1
33	2

Technology

Calculators, Software Packages, and Statistics of Central Tendency

Many scientific calculators and all graphing calculators will allow you to enter data items. After you do so, the calculator will automatically display the mean, and perhaps the median and mode. Software packages for statistics automatically give the value for any requested statistic after data items have been entered.

The data value that occurs most often in this distribution is 17. Of the ten longest-running shows, the greatest number ran for 17 seasons; 17 is called the *mode* of this distribution.

The Mode

The **mode** is the data value that occurs most often in a data set.

EXAMPLE 8 Finding the Mode

Find the mode for the following group of data:

$$7, 2, 4, 7, 8, 10.$$

Solution The number 7 occurs more often than any other. Therefore, 7 is the mode.

If no single data value occurs more frequently than any other data value in a group, the group has no mode. For example, no data value in 2, 1, 4, 5, 3 occurs more than once, and the group has no mode. For the group 3, 3, 4, 5, 6, 6, no single value occurs most frequently, and this group has no mode. (You may find some books that call both 3 and 6 the modes of this group because each of these occurs twice.)

4 Determine the midrange for a data set.

The Midrange

Table 12.10 shows the ten hottest cities in the United States. Because temperature is constantly changing, you might wonder how the mean temperatures shown in the table are obtained.

First, we need to find a representative daily temperature. This is obtained by adding the lowest and highest temperatures for the day and then dividing this sum by 2. Next, we take the representative daily temperatures for all 365 days, add them, and divide the sum by 365. These are the mean temperatures that appear in Table 12.10.

Representative daily temperature,

$$\frac{\text{lowest daily temperature} + \text{highest daily temperature}}{2},$$

is an example of a measure of central tendency called the *midrange*.

The Midrange

The **midrange** is found by adding the lowest and highest data values and dividing the sum by 2.

$$\text{Midrange} = \frac{\text{lowest data value} + \text{highest data value}}{2}$$

Table 12.10 Ten Hottest U.S. Cities

City	Mean Temperature
Key West, FL	77.8°
Miami, FL	75.9°
West Palm Beach, FL	74.7°
Fort Myers, FL	74.4°
Yuma, AZ	74.2°
Brownsville, TX	73.8°
Phoenix, AZ	72.6°
Vero Beach, FL	72.4°
Orlando, FL	72.3°
Tampa, FL	72.3°

Source: National Oceanic and Atmospheric Administration

EXAMPLE 9   Finding the Midrange

The best paid state governors are in New York and New Jersey, each earning $130,000 annually. The worst paid is the governor of Montana, earning $59,310 annually. Find the midrange for annual salaries of U.S. governors.

Solution

$$\text{Midrange} = \frac{\text{Lowest annual salary} + \text{highest annual salary}}{2}$$

$$= \frac{\$59,310 + \$130,000}{2} = \frac{\$189,310}{2} = \$94,655$$

The midrange for annual salaries of U.S. governors is $94,655.

We can find the mean annual salary of U.S. governors by adding up the salaries of all 50 governors and then dividing the sum by 50. It is much faster to calculate the midrange, which is often used as an estimate for the mean.

EXAMPLE 10   Finding the Four Measures of Central Tendency

Suppose your six exam grades in a course are

$$52, 69, 75, 86, 86, \text{ and } 92.$$

Compute your final course grade (90–100 = A, 80–89 = B, 70–79 = C, 60–69 = D, below 60 = F) using the

a. mean   b. median   c. mode   d. midrange

Solution

a. The mean is the sum of the data items divided by the number of items, 6.

$$\text{Mean} = \frac{52 + 69 + 75 + 86 + 86 + 92}{6} = \frac{460}{6} \approx 76.67$$

Using the mean, your final course grade is C.

b. The data items are arranged in order. Because the number of data items is even, the median is the mean of the two middle items.

$$\text{Median} = \frac{75 + 86}{2} = \frac{161}{2} = 80.5$$

Using the median, your final course grade is B.

c. The mode is the data value that occurs most frequently. Because 86 occurs most often, the mode is 86. Using the mode, your final course grade is B.

d. The midrange is the mean of the lowest and highest data values.

$$\text{Midrange} = \frac{52 + 92}{2} = \frac{144}{2} = 72$$

Using the midrange, your final course grade is C.

Shrinking Means

The mean number of persons per U.S. household declined from 1850 through 1990. The mean has remained relatively stable since 1990.

Year	Mean Number of Persons per Household
1850	5.55
1860	5.28
1870	5.09
1880	5.04
1890	4.93
1900	4.76
1910	4.54
1920	4.34
1930	4.11
1940	3.67
1950	3.37
1960	3.35
1970	3.14
1975	2.94
1980	2.76
1985	2.69
1990	2.63
1997	2.64

Source: Bureau of the Census

Exercise Set 12.2

✓ Practice Exercises

In Exercises 1–8, find the mean for each group of data items.

1. 7, 4, 3, 2, 8, 5, 1, 3
2. 11, 6, 4, 0, 2, 1, 12, 0, 0
3. 91, 95, 99, 97, 93, 95
4. 100, 100, 90, 30, 70, 100
5. 100, 40, 70, 40, 60
6. 1, 3, 5, 10, 8, 5, 6, 8
7. 1.6, 3.8, 5.0, 2.7, 4.2, 4.2, 3.2, 4.7, 3.6, 2.5, 2.5
8. 1.4, 2.1, 1.6, 3.0, 1.4, 2.2, 1.4, 9.0, 9.0, 1.8

In Exercises 9–12, find the mean for the data items in the given frequency distribution.

9.

Score x	Frequency f
1	1
2	3
3	4
4	4
5	6
6	5
7	3
8	2

10.

Score x	Frequency f
1	2
2	4
3	5
4	7
5	6
6	4
7	3

11.

Score x	Frequency f
1	1
2	1
3	2
4	5
5	7
6	9
7	8
8	6
9	4
10	3

12.

Score x	Frequency f
1	3
2	4
3	6
4	8
5	9
6	7
7	5
8	2
9	1
10	1

In Exercises 13–20, find the median for each group of data items.

13. 7, 4, 3, 2, 8, 5, 1, 3
14. 11, 6, 4, 0, 2, 1, 12, 0, 0
15. 91, 95, 99, 97, 93, 95
16. 100, 100, 90, 30, 70, 100
17. 100, 40, 70, 40, 60
18. 1, 3, 5, 10, 8, 5, 6, 8
19. 1.6, 3.8, 5.0, 2.7, 4.2, 4.2, 3.2, 4.7, 3.6, 2.5, 2.5
20. 1.4, 2.1, 1.6, 3.0, 1.4, 2.2, 1.4, 9.0, 9.0, 1.8

Find the median for the data items in the frequency distribution in

21. Exercise 9.
22. Exercise 10.
23. Exercise 11.
24. Exercise 12.

In Exercises 25–32, find the mode for each group of data items. If there is no mode, so state.

25. 7, 4, 3, 2, 8, 5, 1, 3
26. 11, 6, 4, 0, 2, 1, 12, 0, 0
27. 91, 95, 99, 97, 93, 95
28. 100, 100, 90, 30, 70, 100
29. 100, 40, 70, 40, 60
30. 1, 3, 5, 10, 8, 5, 6, 8
31. 1.6, 3.8, 5.0, 2.7, 4.2, 4.2, 3.2, 4.7, 3.6, 2.5, 2.5
32. 1.4, 2.1, 1.6, 3.0, 1.4, 2.2, 1.4, 9.0, 9.0, 1.8

Find the mode for the data items in the frequency distribution in

33. Exercise 9.
34. Exercise 10.
35. Exercise 11.
36. Exercise 12.

In Exercises 37–44, find the midrange for each group of data items.

37. 7, 4, 3, 2, 8, 5, 1, 3
38. 11, 6, 4, 0, 2, 1, 12, 0, 0
39. 91, 95, 99, 97, 93, 95
40. 100, 100, 90, 30, 70, 100
41. 100, 40, 70, 40, 60
42. 1, 3, 5, 10, 8, 5, 6, 8
43. 1.6, 3.8, 5.0, 2.7, 4.2, 4.2, 3.2, 4.7, 3.6, 2.5, 2.5
44. 1.4, 2.1, 1.6, 3.0, 1.4, 2.2, 1.4, 9.0, 9.0, 1.8

Find the midrange for the data items in the frequency distribution in

45. Exercise 9.

46. Exercise 10.

47. Exercise 11.

48. Exercise 12.

Application Exercises

49. The mean annual cost for automobile insurance in the United States is $665.52. The cost in each of the five most expensive states is shown. By how much does the mean cost for these five states exceed the national mean?

Rank	State	Cost for Auto Insurance
1	New Jersey	$1013.47
2	Hawaii	963.08
3	District of Columbia	958.58
4	New York	905.90
5	Massachusetts	898.21

Source: National Association of Insurance Commissioners

50. Use the graph to find the mean number of business failures in the United States for the 1990–1997 period.

Number of Business Failures in the U.S.

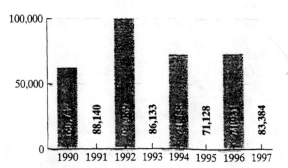

Source: Dun & Bradstreet

51. The greatest rainfall amount recorded in the United States occurred in Alvin, Texas in a 24-hour period on July 25–26, 1979. It was 43 inches.
    a. What was the mean hourly rainfall during that period?
    b. Does your answer in part (a) mean that this is the number of inches of rain that fell during each hour on July 25–26? Explain your answer.
    c. What was the least amount of rain that could have fallen in Alvin in a single hour on July 25–26?

The weights (to the nearest whole pound) of 40 randomly selected male college students are organized in a histogram with a superimposed frequency polygon, shown at the top of the next column. Use the graph to answer Exercises 52–55.

52. Find the mean weight.

53. Find the median weight.

54. Find the modal weight.

55. Find the midrange weight.

Weights of 40 Male College Students

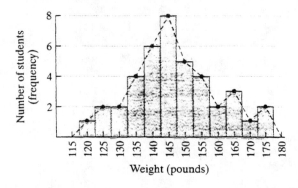

56. The list shows the total worldwide sales of the top-selling albums of the twentieth century. For these top-selling 11 albums, find
    a. the mean number of sales.
    b. the median number of sales.
    c. the modal number of sales.
    d. the midrange number of sales.

Artist/Album	Worldwide Sales to the Nearest Million
Michael Jackson, *Thriller*	40,000,000
Pink Floyd, *Dark Side of the Moon*	28,000,000
Meat Loaf, *Bat out of Hell*	27,000,000
Soundtrack, *The Bodyguard*	26,000,000
Soundtrack, *Saturday Night Fever*	25,000,000
The Beatles, *Sgt. Pepper's Lonely Hearts Club Band*	24,000,000
Eagles, *Their Greatest Hits 1971–1975*	24,000,000
Mariah Carey, *Music Box*	23,000,000
Carole King, *Tapestry*	22,000,000
Simon and Garfunkel, *Bridge over Troubled Water*	22,000,000
Soundtrack, *Grease*	22,000,000

Source: RIAA

57. An advertisement for a speed-reading course claimed that the "average" reading speed for people completing the course was 1000 words per minute. Shown on page 617 are the actual data for the reading speeds per minute for a sample of 24 people who completed the course.

1000	900	800	1000	900	850
650	1000	1050	800	1000	850
700	750	800	850	900	950
600	1100	950	700	750	650

a. Find the mean, median, mode, and midrange. (If you prefer, first organize the data in a frequency distribution.)

b. Which measure of central tendency was given in the advertisement?

c. Which measure of central tendency is the best indicator of the "average" reading speed in this situation? Explain your answer.

Writing in Mathematics

58. What is the mean and how is it obtained?

59. What is the median and how is it obtained?

60. What is the mode and how is it obtained?

61. What is the midrange and how is it obtained?

Use the median sales prices of existing single-family homes to answer Exercises 62–64.

Median Sales Price of Existing Single-Family Homes

Year	United States	Northeast	Midwest	South	West
1996	118,200	140,900	99,800	102,800	152,900
1997	124,100	145,100	106,100	109,000	160,300

Source: U.S. Department of Housing and Urban Development

62. The median sales price in 1997 for the entire country was $124,100. Explain what this means.

63. Explain why median sales prices, rather than mean sales prices, are reported.

64. Without using specific numbers, write two statements that summarize the trends shown by the median sales prices.

65. The "average" income in the United States can be given by the mean or the median.
   a. Which measure would be used in anti-U.S. propaganda? Explain your answer.
   b. Which measure would be used in pro-U.S. propaganda? Explain your answer.

66. In a class of 40 students, 21 have examination scores of 77%. Which measure or measures of central tendency can you immediately determine? Explain your answer.

67. A student's parents promise to pay for next semester's tuition if an A average is earned in chemsitry. With examination grades of 97%, 97%, 75%, 70%, and 55%, the student reports that an A average has been earned. Which measure of central tendency is the student reporting as the average? How is this student misrepresenting the course performance with statistics?

68. According to the National Oceanic and Atmospheric Administration, the coldest city in the United States is International Falls, Minnesota, with a mean temperature of 36.8°. Explain how this mean is obtained.

Critical Thinking Exercises

69. Make up a set of six examination grades (from 0 to 100) with each of the following characteristics:
   a. The mean and the median have the same value, but the mode has a different value.
   b. The mean and the mode have the same value, but the median has a different value.
   c. The mean is greater than the median.
   d. The mode is greater than the mean.
   e. The mean, median, and mode have the same value.
   f. The mean and mode have values of 72.

70. On an examination given to 30 students, no student scored below the mean. Describe how this occurred.

Technology Exercises

71. Use the statistical mode of a calculator to determine the mean for the following data items: 3, 9, 6, 10, 5, 6, 9, 9, 3, 6.

72. Use the statistical mode of a calculator to determine the mean for the following data items: 13, 29, 65, 23, 65, 96, 91, 95, 73, 66.

Group Exercise

73. Select a characteristic, such as shoe size or height, for which each member of the group can provide a number. Choose a characteristic of genuine interest to the group. For this characteristic, organize the data collected into a frequency distribution and a graph. Compute the mean, median, mode and midrange. Discuss any differences among these values. What happens if the group is divided (men and women or people under a certain age and people over a certain age) and these measures of central tendency are computed for each of the subgroups? Attempt to use measures of central tendency to discover something interesting about the entire group or the subgroups.

SECTION 12.3   Measures of Dispersion

Objectives

1. Determine the range for a data set.
2. Determine the standard deviation for a data set.

When you think of Houston, Texas and Honolulu, Hawaii, do balmy temperatures come to mind? Both cities have a mean temperature of 75°. However, the mean temperature does not tell the whole story. The temperature in Houston differs seasonally from a low of about 40° in January to a high of close to 100° in July and August. By contrast, Honolulu's temperature varies less throughout the year, usually ranging between 60° and 90°.

Measures of dispersion are used to describe the spread of data items in a data set. Two of the most common measures of dispersion, the *range* and the *standard deviation*, are discussed in this section.

1 Determine the range for a data set.

The Range

A quick but rough measure of dispersion is the **range**, the difference between the highest and lowest data values in a data set. For example, if Houston's hottest annual temperature is 103° and its coldest annual temperature is 33°, the range in temperature is

$$103° - 33°, \quad \text{or} \quad 70°.$$

If Honolulu's hottest day is 89° and its coldest day 61°, the range in temperature is

$$89° - 61°, \quad \text{or} \quad 28°.$$

The Range

The **range**, the difference between the highest and lowest data values in a data set, indicates the total spread of the data.

$$\text{Range} = \text{highest data value} - \text{lowest data value}$$

EXAMPLE 1   Computing the Range

Table 12.11 gives the ten most expensive markets for new homes in the United States. The figures are based on the mean cost of a new home and are drawn from a database of approximately 300 cities encompassing the largest metropolitan areas in the country. Find the range of home costs for the ten most expensive cities.

Table 12.11   Highest New Home Costs

City	Mean Home Cost (in thousands of dollars, to the nearest thousand $)
Honolulu	$332
San Francisco	256
San Jose, CA	251
Santa Cruz, CA	235
Stamford, CT	223
Orange County, CA	215
Bergen County, NJ	215
Salinas, CA	213
Long Island, NY	210
Ventura, CA	210

Source: Places Rated Almanac

Solution

$$\text{Range} = \text{highest data value} - \text{lowest data value}$$

$$= \$332 - \$210 = \$122$$

Because new home costs are shown in thousands of dollars in Table 12.11, the range of this data is $122,000.

The Standard Deviation

A second measure of dispersion, and one that is dependent on *all* of the data items, is called the **standard deviation**. The standard deviation incorporates how much each data item differs from the mean. To determine how much a data item deviates from the mean, first compute the mean. Then subtract the mean from the data item.

EXAMPLE 2   Finding Deviations from the Mean

Find the deviations from the mean for the ten data items in Table 12.11.

Solution   First, calculate the mean.

$$\text{Mean} = \frac{\Sigma x}{n} = \frac{332 + 256 + 251 + 235 + 223 + 215 + 215 + 213 + 210 + 210}{10}$$

$$= \frac{2360}{10} = 236$$

The mean home cost for the ten most expensive markets is $236,000. Now, let's find out by how much the home cost for each city differs from this amount. We do so by subtracting 236, the mean, from the ten data items. For Honolulu, the computation is shown as follows:

$$\text{Deviation from mean} = \text{data item} - \text{mean}$$

$$= 332 - 236 = 96$$

This indicates that home costs in Honolulu exceed the $236,000 mean by $96,000. The computation for Ventura is given by:

$$\text{Deviation from mean} = \text{data item} - \text{mean}$$

$$= 210 - 236 = -26$$

This indicates that home costs in Ventura are $26,000 below the mean.

The deviations from the mean for each of the ten given data items are shown in Table 12.12.

Table 12.12   Deviations from the Mean

Data item	Deviation: Data item − mean
332	$332 - 236 = 96$
256	$256 - 236 = 20$
251	$251 - 236 = 15$
235	$235 - 236 = -1$
223	$223 - 236 = -13$
215	$215 - 236 = -21$
215	$215 - 236 = -21$
213	$213 - 236 = -23$
210	$210 - 236 = -26$
210	$210 - 236 = -26$

The sum of deviations for a set of data is always zero. For the deviations shown in Table 12.12,

$$96 + 20 + 15 + (-1) + (-13) + (-21) + (-21) + (-23) + (-26) + (-26)$$

$$= 131 + (-131) = 0$$

This shows that we cannot find a measure of dispersion by finding the mean of the deviations, because this value is always zero. However, a kind of average of the deviations from the mean, called the **standard deviation**, can be computed. We do so by squaring each deviation and later introducing a square root in the computation. Here are the details on how to find the standard deviation of a set of data.

2 Determine the standard deviation for a data set.

Computing the Standard Deviation for a Data Set

1. Find the mean of the data items. $\bar{x}$

2. Find the deviation of each data item from the mean:

$$\text{data item} - \text{mean} \qquad x - \bar{x}$$

3. Square each deviation:

$$(\text{data item} - \text{mean})^2 \qquad (x - \bar{x})^2$$

4. Sum the squared deviations:

$$\Sigma(\text{data item} - \text{mean})^2$$

5. Divide the sum in step 4 by $n - 1$, where n represents the number of data items:

$$\frac{\Sigma(\text{data item} - \text{mean})^2}{n - 1}$$

6. Take the square root of the quotient in step 5. This value is the standard deviation for the data set.

$$\text{standard deviation} = \sqrt{\frac{\Sigma(\text{data item} - \text{mean})^2}{n - 1}}$$

memorize these steps.

Table 12.11   Highest New Home Costs

City	Mean Home Cost (in thousands of dollars, to the nearest thousand $)
Honolulu	$332
San Francisco	256
San Jose, CA	251
Santa Cruz, CA	235
Stamford, CT	223
Orange County, CA	215
Bergen County, NJ	215
Salinas, CA	213
Long Island, NY	210
Ventura, CA	210

Source: Places Rated Almanac.

The computation of the standard deviation can be organized using a table with three columns:

Data item	Deviation: Data item − mean	(Deviation)²: (Data item − mean)²

In Example 2, we worked out the first two columns of such a table. Let's continue working with the data for the most expensive homes in the United States and compute the standard deviation.

EXAMPLE 3   Computing the Standard Deviation

Table 12.11, showing the ten most expensive markets for new homes in the United States, is repeated in the margin. Find the standard deviation of the home costs.

Solution

1. **Find the mean.**

   From our work in Example 2, the mean is 236.

2. **Find the deviation of each data item from the mean: data item − mean.**

This, too, was done in Example 2 for each of the ten data items.

3. **Square each deviation: (data item − mean)^2.** We square each of the numbers in the (data item − mean) column, shown in Table 12.13. Notice that squaring the difference always results in a positive number.

Table 12.13 Computing the Standard Deviation

Data item	Deviation: Data item − mean	(Deviation)^2: (Data item − mean)^2
332	$332 - 236 = 96$	$96^2 = 96 \cdot 96 \quad = 9216$
256	$256 - 236 = 20$	$20^2 = 20 \cdot 20 \quad = 400$
251	$251 - 236 = 15$	$15^2 = 15 \cdot 15 \quad = 225$
235	$235 - 236 = -1$	$(-1)^2 = (-1)(-1) \quad = 1$
223	$223 - 236 = -13$	$(-13)^2 = (-13)(-13) = 169$
215	$215 - 236 = -21$	$(-21)^2 = (-21)(-21) = 441$
215	$215 - 236 = -21$	$(-21)^2 = (-21)(-21) = 441$
213	$213 - 236 = -23$	$(-23)^2 = (-23)(-23) = 529$
210	$210 - 236 = -26$	$(-26)^2 = (-26)(-26) = 676$
210	$210 - 236 = -26$	$(-26)^2 = (-26)(-26) = 676$
		12,774

Adding the ten numbers in the third column
gives the sum of the squared deviations:
Σ(data item−mean)^2.

4. **Sum the squared deviations: Σ(data item − mean)^2.** This step is shown in Table 12.13. The squares in the third column were added.

5. **Divide the sum in step 4 by $n − 1$, where n represents the number of data items.** The number of data items is 10, so we divide by 9.

$$\frac{\Sigma(\text{data item} - \text{mean})^2}{n - 1} = \frac{12{,}774}{10 - 1} = \frac{12{,}774}{9} \approx 1419.33$$

6. **The standard deviation is the square root of the quotient in step 5.**

$$\text{Standard deviation} = \sqrt{\frac{\Sigma(\text{data item} - \text{mean})^2}{n - 1}} = \sqrt{\frac{12{,}774}{9}} \approx 37.67$$

The standard deviation of the home costs in Table 12.11 is $37.67 thousand, or $37,670.

Example 4 illustrates that as the spread of data items increases, the standard deviation gets larger.

EXAMPLE 4 Computing the Standard Deviation

Find the standard deviation of the data items in each of the samples on page 622.

Sample A:

$$17, 18, 19, 20, 21, 22, 23$$

Sample B:

$$5, 10, 15, 20, 25, 30, 35$$

Solution Begin by finding the mean for each sample.
Sample A:

$$\text{Mean} = \frac{17 + 18 + 19 + 20 + 21 + 22 + 23}{7} = \frac{140}{7} = 20$$

Sample B:

$$\text{Mean} = \frac{5 + 10 + 15 + 20 + 25 + 30 + 35}{7} = \frac{140}{7} = 20$$

Although both samples have the same mean, the scores in sample B are more spread out. Thus, we would expect sample B to have the greater standard deviation. The computation of the standard deviation requires that we find $\Sigma(\text{data item} - \text{mean})^2$, shown in Table 12.14.

Table 12.14 Computing Standard Deviations for Two Samples

	Sample A			Sample B	
Data item	Deviation: Data item − mean	(Deviation)^2: (Data item − mean)^2	Data item	Deviation: Data item − mean	(Deviation)^2: (Data item − mean)^2
17	$17 - 20 = -3$	$(-3)^2 = 9$	5	$5 - 20 = -15$	$(-15)^2 = 225$
18	$18 - 20 = -2$	$(-2)^2 = 4$	10	$10 - 20 = -10$	$(-10)^2 = 100$
19	$19 - 20 = -1$	$(-1)^2 = 1$	15	$15 - 20 = -5$	$(-5)^2 = 25$
20	$20 - 20 = 0$	$0^2 = 0$	20	$20 - 20 = 0$	$0^2 = 0$
21	$21 - 20 = 1$	$1^2 = 1$	25	$25 - 20 = 5$	$5^2 = 25$
22	$22 - 20 = 2$	$2^2 = 4$	30	$30 - 20 = 10$	$10^2 = 100$
23	$23 - 20 = 3$	$3^2 = 9$	35	$35 - 20 = 15$	$15^2 = 225$
	$\Sigma(\text{data item} - \text{mean})^2 = 28$			$\Sigma(\text{data item} - \text{mean})^2 = 700$	

Each sample contains seven pieces of data, so we compute the standard deviation by dividing the sums in Table 12.14 by $7 - 1$, or 6, and taking the square root of each quotient.

$$\text{Standard deviation} = \sqrt{\frac{\Sigma(\text{data item} - \text{mean})^2}{n - 1}}$$

Sample A:

$$\text{Standard deviation} = \sqrt{\frac{28}{6}} \approx 2.16$$

Sample B:

$$\text{Standard deviation} = \sqrt{\frac{700}{6}} \approx 10.80$$

Sample A has a standard deviation of approximately 2.16, and sample B has a standard deviation of approximately 10.80. The scores in sample B are more spread out than those in sample A.

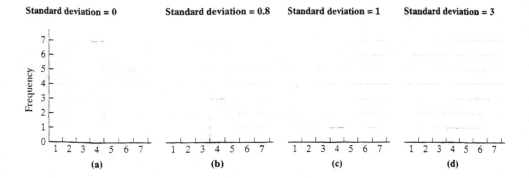

Figure 12.12 The standard deviation gets larger with increased dispersion among scores. In each case, the mean is 4.

Figure 12.12 illustrates four sets of data items organized in histograms. From left to right, the data items are

Figure 12.12 (a): 4, 4, 4, 4, 4, 4, 4
Figure 12.12 (b): 3, 3, 4, 4, 4, 5, 5
Figure 12.12 (c): 3, 3, 3, 4, 5, 5, 5
Figure 12.12 (d): 1, 1, 1, 4, 7, 7, 7

Each data set has a mean of 4. However, as the spread of data items increases, the standard deviation gets larger. Observe that when all the data items are the same, the standard deviation is 0.

EXAMPLE 5   Interpreting Standard Deviation

Two fifth grade classes have nearly identical mean scores on an aptitude test, but one class has a standard deviation three times that of the other. All other factors being equal, which class is easier to teach, and why?

Solution   The class with the smaller standard deviation is easier to teach because there is less variation among student aptitudes. Course work can be aimed at the average student without too much concern that the work will be too easy for some or too difficult for others. By contrast, the class with greater dispersion poses a greater challenge. By teaching to the average student, the students whose scores are significantly above the mean will be bored; students whose scores are significantly below the mean will be confused.

In our discussion of measures of central tendency, we saw that these measures are sometimes given for the entire population. For example, in 1997 the mean salary for National Football League quarterbacks was $1,346,000 (source: NFL Players Association). We can use this mean for the population of NFL quarterbacks to find the standard deviation for their salaries. Subtract the mean salary from each player's salary and use the procedure for computing the standard deviation.

By contrast to the population of NFL quarterbacks, most populations are too large to obtain data items for all members. Means and standard deviations are calculated using data items from a random sample of the population. Over the long run, statisticians expect the mean and the standard deviation for the sample to agree with the mean and the standard deviation for the population. By calculating the standard deviation for a random sample, statisticians can gain a good estimate for the standard deviation of the entire population.

In 1997, the mean salary for a U.S. public school teacher was approximately $40,000. Nearly 34 teachers can be hired for the salary of one NFL quarterback.

Technology

Standard Deviation on a Calculator

Many scientific calculators and all graphing calculators will allow you to enter data items, automatically displaying the standard deviation. Graphing calculators require that you specify if data items are from an entire population or a sample of the population. Many calculators use s to represent the sample standard deviation and σ to represent the population standard deviation.

Exercise Set 12.3

 Practice Exercises

In Exercises 1–10, find the range for each group of data items.

1. 1, 2, 3, 4, 5
2. 16, 17, 18, 19, 20
3. 7, 9, 9, 15
4. 11, 13, 14, 15, 17
5. 3, 3, 4, 4, 5, 5
6. 3, 3, 3, 4, 5, 5, 5
7. 1, 1, 1, 4, 7, 7, 7
8. 6, 6, 6, 6, 7, 7, 7, 4, 8, 3
9. 9, 5, 9, 5, 9, 5, 9, 5
10. 6, 10, 6, 10, 6, 10, 6, 10

In Exercises 11–14, a group of data items and their mean are given. Find a. the deviation from the mean for each of the data items and b. the sum of the deviations in part (a).

11. 3, 5, 7, 12, 18, 27; Mean = 12
12. 84, 88, 90, 95, 98; Mean = 91
13. 29, 38, 48, 49, 53, 77; Mean = 49
14. 60, 60, 62, 65, 65, 65, 66, 67, 70, 70; Mean = 65

In Exercises 15–20, find a. the mean; b. the deviation from the mean for each data item; and c. the sum of the deviations in part (b).

15. 85, 95, 90, 85, 100
16. 94, 62, 88, 85, 91
17. 146, 153, 155, 160, 161
18. 150, 132, 144, 122
19. 2.25, 3.50, 2.75, 3.10, 1.90
20. 0.35, 0.37, 0.41, 0.39, 0.43

In Exercises 21–30, find the standard deviation for each group of data items.   (by hand)

21. 1, 2, 3, 4, 5
22. 16, 17, 18, 19, 20
23. 7, 9, 9, 15
24. 11, 13, 14, 15, 17
25. 3, 3, 4, 4, 5, 5
26. 3, 3, 3, 4, 5, 5, 5
27. 1, 1, 1, 4, 7, 7, 7
28. 6, 6, 6, 6, 7, 7, 7, 4, 8, 3
29. 9, 5, 9, 5, 9, 5, 9, 5
30. 6, 10, 6, 10, 6, 10, 6, 10

In Exercises 31–32, compute the mean, range, and standard deviation for the data items in each of the three samples. Then describe one way in which the samples are alike and one way in which the samples are different.

31. Sample A: 6, 8, 10, 12, 14, 16, 18
    Sample B: 6, 7, 8, 12, 16, 17, 18
    Sample C: 6, 6, 6, 12, 18, 18, 18
32. Sample A: 8, 10, 12, 14, 16, 18, 20
    Sample B: 8, 9, 10, 14, 18, 19, 20
    Sample C: 8, 8, 8, 14, 20, 20, 20

 Application Exercises

33. The table at the top of the next column gives the number of police officers (in thousands, rounded to the nearest thousand) for the ten largest police forces in the United

States. (Miami is included because the city has more police officers than most states.) Find the mean and the standard deviation for this set of data.

State	Police Officers (thousands)
1. New York	68
2. California	66
3. Texas	41
4. Illinois	36
5. Florida	33
6. New Jersey	27
7. Pennsylvania	24
8. Ohio	21
9. Miami	20
10. Georgia	17

Source: U.S. Bureau of Justice Statistics

34. The accompanying table gives the number of U.S. citizens (in thousands) residing in other countries. Find the mean and the standard deviation for this set of data.

Nation	U.S. Citizens (thousands)
1. Mexico	539
2. Germany	354
3. Canada	296
4. United Kingdom	259
5. Israel	112
6. Italy	104
7. Dominican Republic	97
8. Spain	79
9. Australia	62
10. France	59

Source: U.S. Census Bureau

35. From 1918 to 1931, Babe Ruth was the American League home-run champion 12 times. The number of home runs Ruth hit per year for each of the 12 years is shown below. Find the mean and the standard deviation for this set of data.

11, 29, 54, 59, 41, 46, 47, 60, 54, 46, 49, 46

A 1996 study of student achievement in math and science ranked 41 countries. Scoring was on a scale of 200 to 800 points. Results for 15 of the countries in science are shown on the next page. Use these results to solve Exercises 36–38.

Science Scores
Top Five

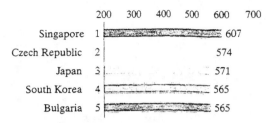

In the Middle

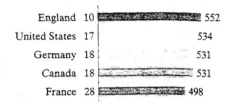

Bottom Five

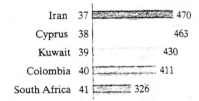

Source: International Mathematics and Science Study, 1996

36. Find the mean and the standard deviation for the top five countries.

37. Find the mean and the standard deviation for the five countries in the middle.

38. Find the mean and the standard deviation for the bottom five countries.

39. The bar graph shows the number of children home-educated in the United States. Find the mean and the standard deviation for the six data items.

Number of Children Home-Educated in the U.S.

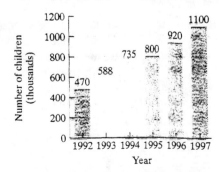

Source: National Home Education Research Institute

40. (Work this exercise with a calculator.) Shown below is the yearly per capita expenditure for the fifty U.S. states and Washington D.C. for police protection. Find the mean per capita expenditure and the standard deviation for the 51 data items.

AL	102.9	AK	532.9	AZ	194.8
AR	76.1	CA	202.6	CO	152.0
CT	135.8	DE	175.9	DC	548.8
FL	160.9	GA	123.9	HI	165.6
ID	102.1	IL	152.7	IN	92.1
IA	108.6	KS	108.9	KY	92.2
LA	144.7	ME	87.5	MD	175.6
MA	139.9	MI	170.8	MN	128.1
MS	74.8	MO	113.6	MT	117.1
NE	111.3	NV	276.4	NH	104.7
NJ	180.5	NM	184.4	NY	216.3
NC	109.0	ND	101.8	OH	121.7
OK	110.8	OR	147.9	PA	124.7
RI	143.2	SC	94.0	SD	103.8
TN	102.1	TX	112.8	UT	133.1
VT	109.9	VA	138.9	WA	169.3
WV	67.2	WI	153.0	WY	202.5

Source: Statistical Abstract of the U.S.

 Writing in Mathematics

41. Describe how to find the range of a data set.

42. Describe why the range might not be the best measure of dispersion.

43. Describe how the standard deviation is computed.

44. Describe what the standard deviation reveals about a data set.

45. If a set of test scores has a standard deviation of zero, what does this mean about the scores?

46. Two classes took a statistics test. Both classes had a mean score of 73. The scores of class A had a standard deviation of 5.6, and those of class B had a standard deviation of 10. Discuss the difference between the two classes' performance on the test.

47. A sample of cereals indicates a mean potassium content per serving of 93 milligrams, and a standard deviation of 2 milligrams. Write a description of what this means for a person who knows nothing about statistics.

Critical Thinking Exercises

48. Which one of the following is true?
    a. If the same number is added to each data item in a set of data, the standard deviation does not change.
    b. If each number in a data set is multiplied by 4, the standard deviation is doubled.
    c. It is possible for a set of scores to have a negative standard deviation.
    d. Data sets with different means cannot have the same standard deviation.

49. Describe a situation in which a relatively large standard deviation is desirable.

50. If a set of test scores has a large range but a small standard deviation, describe what this means about students' performance on the test.

51. Use the data 1, 2, 3, 5, 6, 7. Without actually computing the standard deviation, which of the following best approximates the standard deviation?
    a. 2   b. 6   c. 10   d. 20

Technology Exercises

52. Use the statistical mode of a calculator to determine the standard deviation of the following data items: 3, 9, 6, 10, 5, 6, 9, 9, 3, 6.

53. Use the statistical mode of a calculator to determine the standard deviation of the following data items: 13, 29, 65, 23, 65, 96, 91, 95, 73, 66.

Group Exercises

54. As a follow up to Group Exercise 73 on page 617, the group should reassemble and compute the standard deviation for each data set whose mean you previously determined. Does the standard deviation tell you anything new or interesting about the entire group or subgroups that you did not discover during the previous group activity?

55. Two fascinating sources of data are the *Wall Street Journal Almanac* (filled with terrific graphs) and the *American Almanac: Statistical Abstract of the United States*. Each volume is updated yearly. Group members should consult these sources (or an equivalent Internet source) and select intriguing data. The group's function is to use statistics to tell a story. Once "intriguing" data are identified, as a group:
    a. Summarize the data. Use words, frequency distributions, and graphic displays.
    b. Compute measures of central tendency and variability, using these statistics to discuss the data.

SECTION 12.4   The Normal Distribution

Objectives

1. Recognize characteristics of normal distributions.

2. Understand the 68–95–99.7 Rule.

3. Find scores at a specified standard deviation from the mean.

4. Use the 68–95–99.7 Rule.

5. Convert a data item to a z-score.

6. Understand and use percentiles.

7. Use and interpret margins of error.

8. Recognize distributions that are not normal.

Mean Adult Heights

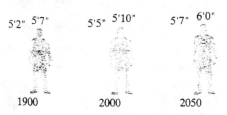

5'2" 5'7"   5'5" 5'10"   5'7" 6'0"

1900   2000   2050

Source: National Center for Health Statistics

Our heights are on the rise! In one million B.C., the mean height for men was 4 feet 6 inches. The mean height for women was 4 feet 2 inches. Because of improved diets and medical care, the mean height for men is now 5 feet 10 inches and for women it is 5 feet 5 inches. Mean adult heights are expected to plateau by 2050.

Suppose that a researcher selects a random sample of 100 adult men, measures their heights, and constructs a histogram. The graph is shown in Figure 12.13(a) at the top of the next page. Figure 12.13 illustrates what happens as the sample size increases. In Figure 12.13(c), if you were to fold the graph down the middle, the left side would fit the right side. As we move out from the middle, the heights of the bars are the same to the left and right. Such a histogram is called

116. Give an example of a phenomenon that is normally distributed. Explain why. (Try to be creative and not use one of the distributions discussed in this section.) Estimate what the mean and the standard deviation might be and describe how you determined these estimates.

117. Give an example of a phenomenon that is not normally distributed and explain why.

 Critical Thinking Exercises

118. Find two z-scores so that 40% of the data in the distribution lies between them. (More than one answer is possible.)

119. A woman insists that she will never marry a man as short or shorter than she, knowing that only one man in 400 falls into this category. Assuming a mean height of 69 inches for men with a standard deviation of 2.5 inches (and a normal distribution), approximately how tall is the woman?

120. The placement test for a college has scores that are normally distributed with a mean of 500 and a standard deviation of 100. If the college accepts only the top 10% of examinees, what is the cutoff score on the test for admission?

 Group Exercise

121. For this activity, group members will conduct interviews with a random sample of students on campus. Each student is to be asked, "What is the worst thing about being a student?" One response should be recorded for each student.
   a. Each member should interview enough students so that there are at least 50 randomly selected students in the sample.
   b. After all responses have been recorded, the group should organize the four most common answers. For each answer, compute the percentage of students in the sample who felt that this is the worst thing about being a student.
   c. Find the margin of error for your survey.
   d. For each of the four most common answers, write a statement about the percentage of all students on your campus who feel that this is the worst thing about being a student.

SECTION 12.5   Scatter Plots, Correlation, and Regression Lines

Objectives

1. Make a scatter plot for a table of data items.
2. Interpret information given in a scatter plot.
3. Compute the correlation coefficient.
4. Write the equation of the regression line.
5. Use a sample's correlation coefficient to determine if there is a correlation in the population.

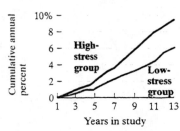

Cumulative Annual Heart-Disease Incidents for High- and Low-Stress Groups

During a 13-year study, men in a high-stress group were more likely to have heart attacks than those in a low-stress group.
Source: "Self-Perceived Psychological Stress and Incidence of Coronary Artery Disease in Middle-Aged Men."

Have you ever noticed that during periods of high stress you tend to get sick? A random sample of 232 subjects each filled in two questionnaires. The first dealt with the amount of stress he or she experienced in the past 12 months. The second questionnaire assessed how often he or she became ill during that period. The researchers found that there is a relationship between stress and illness. An increase in stress tends to be accompanied by increased episodes of ill health. This 1971 study lead to hundreds of followup studies that have enabled medical professionals to better understand how stress is related to physical health.

Up to this point in the chapter, we have studied situations in which data sets involve a single variable, such as SAT scores, weights, cholesterol levels, and lengths of pregnancies. By contrast, the stress-illness study involved data collected on two variables—amount of stress and frequency of illness. In this section, we consider situations in which there are two data items for each randomly selected person or thing. Our interest is in determining whether or not there is a relationship between the two variables and, if so, the strength of that relationship.

1 Make a scatter plot for a table of data items.

Scatter Plots and Correlation

Is there a relationship between education and prejudice? With increased education, does a person's level of prejudice tend to decrease? Notice that we are interested in two quantities—years of education and level of prejudice. For each person in our sample, we will record the number of years of school completed and the score on a test measuring prejudice. Higher scores on this 1 to 10 test indicate greater prejudice. Using x to represent years of education and y to represent scores on a test measuring prejudice, Table 12.16 shows these two quantities for a random sample of ten people.

Table 12.16   Recording Two Quantities in a Sample of Ten People

Respondent	A	B	C	D	E	F	G	H	I	J
Years of education (x)	12	5	14	13	8	10	16	11	12	4
Score on prejudice test (y)	1	7	2	3	5	4	1	2	3	10

When two data items are collected for every person or object in a sample, the data items can be visually displayed using a *scatter plot*. A **scatter plot** is a collection of data points, one data point per person or object. We can make a scatter plot of the data in Table 12.16 by drawing a horizontal axis to represent years of education and a vertical axis to represent scores on a test measuring prejudice. We then represent each of the ten respondents with a single point on the graph. For example, the dot for respondent A is located to represent 12 years of education on the horizontal axis and 1 on the prejudice test on the vertical axis. Plotting each of the ten pieces of data in a rectangular coordinate system results in the scatter plot shown in Figure 12.26.

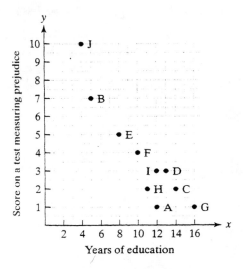

Figure 12.26 A scatter plot for education-prejudice data

A scatter plot like the one in Figure 12.26 can be used to determine if two quantities are related. If there is a clear relationship, the quantities are said to be **correlated**. The scatter plot shows a downward trend among the data points, although there are a few exceptions. People with increased education tend to have a lower score on the test measuring prejudice. **Correlation** is used to determine if there is a relationship between two variables and, if so, the strength and direction of that relationship.

Correlation and Causal Connections

Correlations can often be seen when data items are displayed on a scatter plot. Although the scatter plot in Figure 12.26 indicates a correlation between education and prejudice, we cannot conclude that increased education

Study Tip

The numbered list on the right represents three possibilities. Perhaps you can provide a better explanation about decreasing prejudice with increased education.

causes a person's level of prejudice to decrease. There are at least three possible explanations.

1. The correlation between increased education and decreased prejudice is simply a coincidence.

2. Education usually involves classrooms with a variety of different kinds of people. Increased exposure to diversity in the classroom setting, which accompanies increased levels of education, might be an underlying cause for decreased prejudice.

3. Education, the process of acquiring knowledge, requires people to look at new ideas and see things in different ways. Thus, education causes one to be more tolerant and less prejudiced.

Establishing that one thing causes another is extremely difficult, even if there is a strong correlation between these things. For example, as the air temperature increases, there is an increase in the number of people stung by jellyfish at the beach. This does not mean that an increase in air temperature causes more people to be stung. It might mean that because it is hotter, more people go into the water. With an increased number of swimmers, more people are likely to be stung. In short, correlation is not necessarily causation.

Regression Lines and Correlation Coefficients

Figure 12.27 shows the scatter plot for the education-prejudice data for a second time. Also shown is a straight line that seems to "fit" the data points fairly well. Most of the data points lie either near or on this line. A line that best fits the data points in a scatter plot is called a **regression line**. The regression line is the particular line in which the spread of the data points around it is as small as possible.

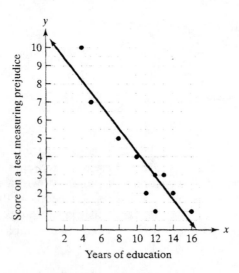

Figure 12.27 A scatter plot with a regression line

The scatter plot in Figure 12.28 on page 645 indicates that as years of education increase, income tends to increase. Each point in the scatter plot depicts two variables, education and income, obtained from one randomly selected person. Also shown is the regression line, the line that best fits the data points. The

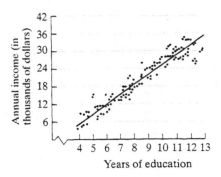

Figure 12.28 As years of education increase, income tends to increase

scatter plot indicates a relationship, or correlation, between education and income. However, we cannot conclude that increased education causes annual income to increase.

A measure that is used to describe the strength and direction of a relationship between variables whose data points lie on or near a line is called the **correlation coefficient**, designated by r. Figure 12.29 shows scatter plots and correlation coefficients. Variables are **positively correlated** if they tend to increase or decrease together, as in Figure 12.29 (a), (b), and (c). By contrast, variables are **negatively correlated** if one variable tends to decrease while the other increases, as in Figure 12.29 (e), (f), and (g). Figure 12.29 illustrates that a correlation coefficient, r, is a number between -1 and 1, inclusive. Figure 12.29 (a) shows a value of 1. This indicates a **perfect positive correlation** in which all points in the scatter plot lie precisely on the regression line that rises from left to right. On the far right, Figure 12.29 (g) shows a value of -1. This indicates a **perfect negative correlation** in which all points in the scatter plot lie precisely on the regression line that falls from left to right.

2 Interpret information given in a scatter plot.

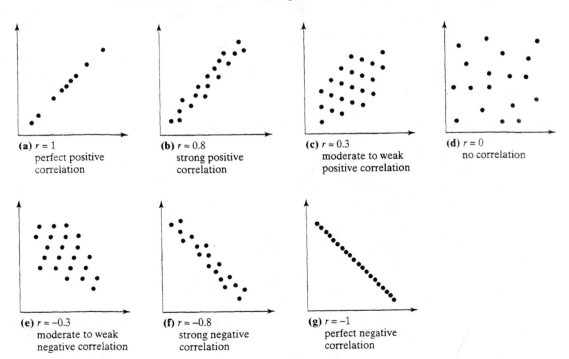

(a) $r = 1$
perfect positive correlation

(b) $r \approx 0.8$
strong positive correlation

(c) $r \approx 0.3$
moderate to weak positive correlation

(d) $r = 0$
no correlation

(e) $r \approx -0.3$
moderate to weak negative correlation

(f) $r \approx -0.8$
strong negative correlation

(g) $r = -1$
perfect negative correlation

Figure 12.29 Scatter plots and correlation coefficients

Beneficial Uses of Correlation Coefficients

- A Florida study showed a high positive correlation between the number of powerboats and the number of manatee deaths. Many of these deaths were seen to be caused by boats' propellers gashing into the manatees' bodies. Based on this study, Florida set up coastal sanctuaries where power boats are prohibited so that these large gentle mammals that float just below the water's surface could thrive.

- In 1986, researchers studied how psychiatric patients readjusted to their community after their release from a mental hospital. A moderate positive correlation ($r = 0.38$) was found between patients' attractiveness and their postdischarge social adjustment. The better-looking patients were better off. The researchers suggested that physical attractiveness plays a role in patients' readjustment to community living because good-looking people tend to be treated better by others than homely people are.

Take another look at Figure 12.29. If r is between 0 and 1, as in (b) and (c), the two variables are positively correlated, but not perfectly. Although all the data points will not lie on the regression line, as in (a), an increase in one variable tends to be accompanied by an increase in the other.

Negative correlations are also illustrated in Figure 12.29. If r is between 0 and −1, as in (e) and (f), the two variables are negatively correlated, but not perfectly. Although all the data points will not lie on the regression line, as in (g), an increase in one variable tends to be accompanied by a decrease in the other.

EXAMPLE 1   Interpreting a Correlation Coefficient

We opened this section with a 1971 study involving 232 subjects. Researchers found a relationship between subjects' level of stress and how often they became ill. The correlation coefficient in this study was 0.32. Does this indicate a strong relationship between stress and illness?

Solution   The correlation coefficient $r = 0.32$ means that as stress increases, frequency of illness also tends to increase. However, 0.32 is only a moderate correlation, illustrated in Figure 12.29(c) on page 645. There is not, based on this study, a strong relationship between stress and illness. In this study, the relationship is somewhat weak.

EXAMPLE 2   Interpreting Information Given in a Scatter Plot

The scatter plot in Figure 12.30 shows the relationship between fat intake and deaths per 100,000 women from breast cancer. Use the scatter plot to determine whether each of the statements on page 647 is true or false.

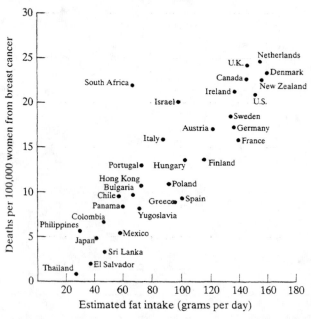

Figure 12.30 *Source:* From "Diet and Cancer" by Leonard A. Cohen, Copyright © 1987 by Scientific American, Inc. All rights reserved

a. Increased fat intake is a cause of breast cancer.

Solution The variables in the scatter plot, daily fat intake and deaths per 100,000 women, tend to increase together in Figure 12.30. Thus, the values of the first variable (daily fat intake) are positively correlated with those for the second variable (deaths per 100,000 women). However, correlation does not tell us whether there is a cause-and-effect relationship between the first and second variables. Other factors may influence the death rate from breast cancer. (Recent studies from Great Britain show that there is no causal relationship between fat intake and breast cancer.) Based on Figure 12.30, we cannot conclude that increased fat intake is a cause of breast cancer. Correlation is not necessarily causation. The given statement is false.

b. With a fat intake of approximately 150 grams per day in the United States, there are 26 deaths per 100,000 women from breast cancer.

Solution Find the point in the scatter plot that represents the United States. This point is over about 150 units on the horizontal axis and up about 21 units. This means that with a fat intake of approximately 150 grams per day in the United States, there are 21 deaths per 100,000 women from breast cancer. The given statement is false because of its claim that there are 26 deaths per 100,000 women.

c. There is a strong positive correlation between fat intake and deaths from breast cancer.

Solution The variables in the scatter plot, daily fat intake and deaths per 100,000 women from breast cancer, tend to increase together. It would not be too difficult to draw a straight line that rises from left to right on or near which most of the data points lie. This indicates that there is a strong positive correlation between fat intake and deaths from breast cancer. The given statement is true.

Cigarettes and Lung Cancer

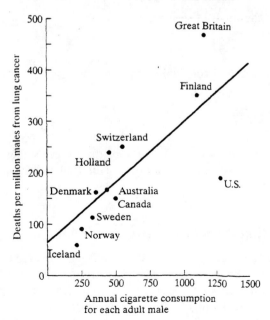

This scatter plot shows a relationship between cigarette consumption among males and deaths due to lung cancer per million males. The data are from 11 countries and date back to a 1964 report by the U.S. Surgeon General. The correlation coefficient for this study was computed to be 0.73, a relatively high positive correlation. At that time, the tobacco industry argued that in spite of this correlation, tobacco use is not the cause of cancer. Although correlation is not causation, recent data do, indeed, show a causal effect between tobacco use and numerous diseases.

Source: Smoking and Health, Washington, D.C., 1964

3 Compute the correlation coefficient.

How to Obtain the Correlation Coefficient and the Equation of the Regression Line

The easiest way to find the correlation coefficient and the equation of the regression line is to use a graphing or statistical calculator. Graphing calculators have statistical menus that enable you to enter the x and y data items for the variables. Based on this information, you can instruct the calculator to display a scatter plot, the equation of the regression line, and the correlation coefficient.

We can also compute the correlation coefficient and the equation of the regression line by hand using formulas. First, we compute the correlation coefficient.

Technology

Gaphing Calculators, Scatter Plots, and Regression Lines

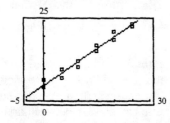

This calculator display was obtained by entering x and y data items and instructing the calculator to display a scatter plot and the regression line.

```
LinReg
 y=ax+b
 a=.7171428571
 b=4.785714286
 r=.9803266536
```

Calculators display equations of regression lines and calculate correlation coefficients. The slope shown above is approximately 0.7. The positive slope reinforces the fact that there is a positive correlation between the variables.

Computing the Correlation Coefficient by Hand

The following formula is used to calculate the correlation coefficient, r.

$$r = \frac{n(\Sigma xy) - (\Sigma x)(\Sigma y)}{\sqrt{n(\Sigma x^2) - (\Sigma x)^2}\sqrt{n(\Sigma y^2) - (\Sigma y)^2}}$$

In the formula

$n =$ the number of data points (x, y)

$\Sigma x =$ the sum of the x-values

$\Sigma y =$ the sum of the y-values

$\Sigma xy =$ the sum of the product of x and y in each pair

$\Sigma x^2 =$ the sum of the squares of the x-values

$\Sigma y^2 =$ the sum of the squares of the y-values

$(\Sigma x)^2 =$ the square of the sum of the x-values

$(\Sigma y)^2 =$ the square of the sum of the y-values

When computing the correlation coefficient by hand, organize your work in five columns:

x	y	xy	x^2	y^2

Find the sum of the numbers in each column. Then, substitute these values into the formula for r. Example 3 illustrates computing the correlation coefficient for the education-prejudice test data.

EXAMPLE 3 Computing the Correlation Coefficient

Shown again on page 649 are the number of years of school, x, completed by ten randomly selected people and their scores on a test measuring prejudice, y. Recall that higher scores on the measure of prejudice (1 to 10) indicate greater levels of prejudice. Determine the correlation coefficient between years of education and scores on a prejudice test.

Respondent		A	B	C	D	E	F	G	H	I	J
Years of education (x)		12	5	14	13	8	10	16	11	12	4
Score on prejudice test (y)		1	7	2	3	5	4	1	2	3	10

Solution As suggested, organize the work in five columns.

x	y	xy	x^2	y^2
12	1	12	144	1
5	7	35	25	49
14	2	28	196	4
13	3	39	169	9
8	5	40	64	25
10	4	40	100	16
16	1	16	256	1
11	2	22	121	4
12	3	36	144	9
4	10	40	16	100
$\Sigma x = 105$	$\Sigma y = 38$	$\Sigma xy = 308$	$\Sigma x^2 = 1235$	$\Sigma y^2 = 218$

| Add all values in the x-column. | Add all values in the y-column. | Add all values in the xy-column. | Add all values in the x^2-column. | Add all values in the y^2-column. |

We use these five sums in calculating the correlation coefficient.

Another value in the formula for r that we have not yet determined is n, the number of data points (x, y). Because there are ten items in the x-column and ten items in the y-column, the number of data points (x, y) is ten. Thus, $n = 10$.

In order to calculate r, we also need to find the square of the sum of the x-values and the y-values:

$$(\Sigma x)^2 = (105)^2 = 11{,}025 \text{ and } (\Sigma y)^2 = (38)^2 = 1444$$

We are ready to determine the value for r.

$$r = \frac{n(\Sigma xy) - (\Sigma x)(\Sigma y)}{\sqrt{n(\Sigma x^2) - (\Sigma x)^2}\sqrt{n(\Sigma y^2) - (\Sigma y)^2}}$$

$$= \frac{10(308) - 105(38)}{\sqrt{10(1235) - 11{,}025}\sqrt{10(218) - 1444}}$$

$$= \frac{-910}{\sqrt{1325}\sqrt{736}}$$

$$\approx -0.92$$

This value for r is fairly close to -1 and indicates a strong negative correlation. This means that the more education a person has, the less prejudiced that person is (based on scores on the test measuring levels of prejudice).

Once we have determined that two variables are related, we can use the equation of the regression line to determine the exact relationship. Here is the formula for writing the equation of the line that best fits the data.

4 Write the equation of the regression line.

Writing the Equation of the Regression Line by Hand

The equation of the regression line is

$$y = mx + b$$

where

$$m = \frac{n(\Sigma xy) - (\Sigma x)(\Sigma y)}{n(\Sigma x^2) - (\Sigma x)^2}, \text{ and } b = \frac{\Sigma y - m(\Sigma x)}{n}.$$

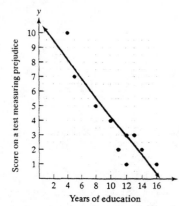

Years of education

Figure 12.27

EXAMPLE 4 Writing the Equation of the Regression Line

a. Shown, again, in Figure 12.27 is the scatter plot and the regression line for the data in Example 3. Use the data to find the equation of the regression line that relates years of education and scores on a prejudice test.

b. Approximately what score on the test can be anticipated by a person with nine years of education?

Solution

a. We use the sums obtained in Example 3. Thus,

$$m = \frac{n(\Sigma xy) - (\Sigma x)(\Sigma y)}{n(\Sigma x^2) - (\Sigma x)^2} = \frac{10(308) - 105(38)}{10(1235) - (105)^2} = \frac{-910}{1325} \approx -0.69$$

With a negative correlation coefficient, it makes sense that the slope of the regression line is negative. This line falls from left to right, indicating a negative correlation.

Now, we find the y-intercept, b.

$$b = \frac{\Sigma y - m(\Sigma x)}{n} = \frac{38 - (-0.69)(105)}{10} = \frac{110.45}{10} \approx 11.05$$

Therefore, the equation of the regression line is

$$y = mx + b$$

$$y = -0.69x + 11.05$$

where x represents the number of years of education and y represents the score on the prejudice test.

b. To anticipate the score on the prejudice test for a person with nine years of education, substitute 9 for x in the regression line's equation.

$$y = -0.69x + 11.05$$

$$y = -0.69(9) + 11.05 = 4.84$$

5 Use a sample's correlation coefficient to determine if there is a correlation in the population.

A person with nine years of education is anticipated to have a score close to 5 on the prejudice test.

The Level of Significance of r

In Example 3, we found a strong negative correlation between education and prejudice, computing the correlation coefficient, r, to be -0.92. However, the sample size ($n = 10$) was relatively small. With such a small sample, can we truly conclude that a correlation exists in the population? Or could it be that education and prejudice are not related? Perhaps the results we obtained were simply due to sampling error and chance.

Mathematicians have identified values to determine if r, the correlation coefficient for a sample, can be attributed to a relationship between variables in the population. These values are shown in the second and third columns of Table 12.17. They depend on the sample size, n, listed in the left column. If $|r|$, the absolute value of the correlation coefficient computed for the sample, is greater than the value given in the table, a correlation exits between the variables in the population. The column headed $\alpha = 0.05$ denotes a **significance level of 5%**, meaning that there is a 0.05 probability that, when the statistician says the variables are correlated, they are actually not related in the population. The column on the right, headed $\alpha = 0.01$, denotes a **significance level of 1%**, meaning that there is a 0.01 probability that, when the statistician says the variables are correlated, they are actually not related in the population. Values in the $\alpha = 0.01$ column are greater than those in the $\alpha = 0.05$ column. Because of the possibility of sampling error, there is always a probability that when we say the variables are related, there is actually not a correlation in the population from which the sample was randomly selected.

Table 12.17 Values for Determining Correlations in a Population

n	$\alpha = 0.05$	$\alpha = 0.01$
4	0.950	0.990
5	0.878	0.959
6	0.811	0.917
7	0.754	0.875
8	0.707	0.834
9	0.666	0.798
10	0.632	0.765
11	0.602	0.735
12	0.576	0.708
13	0.553	0.684
14	0.532	0.661
15	0.514	0.641
16	0.497	0.623
17	0.482	0.606
18	0.468	0.590
19	0456	0.575
20	0.444	0.561
22	0.423	0.537
27	0.381	0.487
32	0.349	0.449
37	0.325	0.418
42	0.304	0.393
47	0.288	0.372
52	0.273	0.354
62	0.250	0.325
72	0.232	0.302
82	0.217	0.283
92	0.205	0.267
102	0.195	0.254

The larger the sample size n, the smaller is the value of r needed for a correlation in the population.

EXAMPLE 5 Determining a Correlation in the Population

In Example 3, we computed $r = -0.92$ for $n = 10$. Can we conclude that there is a negative correlation between education and prejudice in the population?

Solution Begin by taking the absolute value of the calculated correlation coefficient.

$$|r| = |-0.92| = 0.92$$

Now, look to the right of $n = 10$ in Table 12.17. Because 0.92 is greater than both of these values (0.632 and 0.765), we may conclude that a correlation does exist between education and prejudice in the population. (There is a probability of 0.01 that the variables are not really correlated in the population and our results could be attributed to chance.)

Exercise Set 12.5

✓ Practice and Application Exercises

In Exercises 1–8, make a scatter plot for the given data. Use the scatter plot to describe whether or not the variables appear to be related.

1.

x	1	6	4	3	7	2
y	2	5	3	3	4	1

2.

x	2	1	6	3	4
y	4	5	10	8	9

3.

x	8	6	1	5	4	10	3
y	2	4	10	5	6	2	9

4.

x	4	5	2	1
y	1	3	5	4

5.

Respondent	A	B	C	D	E	F	G
Years of education of parent (x)	13	9	7	12	12	10	11
Years of education of child (y)	13	11	7	16	17	8	17

6.

Respondent	A	B	C	D	E
IQ (x)	110	115	120	125	135
Annual income (y) (in thousands of dollars)	30	32	36	40	44

7. The data show the number of registered automatic weapons (in thousands) and the murder rate (in murders per 100,000) for eight randomly selected states.

Automatic weapons, x	11.6	8.3	6.9	3.6	2.6	2.5	2.4	0.6
Murder rate, y	13.1	10.6	11.5	10.1	5.3	6.6	3.6	4.4

Source: FBI and Bureau of Alcohol, Tobacco, and Firearms

8. The data show the number of marriages and divorces (in millions) for six selected years in the United States

Year	1970	1975	1980	1985	1990	1994
Marriages, x	2.159	2.153	2.39	2.413	2.443	2.362
Divorces, y	0.708	1.036	1.189	1.19	1.182	1.191

Source: U.S. Center for Health Statistics

The scatter plot in the figure shows the relationship between the percentage of married women of child bearing age and births per woman in selected countries. Use the scatter plot to determine whether each of the statements in Exercises 9–16 is true or false.

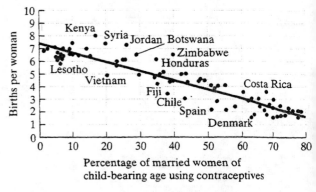

Source: Population Reference Bureau

9. There is a strong positive correlation between contraceptive use and births per woman.

10. There is no correlation between contraceptive use and births per woman.

11. There is a strong negative correlation between contraceptive use and births per woman.

12. There is a causal relationship between contraceptive use and births per woman.

13. With approximately 43% of women of child-bearing age using contraceptives, there are 3 births per woman in Chile.

14. With 20% of women of child-bearing age using contraceptives, there are 6 births per woman in Vietnam.

15. No two countries have a different number of births per woman with the same percentage of married women using contraceptives.

16. The country with the greatest number of births per woman also has the smallest percentage of women using contraceptives.

The scatter plot in the figure shows the relationship between SAT scores and grade point average for the first year in college for a group of randomly selected college students. Use the scatter plot to determine whether each of the statements in Exercises 17–24 is true or false.

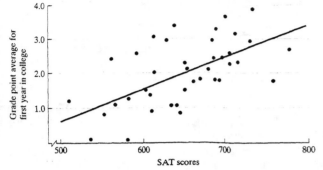

17. There is no correlation between SAT scores and grade point averages.
18. There is an almost-perfect positive correlation between SAT scores and grade point averages.
19. There is a positive correlation between SAT scores and grade point averages.
20. As SAT scores decrease, grade point averages also tend to decrease.
21. Most of the data points lie on the regression line.
22. The number of college students in this sample is approximately 200.
23. The student with the lowest SAT score has the worst grade point average.
24. The student with the highest SAT score has the best grade point average.

The scatter plot shows the relationship between the Olympic year and the men's and women's winning times (in seconds) in the Olympic 100-meter freestyle swimming race. Also shown are the regression lines. Use the information given in the figure to determine whether each statement in Exercises 25–28 is true or false.

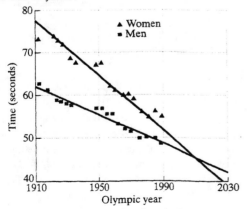

Men's and women's winning times in the Olympic 100-meter freestyle swimming race

25. There is a strong positive correlation between the Olympic year and winning time in the race for both women and men.
26. Even if present trends continue, women will not swim faster than men in this Olympic event.
27. Many of the data points do not fall exactly on the regression lines for the two sets of data.
28. A reasonable estimate of the correlation coefficient for the data for the women is −0.2.

Use the scatter plots shown, labeled (a)–(f), to solve Exercises 29–32.

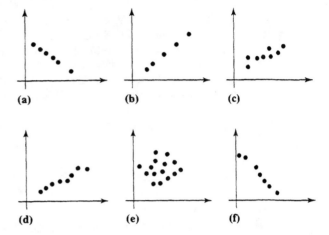

29. Which scatter plot indicates a perfect negative correlation?
30. Which scatter plot indicates a perfect positive correlation?
31. In which scatter plot is $r = 0.9$?
32. In which scatter plot is $r = 0.01$?

Compute r, the correlation coefficient, rounded to the nearest thousandth, for the data in

33. Exercise 1.   34. Exercise 2.
35. Exercise 3.   36. Exercise 4.

37. Use the data in Exercise 5 to solve this exercise.
   a. Determine the correlation coefficient between years of education of parent and child.
   b. Find the equation of the regression line for years of education of parent and child.
   c. Approximately how many years of education can we predict for a child with a parent who has 16 years of education?

38. Use the data in Exercise 6 to solve this exercise.
   a. Determine the correlation coefficient between IQ and income.
   b. Find the equation of the regression line for IQ and income.
   c. Approximately what annual income can be anticipated by a person whose IQ is 123?

39. Use the data in Exercise 7 to solve this exercise.
    a. Determine the correlation coefficient between the number of automatic weapons and the murder rate.
    b. Find the equation of the regression line.
    c. Approximately what murder rate can we anticipate in a state that has 14 thousand registered weapons?

40. Use the data in Exercise 8 to solve this exercise.
    a. Determine the correlation coefficient between the number of marriages and the number of divorces.
    b. Find the equation of the regression line.
    c. Approximately how many divorces can we anticipate for a year in which there are 2.7 million marriages?

In Exercises 41–47, the correlation coefficient, r, is given for a sample of n data points. Use the $\alpha = 0.05$ column in Table 12.17 on page 651 and determine whether or not we may conclude that a correlation does exist in the population. (Using the $\alpha = 0.05$ column there is a probability of 0.05 that the variables are not really correlated in the population and our results could be attributed to chance. Ignore this possibility when concluding whether or not there is a correlation in the population.)

41. $n = 20, r = 0.5$ 42. $n = 27, r = 0.4$

43. $n = 12, r = 0.5$ 44. $n = 22, r = 0.04$

45. $n = 72, r = -0.351$ 46. $n = 37, r = -0.37$

47. $n = 20, r = -0.37$

48. In the 1964 study on cigarette consumption and deaths due to lung cancer (see the essay on page 647), $n = 11$ and $r = 0.73$. What can you conclude using the $\alpha = 0.05$ column in Table 12.17?

Writing in Mathematics

49. What is a scatter plot?

50. How does a scatter plot indicate that two variables are correlated?

51. Give an example of two variables with a strong positive correlation and explain why this is so.

52. Give an example of two variables with a strong negative correlation and explain why this is so.

53. What is meant by a regression line?

54. When all points in a scatter plot fall on the regression line, what is the value of the correlation coefficient? Describe what this means.

For the pairs of quantities in Exercises 55–58, describe whether a scatter plot will show a positive correlation, a negative correlation, or no correlation. If there is a correlation, is it strong, moderate, or weak? Explain your answers.

55. Height and weight

56. Number of days absent and grade in a course

57. Height and grade in a course

58. Hours of television watched and grade in a course

59. Explain how to use the correlation coefficient for a sample to determine if there is a correlation in the population.

Critical Thinking Exercises

60. Which one of the following is true?
    a. A scatter plot need not define y as a function of x.
    b. The correlation coefficient and the slope of the regression line for the same set of data can have opposite signs.
    c. When all points in a scatter plot fall on the regression line, the value of the correlation coefficient is 0.
    d. If the same number is subtracted from each x-item, but the y-item stays the same, the correlation coefficient for these new data points decreases.

61. Give an example of two variables with a strong correlation, where each variable is not the cause of the other.

Technology Exercises

62. Enter the data items from Table 12.16 on page 643 into an Excel spreadsheet.

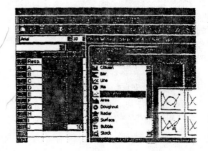

After you have entered the data, use the computer mouse to highlight the cells containing the data corresponding to the years of education and test scores. Then activate the Chart Option of the spreadsheet by clicking on the Insert pull-down menu and selecting Chart. Select the XY(Scatter) option (see picture). Then, click the "Next" button to work your way through the options, including the labels and cosmetic effects. Once you have decided on all of the options (don't worry, you can go back and change them), click the "Finish" button. Excel should generate a scatter plot that looks like Figure 12.2 on page 643.

63. Use MS Excel (or another spreadsheet program) to create a scatter plot for the data in Exercise 6.

Group Exercises

64. The group should select two variables that it believes have a strong positive or negative correlation. Once these variables have been determined,
    a. Collect at least 30 ordered pairs of data (x, y) from a sample of people on your campus.
    b. Draw a scatter plot for the data collected.
    c. Does the scatter plot indicate a positive correlation, a negative correlation, or no relationship between the variables?
    d. Calculate r. Does the value of r reinforce the impression conveyed by the scatter plot?
    e. Find the equation of the regression line.
    f. Use the regression line's equation to make a prediction about a y-value given an x-value.

g. Are the results of this project consistent with the group's original belief about the correlation between the variables, or are there some surprises in the data collected?

65. Group members should consult an almanac, a magazine, or a newspaper in which data about two variables are presented. (See, for example, Exercises 7 and 8 in this exercise set.)
    a. Draw a scatter plot for the data selected by the group.
    b. Does the scatter plot indicate a positive correlation, a negative correlation, or no correlation between the variables?
    c. Calculate r. Does the value of r reinforce the impression conveyed by the scatter plot?
    d. Find the equation of the regression line and use the equation to make a prediction.

CHAPTER SUMMARY, REVIEW, AND TEST

SUMMARY

12.1 Sampling, Frequency Distributions, and Graphs

a. A population is the set containing all objects whose properties are to be described and analyzed. A sample is a subset of the population.

b. Random samples are obtained in such a way that each member of the population has an equal chance of being selected.

c. Data can be organized and presented in frequency distributions, grouped frequency distributions, histograms, frequency polygons, and stem-and-leaf plots.

12.2 Measures of Central Tendency

a. The mean is the sum of the data items divided by the number of items. Mean $= \dfrac{\Sigma x}{n}$.

b. The mean of a frequency distribution is computed using

$$\text{Mean} = \frac{\Sigma xf}{n}$$

where x is each data value, f is its frequency, and n is the total frequency of the distribution.

c. The median of data arranged in order is the item in the middle or the mean of the two middlemost items. The median is the value in the $\frac{n+1}{2}$ position.

d. The mode of a data set is the value that occurs most often. If there is no such value, there is no mode.

e. The midrange is computed using

$$\frac{\text{lowest data value} + \text{highest data value}}{2}.$$

12.3 Measures of Dispersion

a. Range $=$ highest data value $-$ lowest data value

b. Standard deviation $= \sqrt{\dfrac{\Sigma(\text{data item} - \text{mean})^2}{n-1}}$

c. As the spread of data items increases, the standard deviation gets larger.

12.4 The Normal Distribution

a. The normal distribution is a theoretical distribution for the entire population. The distribution is bell-shaped and symmetric about a vertical line through its center, where the mean, median, and mode are located.

CHAPTER 10

Exercise Set 10.1

1. a. C **b.** Ray CD and ray CB **c.** $\angle C, \angle DCB, \angle BCD$ **3.** 30° **5.** 90° **7.** 65°; acute **9.** Obtuse **11.** Straight
13. 65° **15.** 146° **17.** 42° **19.** 1° **21.** 52.6° **23.** 69° **25.** 164° **27.** 90° **29.** $86\frac{3}{4}°$ **31.** 108°; 72°; 108°
33. 50°; 90°; 50° **35.** 68°; 68°; 112°; 112°; 68°; 68°; 112° **37.** Answers may vary. **39.** Answers may vary. **41.** Answers may vary.
53. 45° **55.** 90°

Exercise Set 10.2

1. 67° **3.** 32° **5.** 50°; 130°; 50°; 130°; 50° **7.** Angles A and D, angles B and E, angles C and F; $\overline{AB}$ and $\overline{DE}$, $\overline{AC}$ and $\overline{DF}$, $\overline{BC}$ and $\overline{EF}$
9. Angles N and R, angles P and S, angles M and T; $\overline{NM}$ and $\overline{RT}$, $\overline{NP}$ and $\overline{RS}$, $\overline{MP}$ and $\overline{TS}$ **11.** 5 in. **13.** 6 m **15.** 16 in.
17. 17 m **19.** 39 m **21.** 12 cm **23.** 13.2 m **25.** No; 0.3° **27.** 32 yd **29.** 600 yd **31.** 34 ft **43.** 21 ft

Exercise Set 10.3

1. Quadrilateral **3.** Pentagon **5.** a (square), b (rhombus), d (rectangle), e (parallelogram) **7.** a (square), d (rectangle)
9. c (trapezoid) **11.** 30 cm **13.** 28 yd **15.** 1000 in. **17.** 27 ft **19.** 18 yd **21.** 84 yd **23.** 32 ft **25.** 540°
27. 360° **29.** 108° **31.** 540; 140° **33.** No entry **35.** Stop, yield, deer crossing **37.** Equilateral triangle **39.** Yield
41. $5600 **43.** $9.50 **51.** $6a$

Exercise Set 10.4

1. 18 m² **3.** 16 in.² **5.** 2100 cm² **7.** 56 in.² **9.** 20.58 yd² **11.** 91 m² **13.** 25 cm; 50 cm² **15.** 38 yd²; 113 yd²
17. 72 m² **19.** 300 m² **21.** $556.50 **23.** 148 ft² **25.** $910 **27. a.** 18 bags **b.** $215.55 **29.** 126 m **31.** 376 plants
33. Large pizza **35.** $34,741.50 (using π) or $34,732 (using 3.14) **41.** By a factor of $\frac{9}{4}$ **43.** $13,033.60 **45.** 15.3 cm²

Exercise Set 10.5

1. 36 in.³ **3.** 64 cm³ **5.** 175 yd³ **7.** 56 in.³ **9.** 471 cm³ **11.** 9500 in.³ (using π) or 9495 in.³ (using 3.14) **13.** 151 m³
15. 47 yd³ **17.** 905 m³ (using π) or 904 m³ (using 3.14) **19.** 3054 cm³ (using π) or 3052 cm³ (using 3.14) **21.** 62 m² **23.** 96 ft²
25. 1018 cm³ (using π) or 1017 cm³ (using 3.14) **27.** $40 **29.** No **31. a.** 3,386,880 yd³ **b.** 2,257,920 blocks **33.** Yes
35. 260,120,252,600 mi³ (using π) or 259,988,382,700 mi³ (using 3.14) **39.** Multiplied by 8 **41.** 168 cm³ **43.** 84 cm²

Exercise Set 10.6

1. $\frac{3}{5}, \frac{4}{5}, \frac{3}{4}$ **3.** $\frac{20}{29}, \frac{21}{29}, \frac{20}{21}$ **5.** $\frac{5}{13}, \frac{12}{13}, \frac{5}{12}$ **7.** $\frac{4}{5}, \frac{3}{5}, \frac{4}{3}$ **9.** 188 cm **11.** 182 in. **13.** 7 m **15.** 22 yd **17.** 40 m
19. $m\angle B = 50°$; $a = 18$ yd, $c = 28$ yd **21.** $m\angle B = 38°$; $a = 43$ cm, $b = 33$ cm **23.** 37° **25.** 28° **27.** 529 yd **29.** 2880 ft
31. 86 ft **33.** 50° **35.** 150 ft **37.** 410 ft **47.** tan gets very large; tan 90° is undefined

Exercise Set 10.7

1. a. Yes **b.** Sample path: $DABDCB$ **3. a.** Yes **b.** Sample path: $ADCBDEAB$ **5. a.** No **7.** 4 **9.** 2
11. Pitcher and wrench, pretzel and button **13.** The sum of the angles is greater than 180°. **15.** Yes **17.** No
19. Carbon: even; hydrogen: odd

21. a.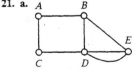
b. Yes
c. Answers may vary.

23. a.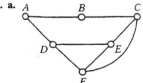
b. No

25. a.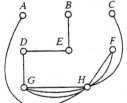

b. No

27. Answers may vary.

CHAPTER 12

Exercise Set 12.1

1. College professors in the United States **3.** Residents of the United States **5.** All high school students in Connecticut

9.

Time Spent on Homework (in hours)	Number of Students
15	4
16	5
17	6
18	5
19	4
20	2
21	2
22	0
23	0
24	2
	30

11.

Age	Number of Runners
10–19	8
20–29	13
30–39	7
40–49	6
50–59	4
60–69	2
	40

13.

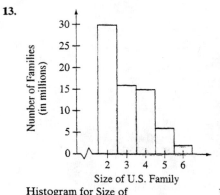
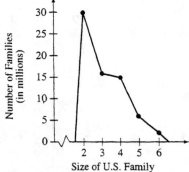

Histogram for Size of
United States Family

Frequency Polygon for Size of
United States Family

15.

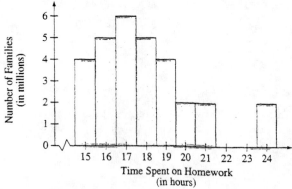
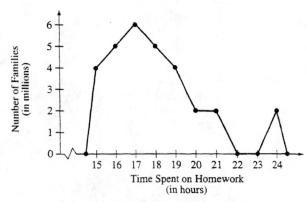

Histogram for Time Spent on Homework

Frequency Polygon for Time Spent on Homework

17. c

19.

Stems	Leaves
2	8 8 9 5
3	8 7 0 1 2 7 6 4 0 5
4	8 2 2 1 4 5 4 6 2 0 8 2 7 9
5	9 4 1 9 1 0
6	3 2 3 6 6 3

21. Ages of the actors: 31, 32, 32, 33, 35, 37, 38, 39, 40, 40, 41, 42, 42, 43, 43, 44, 45, 47, 46, 47, 48, 48. 51, 55, 56, 56, 60, 61, 62, 76
Ages of the actresses: 21, 24, 26, 26, 26, 27, 30, 30, 31, 31, 33, 33, 34, 34, 34, 35, 35, 37, 37, 38, 41, 41, 41, 42, 49, 60, 61, 61, 74, 80

23. Answers may vary.   **37.** Answers may vary.

Exercise Set 12.2

1. 4.125   **3.** 95   **5.** 62   **7.** 3.45   **9.** 4.71   **11.** 6.26   **13.** 3.5   **15.** 95   **17.** 60   **19.** 3.6   **21.** 5   **23.** 6   **25.** 3
27. 95   **29.** 40   **31.** No mode   **33.** 5   **35.** 6   **37.** 4.5   **39.** 95   **41.** 70   **43.** 3.3   **45.** 4.5   **47.** 5.5   **49.** $282.33
51. a. 1.79 inches per hour   **b.** No   **c.** 0 in.   **53.** 147.5 lb   **55.** 147.5 lb
57. a. 854.17 words per minute; 850 words per minute; 1000 words per minute; 850 words per minute   **b.** Mode   **c.** Answers may vary.
69. Answers may vary.

Exercise Set 12.3

1. 4   **3.** 8   **5.** 2   **7.** 6   **9.** 4   **11. a.** $-9, -7, -5, 0, 6, 15$ **b.** 0   **13. a.** $-20, -11, -1, 0, 4, 28$ **b.** 0
15. a. 91   **b.** $-6, 4, -1, -6, 9$ **c.** 0   **17. a.** 155   **b.** $-9, -2, 0, 5, 6$ **c.** 0
19. a. 2.70   **b.** $-0.45, 0.80, 0.05, 0.40, -0.80$ **c.** 0   **21.** 1.58   **23.** 3.46   **25.** 0.89   **27.** 3   **29.** 2.14
31. 12, 12, 4.32; 12, 12, 5.07; 12, 12, 6; The samples have the same mean, but different standard deviations.   **33.** 35.3; 18.32
35. 45.2; 13.60   **37.** 529.2; 19.51   **39.** 768.83, 226.56   **49.** Answers may vary.   **51.** a

Exercise Set 12.4

1. 120   **3.** 160   **5.** 150   **7.** 60   **9.** 90   **11.** 68%   **13.** 34%   **15.** 47.5%   **17.** 49.85%   **19.** 16%   **21.** 2.5%
23. 95%   **25.** 47.5%   **27.** 16%   **29.** 2.5%   **31.** 0.15%   **33.** 1   **35.** 3   **37.** 0.5   **39.** 1.75   **41.** 0   **43.** -1
45. -1.5 **47.** -3.25 **49.** 1.5   **51.** 2.25   **53.** -0.5 **55.** -1.5 **57.** Math test   **59.** 500   **61.** 475   **63.** 250
65. 275   **67. a.** 72.57%   **b.** 27.43%   **69. a.** 88.49%   **b.** 11.51%   **71. a.** 24.20%   **b.** 75.8%   **73. a.** 11.51%   **b.** 88.49%
75. 33.99%   **77.** 15.74%   **79.** 86.64%   **81.** 28.57%   **83.** 93.32%   **85.** 27.43%   **87.** 88.49%   **89.** 6.29%   **91.** 45.14%
93. 6.68%   **95.** 24.17%   **97. a.** ±5.0%   **b.** We can be 95% confident that between 21% and 31% of all parents feel that crime is a
bad thing about being a kid.   **99. a.** ±1.6%   **b.** We can be 95% confident that between 58.6% and 61.8% of all TV households watched
the final episode of $M*A*S*H$.   **101.** 0.2%   **103.** No   **105.** Answers may vary.   **119.** 62 in.

Exercise Set 12.5

1.

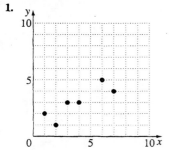

There appears to be a strong positive correlation.

3.

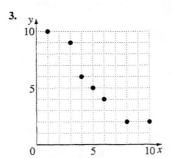

There appears to be a strong negative correlation.

5.

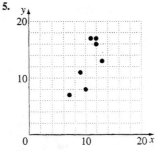

There appears to be a moderate positive correlation.

7.

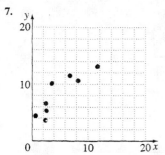

There appears to be a moderate positive correlation.

9. False   **11.** True   **13.** True   **15.** False   **17.** False
19. True   **21.** False   **23.** False   **25.** False   **27.** True   **29.** a
31. d   **33.** 0.855   **35.** −0.954
37. a. 0.75   **b.** $y = 1.52x - 3.38$ **c.** 21 yrs
39. a. 0.885   **b.** $y = 0.85x + 4.05$ **c.** 16 murders per 100,000 people
41. Correlation does exist   **43.** Correlation does not exist
45. Correlation does exist   **47.** Correlation does not exist
61. Answers may vary.

Chapter 12 Review

1. American adults earning $100,000 or more each year   **2.** Rental apartments in San Francisco   **3.** a

4.

Time Spent on Homework (in hours)	Number of Students
6	1
7	3
8	3
9	2
10	$\frac{1}{10}$

5.

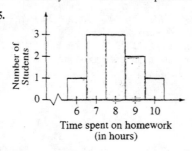

6.

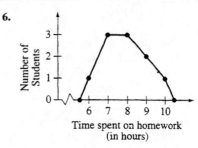

7.

Grades	Number of Students
0–39	19
40–49	8
50–59	6
60–69	6
70–79	5
80–89	3
90–100	$\frac{3}{50}$

8.

Stems	Leaves
1	3 4 1 3 7 8
2	4 9 6 9 2 7
3	4 9 6 5 1 1 1
4	4 0 2 7 9 1 2 5
5	7 9 6 4 0 1
6	3 3 7 0 8 9
7	2 3 4 0 5
8	7 1 6
9	5 1 0

9. Answers may vary.
10. 91.2   **11.** 17   **12.** 2.3
13. 11   **14.** 28   **15.** 2
16. 27   **17.** No mode   **18.** 2
19. 91   **20.** 19.5   **21.** 2.5
22. Answers may vary.
23. Answers may vary.